Cereal Crops

A field of hybrid corn or maize.

(Courtesy US Department of Agriculture)

Cereal Crops

WARREN H. LEONARD

Professor of Agronomy
Colorado State University
Fort Collins, Colorado

and

JOHN H. MARTIN

Research Agronomist
Agricultural Research Service
United States Department of Agriculture
Beltsville, Maryland

The Macmillan Company
Collier-Macmillan Limited, *London*

PRINTING   78910   YEAR   56789

Library of Congress catalog card number: 63-9596

THE MACMILLAN COMPANY
866 THIRD AVENUE, NEW YORK, NEW YORK 10022
COLLIER-MACMILLAN CANADA, LTD., Toronto

Printed in the United States of America

Preface

This book is designed as a college text for a course in Cereal Crops, to be taught after a general course in crop production or botany. The subject matter is presented in a style more advanced than that in an earlier and more general book by the same authors, *Principles of Field Crop Production*. The present book also should be instructive to anyone interested in the production, use, and history of the cereal grains. This would include farmers as well as members of firms that handle or process grains and their products. The subject matter presented, together with the extensive literature citations, should serve as helpful reference material to many agricultural technicians.

As a text, *Cereal Crops* may be too extensive to be covered in a one-term course. In that event, certain sections might be omitted, particularly those that deal with cytology, genetics, diseases, or insect pests.

This book is concerned wholly with the cereal crops. Buckwheat is omitted because it is not a true cereal, although its seeds serve some of the same purposes as do the cereal grains.

It may interest the reader to know that this book is the culmination of many years of experience with cereals by the authors. This experience includes the production, handling, and processing of the cereal grains, as well as intensive study, research, and teaching. Separately or jointly, the authors have conducted or observed cereal research and production in most of the states in the United States and also in eight foreign countries.

Warren H. Leonard
John H. Martin

ACKNOWLEDGMENTS

The authors are deeply indebted to their associates as well as others who have assisted in the preparation of this book. Some of these workers read portions of the manuscript, offered suggestions for improvement, and sometimes supplied new subject-matter material. The authors gratefully acknowledge assistance from C. R. Adair, Wray M. Bowden (Canada), L. W. Briggle, F. A. Coffman, F. F. Dicke, Harold D. Harrington, Elmer Heyne, Nelson E. Jodon, T. A. Kiesselbach, Willard L. Lindsay, H. C. Murphy, B. P. Pal (India), D. A. Reid, L. P. Reitz, D. W. Robertson, Frank B. Salisbury, G. F. Sprague, Coit Suneson, Arnold J. Ullstrup, O. J. Webster, and G. A. Wiebe.

Many illustrations used in this book were supplied by the International Harvester Company, John Deere Company, and J. I. Case. Illustrations not otherwise credited were obtained from agencies of the United States Department of Agriculture. These included the Agricultural Research Service, Economic Research Service, Agricultural Marketing Service, Foreign Agricultural Service, and the Extension Service.

Contents

PART I General Principles

1. ECONOMIC ROLE OF THE CEREALS

IMPORTANCE OF THE CEREAL GRAINS

The cereals are crop plants belonging to the grass family (*Gramineae*) that are grown for their edible starchy seeds. The term *cereal* applies to the entire plant as well as the grain, and it is also loosely applied to the grain products. Grain is a collective term applied to cereals. The cereal grains are wheat, rice, maize, rye, barley, oats, grain sorghum, and various millets. In the United States, the term *food grains* is sometimes applied to wheat, rye, and rice, while the term *feed grains* is used for corn, barley, oats, and grain sorghum.

About half the plowed land of the world is given to growing the principal cereals [38]. Cereal grains dominate world agricultural production because they directly or indirectly provide a large portion of the human sustenance. They are by far the most important source of concentrated carbohydrates for man and beast. Cereals are the chief items in the diet for many people, particularly in the Orient, because they are a comparatively cheap source of calories. Grains represent the flexible fraction in the feed ration of the domestic animals which supply meat, milk, and other food products. Cereals also are used as forage for livestock.

A large percentage of the world population subsists mainly on either wheat, rice, or maize. Consumption of wheat as a food generally increases as a nation develops from a totally agrarian mode of life to a diversified one. Wheat (Fig. 1-1) is an important basic food item in the United States as well as in other advanced countries. In the Orient, rice is an essential food for a large segment of the world population. Many people in the poorer, more thickly populated areas of the rice-growing regions depend almost entirely on rice for their subsistence. The inhabitants of some countries depend primarily on corn, rye, barley, grain sorghum, or millets for

FIGURE 1-1. **Wheat — the staff of life.**
(*Courtesy US Department of Agriculture*)

their main staple food. This is particularly true of the underprivileged classes of such countries [23].

Corn (see frontispiece) provides more than half of all feed grain in the United States; in the cooler climates of Canada and northern Europe, oats and barley are the principal feed grains produced. Rye, grain sorghum, and the millets provide feed grain, but very little grain is fed to livestock in Asia, Africa, South America, and Central America.

WORLD DISTRIBUTION OF CEREALS

The principal regions of small grain production are in North America, China, Europe, India, Argentina, and Australia. Northern Africa grows considerable barley and wheat. The most important areas of small grain production in the world, exclusive of China, are within Europe, where more than 95 per cent of the rye, 60 per cent of the oats, about 50 per cent of the barley and wheat, and approximately one per cent of the rice are produced [30]. The principal small grain of Australia is wheat, grown in a narrow belt that parallels the seacoast in the south and borders the interior desert. The United States and Canada combined grow about one-sixth of the world supply of small grains.

About 95 per cent of the world rice crop is produced and consumed in Monsoon Asia, an area that extends across the southeastern part of Asia from India to Japan and includes most of the adjacent tropical and subtropical islands. India and Burma produce more than 50 per cent of the world rice crop, exclusive of China.

Corn is produced from latitude 58°N. in Canada and the Soviet Union to latitude 40°S. It is largely a New World crop; about half the world acreage is in the United States. The principal corn countries in South America are Argentina and Brazil; in Europe, the most important corn regions are the Danube Basin, Soviet Russia, Italy, and Spain.

Sorghum is fairly important throughout the world, but particularly so in India, Africa, and the United States.

Millets are used as food primarily in eastern and southern Asia, parts of Africa, and parts of the Soviet Union [16].

CEREAL GRAIN STATISTICS

The total world production of all cereal grains generally varies little from year to year. Shortages of certain crops in some areas are often balanced by above-average production elsewhere. However, immediately after World War II there was a world food shortage, primarily because of a cereal grain scarcity. The shortages were over late in 1948 due largely to production recovery in deficit regions. By 1950, the world was confronted with grain surpluses.

The principal grain export nations are Australia, Argentina, Canada, and the United States. Europe has long been the world's major grain importer.

The world acreage, yield per acre, and production for various cereal crops for the period from 1959–61 are given in Table 1-1 [1].

TABLE 1-1. **Cereal Grains: Average Annual World Acreage, Yield, and Production, 1959–61.**

Crop	Average Acreage	Yield per Acre	Weight per Bushel	Average Production
	(1000 A)	(Bu)	(Lb)	(1000 T)[1]
Wheat	501,000	18.3	60	275,000
Corn	260,000	32.5	56	236,000
Rice[2]	290,000	1750.0[3]	45	255,000
Barley	152,000	26.4	48	96,000
Oats	113,000	37.1	32	67,000
Rye	75,000	18.2	56	41,000
Sorghum	125,000	16.1	56	56,000
Millet	119,000	419.0[3]	—	25,000

[1]Short tons   [3]Pounds
[2]Rough rice

Preliminary average estimates of cereal grain acreages, yields, and production in the United States for the period 1952–61 are given in Table 1-2.

TABLE 1-2. **Cereal Grains: Average Annual United States Acreage, Yield, and Production 1952–61.**

Crop	Harvested Acreage	Yield per Harvested Acre	Average Production
	(1000 A)	(Bu)	(1000 Bu)
Wheat	54,200	21.2	1,150,000
Corn (all)	77,410	46.3	3,600,000
Rice (rough)	1,760	65.8	116,000
Barley	12,900	29.2	377,000
Oats	33,100	37.1	1,230,000
Rye	1,640	15.5	25,000
Grain sorghum	12,400	32.9	409,000

EARLY HISTORY OF THE CEREALS

Cultivation of all the cereal grains except oats and rye began before the dawn of history. Wheat, barley, and millets were cultivated in many parts of the Old World 10–15 thousand years before the Christian era [25]. Cultivation of the cereal grains was already a highly developed art by the time of the first written histories of the Greeks and Romans [35]. All important civilizations were founded on the basis of one or another of the cereal grains. When man learned to cultivate cereals he did not have to wander in search of food. Cereal production gave him a stable mode of life and the leisure that nurtured arts, crafts, and sciences [24]. Babylonia, Egypt, Greece, and Rome were all based on the growing of wheat, barley, and the millets; the ancient cultures of India, China, and Japan were based on the rice crop. The pre-Columbian people of the Inca, Maya, and Aztec civilizations in the New World depended on Indian corn (maize) for their daily bread [24].

Whole cereal grains roasted or parched were common in the diets of the ancient peoples of the Stone Age. Grains were also ground between stones, with the meal stored in crude earthenware pots for a reserve food supply. Ancient peoples ate a heavy, unleavened flatbread made of coarsely ground meal. Such bread has been found along with parched or uncooked stores of wheat, barley, and millet in the ruins of the Swiss Lake Dwellers, a people who lived 6–7 thousand years ago, and in Egyptian Tombs [35].

The cereals contained carbohydrates, proteins, fats, minerals, and vitamins. Whole-grain cereals come closer to being in themselves an adequate human diet than any other plant product [24], although heavy consumption of unmilled wheat and rice often leads to digestive troubles. Famines and food shortages have long been associated with failures of the cereal crops upon which man depends for a large proportion of his total food. As man migrated, he carried cereal seeds to new regions, spreading them over the world wherever they could be grown.

ORIGIN OF CEREALS

The progenitors of the cultivated cereals were wild grasses that shed seeds at maturity, thus reseeding themselves.

Widespread systematic geographical investigations of a large number of crop plants were made by the great Russian geneticist N. I. Vavilov [36, 37]. He conceived a species as a more or less distinct heterogeneous as well as variable morphophysiological system, the origin of which is associated with a particular environment and area. A center of origin is characterized by the presence of a great diversity of genotypes of a particular species; consequently, each is an important source of germplasm for use in plant breeding. The locations of the principal phytogeographic centers of origin Vavilov established by a study of the diversity of each botanical species, including its genetics, cytology, and immunology. He also studied related wild species and their interrelationships with cultivated forms. He found one or more cereals in each of the eight world centers he described: China, India, Central Asia, Near East, Mediterranean, Abyssinia, Central America, and South America.

Archaeological evidence suggests possible centers of origin of the cereals. The cultures of the Old World region of Europe, North Africa, and the temperate zone of western Asia to the Indus Valley were based on wheat and barley. Discoveries at the Jarmo site in Iraq, which date from about 6750 BC, reveal the crucial combination of the wild prototype and its more advanced domesticated form for both of these cereals [15].

CLIMATE IN RELATION TO CEREAL PRODUCTION

Climatic factors determine those areas where each of the cereals can be grown economically. Within areas favorable to production, weather conditions have a marked influence on growth, yield, and quality of the harvested crop. Cereals generally grown in the temperate climates of the world are wheat, maize, rye, barley, oats, grain sorghum, and some of the millets; the important cereals grown in hot climates are rice, sorghum, pearl millet, and finger millet.

Climate for Wheat, Rye, Barley, and Oats

Wheat, rye, barley, and oats generally are grown where annual precipitation is 15–45 inches, but most extensively where it is less than 30

FIGURE 1-2. **Harvesting and threshing rice with a self-propelled combine. The threshed grain is being transferred to a dump cart (or bankout cart) in which the rice is hauled from the field.**

(Courtesy J. I. Case Company)

inches. Because of other climatic factors, as well as economic conditions, neither the minimum nor maximum limit is sharply defined [31]. Scarcity of small grains other than rice in areas of adequate rainfall is due to indirect effects, such as prevalence of diseases, notably rusts, scabs, mildews, and leaf spots of various kinds; poor soil; excessive growth and lodging; and difficulties in preparation of land or in seeding, harvesting, and care of the crop. In India, wheat is grown where the annual rainfall is 60 inches or more, but most of the rain falls during a season of the year when the crop is not growing.

In most areas where growing seasons are severely restricted, only spring-sown small grains are grown. They are seeded as early in the spring as possible, usually several weeks before the last killing frost. Length of frost-free period is a good index of the practicability of small grain production [30]. Extensive small-grain production requires a frost-free period of 100 days or more; a period less than 90 days is precarious, demanding not only prompt seeding but the use of the earliest-maturing varieties. All cereals are damaged by freezing during heading, pollination, and early grain de-

velopment. Oats and wheat are grown farther north and at higher elevations than other small grains except spring barley [39].

The northern limits of fall-seeded small grains in the Northern Hemisphere are largely determined by winter temperatures. Winter rye is far
more resistant to low temperatures, and it is grown farther north than is
any other winter cereal. Next in order are winter wheat, winter barley, and
winter oats. Warm, moist weather limits the production of winter grains in
the southern parts of the Northern Hemisphere. The fall-sown cereals grown
in areas with mild winters are almost all varieties with a spring growth
habit.

Rice

The rice plant (Fig. 1-2) requires warm temperatures and abundant
rainfall or irrigation. In Monsoon Asia, rice is grown where annual rainfall
is 40 inches or more [38]. Little rice is grown at elevations above 3000
feet or where the average January temperature is below freezing. Rice has
a high moisture requirement but is not attacked by rusts, as are other small
grains. Rice is unable to survive temperatures appreciably below freezing,
and requires a somewhat longer frost-free season than do the other small
grains. True winter varieties of rice are unknown, although rice frequently
is grown as a winter crop in the tropics.

Of all the cereals, rice is the best adapted to the moister parts of
Monsoon Asia [38]. Conditions there include a hot moist climate, high
rainfall, and wide stretches of land flooded naturally at certain seasons, or
by irrigation by primitive or inexpensive means. Millets, grain sorghums,
and maize can be grown under hot moist conditions, but they can compete
with rice only in areas of lower summer rainfall. In places where lowland
rice thrives, no other cereal can produce as much food per unit area of
land.

Other Cereal Grains

Corn is cultivated in more widely divergent climates than is any other
cereal. It is grown below sea level in Caspian Plain and above 12 thousand
feet in the Peruvian Andes. It is unique among the cereals in point of the
enormous diversity of strains developed to fit widely differing conditions of
temperature, moisture, length of frost-free season, and other environmental
factors [17].

Sorghum has proved enormously useful in areas too hot or too dry to
grow corn well. Although many varieties are adapted to the temperate
regions, warm weather is required for the successful growth of sorghums.

With the development of improved early varieties, the limits of grain sorghum production in the United States now extend into sections where the average annual precipitation is only 15–17 inches, the average frost-free period 130–140 days, and the mean July temperature as low as 75°F [26].

TRENDS IN GRAIN PRODUCTION

Reliable statistics on world grain production and trade have been available only since about 1900. Five general periods are distinguishable in the world grain situation in the first half of the twentieth century [14].

The years 1900–14 were a period of expansion in production and trade, associated with increased consumption, free markets, and relatively limited price movement. Wheat utilization was increased with the progress of industrialization, principally in Europe, and with the increased per capita wheat consumption in most western countries characteristic of the early stages of a rise in living standards. Exports in wheat and flour rose from 475 million bushels in 1900 to 735 million annually in 1911–13. Exports of barley, oats, and maize also showed substantial increases.

During World War I (1914–18) and the immediate postwar years, domestic production in Europe declined significantly. Government controls on production and distribution were first extensively applied in European and other countries. War experience also reinforced the tendencies towards programs for national self-sufficiency.

The 1920's was a decade of postwar recovery and adjustment. The sharp expansion in North American grain cultivation was generally maintained, and significant increases occurred in Argentina and in Australia. World wheat trade averaged somewhat above pre-1914 levels, but the trade in coarse grains remained below prewar average volume throughout most of this period as a result of decreased livestock populations in Europe.

The 1930's was a decade of surplus supplies, low prices, and governmental controls. Increased utilization in import countries was limited by foreign exchange difficulties. In 1932 prices dropped to the lowest ever recorded. In the export countries, loans, price supports, and other measures were instituted to protect wheat growers from the worst effects of the market collapse. Import countries acted to protect or increase the domestic output in order to lessen foreign exchange difficulties.

World War II also caused changes in the world grain production pattern. Production in North America was increased sharply during the war and early postwar years. World trade was carried on largely on a government-to-government basis. A world food crisis arose in many countries during and after the war because of short crops due to various dislocations.

International allocation machinery directly or indirectly controlled practically all world grain supplies until the shortage was relieved late in 1948.

As surplus supplies became available the world grain trade entered a system of controlled barter, subsidized exports, import restrictions, and price supports.

CEREALS IN HUMAN NUTRITION

The cereals are used directly for human food or, as livestock and poultry feed indirectly for conversion into meat, milk, and eggs. In the more advanced countries, there has been a gradual shift from use of cereals directly as food to livestock feed.

Proportion of Cereals in Diet

In nations where population presses on the food supply, most food—in terms of calories—comes directly from the cereal grains. Cereals are a cheap source of calories in terms of effort and costs of production. One acre of rice in Japan will produce as many calories for direct human consumption as five or six acres of crops converted to animal food products. Consequently, production of animals for food in overpopulated countries generally is economical only on lands where cereal production is impossible.

Cereal-potato crops supplied about 75 per cent of the world's food calories in the period 1933–38 [2, 3]; about 70 per cent was contributed by the cereal grains alone. With respect to total food calories, national averages of cereal-potato calories varied from 30-90 per cent. A high percentage of cereal-potato calories consumed directly as human food signifies a low dietary standard. As an average for all nations in Asia except Japan, 80–90 per cent of the calories in the human diet come from the cereal-potato group. The Soviet Union falls within this category. In advanced Occidental countries—for example, the United States, United Kingdom, Switzerland, Sweden, Canada, Australia, and New Zealand—only 30–40 per cent of the food calories come directly from the cereal-potato groups. National diets exceeding 70 per cent of cereal-potato calories are deficient in animal proteins, minerals, and vitamins, and are likely to be so qualitatively inadequate that the human organism is damaged. Probably three-fourths of the world population subsists on such diets.

Cereal Consumption in the United States

The average American diet has improved greatly in quality since 1909. As indicated in Table 1-3, per capita consumption of cereals was 134.5 pounds greater in 1909 than in 1958 [7, 1].

TABLE 1-3. **Cereal Products: Pounds Per Capita Consumption
in the United States, 1909–58.**

Year	Wheat	Rye	Rice	Corn	Oats	Barley	Total
1909	216.7	3.4	7.2	59.0	3.2	3.6	293.1
1958	122.8	1.2	5.7	24.6	3.2	1.1	158.6

There has been a shift from foods relatively high in calorie content to foods relatively high in minerals and vitamins, such as fruits, vegetables, and dairy products. Improvement in the nutritional quality of certain foods themselves has also been important. For example, the enrichment of flour together with the fortification of cereal products has been responsible for a large part of the increases shown for iron, thiamine, riboflavin, and niacin since before World War II [6].

Grain products contributed to the average civilian diet in 1959 approximately 20.7 per cent of the calories, 19.5 per cent of the protein, and 1.5 per cent of the fat. Grain products also provided the national diet nearly one-fourth its iron and niacin and nearly one-third its thiamine. The production of these grains used for food required only 7 per cent of the cropland and 3 per cent of the farm labor.

Cereals used indirectly as livestock and poultry feed provide about one-third of all food energy contained in the national diet. Approximately one-third of the livestock feed consists of concentrate feeds, most of which are grain or grain products [19].

The equivalent of nearly 2.7 acres of cropland was used in 1943–45 to produce the average American civilian diet. About 12 per cent of the 2.7 acres (0.4 acres) was used to grow food crops for direct human consumption.

ROLE OF CEREALS IN WORLD FOOD PROBLEM

Cereals will assume a more and more important role in attempts to meet future world food requirements as the population continues to increase. Consequently, potentialities for increased cereal production are significant.

There were an estimated 3000 million people in the world in 1961. The world population quadrupled between 1650 and 1950. The present rate of world population growth is 1.7 per cent per year—at that rate, there is a prospect of a world population of 6280 million people by AD 2000, an increase of 150 per cent over the population of 2406 million in 1950. Such a population would necessitate a tremendous increase in food production.

The present problem of surpluses in the United States may disappear by 1975, when the population will be an estimated 228.5 million people, based on continued 1954–55 fertility rates. In order to maintain the present

American diet for the increased population, an increased production equivalent to an estimated 100 million more acres of cropland will be necessary. However, most of the additional production will have to come from increased acre yields of food crops on presently cultivated land [34, 20].

Increased cereal production is an important step in the realization of future world food needs. Although a balanced diet is impossible from these crops alone, a minimum calorie requirement can be supplied from the cereals to avert starvation. Acre yields of feed grains in the United States rose 70 per cent during and since World War II (Fig. 1-3); food grain

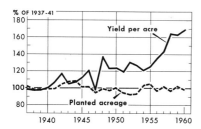

FIGURE 1-3. **Total acreage and yield of feed grains — corn oats, barley, and grain sorghum — in the United States. Yields have increased since 1939.**

(Courtesy US Department of Agriculture)

yields increased more than 60 per cent by 1960. The hazards of production have been controlled more and more through the application of suitable chemicals, improved cultural practices, extended irrigation, and the culture of superior varieties. The widespread use of hybrids has been an important factor in the increased production of the American corn and grain sorghum crops. Fertilizer use has increased. Some of these improved practices are practicable for countries where food is now scarce. Since 1938, wheat yields in Europe have increased about 20 per cent in the Communist countries and 30 per cent in the other European countries. An increase of 10 per cent in rice yields in Monsoon Asia is a reasonable expectation through improvements in varieties grown, cultural methods, fertilizer practices, and irrigation facilities [28, 18]. About 2838 million acres, less than 10 per cent of the total world land area, is now cultivated. The arable land area can be increased by only about 50 per cent from all known suitable soil types [31].

THE AMERICAN GRAIN GROWER

Cereal grain is grown on nearly four million farms in the United States each year. An appreciable portion of the grain on a million or so of these farms is grown for the market; the others produce chiefly for home or local consumption as feed or food. The sale of grain provides 40 per cent or more of the cash income on each of more than 400 thousand American farms.

In the United States, power machinery and improved crop and live-stock production doubled output per farm worker between 1910 and 1945 and reduced the cost per unit of farm output by 25 per cent (in 1935–39 dollars). Improvements in grain production were responsible for much of those gains [8]. The output of grain per man-hour of farm labor increased more than eightfold between 1910 and 1960. The grain growers themselves played an important role in this advance.

Farm Acreages in Cereal Grains

In 1959, approximately 298 thousand farms, 10.8 per cent of all farms in the United States, were classed as commercial cash grain farms. Growers of market grain are located on land smooth enough to be tilled in large tracts. These growers operate from 160–2000 acres, keeping 100–1000 acres in crops (Fig. 1-4). Representative grain farms in eight areas each harvested an average of 206–450 acres of crops, of which 136–434 acres were in grain in 1960, as shown in Table 1-4 [12]. From 85 to 95 per cent of the labor on these grain farms was performed by the operator and his family, except for the wheat-pea growers who hired about 20 per cent of

FIGURE 1-4. **A typical 1400-acre grain farm in North Dakota.**

(Courtesy International Harvester Company)

their labor. Most farms in the humid, subhumid, and irrigated areas have less than 300 acres in crops. Acreages of from 480–1280 prevail on semi-arid farms. There, yields often are low, which means that a large crop area is necessary to produce an adequate family income. It is possible to till, seed, and harvest a large dryland area because of relatively little interference from rain or wet soil.

Where grains are sown regularly on summer-fallowed land, a farmer can operate about twice the area he could where the crop land must be prepared, seeded, and harvested each year. Thus, such farms usually range in size from 640–2000 acres, with perhaps 300–800 acres in grain and an equal area fallowed each year. With modern equipment, a typical farm family produces 200–800 acres of grain largely by its own labor, except for some extra help at harvest time. This seems to be the most efficient farm size in such areas [33].

American growers of market grain in 1960 used tractor power for all field work and hauled the grain in a truck or trailer. Small grains and grain sorghums were harvested with a combine; corn was gathered with a picker or a picker-sheller. Growers either owned these machines or hired a custom operator.

Diversification on Grain Farms

Most market grain growers produced some other crop for cash, such as soybeans, cotton, peas, flax, or broomcorn, where such crops are adapted. The crops were rotated where rotation was deemed to be advantageous and other crops could be grown profitably. Many grain farms had a poultry flock and often some hogs or other livestock. Farms that had some rough land suitable only for pasture had cattle or sheep, and also produced hay and perhaps some silage. The cash grain farms, reported in Table 1-4, had 18–30 per cent of the land in pasture and derived 20–25 per cent of the cash receipts from livestock and livestock products.

Timely operation often is extremely important in cereal grain production, particularly in avoiding storm losses at harvest time and in the early seeding of spring small grains. Consequently, interruptions of even a day or two during critical seasons in order to care for livestock or gardens can prove extremely costly to the grain grower should bad weather follow. This doubtless accounts for the limited diversification in certain semiarid grain regions. Other enterprises are common on grain farms. The growing of several different grains may spread the seeding and harvesting periods and thus permit a farmer to increase his income by operating a larger acreage.

SOIL DEPLETION BY CEREAL GRAINS

The cash grain grower should not be condemned as a "soil miner" because an appreciable portion of its mineral nutrients is sold off his farm

TABLE 1-4. **Average Farm Size, Net Income, and Labor Used in 16 Typical Type-of-Farming Areas in the Corn Belt and Western States.**

Area	Type of Farming	Land in Farm, 1960	Crops Harvested, 1960		Average Net Farm Income, 1947–60	Total Labor Used, 1960
			Total	Grain		
		(A)	(A)	(A)	(Dollars)	(Hours)
Corn Belt	Cash Grain (Illinois-Indiana)	248	206	136	8,030	3,230
	Hog-beef fattening	216	155	128	8,144	4,150
	Hog-beef raising	249	112	60	3,562	3,500
	Hog-dairy	178	109	72	5,217	4,420
	Dairy-hog	163	103	62	3,894	3,990
	Dairy (Wisconsin)	161	84	38	2,936	4,155
Southern Great Plains	Wheat	773	368	303	8,557	3,040
	Wheat-grain sorghum	750	416	371	6,378	3,110
Northern Great Plains	Wheat-small grain-livestock	715	405	274	5,071	2,810
	Wheat-corn-livestock	515	345	229	4,680	3,540
	Wheat-roughage-livestock	810	421	223	4,180	3,190
	Cattle	4,380	255	76	5,320	4,060
	Sheep	6,638	218	75	8,398	8,820
Northwest	Wheat-pea	576	380	266	12,840	3,470
Inter-mountain	Wheat-fallow	1,363	450	434	9,659	3,640
Region	Cattle	1,735	174	16	8,887	5,210

with the grain that took them from the soil. When grain is used for human consumption, most of the minerals in it ultimately pass into sewers and cemeteries and are thus lost to the soil. The collection of "night soil" for use as fertilizer in parts of Asia returns some of what would otherwise be lost.

Feeding grain to livestock sacrifices from 70 to 90 per cent of the protein and calories in the grain otherwise available for human consumption, but nitrogen, minerals, and organic matter are returned to the soil in the form of manure. Feed grain sold off the farm provides manure for other lands. Of the feed grains not required for seed, more than 90 per cent of the oats, 85 per cent of the corn and grain sorghum, and two-thirds of the barley are fed to livestock, and thus provide manure for some locality on or off the home farm. The by-products of food and fermentation grain processing, which amount to about one-third of the corn, grain sorghum, and barley so used, are returned to the farm as feeds containing most of the protein and minerals in the original grain. About 30 per cent of the total weight of the wheat and rye ground for flour is returned to the farm as mill feed, again with a substantial share of the minerals and protein.

The cereal crops do not fix atmospheric nitrogen for soil enrichment as do the legumes, but the residues from cereals return much more organic matter to the soil than do legumes that have been harvested for forage. A large part of the grain processed in food industries is produced on very fertile soils that receive only a small amount of the total fertilizer used. Thus, the commercial grain grower dissipates a relatively small portion of natural resources of phosphorus and potash used in the manufacture of mineral fertilizers. Commercial fertilizers were applied to 60 per cent of the total U. S. corn acreage and 28 per cent of the total wheat acreage in 1954, but only one-fourth the corn acreage and one-eighth the wheat acreage in the fertile but semiarid Great Plains States were fertilized.

Small-grain fields suffer very little erosion, except on unfrozen ground after the stubble has been turned under and before new seedings are established. Sloping fields in intertilled corn and grain sorghum, like those in other row crops, often are subject to heavy erosion. Contoured rows of corn and sorghum and close drilling of grain sorghum reduce erosion hazards.

PROFITS FROM GRAIN PRODUCTION

Grain growing is not always profitable. It is most profitable during wars or other periods of food scarcity. Grain growing is as profitable as other farm enterprises in important grain-production regions over a period of average seasons. Intensive types of agriculture that bring a higher acre return than grain growing may be even less profitable because of the smaller operation and the large labor requirement. The average net returns per farm in 16 type-of-farming areas 1949–58, as determined by the Department of Agriculture, are shown in Table 1-4. The grain farms yielded a higher average net income than the dairy farms, and an equal or higher net income than the diversified farms. Dairy farms provide a relatively stable but somewhat low net income and utilize more labor throughout the year. Grain growers realize a relatively high return per hour of labor. Modern dairy farms require the labor of one man to care for a herd of 30–50 cows, along with the young stock. Cash grain growers thus have the time to crop a larger acreage than do dairy farmers; they often rent additional land to provide more employment in order to obtain a larger income. Cash grain growing is popular also because the operator is not confined to the farm throughout the year in order to care for livestock.

In a given locality the income of the grain grower is roughly proportional to the area that he and his family operate, provided that suitable large equipment is used for the larger crop acreages. On the larger farms the investment per acre in buildings and equipment is less, the output per worker is greater, and the gross receipts are proportional to the crop acreage [4, 29]. Farm size in an American grain region is not fixed, as so often has been assumed. Market grain growers regularly buy or rent additional land when necessary to provide a crop area large enough to justify the operation of efficient equipment. The average size of grain farms increased 10 per cent between 1939–49, according to the United States Census. Enlargements in farm size reduce the farm population and increase the output per worker. Modern rubber-tired tractors and implements, which travel much faster than horses, have eliminated the chief drawback to cropping areas a mile or more from the farmstead.

COST FACTORS IN GRAIN PRODUCTION

Production costs for the entire domestic crops of wheat, oats, and corn in the United States were estimated from 1932–46 [13]. Production expenses per acre in 1960 were three to four times higher than in 1932, but higher yields partly offset increased bushel costs. The increase in acre costs resulted from higher rates paid for labor, equipment, supplies, and land use. The total increase was almost directly proportional to the increase in the national wholesale commodity price index.

Effect of Type of Cereal Crop

The lowest average cost per acre of wheat produced was in the hard red winter wheat region of Nebraska, Kansas, Colorado, Oklahoma, and

FIGURE 1-5. **A ground-powered combine cutting an 18-foot swath of grain, drawn by 27 horses, used in the Pacific Northwest in the early part of the century.**

(Courtesy US Department of Agriculture)

Texas. This region had the lowest expenses for soil preparation, harvesting, hauling, fertilizers, and seed. Nearly all of these farms were highly mechanized, tillage operations were simple, the topography was generally smooth, seeding rates were low, and practically no fertilizer was used for wheat. The lowest average cost per bushel of wheat was in the western states where high acre yields with few crop failures prevailed. This region was the first to adopt combine harvesting (Fig. 1-5) and other mechanized methods.

The lowest cost per bushel of oats was in the Great Lakes and Corn Belt states, where acre yields were highest.

The southwestern, western, and southeastern states had the lowest per acre cost of corn production, but the lowest bushel costs were in the northern Great Lakes and Corn Belt states where acre yields were the highest. The cost of producing an acre of corn is half again higher than that of wheat or oats because of need for intertillage, heavier fertilization, and the extra labor involved in harvesting the higher yield of grain, often on no more than two rows at a time.

In the Great Plains, where most of the grain sorghum is grown, the acre cost of production is higher than for wheat because of the several intertillage operations and a higher cost for combining and hauling the extra bushels of grain sorghum. The lower acre seed cost for grain sorghum is offset by the necessity of frequent replanting.

The cost of rice production in California in 1948 was estimated at nearly $90 an acre, or $2.57 per 100 pounds of rough rice, exclusive of management costs. Of the total expenditures, tractor and truck power cost about $7 an acre, man labor cost $12.50, machinery about $9, materials $25.50, and a hired airplane and pilot for seeding, fertilizing, spraying, and bird protection cost about $5 an acre. The remaining items were interest, taxes, insurance, general expenses, and overhead [9]. In Arkansas, the 1947 average cost of materials and service for rice production on farms that averaged 110 acres of rice was $42.40 an acre where harvested with a binder, $40.13 where harvested with a tractor-drawn combine, and $38.61 where harvested with a self-propelled combine [32]. For a yield of 50 bushels or 2250 pounds an acre the cost per 100 pounds was $1.70–1.90. This was similar to the cost per 100 pounds for the same items in California, where wages and acre yields were higher.

In Texas, with wage rates computed at 50–60 cents an hour and other expenses less than in 1948, the 1945 total cost of producing rice cut with a self-propelled combine was about $44 an acre [21]. The cost of producing rice cut with the binder was about $50 an acre. The combine method of harvest saved 6–9 man-hours per acre. The greatest saving of labor was possible with a large self-propelled combine. Bulk combining of rice saves 1.25 to 1.50 man-hours of labor per acre as compared with sacking the grain.

Effect of Power Machinery

Power machinery reduces production costs [22]. However, in many countries, tractor fuel costs several times more than in the United States, and tractors are more costly, and fields often are too small for economical use of machines. Manual labor is much cheaper. Rice often is produced as cheaply by hand methods in some countries as it is in other countries that use the most modern equipment. Rice produced in Southeast Asia competes successfully with that grown in the United States.

Power farming is most profitable where wages are high and machines are built by mass production. Between 1933–48 farm wage rates in the United States increased more than fourfold and the price of horse feed increased more than threefold. In the same period, the costs of farm machinery and motor supplies not quite doubled. Rapid mechanization of farm operations was inevitable under such circumstances. Since WW II the total operating hourly cost of a tractor, exclusive of the driver, having the power of about 80 men or 8 horses has averaged little more than the hourly wage of a farm worker in the grain regions and about the same as the hourly cost of 4 work horses.

Effect of Yield on Production Costs

Relatively high acre yields are the chief factor in low cost grain production in a region where land values are similar and farm equipment fairly standardized. The acre cost of growing grain increases with higher yields, but not proportionally, because the charges for land use, soil preparation, seed, seeding, cultivation, and equipment are similar for low- and high-yielding fields, up to harvest time. But increased yields entail extra harvesting costs and, often, higher costs for better land, increased fertilizer applications, spraying for weed control, or more intensive tillage. On the other hand, the sowing of good quality seed of the best varieties, seed treatment, and correct and timely field operations cost little more than ordinary practices. An increase of one bushel an acre over a 30-bushel yield of wheat, a 3.3 per cent increase, may increase net income by 5.5–8.7 per cent.

Rates for custom combining and corn picking usually are assessed at a fixed rate per acre, or at a basic rate per acre plus a stated premium per bushel. Thus, harvesting costs per acre may be somewhat greater for a large yield. Hauling costs are directly proportional to crop yield.

In earlier years, when grain was harvested with a binder, high yields reduced costs. The cutting time per acre with a binder is nearly the same for high as for low yields. Twine requirements for binding increase from about 1.25 pounds per acre for a 10-bushel yield to 3 pounds for a 40-bushel yield of wheat. One man can shock an acre of bound wheat yielding 10 to 15 bushels in about 1 hour, 20-bushel yield in 1.25 hours, 30-bushel yield in 1.50 hours, and a 40-bushel yield in 1.75 hours. Custom threshing rates for bound grain usually are based on fixed rates per bushel, although the number of bushels threshed per hour of man labor increases appreciably with higher acre yields [4].

Effect of Land Prices on Grain Production

Much of the wheat and grain sorghum and considerable acreages of corn and barley produced in the United States and throughout the world are grown in semiarid regions where land prices are relatively low. Barley is grown mostly on land of medium value. Corn and oats are common crops on highly productive soils. In the Corn Belt of the United States, land prices are based on the direct or indirect returns from the corn crop. In California, Texas, and Louisiana, rice is grown mostly on heavy soils of limited value for other crops; the selling price of such land depends upon the returns from the rice crop. In overpopulated sections of the world where grains are grown mostly for home food use, land often has been priced far above its productive value, but costs of production are a minor consideration

TABLE 1-6. **Cost Per Acre for Harvesting Grain with Tractor Equipment in Nebraska, 1948.**

Machine	Size	Tractor Drawbar Horsepower	Acres per Hour	Cost per Acre[1]				
				Machine Use (dollars)	Power (dollars)	Labor[2] (dollars)	Preparation (dollars)	Total (dollars)
Combine								
Without motor	5-foot	11-20	1.2	1.11	0.66	0.58	0.47	2.82
"	6-foot	11-20	1.4	1.11	0.57	0.50	0.44	2.62
With motor	6-foot	11-20	1.4	1.53	0.57	0.50	0.52	3.12
"	8-foot	11-20	1.7	1.53	0.47	0.41	0.48	2.89
" " (2 men)	10-foot	21-25	2.0	1.53	0.51	0.70	0.55	3.29
" " (2 men)	12-foot	21-25	2.7	1.53	0.38	0.52	0.49	2.92
" " (2 men)	16-foot	21-25	3.1	1.53	0.33	0.45	0.46	2.77
Self-propelled	14-foot	—	3.6	1.72	[3]	0.20	0.38	2.30
Grain binder (1 man)	8-foot	11-20	1.9	0.97	0.42	0.37	0.35	2.11
" " (2 men)	10-foot	11-20	2.4	0.66	0.33	0.58	0.32	1.89
Corn picker								
Pull type	1-row	11-20	0.9	1.00	0.89	0.78	0.53	3.20
" "	2-row	21-25	1.3	1.00	0.78	0.54	0.46	2.78
Mounted	1-row	11-20	0.9	1.00	0.89	0.78	0.53	3.20
"	2-row	21-25	1.5	1.00	0.68	0.47	0.43	2.58
Picker and sheller	2-row	21-25	1.0	1.41	1.02	0.70	0.63	3.76
Corn Snapper	1-row	11-20	0.7	0.80	1.14	1.00	0.59	3.53
Corn Binder	1-row	11-20	1.2	0.95	0.66	0.58	0.44	2.63

[1]These costs are shown for comparative purposes only. By 1961, wage rates in Nebraska exceeded $1.00 per hour, the cost of machinery and supplies had increased appreciably, and interest rates were higher.

[2]At 70 cents per hour.

[3]Included in machine use.

in light of the need for food. Land prices in the grain areas of the United States vary with average acre returns.

Farm ownership in American grain regions becomes unprofitable when land prices per acre rise much above four times the gross annual acre value of the grain crop. A one-third share rental of a crop worth 25 per cent of the land price yields no more than 5 per cent interest on the investment after realty taxes, insurance, and upkeep are deducted.

Effect of Size of Machine on Operating Costs

The cost per acre for machinery use decreases as the size of the machine increases, provided all machines are utilized in proportion to their capacity [11]. Thus, under the conditions indicated, a large tractor is a more economical power unit because it saves labor (Table 1-5). The cost of

TABLE 1-5. **Tractor Operating Costs in Nebraska, 1948.**

Drawbar Horsepower	*Operating Cost*	
	Per Hour	*Approximate Average per Horsepower Hour*
	(dollars)	(dollars)
6–10	0.71	.090
11–20	0.80	.053
21–25	1.02	.045
26–30	1.16	.040

horse work under comparable conditions was about 20 cents an hour. Likewise, the total cost per acre for tillage and seeding is less for large machines. Acre costs for harvesting also are less for larger machines except when extra labor or an additional motor is required (Table 1-6.).

Fixed costs for depreciation, interest, insurance, taxes, and housing made it advisable to use high-priced machines costing $800 or more in 1960 on as large an acreage as possible. Such machines should be used 100–200 hours a year. The cost per acre for fixed items is reduced directly as the acreage covered or number of hours operated during a season is increased. Less expensive machines may be operated economically with 30–100 hours use a year [27]. The normal seasonal capacity of many farm machines is 50–100 per cent greater than the average use they are given in the United States. However, ample machine capacity insures against losses from delayed field operations.

Grain growers may have to choose between the economic feasibility of ownership of combines and custom harvesting. With a custom rate of $5 per acre for harvesting small grains, custom harvesting in Arkansas has a cost advantage over ownership of a 7-foot pull-type combine where annual use is less than 130 acres of small grains. Custom harvesting would have a cost advantage over ownership of a 12- or 14-foot self-propelled combine where fewer than 275 acres of small grains were harvested annually. Above these respective levels of use, ownership would have a cost advantage [5].

Fully 90 per cent of the combines and corn pickers in the United States are owned by their operators. The remainder are owned in partnership. Many operators do custom work for others. About 30 per cent of the corn and grain sorghum growers and more than 40 per cent of the wheat and oat growers hire custom machines for some of their harvesting, spraying, and other field operations.

REFERENCES

1. *Agricultural statistics, 1959.* USDA, pp 1–632. 1960.
2. Bennett, M. K., "International contrasts in food consumption." *Geog. Rev.,* **31**: 365–376. 1941.
3. ———, *The World's Food.* New York: Harper. pp 1–282. 1954.
4. Bonnen, C. A., and J. B. Hutson, "Profitable farming systems for central South Dakota." S.Dak. Ag. Exp. Sta. *Bul. 226.* pp 1–80. 1927.
5. Capstick, D. F., "Costs of harvesting with grain combines." Ark. Ag. Exp. Sta. *Bul. 630.* 1960.
6. Christensen, R. P., "Efficient use of food resources in the United States." USDA *Tech. Bul. 963.* pp 1–98. 1948.
7. *Consumption of food in the United States, 1909-52.* USDA Ag. Hndbk. No. 62. pp 249. 1953.
8. Cooper, M. R., G. T. Barton, and A. P. Brodell, "Progress of farm mechanization." USDA *Misc. Publ. No. 630.* 1947.
9. Davis, L. L., "California rice production." Cal. Ag. Exten. *Cir. 163.* 1950.
10. DeCandolle A., *Origin of Cultivated Plants,* 2d. ed., New York: Hafner, pp 1–468. (Reprinted 1959.) 1886.
11. Epp, A. W., "Cost of operating machinery on Nebraska farms." Nebr. Ag. Exp. Sta. *Bul. 413.* 1952.
12. "Farm costs and returns—commercial farms by type, size, and location." USDA Ag. Info. *Bul. 230.* 1960.
13. "Farm production practices, costs and returns." USDA Ec. Stat. *Bul. 83.* pp 1–115. 1949.
14. "Grain." FAO-UN Comm. Ser. *Bul. 18.* 1950.
15. Helbaek, H., "Domestication of food plants in the Old World." *Sci.,* **130**(3372): 365–372. 1959.
16. Jasny, N., *Competition Among Grains.* Stanford U., Food Res. Inst. pp 1–606. 1940.
17. Jenkins, M. T., "Influence of climate and weather on growth of corn," in *Climate and Man.* USDA Yrbk. of Ag. pp 308–320. 1941.
18. ———, "Genetic improvement of food plants for increased yield." Amer. Phil. Soc. *Proc.,* **95**(1): 84–91. 1951.

19. Jennings, R. D., "Consumption of feed by livestock, 1909–47." USDA *Cir. 836.* pp 1–105. 1949.
20. Leonard, W. H., "World population in relation to potential food supply." *Sci. Mo.,* **85:** 113–125. 1957.
21. Magee, A. C., and C. A. Bonnen, "Information basic to adjustments in rice production in Texas." Tex. Ag. Exp. Sta. *Bul. 676.* pp 1–46. 1945.
22. ———, C. A. Bonnen, and B. H. Thibodeaux, "Information basic to farm adjustments in the high plains cotton area of Texas." Tex. Ag. Exp. Sta. *Bul. 652.* pp 1–81. 1944.
23. Majors, K. R., "Cereal grains as food and feed," in *Crops in Peace and War.* USDA Yrbk. of Ag. pp 331–340. 1950–51.
24. Mangelsdorf, P. C., "Wheat." *Sci. Am.,* **189**(1): 50–59. July 1953.
25. Mann, H. H., "Wheat in the Middle East." *Emp. J. Exp. Ag.,* **14:** 31–42. 1946.
26. Martin, J. H., "Climate and sorghum," in *Climate and Man.* USDA Yrbk. of Ag. pp 343–347. 1941.
27. Miller, F., Q. W. Lindsey, and A. G. George, "Cost of operating machinery on Nebraska farms." Nebr. Ag. Exp. Sta. *Bul. 391.* pp 1–35. 1948.
28. Quisenberry, K. S., "Crop production potentials in relation to freedom from want," in *Freedom from Want, Chronica Botanica,* **11**(4): 237–245. 1948.
29. Ruden, W. L., "Farm size and its relation to volume of production, operating costs, and net returns, Southeastern Nebraska, 1930–1939." Nebr. Ag. Exp. Sta. *Bul. 346.* pp 1–16. 1943.
30. Salmon, S. C., "Climate and small grains," in *Climate and Man.* USDA Yrbk. of Ag. pp. 321–342. 1941.
31. Salter, R. M., "World soil and fertilizer resources in relation to food needs," in *Freedom from Want, Chronica Botanica,* **11**(4): 227–235. 1948.
32. Slusher, M. W., and F. Mullins, "Production items and costs for enterprises on rice farms." Ark. Ag. Exp. Sta. *Bul. 489.* pp 1–35. 1949.
33. Stippler, H. H., and E. M. Castle, "Wheat farming in the Columbia Basin of Oregon. Part 2: Cost and returns on specialized wheat-summerfallow farms." Ore. Ag. Exp. Sta. *Bul. 578.* 1961.
34. "The fifth plate." USDA PA *Cir. 191.* 1951.
35. "The story of the cereal grains." General Mills, Inc. pp 1–26. 1944.
36. Vavilov, N. I., "Origin of cultivated plants." Int. Congr. Pl. Sci. *Proc.,* **1:** 167–169. 1926.
37. ———, "The origin, variation, immunity, and breeding of cultivated plants." (Trans. K. Starr Chester.) *Chronica Botanica,* **13**(1–6): 1–364. 1949–50.
38. Wickizer, V. D., and M. K. Bennett, *The Rice Economy of Monsoon Asia.* Stanford U. Food Res. Inst., pp 1–358. 1941.
39. Zinserling, G. D., "Northern limits of agriculture." *Bul. Appl. Bot. and Plant Breed.,* **15:** 127–142. (Eng. summary.) 1925.

2. BOTANY OF THE CEREALS

GENERAL DESCRIPTION

All cereals are normally annuals; that is, they complete the life cycle in one season. However, rice and sorghum plants are able to live as perennials for several years in mild climates. Except in very cold climates, some cereals behave as winter annuals; that is, live through the winter as small plants in the vegetative stage and send up flower stalks in the spring. There are spring and winter types of wheat, barley, oats, and rye. Spring varieties of these crops live through the winter in mild climates.

Cereal plants have a bunch or tussock habit of growth, because new stalks develop only from the basal buds of the axis. The buds on the main stalk may produce several basal branch culms or tillers, but the tillers may repeat the process to form additional tillers [31].

ROOTS

Cereal plants have fibrous roots, *i.e.,* many slender roots of similar diameter and length, and somewhat smaller branches.

FIGURE 2-1. Stages in corn germination: (1) before germination (2) germinated 36 hours (3) 48 hours (4) 4 days (5) 8 days. In the 2 upper views the seedcoat has been removed to expose the embryo. In germinating, the radicle or first seminal root (r) pushes out quickly, the nodel region (n) swells; the coleoptile, which encloses the first leaves and has a vent at the tip (c') grows upward; additional seminal roots (se) arise, usually in pairs above the radicle, after 3 days. Finally the coronal or crown roots (cr) develop and the food substance in the seed (s) is practically exhausted. At (6) a wheat germ enlarged about 25 times shows the scutellum (sc), vent in coleoptile (v), epiblast (e), seminal root swellings (se), and radicle (r) which is enclosed in the coleorhiza.

(*Courtesy US Department of Agriculture*)

26

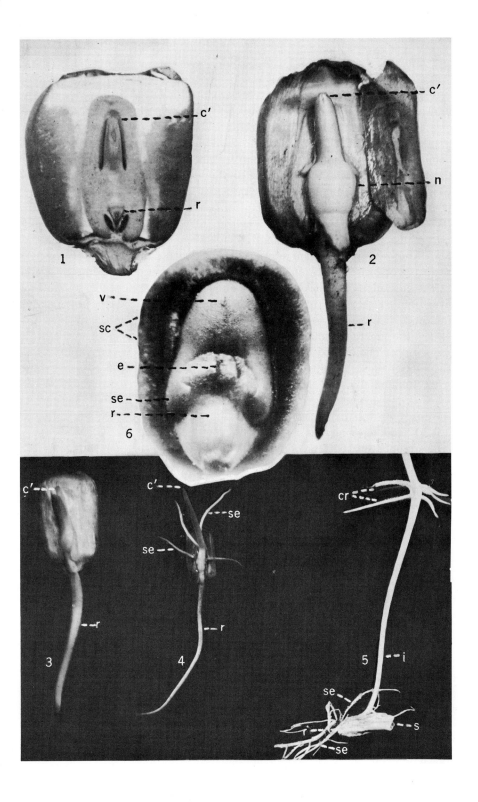

Types of Cereal Roots

Seminal or primary roots develop when the seed germinates (Fig. 2-1), growing downward from the radicle or lower end of the embryo. Wheat, oats, barley, rye, and corn normally develop 3, 5, or 7 seminal roots. Sorghum, rice, and proso produce only a single branched seminal root. Seminal roots sometimes have been erroneously called "temporary roots," the belief being that they function only in early growth stages. Seminal roots may function until the plant matures [70]. Seminal roots of corn may penetrate to a depth of five or six feet, but frequently they die soon after the coronal roots appear [71]. In wheat, they may serve as the chief support of the main stem of the plant [43].

After the young plant unfolds a few leaves, the coronal (crown or nodal) roots arise from stem nodes underground and develop into an elaborate root system. Coronal roots arise about one inch below the soil surface, even though the seed may be planted deeper (Fig. 2-2). The subcrown internode between the seed and crown elongates until stopped by light that strikes the emerging coleoptile. At that stage the crown node is still below the surface. The number of coronal roots at a single node varies, but usually the roots form a definite whorl. Coronal roots initially tend to grow somewhat horizontally, but later they turn abruptly downward [37]. Winter wheat coronal roots show very slow development in the fall, but greatly increased growth in the spring [75]. Coronal roots in corn are ultimately 15–20 times as numerous as the seminal roots [71].

Frequently, roots grow from the nodes above the soil surface as, for example, brace (or aerial) roots of corn. They are unbranched above the ground but appear the same as other coronal roots once they enter the soil.

Extent of Root Systems

Some cereal roots may elongate as rapidly as a half-inch per day; seminal roots of winter wheat may grow at that rate for 70 days [68, 69]. The main vertical roots of corn may grow at the rate of 2.0–2.5 inches per day for three or four weeks. The mature root system of a corn plant may occupy 200 cubic feet of soil. A corn plant grown in loess soil produced 19 main roots with 1462 branches of the second and third orders. The main roots consisted of 4–5 per cent of the total length; the primary branches, 47–67 per cent; the finer secondary and tertiary laterals, 29–48 per cent of the total [71].

With ample space, the roots of a single plant may have a total spread of 4 feet in wheat, 8 feet in corn, and 12 feet in sorghum. Roots of small grains, corn, and sorghum normally penetrate downward 3–6 feet, but may reach a depth of 8–10 feet or more.

FIGURE 2-2. Corn plants 2, 4, 6 and 10 inches deep. The crown was formed at nearly the same depth regardless of planting depth.

(*Courtesy US Department of Agriculture*)

A single winter rye plant that bore 80 culms with 420 leaves had a total external surface of 51.38 square feet, while the surface area of subterranean parts was 6875.4 square feet, 130 times greater [17].

A high correlation between root and top growth occurs in corn (Table 2-1). In a comparison of small, medium, and large types of corn in Nebraska, the rates of root and top growth were approximately the same for all types until the small varieties tasseled. Thereafter, continued vegetative top growth caused the medium and large types to surpass the small type in root growth. As the medium type commenced tasseling, its vegetative

TABLE 2-1. **Comparison of Root Systems of Small, Medium, and Large Types of Corn**

Character observed	Varietal Type		
	Small	Medium	Large
Lateral spread of roots:			
Maximum (in.)	36	48	54
Average for node of greatest spread (in.)	35	39	38
Depth of root penetration:			
Maximum (in.)	67	73	74
Average (in.)	47	54	58
Functional roots (number)	60	85	99
Combined length of main roots (ft)	283	346	545
Root volume (cc)	403	749	1484
Root weight (gm)	36	77	148

development was exceeded by that of the large [71]. In seedling oat plants, top growth and root development are highly correlated. Root growth is reduced proportionally by the removal of top growth [65].

Like the roots of most other crop plants, roots of cereal plants do not extend into water-logged soil. A wet surface soil in the early stage of plant growth promotes a shallow root habit that may cause the plant to suffer in drought. Delayed irrigation may encourage deeper root penetration in spring wheat. Roots penetrate dry soil only slightly beyond available soil moisture supplies. There are fewer roots in the third and fourth foot depths when irrigated only at the heading, blossoming, or grain-filling stages than when irrigated only once at germination, tillering, or the jointing stage [60]. Roots of mature winter wheat plants were observed at a depth of 13 feet where moisture conditions were favorable; *i.e.,* soil wetted to a depth of 6 feet just before seeding. Nitrogen fertilizer increased root weights as well as moisture utilization at all moisture levels [38].

Absorption by Roots

Plants absorb water and mineral nutrients largely through the root hairs. The roots absorb water by osmosis, while the cytoplasmic membrane of the cell is the selective tissue that restricts the free entry or exit of nutrient ions that plants absorb. When the cell sap is more concentrated than the soil solution, water passes into the root hairs, except under very abnormal soil conditions. The rate of absorption of water varies with the osmotic potential of the cell [63]. In corn, the most rapid entry of water into the roots occurs in the zone between the 6 and 10 cm levels above the root tip [30]. Increasing the soil moisture tension progressively to 12 atmospheres brings about progressively diminishing absorption, fresh weight, dry weight, and seedling hydration in corn. Growth behavior is most sensitive in the range 1–3 atmospheres [22].

The more a plant needs water the more vigorously it absorbs it, provided the water supply remains ample. Water taken up in excess of the ability of the plant to transpire water vapor through the stomata is forced out through pores in the leaf called *hydathodes.* Most so-called dewdrops are actually water globules from hydathodes. Plasmolysis (cell collapse) results when the soil solution is more concentrated than that in the root hair and other cells. Such a condition may be found in saline, or "alkali," soils where water is actually withdrawn from the plant [48].

Nutrients are absorbed as ions by active uptake processes associated with the metabolism of the root. For instance, potassium nitrate (KNO_3) dissolves and becomes dissociated into K^+ and NO_3^- ions. These ions are transported across the semipermeable membrane independently of water uptake. Thus, it is possible for mineral nutrients to be absorbed when the atmosphere is saturated, little water is being taken up, and none transpired. Mineral nutrients can be concentrated in the cell at concentrations far above that in the external solution. However, water movement in soil may help transport nutrients to the root.

FIGURE 2-3. Tillers and tiller buds in a sorghum plant. The swollen portion of the culm in the front center is a node.

(*Courtesy US Department of Agriculture*)

FIGURE 2-4. A wheat plant with about 150 tillers.

(*Courtesy US Department of Agriculture*)

STEMS OR CULMS

After a cereal seed germinates, the plumule internodes elongate into the first young stem. The lower internodes, which are formed first, are very short. While the cells are young and active, stem elongation continues by cell division as well as cell elongation at the growth ring above each successive node. As many as three internodes may be elongating at the same time. Growth in diameter of the stem of cereals is a consequence of cell enlargement, not cell division, after the essential structures have been formed.

General Properties of Stems

The stem of a cereal plant is divided into nodes (Fig. 2-3) and internodes, the stem section between the nodes being called internodes. Young internodes are filled with pith; except in corn, sorghum, and some wheats, the pith usually disappears before maturity. The length attained by internodes varies with position and by species. In general, the basal internodes remain short. With some exceptions, the upper ones become progressively longer. The uppermost internode (the peduncle) bears the inflorescence and is usually the longest one. The stem or culm of a cereal is cylindrical, or nearly so. The stems die down to the soil surface after the seed has matured [32, 31], except in sorghum and proso millet. They often develop axillary branches after the seed is ripe.

In addition to the main stem, branches known as *tillers* (Fig. 2-3) may arise from each of the subterranean nodes in most cereals. They often produce a number of tillers from the primary stem, and they in turn produce others. Usually 30–40 tillers, occasionally as many as 150, may arise from a single seed under favorable environmental conditions (Fig. 2-4). Each tiller develops its own root system.

The stem may change type during the life of the cereal plant. Sometimes the primary axis within the plumule remains so short that the leaves are crowded together in a rosette. Winter annuals, such as winter wheat, exhibit this habit until sometime in the spring.

Temperature and day length affect the growth habit of cereals. Certain varieties of winter oats may show a spreading habit when sown in the fall, but an erect habit when sown in the spring.

Lodging in Cereals

Resistance to lodging (*i.e.,* the capacity of stems to withstand the adverse effects of rain and wind) is an important quality in cereals. Often varietal in character, its expression is modified by environment. For example, a thick heavy growth keeps much of the sunlight from reaching the base of the stems, and shade causes the cell walls of the stems to be thin and weak.

Most analyses of morphological characters of cereals reveal no single factor that can be used as an infallible index of standability [44]. Large culm diameter often has been associated with lodging resistance in small grains [72, 10, 26, 50]; but stiffness of straw may not be a reliable guide to the lodging resistance of a plant having a weak root system [26]. More important factors are length of straw, leaf area, and resistance to bending. Semidwarf wheats, about two-thirds as tall as common commercial varieties, offer a possible reduction in lodging without a loss in yield [66]. Apparently, there is no relationship between wheat tillering rates and lodging in the field [10]. Breaking strength of straw [14], as well as weight per unit length of basal culm [3] have been associated with lodging resistance. Short, thick, heavy stems with thick walls are the best insurance against lodging [3].

Lodging also may result from a low content of dry matter per unit length of culm, a reduced content of lignin, or of certain di- or polysaccharides in the stem [72]. Yield decreases in winter wheat caused by lodging two weeks after heading may be a result of restricted photosynthesis and subsequent translocation and water intake imposed by the crushed tissue. Reduced light exposure and lower water content of lodged plants may contribute to decreased rates of photosynthesis, decreased carbohydrate production, reduction in amino acid synthesis, and decreased protein production. Production of carbohydrates was decreased proportionally more than that of protein when the plants were lodged, with resultant higher percentages of protein in the grain [52].

Abundant soil nitrogen may produce a lush growth of cereals that leads to increased lodging. Such effects often result from nitrogen fertilizer applications [8, 23, 42]. Lodging usually has been decreased in small grains by applications of phosphorus and potash on deficient soils because these nutrients promote root development [8, 26]. Corn plants also lodge in soils deficient in potash [42]. A proper balance of nitrogen, phosphorus, and potash in the soil reduces lodging to a minimum.

Cereal pests also contribute to lodging. In wheat, lodging may be aggravated by infestations of the Hessian fly, wheat jointworm, billbugs, and sawflies which weaken the stems, or of root worms which feed on the roots. Diseases that cause deterioration of the stems or roots, such as the foot rots, rusts, take-all, and eyespot, contribute to lodging [21] (Fig. 2-5).

When a grass or cereal stem lodges before maturity, it usually bends upward as a result of cell elongation on the lower side of the nodes. This in turn is the result of a response to an apogeotropic (opposed to gravity) stimulus. The thickened nodal tissue, which functions to bend up the stem, occurs in both the sheath and culm in some of the cereal grasses; *e.g.,* corn and sorghums. However, it is found only at the base of the sheath in wheat, oats, barley, and rye.

LEAVES

Leaves of cereals arise from buds which are lateral appendages of the plant stem. Leaves are functional in photosynthesis and transpiration.

General Characteristics

Grass leaves are 2-ranked, or *distichous*. There are two parts of the foilage leaf, the sheath and blade or lamina. Most grasses are characterized by a long, narrow, flat blade that tapers to a point. The leaves are parallel-veined; *i.e.,* contain many veins about equal in size that run parallel and are joined by inconspicuous veinlets. Such leaves grow from the base.

At the junction of the sheath and blade there occurs a thin membranous outgrowth known as the *ligule*. Because its relative development varies greatly in different species, the ligule often is of taxonomic value. Absence of the ligule in a cereal is usually a recessive character. Lateral outgrowths known as *auricles* may occur above the ligule, being well developed in *Hordeum* (Fig. 2-6) and in *Oryza*. The region on the back of the leaf at the junction of the sheath and blade is called the collar.

Modified leaves include: (1) Scale leaves or reduced leaves below the foliage leaves; (2) bracts or reduced leaves above the foliage leaves, which include glumes, lemmas, and paleas; and (3) flower parts; *i.e.,* stamens and pistils.

FIGURE 2-5. **A type of lodging or stem breaking called crinkling which occurs after the culm is ripe, dead and attacked by saprophytic fungi.**

(*Courtesy US Department of Agriculture*)

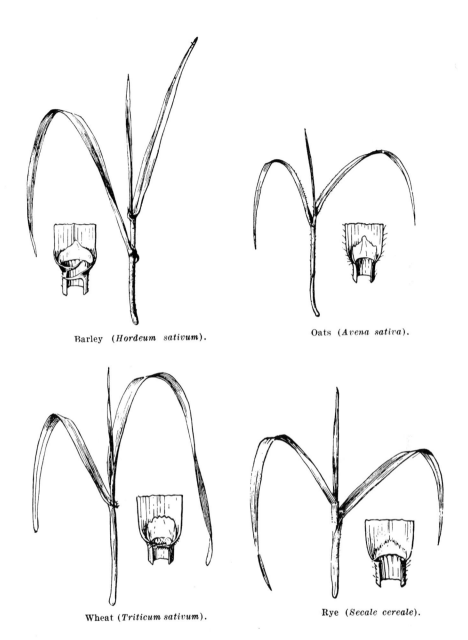

Barley (*Hordeum sativum*).

Oats (*Avena sativa*).

Wheat (*Triticum sativum*).

Rye (*Secale cereale*).

FIGURE 2-6. **Distinguishing characters of young cereal leaves and sheaths, and of ligules and auricles (see inserts). Barley has long clasping smooth auricles; wheat has shorter hairy auricles; rye has very short auricles, whereas the oat sheath has no auricles. The sheaths of rye and oats and the leaf margins of oats have hairs. Note also the differences in the shape of the shieldlike ligule at the base of each leaf blade.**

(*Courtesy US Department of Agriculture*)

Transpiration

Transpiration is the evaporation of water from the aerial parts of plants, particularly the leaves. Most of the water absorbed by plants is transpired, but a plant is unable to grow unless it has sufficient water at its disposal. A single corn plant has been found to lose by transpiration more than 400 pounds during its life span of 100 days. At this rate, an acre of corn would evaporate about 1200 tons of water in a 100-day season. Most of the water that evaporates from the leaves passes out into the air through the stomata, but a small amount of water vapor diffuses through the cuticles of epidermal layers.

In the transpiration process, liquid water changes to the vapor form as it passes from the walls of the mesophyll cells in the leaves, where such cell walls are exposed to the intercellular spaces of the mesophyll tissues. As water vapor collects in these intercellular spaces, it diffuses through the stomata into the outside air.

Light, temperature, humidity, wind velocity, and soil conditions influence the rate of transpiration in plants. When the stomata are open, transpiration is more rapid in bright light than in diffused light and darkness. High temperatures, low humidity, and wind movement favor increased transpiration. When soil water is readily absorbed, the transpiration rate is higher than where the water is absorbed with difficulty. Cereal plant modifications that check excessive evaporation are reduced leaf surfaces, thickened cuticle, and waxy bloom on the cuticle of leaves and stems. A waxy bloom is conspicuous on sorghum, wheat, and barley.

The ratio of the total water absorbed to the total amount of dry matter produced by the plant is termed the *water requirement* or *transpiration ratio*. It usually is expressed as the number of pounds of water required to produce one pound of dry matter; that ranges from 200 to 1000 pounds for different crops. The transpiration ratio for a given crop is influenced by the transpiration rate, but also by the growth and adaptation of the crop. As an example, oats assume a comparatively high water requirement when temperatures are too high for optimum growth. Under such conditions, a warm-weather crop like sorghum is relatively more efficient in the use of water [61]. In a cool season, the reverse may be true. The mean water requirements of some cereals investigated at Akron, Colorado, 1913–17 were as follows: oats 635, barley 521, wheat 505, corn 372, millet 287, and sorghum 271. All of these water requirements were based upon the total dry matter in the plants above the ground.

A more practical measure of the water requirement for crops is termed *consumptive use,* which includes evaporation from the soil surface as well as transpiration through the plant.

Effects of Defoliation

Defoliation of cereals during active growth reduces the photosynthetic area of the plants and may result in serious reductions in yield. The extent of injury depends largely on the stage of plant development. The principal causes of defoliation are hail injury and leaf diseases.

Experiments to ascertain the effects of hail injury on cereals have included whipping, shredding, and removal of the leaves. In Illinois, untreated corn yielded 62.1 bushels of grain per acre, while corn lightly whipped when the tassels began to emerge produced 59.4 bushels. Plants in full tassel whipped a week later yielded 52.2 bushels. Corn that was defoliated in the early silking stage yielded only 4.8 bushels per acre. The reduction in yield was progressively less as the treatment was administered later in plant development [18]. In Iowa, a yield reduction of less than 10 per cent followed defoliation of corn at the 6-leaf stage, but the yield was almost nothing when defoliation occurred after all the leaves had unrolled [19]. The most serious injury occurred at the flowering stage. Defoliation delayed flowering 2–5 days.

Leaf removal was inflicted on oats, barley, and wheat in Iowa at weekly intervals from the seedling stage to the hard-dough stage of the grain. Cutting off all leaves above the growing point reduced yields about in proportion to the percentage of leaf area removed at each weekly interval [20]. Winter wheat yields in Kansas were reduced 23.5–31.7 per cent when the leaf blades were removed at or just prior to heading. This decrease apparently was associated with the loss of nitrogen accumulated in the leaves and with the decreased photosynthetic tissue. Removal of the leaf blades also reduced the protein content of the grain [52].

Leaf diseases, such as heavy infections of leaf rust (*Puccinia triticina*), often reduce the photosynthetic area and consequently the yields of wheat [34] by a reduction in the number and size of the kernels. The yield of resistant varieties may suffer one third as much yield reduction as a susceptible variety, from the killing of many green leaf cells; *i.e.,* flecking.

Spraying leaves with chemical desiccants to hasten drying has been ineffective on corn, grain sorghum, wheat, oats, and barley, but has been used to a limited extent in California on rice grown for seed [1]. Spraying nearly mature corn with endothal did not reduce the grain moisture significantly; water from the stalk continued to move into the ear [11].

INFLORESCENCE

As in other grasses, the flowers of cereals are grouped on an axis of the inflorescence, called a *rachis*; in maize, a *cob*. An individual flower stalk is a *pedicel*. The inflorescence of wheat, barley, and rye is a spike in which the sessile spikelets are attached along a rachis. The inflorescence in oats, rice, sorghum, and most of the millets is a branched panicle bearing spikelets on pedicels (Fig. 2-7).

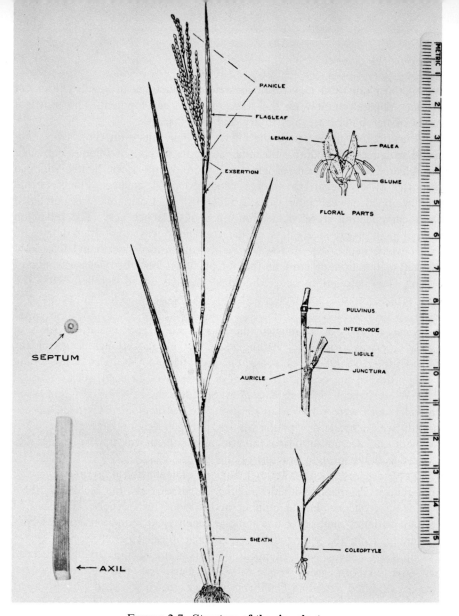

SEPTUM

AXIL

FIGURE 2-7. **Structure of the rice plant.**

(*Courtesy US Department of Agriculture*)

Spikelet

The spikelet consists of one or more florets subtended by two bracts called *glumes*. The floret is subtended or enclosed by two bracts, the *lemma* and the *palea* (Fig. 2-8). In the floret are the stamens, pistil, and lodicules. There are three stamens in each floret of the cereals, except for rice which has six. The stamen is composed of a filament or stalk which bears an anther. The interior lobes of the anthers are pollen sacs in which pollen is produced in the form of loose, round pollen grains. Finally, each sac splits open or dehisces to allow the pollen to escape. The pistil is single with a one-celled ovary that bears a style topped by a bifurcate (divided) stigma. The lodicules (usually two) are small, greenish, scalelike structures which lie between the ovary and the lemma and palea. At the time of fertilization, the lodicules swell to force open the floret. Individual florets are borne on rachillas, an extension of the pedicel within the spikelet. Awns if present usually occur on the lemma. The awn usually is a prolongation of the apex of the lemma, but it may arise dorsally, as in *Avena* [31, 48].

FIGURE 2-8. **Oat floret, showing the anthers and stigma within the lemma and palea, with a detached ovary at right.**

(*Courtesy US Department of Agriculture*)

Mode of Pollination

Most cereals have perfect or bisexual flowers that contain both stamens and pistils. Corn and wild rice are monoecious and have separate staminate and pistillate flowers borne on the same plant. Cereal crops also may be naturally self-pollinated, often cross-pollinated, or naturally cross-pollinated.

Naturally self-pollinated cereals, (wheat, oats, barley, and rice) usually show less than 1–4 per cent of cross-pollination, the amount being dependent upon variety and environment [5, 64]. The pistil generally is pollinated by pollen from the same flower. Barley grown in adjacent rows usually cross-pollinates less than 0.15 per cent, but Nudideficiens, a two-rowed barley never grown commercially in the United States, showed 3–21 per cent of natural crossing in different years. The floral bracts of this variety remained open during the pollination period [55].

FIGURE 2-9. **The barley pistil: (c) cone-shaped tip of outer integument, (ie) inner epidermis of ovary wall, (ii) inner integument, (lps) lateral procambium strands, (m) micropyle, (n) nucellus which contains the embryo sac, (oi) outer integument, (pg) pollen grain, (s) style, and (sh) stigma hair. The broken line shows the course of the pollen tube from pollen grain to micropyle (m). Above the micropyle are 2 synergids and the egg nuclei. The 3 antipodal cells higher up have already divided several times.**

(Courtesy US Department of Agriculture)

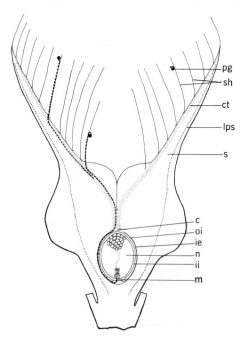

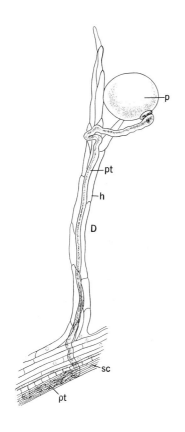

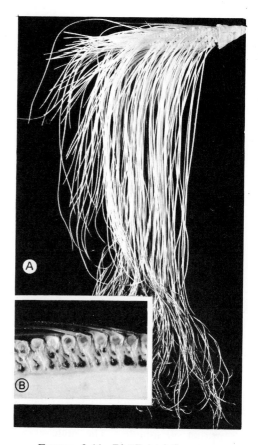

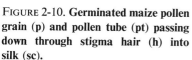

FIGURE 2-10. **Germinated maize pollen grain (p) and pollen tube (pt) passing down through stigma hair (h) into silk (sc).**
(*Courtesy US Department of Agriculture*)

FIGURE 2-11. **Pistillate inflorescence of maize. (a) unpollinated ear and silks; (b) enlarged ovaries showing attachment of silks.**

Often cross-pollinated cereals include sorghum and the foxtail and proso millets. The pistil may be pollinated by pollen from the same flower, from another flower on the same plant, or from another plant. Crossing among the cereals is largely via air-borne pollen. Self-pollination usually is 90–95 per cent in sorghum [62].

Naturally cross-pollinated cereals include corn, rye, and pearl millet. Cross-pollination is essential to seed production in many plants of rye because they are self-sterile. In corn, self-pollination is effectively restricted by monoecism, being less than 5 per cent [29], even as low as 0.7 per cent [36]. Self-pollination in pearl millet is restricted by protogyny, a condition in which the stigmas are receptive before the stamens shed their pollen.

Process of Fertilization

The ovary of a grass plant contains a single ovule composed of a nucellus surrounded by inner and outer integuments. The embryo sac (Fig. 2-9), which is within the nucellus, is composed of 8 nuclei as follows: 2 synergids and 1 egg cell at the micropylar end, 3 antipodal cells at the opposite end, and 2 endosperm or polar nuclei near the center. When pollen grains fall on the stigma of the pistil, they germinate in the sticky stigmatic excretion. The germinated pollen grain contains a tube nucleus and 2 sperm nuclei. The tube nucleus digests its way down the vascular bundles of the style to the embryo sac. One sperm nucleus unites with the egg cell, while the other fuses with the 2 endosperm nuclei. Fusion of the sperm nucleus with the egg cell is termed fertilization. This union gives rise to the zygote, diploid in chromosome number. The fusion of the second male nucleus with the 2 endosperm nuclei, termed double fertilization, gives rise to the endosperm which is triploid in chromosome number. The process of fertilization has been described in detail for corn [49, 37].

Fertilization in corn (Figs. 2-10, 2-11) takes place 26–28 hours after pollination [49]. In barley, the pollen grain has been found to germinate 5 minutes after it reached the stigma, the male nuclei had entered the embryo sac within 45 minutes, and the fertilized egg had begun division within 15 hours [54]. In common oats, pollen has been observed to germinate on the stigma and send tubes into the style 5 minutes after pollination. The male generative nuclei were near the egg nucleus and polar nuclei within 30 minutes. The male gamete had entered the egg within 4 hours, while the fertilized egg was in prophase 13.5 hours after pollination [6].

Immediate Effect of Foreign Pollen

The mechanism of double fertilization accounts for the phenomenon of xenia, the immediate observable effect of foreign pollen on the endosperm [67], first reported in corn. Endosperm characters of the pollen parent are evident as soon as the outcrossed grains ripen, when the character is determined by a dominant gene. For example, the endosperm of white corn or sorghum strains becomes yellow when pollinated by plants with yellow kernels. Xenia also produces changes in the composition, texture, and weight of the endosperm in corn. As an example, the kernels of waxy or sweet types become starchy and heavier when outcrossed by plants with starchy kernels [37]. Xenia also has been observed in barley, rye, and rice.

CARYOPSIS OR KERNEL

Cereals produce a dry, indehiscent, one-seeded fruit known as a

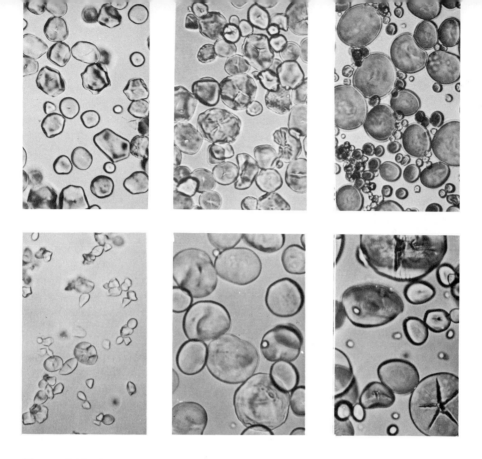

FIGURE 2-12. Corn and sorghum starch granules are roughly spherical or polyhedral, and mostly 10 to 20 microns in diameter, with more large granules in sorghum. Wheat, barley, and rye starch granules are small and spherical or large and lens-shaped. Wheat starch has more small granules and rye starch more large granules. Rye granules often have a prominent hilum with radiating fissures. Oat starch granules are mostly 2 to 3 microns in diameter, but oat starch contains many larger granules.

(*Courtesy US Department of Agriculture*)

caryopsis. It is commonly called a grain, kernel, or seed. The characteristics of the starch granules vary in the different cereals (Fig. 2-12).

General Structure

In the caryopsis, the ovary wall or pericarp is fused with the seedcoat or testa of the seed, technically a matured ovule. The wheat kernel has been described as a kind of nut with a single seed [53]. The kernel (caryopsis) consists of pericarp, endosperm, and embryo. The outer rim of the embryo is the scutellum—a flattened, somewhat fleshy, shield-shaped structure that lies back of the plumule and close to the endosperm. The scutellum is regarded as the single cotyledon of a grass "seed" or caryopsis.

Process of Germination

Cereal seeds must take up water to reach a moisture content of about 30 per cent before germination will take place. The processes of conversion, respiration, and growth begin as the seed first takes up water and swells. An oxygen supply and a temperature of 40°–60°F, depending upon the species, also are necessary for germination.

In the germination process, the compounds in the seed are broken down into simpler ones, chiefly by hydrolysis through enzyme action. Starches are converted to sugars by the action of the enzyme diastase, fats are broken down to fatty acids by the lipases, and proteins are converted to amino acids by proteases. These simple compounds are then transported to the embryo cells in active growth. Respiration, which occurs at a high rate during germination, provides the energy for seedling growth [47].

Seeds of cereals remain in the soil during germination, which is termed hypogeal germination. On germination, the coleorhiza elongates and breaks through the pericarp. Shortly afterwards, the seminal roots break through the end of the coleorhiza. The plumule grows upward. The first leaf, the coleoptile, appears above ground as a single-pole tubelike structure. The first blade soon appears from a slit in the tip of the coleoptile. As the embryo grows, the endosperm becomes soft and decreases in dry weight as roots and leaves develop. The seedling is able to carry on photosynthesis, which makes it independent of the stored food in the seed, usually within 10 days after germination begins [53].

Conditions Affecting Germination

The minimum moisture content of corn seed for germination is about 30.5 per cent; that for rice, about 26.5 per cent. The maximum soil moisture tension for the germination of corn at 77°F is 12.5 atmospheres; for rice, only 7.9 atmospheres. These cereals germinated in different soil types with soil moisture percentages as follows:

Soil Type	Corn %	Rice %
Miami silt loam	4.14	4.59
Nappanee clay loam	6.42	7.09
Brookston sandy clay loam	7.60	9.18
Bono clay	12.80	14.30

Seeds in soil at or near the wilting point do not germinate but will mold [33].

All breaks in the seed coat are deleterious to germination in the cereals [46]. Broken seeds often have low viability. Injury to the embryo usually is the most serious. A crosswise break in barley was less injurious than it was in wheat or rye. Broken seeds show more mold growth than do whole seeds. For example, whole wheat seed germinated 91 per cent, but injured seed only 24 per cent. In sorghums, whole seed germinated 82 per cent, but the germination of injured seed dropped to 28 per cent. A marked decrease in the germination of mutilated seeds of wheat and corn, when the germ was injured, also has been observed [74].

Immature seeds of corn will grow within 20 days after the fertilization of the silks [36]. When planted the following year, mature seed produced an average yield of 64.5 bushels per acre, while immature seed harvested in the late milk stage yielded 63.4 bushels. Immature seeds usually develop more mold growth than do mature seeds. Because there is less food reserves in the endosperm, they also produce smaller sprouts.

The effect of seed size on seedling weight in wheat is shown in Fig. 2-13. These data were computed from tests with numerous grain samples of varying plumpness as a result of different degrees of stem rust attack in the fields from which the samples were obtained.

Dormancy in Cereal Seeds

Seeds of some cereals may be dormant when freshly harvested. They need a period of storage in which to afterripen before they are capable of germination. Most cereal seeds afterripen when stored 1–6 months at 104°F [7]. Dormancy in wheat, barley, and oats often disappears in 20–30 days

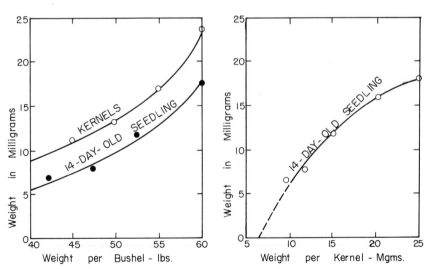

FIGURE 2-13. **Effect of test weight per bushel of hard red spring wheat on kernel weight, and on weight of seedling produced from the seed.**

(Courtesy US Department of Agriculture)

after harvest [16], but may persist for 60 days in wheat [45]. A higher percentage of dormancy also has been observed in wheat harvested before it is mature [73]. Freshly harvested oats and barley, kept at a temperature of 36°F in a relatively high humidity, remained dormant for 3 years. Dormancy is less common in sorghum than in oats or barley [7]. Varieties of the different cereals differ markedly in dormancy [16, 7, 27, 28, 9]. Hullless varieties of barley often show a high germination after harvest, whereas hulled 6-rowed varieties often have dormant periods of 20 days [16].

Temporary dormancy of cereal grains is desirable where prolonged moist weather conditions occur at harvest, as happens in western Canada in some years [27, 28]. Dormancy prevents sprouting in the swath or shock [9], when wet weather prevails. Sorghum often sprouts on the standing stalk. In one very wet season in Colorado, some ripe winter wheat varieties sprouted in the head while still standing in the field, some varieties more than others [16].

For germination tests in seed laboratories, the dormancy of freshly harvested seeds of wheat, barley, oats, and rye can be broken when the seeds are placed in a moist substratum for 5 days at 10°C (50°F) prior to a conventional germination test at 20°C (68°F) [47].

Longevity of Cereal Seeds

Cereal seeds remain viable longer in dry storage in a dry climate than in a humid climate [47]. Longevity of cereal seeds usually is limited to less than two years under warm moist conditions and perhaps forty years under cool dry conditions. Purported germination of mummy wheat from ancient Egyptian tombs is a fable. When seeds are stored in open bins or porous bags their moisture content fluctuates with the relative humidity of the immediate atmosphere [51]. The literature on longevity of cereal and other seeds has been reviewed by several writers [12, 13, 51].

In the warm humid climate of Japan, brown rice stored in straw bags remained fully viable from fall harvest until the next May, but by August germination was only 11–30 per cent, and by October, only 1 per cent. The viability of rough rice was retained longer, but it was less than 10 per cent in November and December, one year after harvest [39]. Wheat, maize, naked barley, and rice seeds were dried to 12 per cent moisture, and stored in rice-straw bags or airtight metal containers. Germination of rice stored in straw bags was very low after one year, but the other grains retained about 80 per cent of their original germination. Naked barley remained viable the longest, but none of the grains germinated after two years. Rice stored in airtight tins still had 64 per cent germination after two years. After 33 months in tins, the germination of maize, naked barley, wheat, and rice was 82, 78, 82.3 and 9.2 per cent, respectively [35].

Wheat, barley, and oats stored in a dry, unheated room in Colorado for ten years germinated 93.7, 85.9, and 87.2 per cent, respectively, small losses in viability. After fifteen years the germination percentages were: wheat, 80.5; hulled barley, 95.8; hull-less barley, 73.9; and oats, 84.8. After twenty years, the average germination percentages for wheat, oats, and barley were 12.8, 49.6, and 46.2, respectively. The 6-rowed hulled barleys maintained their viability better than did the 2-rowed hulled and 6-rowed naked varieties. Rosen rye lost viability after five years; all seeds were dead after eighteen years. Black Amber sorghum maintained its viability, with 97.9 per cent germination in the seventeenth year. Yellow dent maize gradually declined over the 21 years, with a germination of 32 per cent at the end of the period. Thus, in a dry cool climate, like that of Colorado, wheat, oats, barley, sorghum, and maize can be stored for twenty years and there will be enough viable seeds left to maintain the different stocks [56, 57, 59].

Cereal seeds were stored up to thirty-two years in unsealed containers in a semiarid section of Washington, where the average annual precipitation is 11.41 inches and the average yearly temperature 49.7°F. Barley remained viable longest, followed by wheat, oats, corn, and rye. Beldi barley germinated 96 per cent after thirty-two years, whereas Marquis wheat germinated 85 per cent and several other wheat varieties had lost all viability; Banner oats germinated 84 per cent, while Richland oats showed only 6 per cent germination; Dakota flint maize germinated 70 per cent after 32 years, while other varieties showed much lower percentages. Rye failed to germinate after 24–32 years. Viability seemed to be retained longer by unthreshed seeds than by those threshed before storage [25].

Wheat, oats, and barley seeds stored in a saturated atmosphere deteriorated seriously by mold growth within 30 days. Only a slight loss in viability occurred in some samples stored for 1032 days at 57.6 per cent relative humidity [58].

Ideal temperature for storage of dry seeds in airtight containers is 23–41°F. [51]. The optimum condition for storage of cereal seeds is drying followed by sealed storage in the absence of oxygen and at a low temperature. The germination of brown rice was maintained perfectly for four years, stored in airtight containers or in carbon dioxide at a moisture content of 10–12 per cent and at a temperature less than 30°C (86°F) [40, 41].

There is evidence that mutations as well as structural chromosome changes arise in aged seeds of several cereal species. Chlorophyll defects and a few morphological mutations have been reported in maize plants grown from aged seeds. Barley plants raised from seeds 4–7 years old had a mutation frequency 15 times greater than plants raised from fresh seeds. In wheat, the frequency of structural chromosome changes increases with the age of seed. These changes are more pronounced in wheat than in barley or rye in which gene mutations are more prevalent [24, 15].

Conditions at the National Seed Storage Laboratory at Fort Collins,

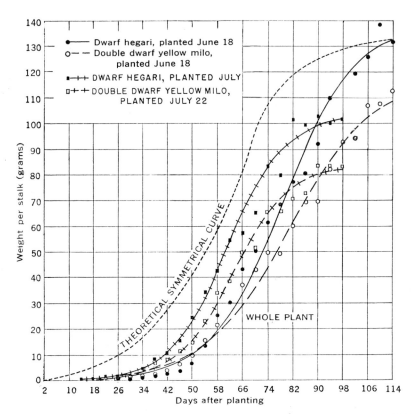

FIGURE 2-14. **Total air-dry weight per stalk of Dwarf hegari and Double Dwarf Yellow milo planted on two different dates. The dots and circles represent the actual weights and the lines the fitted curves. Most crop plants, such as corn and barley, show a growth rate close to the theoretical symmetrical curve. The sorghums, Dwarf hegari, and Double Dwarf Yellow milo have smaller seeds in proportion to ultimate plant size and therefore show a slow gain in weight in the beginning.**

Colorado, that are regarded as ideal for the prolongation of the life of cereal seeds include storage temperatures of 20–40°F and average relative humidity of 35 per cent. At this low humidity, seed moisture content rarely exceeds 9 per cent. Below 50°F respiration is almost completely inhibited, insects become dormant or die, and mold growth rarely occurs [2].

GROWTH PROCESSES IN CEREALS

Growth Cycles

Cereal plants pass through a typical vegetative growth cycle followed by maturity and reproduction [48]. Vegetative growth follows a progressively increasing rate until terminated by the onset of anthesis. Increases in total dry matter, or crop yield, follow a sigmoid (S-shaped) curve up to maturity [4]. Sorghums and millets have small seeds relative to their ultimate plant size. They have apparent but not actual slower growth rates in the initial vegetative period than do other cereals. More time is required to reach a given plant size when the seeds and seedlings are small (Fig. 2-14).

Some approximate but typical growth cycles of wheat in the United States are shown in Fig. 2-15. The growth of spring-sown small grains usually approximates a balanced sigmoid curve, because the temperature is favorable for growth and development most of the time and increasing daylength favors early flowering. Fall-sown grains, on the other hand, are retarded or forced into dormancy by low winter temperatures, and the short photoperiods during the winter in the temperate zones delay flowering. Where winter temperatures are very cold, wheat plants may die back to the ground, then resume growth in the spring.

Factors Affecting Growth Habit

The length of the vegetative period of any cereal or cereal variety is

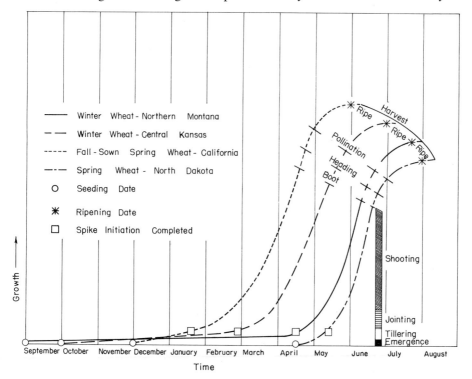

FIGURE 2-15. **Approximate growth cycle of wheat plants when sown on different dates typical of the different areas indicated. Prevailing temperatures and photoperiods affect the growth cycle.**

(Courtesy US Department of Agriculture)

determined largely by temperature, photoperiod, plant nutrition, and growth hormones, and by genetic factors that affect reactions to these conditions. Certain varieties of one cereal may have growth cycles very similar to varieties of another cereal.

Each cereal species has an approximate minimum, optimum, and maximum temperature at which growth occurs, although varieties of a species may differ somewhat in their temperature reactions. When the average temperature is $10°C$ ($50°F$) below the optimum, the time required to grow a crop to maturity is approximately doubled. The plants remain dormant, with a consequent extension of the growing period, whenever temperature falls below the minimum for growth, as occurs in winter-sown cereals in a cold climate. All cereal varieties with a winter growth habit, as well as many spring small-grain varieties, require cold for initiation of the flower primordia. Freezing is not necessary, but extended exposure to cool temperatures of $40-55°F$ or lower may be needed to induce eventual heading. Warmer temperatures favor rapid growth and flowering after the initial floral structure is formed.

Temperature largely determines the length of time a cereal plant takes to flower and mature after the floral structure has been laid down, although unnatural photoperiods may alter the normal period between floral initiation and anthesis.

The long-day cereals—wheat, oats, barley, and rye—flower earlier when nights (daily dark periods) are short and days (photoperiods) long. They will flower even under continuous light. The short-day cereals—corn, rice, sorghum, and millets—flower earlier when the nights are long and days short. They require a daily dark period for 3–5 weeks in order to initiate flowering. Although short-day plants in point of photoperiodic reaction, proso millet varieties may flower and ripen seeds within 75 days of sowing under day lengths no shorter than 15 hours. Any hastened flowering that results from photoperiodic treatment may be expected to reduce vegetative growth. Long photoperiods prolong the vegetative stage of growth of short-day plants, increasing plant size.

Certain temperature and light treatments may be complementary or supplementary in their effects on the time of flowering of a plant. A short-day sorghum plant growing under a long (15-hour) photoperiod may flower earlier under a $70°F$ temperature than one maintained at the nearly optimum growth temperature of $80°F$ (Fig. 2-16).

A soil rich in nitrogen will keep down the carbon-nitrogen ratio and delay flowering in the *nitronegative* cereals—wheat, barley, oats, and rye. The *nitropositive* cereals—corn, sorghum, rice, and millets—flower earlier in such a soil, unless the nitrogen supply is excessive. Ample phosphorus and potassium often favor early flowering. Moisture shortage may cause small-grain plants to flower abnormally early, often observed in a dry season, but a moisture deficiency may force sorghum plants into dormancy until more moisture is available.

Certain growth-regulating chemicals that modify the flowering habits of many plants have only minor effects on cereals, but other plant hormones undoubtedly function in their growth cycles.

Varieties within each of the cereal crops show a wide range in length of growing period. These differences are the expressions of hereditary genes that operate directly on the plant, or that modify or activate the effects of environment.

The cereals may be grouped on the basis of certain botanical characteristics about as follows:

Cool-season, long-day, nitronegative, winter or spring habit plants: Wheat, oats, barley, and rye.

Warm-season, short-day, nitropositive, spring habit plants: Rice, corn, sorghum, and millets.

FIGURE 2-16. **Sorghum plants grown under 15-hour photoperiods at temperatures of 60 to 65° F. (left) 70° F. (center) and 80° F. (right). The 70° F. temperature induced earlier flowering than did the 80° F. temperature that was nearly optimum for growth.**
(Courtesy US Department of Agriculture)

Winter-resistance: Rye > wheat > barley > oats.

Second-growth tendency: Rice > sorghum > millets > oats > barley > wheat > corn.

Seminal roots:
    1 — Rice, sorghum, pearl millet, and proso.
    3 to 7 — Corn, wheat, oats, barley, rye, and foxtail millet.

Stems:
    Solid (pithy) — Corn, sorghum, pearl millet.
    Mostly hollow, except at nodes — Other cereals.

Small seeds and seedlings compared to mature plant size: Sorghum and millets.

CLASSIFICATION OF CEREALS

The different cereal crops may be separated by a key to the genera to which they belong.

1a. Flowers all unisexual, the pistillate crowded on a thick rachis (the cob), the staminate at the top of the plant (the tassel).........................*Zea* (Maize)
1b. At least some of the flowers perfect, nothing resembling a cob or tassel present.
  2a. Inflorescence a spike, one to a culm.
    3a. Cnly one spikelet present at each joint of the rachis.
      4a. Glumes narrow and subulate, one-nerved.................*Secale* (Rye)
      4b. Glumes broad and ovate, at least three nerves present...*Triticum* (Wheat)
    3b. Three spikelets present at each rachis joint (the 2 lateral ones sometimes each reduced to a pair of glumes)...........................*Hordeum* (Barley)
  2b. Inflorescence a panicle or of more than one spikelike raceme.
    5a. Spikelets of two or more similar florets, the whole over 0.75 inch long (15 mm)..*Avena* (Oats)
    5b. Spikelets of only one floret or of two very unlike florets, the whole much less than 0.75 inch long.
      6a. Spikelets definitely compressed laterally; glumes both much shorter than the spikelet....................................*Oryza* (Rice)
      6b. Spikelets round or dorsally compressed; second glume (at least) about as long as the spikelet.
        7a. Lemma and palea thin and papery in texture, much thinner than the two glumes...........................*Sorghum* (Grain sorghum)
        7b. Lemma and palea of the perfect flowers hard and shiny, never thin in texture, much thicker than the two glumes.
          8a. Spikelets subtended by bristles.
            9a. Bristles falling with the spikelet at maturity.................
                                Pennisetum (Pearl millet)
            9b. Bristles not falling with the spikelet........................
                                Setaria (Foxtail millet)

8b. Spikelets not subtended by bristles.
    10a. Spikelets with awns at least one mm long...............
                            Echinochloa (Japanese millet)
    10b. Spikelets awnless or merely awn pointed, less than one mm
    long...*Panicum*
        11a. Inflorescence a diffuse panicle......................
                    Panicum miliaceum (Proso millet)
        11b. Inflorescence of several spikelike racemes
            12a. Racemes along an angled axis.....................
                    Panicum ramosum (Browntop millet)
            12b. Raceme digitate with two to six spikes..............
                    Eleusine (Finger millet)

REFERENCES

1. Addicott, F. T., and R. S. Lynch, "Defoliation and desiccation: Harvest-aid practices," in *Advances in Agronomy*, Vol. 9. New York: Academic Press. pp 67–93. 1957.
2. Anderson, J. A., and A. W. Alcock, *Storage of Cereal Grains and their Products.* Am. Assn. Cer. Chem. Monograph Ser. Vol. II. pp 515. 1954.
3. Atkins, I. M., "A simplified method for testing the lodging resistance of varieties and strains of wheat." *J. Am. Soc. Agron.*, **30**: 309–313. 1938.
4. Bartel, A. T., and J. H. Martin, "The growth curve of sorghum." *J. Ag. Res.*, **57**(11): 843–849. 1938.
5. Beachell, H. M., *et al.*, "Extent of natural crossing in rice." *J. Am. Soc. Agron.*, **27**: 971–973. 1935.
6. Brown, C. M., and H. L. Shands, "Pollen tube growth, fertilization, and early development in *Avena sativa*." *Agron. J.*, **49**(6): 286–288. 1957.
7. Brown, E., *et al.*, "Dormancy and the effect of storage on oats, barley, and sorghum." USDA *Tech. Bul. 953.* 1948.
8. Casserly, L. M., "The effect of nitrogen, phosphorus, and potassium on lodging of oats." *Can. J. Plant Sci.*, **37**: 245–251. 1957.
9. Chang, S. C., "Length of dormancy in cereal crops and its relationship to after-harvest sprouting." *J. Am. Soc. Agron.*, **35**: 482–490. 1943.
10. Clark, E. R., and H. K. Wilson, "Lodging in small grains." *J. Am. Soc. Agron.*, **25**: 561–572. 1933.
11. Crane, P. L., "The use of pre-harvest sprays as an aid in field drying corn." *Agron. J.*, **50**(1): 35–36. 1958.
12. Crocker, W., "Life-span of seeds." *Bot. Rev.*, **4**: 235–274. 1938.
13. ———, and L. V. Barton, *Physiology of Seeds.* Waltham, Mass.: *Chronica Botanica*, pp 267. 1953.
14. Davis, L. L., and T. R. Stanton, "Studies on the breaking strength of straw of oat varieties at Aberdeen, Idaho." *J. Am. Soc. Agron.*, **24**: 290–300. 1932.
15. D'Amato, F., and O. Hoffman-Ostenhof, "Metabolism and spontaneous mutations in plants," in *Advances in Genetics*, Vol. VIII. New York: Academic Press. pp 1–28. 1956.

16. Deming, G. W., and D. W. Robertson, "Dormancy in small grain seeds." Colo. Ag. Exp. Sta. *Tech. Bul. 5.* 1933.

17. Dittmer, H. J., "A quantitative study of the roots and root hairs of a winter rye plant." *Am. J. Bot.,* **24**: 417–420. 1937.

18. Dungan, G. H., "Effect of hail injury on the development of the corn plant." *J. Am. Soc. Agron.,* **20**: 51–54. 1928.

19. Eldredge, J. C., "Hail damage to corn." Ia. Ag. Exp. Sta. *Bul. 348.* 1936.

20. ———, "The effect of injury in imitation of hail damage on the development of small grain." Ia. Ag. Exp. Sta. *Res. Bul. 219.* 1937.

21. Fellows, H., "Falling of wheat culms due to lodging, buckling, and breaking." USDA *Cir. 767.* 1948.

22. Gingrich, J. R., and M. B. Russell, "Effect of soil moisture tension and oxygen concentration on the growth of corn roots." *Agron. J.,* **48**(11): 517–520. 1956.

23. Glynne, M. D., and D. G. Slope, "The effect of seed rate and nitrogen on lodging and yield of spring barley." *J. Ag. Sci.,* **49**: 454–458. 1959.

24. Gunthardt, H., *et al.,* "Studies on aged seeds. II: Relation of age of seeds to cytogenetic effects." *Agron. J.,* **45**: 438–441. 1953.

25. Haferkamp, M. E., L. Smith, and R. A. Nilan, "Studies on aged seeds. I: Relation of age of seed to germination and longevity." *Agron. J.,* **45**: 434–437. 1953.

26. Hamilton, D. G., "Culm, crown, and root development in oats as related to lodging." *Sci. Ag.,* **31**: 286–315. 1951.

27. Harrington, J. B., "The comparative resistance of wheat varieties to sprouting in the shock and windrow." *Sci. Ag.,* **12**: 635–645. 1932.

28. ———, "Testing cereal varieties for dormancy," *Sci. Ag.,* **29**: 538–550. 1949.

29. Hayes, H. K., "Normal self-fertilization in corn." *J. Am. Soc. Agron.,* **10**: 123–126. 1918.

30. Hayward, H. E., and W. B. Spurr, "Effects of osmotic concentration of substrate on the entry of water into corn roots." *Bot. Gaz.,* **105**: 152–164. 1943.

31. Hector, J. M., *Introduction to the Botany of Field Crops.* Vol. I, *Cereals.* Johannesburg, S. Africa: Central News Agency, pp 5–20. 1936.

32. Hitchcock, A. S., *A Textbook of Grasses.* New York: Macmillan. pp 95–132. 1914.

33. Hunter, J. R., and A. E. Erickson, "Relation of seed germination to soil moisture tension." *Agron. J.* **44**: 107–109. 1952.

34. Johnston, C. O., "Effect of leaf rust infection on the yield of certain varieties of wheat." *J. Am. Soc. Agron.,* **23**: 1–12. 1931.

35. Kaihara, H., "Comparative storage-tolerance of some cereal grains in Japan." *Ber. Ohara Inst. Landw. Forsch* 9(4): 435–440. 1951.

36. Kiesselbach, T. A., "Corn investigations." Nebr. Ag. Exp. Sta. *Res. Bul. 20.* 1922.

37. ———, "The structure and reproduction of corn." Nebr. Ag. Exp. Sta. *Res. Bul. 161.* 1949.

38. Kmock, H. G., *et al.,* "Root development of winter wheat as influenced by soil moisture and nitrogen fertilization." *Agron. J.,* **49**: 20–25. 1957.

39. Kondo, M., "The storage of rice and change of its physical properties during this period." *Ber. Ohara Inst. Landw. Forsch.* 3(2): 153–175. 1926.

40. ———, and T. Okamura, "Storage of rice. IV: On the influence of various temperatures in duration of storage and various moistures of rice upon the preservation of germination power of hulled rice." *Ber. Ohara Inst. Landw. Forsch.* (Japan), 4(3): 315–341. 1930a.

41. ———, and T. Okamura, "Germination power, analysis, and vitamin B of hulled rice stored during 4 years, either air-tight or in carbon dioxide." *Ber. Ohara Inst. Landw. Forsch.* **4**(3): 343–348. 1930b.

42. Krantz, B. A., and W. V. Chandler, "Lodging, leaf composition, and yield of corn influenced by heavy application of nitrogen and potash." *Agron. J.*, **43**: 547–552. 1951.

43. Locke, L. F., and J. A. Clark, "Normal development of wheat plants from seminal roots." *J. Am. Soc. Agron.*, **16**: 261–268. 1924.

44. "Lodging of cereals (bibliography)." Cambridge: Imp. Bur. Plant Gen. 1930.

45. Lute, A. M., "A special form of delayed germination." Assn. Off. Seed. Analysts *Proc.* 1924.

46. ———, "Some notes on the behavior of broken seeds of cereals and sorghums." Assn. Off. Seed Analysts *Proc.* 1925.

47. *Manual for Testing Agricultural and Vegetable Seeds.* USDA *Hndbk. No. 30*, pp 440. 1952.

48. Martin, J. H., and W. H. Leonard, *Principles of Field Crop Production.* New York: Macmillan. pp 15–50. 1949.

49. Miller, E. C., "Development of the pistillate spikelet and fertilization in *Zea mays.*" *J. Ag. Res.*, **18**: 255–265. 1919.

50. Norden, A. J., and K. J. Frey, "Factors associated with lodging resistance in oats." *Agron. J.*, **51**: 335–338. 1959.

51. Owen, E. S., "The storage of seeds for maintenance of viability." Commonwealth Bur. Past. and Fld. Crops *Bul. 43.* pp 1–81. 1956.

52. Pauli, A. W., and H. H. Laude, "Protein and carbohydrate relationships in winter wheat as influenced by mechanical injury." *Agron. J.*, **51**(1): 55–57. 1959.

53. Percival, J., *Agricultural Botany*, 7th ed. London: Duckworth. pp 839. 1926.

54. Pope, M. N., "The time factor in pollen-tube growth and fertilization in barley." *J. Ag. Res.*, **54**: 525–529. 1937.

55. Robertson, D. W., and G. W. Deming, "Natural crossing in barley at Ft. Collins (Colorado)." *J. Am. Soc. Agron.*, **23**: 402–407. 1931.

56. ———, and A. M. Lute, "Germination of the seed of farm crops in Colorado after storage for various periods of years." *J. Ag. Res.*, **46**: 455–462. 1933.

57. ———, and A. M. Lute, "Germination of seed of farm crops after storage for various periods of years." *J. Am. Soc. Agron.*, **29**: 822–834. 1937.

58. ———, A. M. Lute, and R. Gardner, "Effect of relative humidity on viability, moisture content, and respiration of wheat, oats, and barley in storage." *J. Ag. Res.*, **59**: 281–292. 1939.

59. ———, A. M. Lute, and H. Kroeger, "Germination of 20-year-old wheat, oats, barley, corn, rye, sorghum, and soybeans." *J. Am. Soc. Agron.*, **35**: 786–795. 1943.

60. ———, et al., "Studies on the critical period for applying irrigation water to wheat." Colo. Ag. Exp. Sta. *Tech. Bul. 11.* 1934.

61. Shantz, H. L., and L. N. Piemeisel, "The water requirement of plants at Akron, Colo." *J. Ag. Res.*, **34**(12): 1093–1190. 1927.

62. Sieglinger, J. B., "Cross-pollination in milo in adjoining rows." *J. Am. Soc. Agron.*, **13**: 280–282. 1921.

63. Slayter, R. O., "Absorption of water by plants." *Bot. Rev.*, **26**: 331–392. 1960.

64. Stanton, T. R., and F. A. Coffman, "Natural crossing in oats at Akron, Colo."
    J. Am. Soc. Agron., **16**: 646–659. 1924.

65. Thurman, R. L., and P. Grissom, "Relationship of top growth and root growth
    of oats." *Agron. J.*, **46**: 474–475. 1954.

66. Vogel, O. A., *et al.*, "Semi-dwarf growth habit in winter wheat improvement for
    the Pacific Northwest." *Agron. J.*, **48**: 76–78. 1956.

67. Weatherwax, P., "Gametogenesis and fecundation in *Zea mays* as the basis of
    xenia and heredity in the endosperm." *Bul. Torrey Bot. Club*, **46**: 73–90. 1919.

68. Weaver, J. E., "Investigations of the root habits of plants." *Am. J. Bot.* **12**: 502–
    509. 1925.

69. ———, *Root Development of Field Crops*. New York: McGraw-Hill. pp 33–90.
    1926.

70. ———, and E. Zink, "Extent and longevity of the seminal roots of certain grasses."
    Pl. Phys., *29*(3): 359–379. 1945.

71. Weihing, R. H., "The comparative root development of regional types of corn."
    J. Am. Soc. Agron., **27**: 526–537. 1935.

72. Welton, F. A., and V. H. Morris, "Lodging in wheat and oats." Ohio Ag. Exp.
    Sta. *Bul. 471.* 1931.

73. Whitcomb, W. O., "Dormancy of newly threshed grain." Assn. Off. Seed Analysts
    Proc. 1924.

74. ———, and W. D. Hay, "Notes on the germination of broken seeds." Assn. Off.
    Seed Analysts *Proc.* 1925.

75. Worzella, W. W., "Root development in hardy and non-hardy winter wheat varie-
    ties." *J. Am. Soc. Agron.*, **24**: 626–637. 1932.

3. MACHINERY IN CEREAL PRODUCTION

DEVELOPMENT OF MACHINERY FOR GRAIN PRODUCTION

The greatest advance in grain production since the dawn of history came with agricultural machine developments between 1900 and 1950 [6]. Cereal grain growers usually have led the field in adoption of mechanical equipment on the farm. As a result, cereals now require only 30 per cent of the labor used in farm crop production in the United States, yet they occupy 63 per cent of the crop acreage and constitute 50 per cent of the total crop value. More hours per year are spent on chores in the cowbarn than in production of the grain crop.

Practically all labor involved in modern grain production consists of machine operation. Successful grain production by modern methods depends greatly on choice of suitable farm machines and skillful operation of them. Detailed descriptions of farm machines can be found in catalogs and numerous books [1, 8, 9, 21, 22, 23].

Range of Grain-Production Methods

All grain production methods, from early Iron Age hand culture to the latest mechanized techniques, may be observed in certain countries of the world today. In the United States, the Hopi Indians of Arizona still dig random holes with a stick, 8–10 inches deep in the sand of a small dry wash, and drop a dozen or so kernels of corn in each (Fig. 3-1). Modern machines are unsuited to such a site. The one-handled wooden plow, hand seeding, hand weeding, cutting with a hand sickle, and hand threshing still prevail in parts of the world where fields are too small to accommodate large machines. In Oriental rice fields most of the crop is transplanted by hand, but a draft animal may be used for stirring and puddling the soil.

FIGURE 3-1. **Planting corn in a deep hole with a stick (above), and a 4-row tractor corn planter (below).**

(*Courtesy US Department of Agriculture*)

Under these conditions, about 500–600 man-hours an acre are required to grow, harvest, dry, thresh, and market the crop. In California, the total labor on an acre of rice may be as low as 7.5 hours. On such farms, large tractors are used for soil preparation, airplanes are used for seeding and for applying fertilizers and herbicides, and the crop is harvested with a large one-man self-propelled combine [4].

Progress in Wheat Production

The typical American farmer of 1800 could, with the help of 2 men for 20 days during harvest, grow only about 30 acres or 600 bushels of wheat a season. Each acre of wheat required from 50 to 70 hours of man labor for growing, harvesting, threshing, and marketing. These farmers used a walking plow, often a brush harrow, and scattered seed by hand. They cut the crop with a sickle, scythe, or cradle, and raked and bound it by hand. They usually threshed the wheat on the barn floor with a flail, winnowed it in a breeze, and hauled the bagged grain over poor roads to the mill.

When crude reapers and small threshers became available after 1840, an acre of wheat could be grown with about 35 man-hours of labor [2]. From 1890 to 1910, standard implements for wheat production were the moldboard plow, spiketooth harrow, grain drill, binder, and steam thresher [5]. With such implements, the wheat grower of the Midwest could produce and market wheat with about 16–18 hours labor an acre if he used 2-horse teams, or about 10–12 hours an acre if he used 4-horse teams. With the use of a 12-foot header pushed by 6 horses for harvesting, together with 6-horse teams for tillage and seeding operations, labor per acre was reduced to about 6 hours. By 1930, the typical grower of the central wheat belt, using tractor equipment and a combine for harvesting, expended about 3.33 hours labor an acre.

By 1945, the western wheat grower, with 2 truck drivers hired for a 20-day harvest period, could grow and market 700 acres or 14,000 bushels entirely by machinery. The implements required were a 25 drawbar-horsepower tractor, a 10-foot oneway plow, a 24-foot rod weeder, a 30-foot gang of drills, a 14-foot selfpropelled combine (Fig. 3-2), and two hired trucks. The total labor expended was about 1.25 hours an acre.

Progress in Corn Culture

The corn grower of 1800 produced and cribbed an acre of 25-bushel corn with 80–90 hours of labor. Seeds were dropped into holes opened and covered with a hoe, and the crop was hoed by hand. Between 1830

FIGURE 3-2. **Self-propelled combines harvesting barley in Arizona.**
(*Courtesy International Harvester Company*)

and 1870, the use of improved plows, including the 1-horse shovel plow for cultivation, enabled farmers to produce an acre of corn with 40–70 hours of labor. With equipment that became available from 1890 to 1910, notably the gang plow, 2-row planter, and 2-horse cultivator [13], about 15 hours an acre, which included time for hand husking, were required to produce the crop. By 1945, the labor required to produce an acre of corn was 5 hours or less if a 3-plow general purpose tractor, 10-foot tandem disk, 40-foot harrow, 4-row planter, 4-row cultivator, 2-row picker, and a crib dump with elevator were used. Two extra men and a small tractor would be required for hauling and cribbing the corn from the picker. The 6- and 8-row planters and cultivators, corn combine, and picker-sheller have further reduced labor requirements. The latter two machines, which eliminate the shelling operation but require an artificial drier, permit earlier harvest which reduces field losses [2].

The labor peak in corn production is the cultivation period, the 8–10 weeks after the crop is planted. With a hand hoe, one man can control weeds on about 5 acres. One man can keep 20 acres of corn cultivated throughout the season with a 1-horse 2-shovel walking cultivator. He could maintain 40 acres in the Corn Belt with the 1-row 2-horse sulky cultivator of the 1890-1915 period. In 1945, with a 4-row tractor cultivator, a man cared for 200–250 acres with no more effort (Fig. 3-3).

Thus, the potential output of a grain grower was multiplied from 16 to 40 times between 1800 and 1945. At present, however, two men are required to build and maintain equipment and furnish supplies for every one American farmer. In 1800 most of the supplies and equipment were produced or made on the home farm.

TILLAGE IMPLEMENTS

The original tillage implement was a sharpened stick [6]. Later a blade of bone, shell, or stone was attached to a wooden handle; later still, hoes

FIGURE 3-3. **Cultivator for surface-planted row crop.**
(Courtesy International Harvester Company

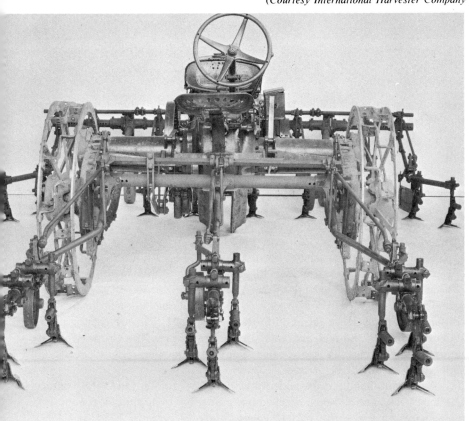

FIGURE 3-4. **Preparing a seedbed with heavy hand hoes in the Middle East.**
(Courtesy US Department of Agriculture)

and knives with metal blades were used (Fig. 3-4). With hand tools, a man may prepare a seedbed on an acre of land in 40–120 hours.

Improved Implements for Seedbed Preparation

Animal power was first used to draw a forked-stick plow by the ancients in Asia, before the day of written records. With this tool, one man could stir an acre of soil once but poorly in 10–20 hours. Plows were mentioned by Theophrastus in 287 BC, as well as in several chapters of the Old Testament. The beating of swords into plowshares, suggested in the Book of Isaiah, shows that metal shares were used in biblical times. The Iron Age began about 1000 BC. A plow with an iron share was mentioned in the rural poem "Georgics," composed by Virgil before 30 BC.

The one-handled wooden plow with a small metal point or blade is still used on many more farms throughout the world than are tractor plows. It neither inverts the soil nor cuts off all growing weeds. Crop yields are likely to be lower than those after moldboard plowing unless weeds are suppressed by other operations.

A second handle was added to the plow before the 14th century. Coulters occasionally were attached to plows by that time. Wrought iron plow shares gave place in part to cast-iron shares between 1785 and 1797. Chilled iron came to be used about 1803; steel shares, after 1833. The modern chilled plow process was patented in 1869. With the metal mold-board plow drawn by 1–4 animals, one man could turn an acre in 4–12 hours. Chilled iron and steel moldboards reduced the draft in plowing. The sulky plow with 2 wheels came into use about 1864; the 3-wheeled sulky plow appeared 20 years later. Gang plow manufacture began in England. Originally these were large plows pulled back and forth across the field by a cable wound on drums on opposite sides of the field, revolved by 2 steam tractors. These cable plows were tried but not adopted in the United States; some were used in other parts of the world until recently. Walking gang plows supported by wheels were used in California in 1867. With the adoption about 1880 of 2-bottom gang plows drawn by 4–6 horses, a man could cover from 0.75 to 1.0 acre per horse in 10 hours. With a 10 drawbar-horsepower tractor to pull 2 plow bottoms, 6–10 acres can be turned in 10 hours; with 3 to 10 plow bottoms and larger tractors or teams, the acreage covered is increased nearly in proportion to the greater width covered (Fig. 3-5).

A disc plow was patented in 1847, but this implement was little used for 50 years until curved, sharp discs were perfected. It is more effective than the moldboard plow only in loose soils or in very compact soils (Fig. 3-6). The one-way or vertical-disc plow (Fig. 3-7) came into extensive use about 1927 and soon largely replaced moldboard plows, disc plows, and the lister for tillage of the wheat lands in the central and southern Great Plains. Its chief advantages are rapid tillage because of the low draft per area of soil stirred, and mixture of residues in the surface layers, which reduces erosion.

An implement called a chisel, which had heavy curved teeth that till the soil as deep as 12 inches or more, was designed in 1895 for breaking and stirring heavy soils in California (Fig. 3-8). Use of it spread to other areas about 1935. About 1940 a modified chisel with a small sweep at the base of each tooth, called the Graham-Hoeme plow, came into use in the southern Great Plains. The lister, introduced in Kansas about 1880, enabled farmers to till a larger area in a day than they could with a moldboard plow. About 1940 the Noble blade cultivator, developed in Canada, was introduced into the central Great Plains of the United States. The original implement had a single long heavy blade for "subtillage" or undercutting grain stubble, but later machines had 1–3 heavy V-shaped sweeps, each 24–100 inches wide (Fig. 3-9). The Graham-Hoeme and Noble implements, although less widely used than the one-way plow, have the advantage of leaving most of the crop residues on the surface of the soil.

Development of Surface-Tillage Implements

Homemade floats or clod mashers of split logs or planks for pulverizing and leveling seed beds were used before steel harrows were perfected. The homemade log roller eventually gave place to the corrugated iron roller. The ancient Japanese used a toothed roller to pulverize and pack the soil.

The brush harrow was used to prepare seedbeds, as well as to cover broadcast seed, from prehistoric times until well into the 19th century. It consisted of a tree limb with branches attached, or logs with many-branched

FIGURE 3-5. **Pulling a 5-bottom moldboard plow, a disc harrow and a grain drill in one operation.**

(Courtesy John Deere & Company)

FIGURE 3-6. **Plowing hard soil with a disc plow.**

(Courtesy International Harvester Company)

FIGURE 3-7. **One-way disc plow which leaves about a third of the crop residue on the soil surface.**

(Courtesy International Harvester Company)

stubs or inserted wooden pegs which served as teeth. Later harrows were made of wood frames into which sharpened pegs were inserted. The Old Testament mentions iron harrows in the time of King David. Pliny illustrated a wooden frame harrow with long iron teeth about AD 30, an implement used until iron and steel frames were introduced in the 18th century. A lever to adjust the tilt of the harrow teeth was added after 1870. The springtooth harrow was patented in 1869; an adjustable type came into use after 1877. Such harrows kill more weeds than do spiketooth harrows.

Unknown in the Western Hemisphere, disc harrows were used by the Japanese of antiquity. A curved-disc tiller was patented in the United States in 1854, and the disc harrow was gradually adopted in later years. The cutaway disc was developed before 1893. The disc harrow is used for preparation of a seedbed on plowed land in humid areas, but it pulverizes dry soils so that they are susceptible to wind erosion.

The Forkner harrow, used for fallow cultivation and seedbed preparation, was on the market by 1915. It had various sets of teeth, shovels, or sweeps mounted on spring shanks similar to those on the springtooth harrow. About three years later, it began to be replaced by duckfoot (field) cultivators with spring-loaded stiff shanks. The rod weeder came into use in the Pacific Northwest about 1910. The forerunner of the rod weeder was the "slicker," a homemade tool with a flat blade 8–12 feet long, forged from a wagon tire, sharpened at the front edge, welded to shanks, and mounted underneath and crosswise on a sled with 3 or 4 wooden runners. The

FIGURE 3-8. **The chisel, a tool for deep tillage.**

(Courtesy Caterpillar Tractor Company)

FIGURE 3-9. (Top) Gang of Noble blades cutting a 56-foot strip, with the grain stubble left on the surface. (Bottom) Noble blade, which cuts 13 feet.

FIGURE 3-10. **A disc drill equipped with packer wheels.**

(*Courtesy Deere and Company*)

FIGURE 3-11. **A one-row corn planter.**

(*Courtesy US Department of Agriculture*)

blades cut off the weeds below the soil surface, but they clogged easily. The revolving square rod on the rotary rod weeder clears itself of weeds and lifts plant residues and clods to the surface. It is useful for maintaining fallow or land kept bare for several weeks or months between plowing and seeding. All of these subsurface tillers provide protection against soil blowing.

Cultivators for intertillage recommended by Jethro Tull in the 17th century were equipped with small shares. Single wide shovels for cultivation were adopted later, followed by cultivators with 2 smaller shovels. Narrow shovels (bull tongues), teeth, and chisels for cultivators were not in general use until late in the 19th century.

The rotary hoe is useful for killing weed seedlings as well as for breaking crusts in fields planted to intertilled crops [15]. It was invented in 1890 and manufactured in 1912, but was not in common use until about 1925. It is used for "blind cultivation" before the corn crop comes up, or later while the young plants are too small to suffer appreciable injury. A spring-tined implement, called the Halleck weeder, supplemented the spike-tooth harrow for blind or early cultivation before the rotary hoe was adopted.

SEEDING OR PLANTING MACHINES

The earliest husbandmen dropped seed into holes in the soil made with a stick, or broadcast the seed and raked it in with a tree branch. Eventually, animal power was used to drag a brush harrow over the scattered seeds or to pull a wooden plow that opened furrows. The seeds were dropped into the furrows by hand, or were dribbled through a tube attached to a gourd or leather bag. The furrows were then covered with a plow or hoe. A plow with an attached funnel, through which seeds were dropped, was used in Iraq about 1700 BC.

Wheeled drills or planters with seed hoppers and 1–3 seed tubes were used in China as early as 2800 BC and in Assyria by 680 BC, but really satisfactory machines for seeding small grains were developed only after the 16th century. Several broadcast seeders and drills were patented in England during the 17th and 18th centuries. The prototype of the modern drill was invented by James Cook in 1782. Force-feed shells and fluted cylinders, developed between 1851 and 1867, replaced the agitator shaft at the bottom of the drill hopper. All drills had hoes, shovels, or coulters for furrow openers until after 1870 when the shoe-type opener was devised. Double and single disc furrow openers, which work better in hard or trashy land, were introduced about 1894 (Fig. 3-10). The end-gate broadcast seeder geared to a wagon wheel was introduced in the early 1870's. It was used chiefly for early spring seeding of oats or cornstubble land. Mechanical trailer-type broadcast seeders came into use after 1940. The deep-furrow

FIGURE 3-12. **Harvesting oats with sickles in southern Europe.**
(Courtesy US Department of Agriculture)

FIGURE 3-13. **Cutting wheat with a cradle.**
(Courtesy Deere and Company)

drill, adopted after 1920, places the seed in moist soil and reduces winter killing and soil blowing.

Improvements on the 1-row hopper planters of the ancients resulted in suitable mechanical corn planters after AD 1800 (Fig. 3-11). A 2-row planter was built in 1839; a hill-drop device operated by hand was invented that year. A 1-row check-row planter was invented in 1857, a 2-row machine appeared in 1860. With these, an extra man was needed to trip the lever at each hill. The automatic check-row planter was introduced in 1875. The lister planter came into use after 1882. However,· hand planters continued to be used on small fields for many years.

GRAIN HARVESTING MACHINES

The sickle or reaping hook was used for cutting grain by Stone Age husbandmen. In biblical times the blades were made of bronze or iron. Steel sickles were made in the 19th century. The sickle is still the chief harvesting tool in Asiatic countries and on small farms in other countries (Fig. 3-12). A man with a sickle can cut, bind, and shock an acre of grain in from 20–50 hours. The scythe was used for cutting grain and hay in ancient Rome, and is still used widely in grain fields of the Orient. Cradle frames were attached to the scythe at some later time, but the "American cradle," an improved type, was not developed until the latter part of the 18th century (Fig. 3-13). Its use was confined largely to the United States. With a cradle, a skilled man can cut, rake, bind, and shock an acre of grain in 10–20 hours. Grain cut with the sickle, scythe, or cradle is bound by hand with straw bands [17].

Development of Harvest Machines

A grain stripper, pushed by oxen and used by the barbarians of Gaul, was described by Pliny in the first century AD. No less than 50 different reapers were designed in Europe and in the United States between 1776 and 1831. Cyrus McCormick patented his first reaper in 1834 [11]. A man walking behind the machine raked the cut stalks off the cutting platform. Commercial manufacture of reapers began in 1840—three machines were built that year. About 500 reapers were built in the United States in 1845; 3000 in 1850; 30,000 in 1870; and 60,000 in 1880. A self-rake reaper built before 1850 was produced in quantity by 1854, but the final form of this machine, which drops the cut grain in gavels, came on the market about 1865. The Marsh Harvester, built in 1858 and first put on the market in 1864, provided a platform on which 2 men could stand and ride while binding the sheafs with straw. A wire binder was perfected in 1873; a twine binder, in 1878. About 3000 twine binders were sold in 1880. The Appleby twine knotter, invented in 1858, is the basic automatic tying device still used. A push binder, cutting 10–12 feet, and propelled by 6 horses, was manufactured after 1890 (Fig. 3-14). The 10-foot binder driven by a tractor power takeoff came into use about 1920.

A grain header was built by William Pitt in England in 1787, but the forerunner of the later headers was invented by Jonathan Haines in Illinois in 1849. The header came into general use only about 1880, and it was largely restricted to western farms in low rainfall areas. The combine replaced it between 1910 and 1940.

For many centuries, grain has been flailed out by hand or threshed by treading out the grain under the feet of men or livestock. With a flail, a man can thresh 7 or 8 bushels a day. A form of threshing machine still used in Asia and Africa consists of stone-studded planks, stone rollers, or metal discs on a shaft drawn by animals over the grain stalks spread on a threshing floor. The grain is winnowed in a breeze. A mechanical thresher equipped with whirling flails was built in England during the 18th century, but the first useful thresher equipped with cylinder, teeth, and concaves, was built by Andrew Meikle in 1786. A successful thresher with a fan for winnowing was built in the United States in 1837. A shaking straw rack was added before 1860. Horses, walking a treadmill or pulling sweeps, furnished the power for operation of the thresher until steam engines replaced them (Fig. 3-15).

A few horse-powered threshers continued in use on small farms for many years. In 1913, in a mountainous section of Oregon, one of the authors worked on one driven by a 14-horse sweep. The fields were too steep for the safe or practical use of a steam tractor.

Stationary steam engines were used occasionally for threshing after 1830 [24]. The first portable steam engines, pulled from place to place by horses, were manufactured for farm use in 1849, but were not used widely until 1865. By 1879, about 80 per cent of the threshing in the principal grain regions was by steam power. A steam tractor was built in the United States in 1858 [14], but successful machines were not available before 1873. Steam tractors were steered by a team of horses hitched to a tongue attached to the front axle—a steering wheel was not attached until 1882. About 38 companies were manufacturing steam tractors by 1888, and 72,000 of these machines were at work on American farms in 1910. Ten-thousand steam tractors were built in 1913, but manufacture of them had stopped by 1925. Gasoline tractors displaced steam tractors.

Early threshers, or separators, were fed by hand. The straw was ejected from the rear of the machine, carried back on a slatted canvas or chain straw carrier. The straw was then dragged ("bucked") to a stack by 2 horses hitched to opposite ends of a long pole. The self-feeder and wind stacker were added to the separator about 1890 (Fig. 3-16). Separators built with cylinders 12–48 inches long had capacities ranging 10–300 bushels

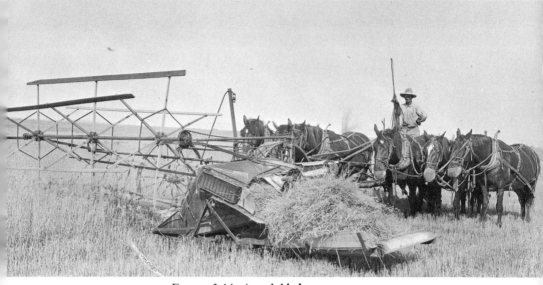

FIGURE 3-14. **A push binder.**
(Courtesy US Department of Agriculture)

FIGURE 3-15. **Thresher powered by a one-horse treadmill.**
(Courtesy J. I. Case Company)

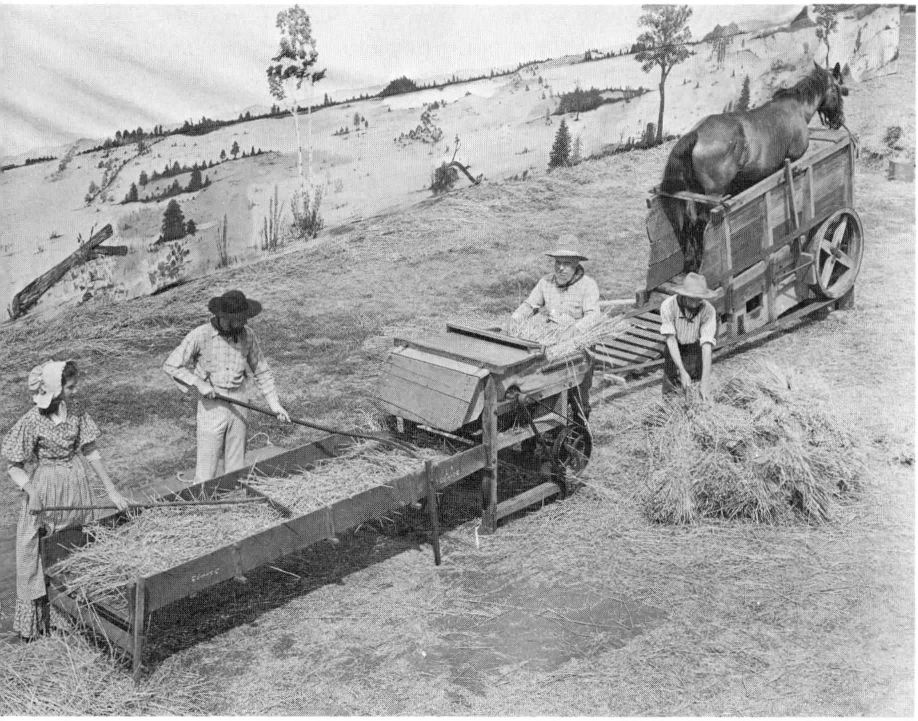

FIGURE 3-16. **Separator with self-feeder and wind-stacker, while threshing rice bundles hauled from the shock.**

(*Courtesy US Department of Agriculture*)

of wheat an hour; the most popular sizes threshed 75–125 bushels of wheat an hour. When the threshed grain haulers and a suitable number of men bringing in the sheaves from the shocked fields are included, about 66 bushels of wheat a day are threshed for each member of the crew nowadays. About 125 bushels of barley or 170 bushels of oats can be threshed in the time required to thresh 100 bushels of wheat [18]. Combines replaced large separators in areas where the latter formerly were popular. In 1941, the 168,000 separators still used in the United States averaged 26 inches in cylinder width, 104 hours in seasonal use, and threshed 829 bushels in 10 hours.

Combine Harvesting

A grain stripper was invented in Australia in 1845 by an Englishman named Ridley. The McKay stripper, built in Australia in 1884, started a method of harvesting that continued in that country for more than 40 years. The stripper had long teeth that caught the wheat heads and a revolving beater that shattered the heads and knocked the grain and chaff into the separating mechanism of the machine.

A combine, first patented in 1828, introduced an attempt to harvest and thresh in a single operation. The Moore-Hascall combine was first tried in the field in Michigan in 1835. One of these machines was shipped around Cape Horn to California, where it harvested 600 acres of wheat in 1854. Other combines were built in California in 1858 and thereafter. About

20 combines were in use in California in 1881; 500–600 in 1888. The combine was a success in the dry summer climate of California; it had failed in the wetter climate of Michigan. Nearly a century elapsed after the combine was invented before farmers in humid climates learned to leave the grain standing in the field until it was sufficiently dry for threshing and safe storage.

The combine (Figs. 3-17, 3-18) had moved into Oregon, Idaho, and Washington by 1898, and into the intermountain states by 1910. Combines were introduced into all the Great Plains states except North Dakota by 1919, and into the remaining grain-growing States by 1927. About 4000 combines were used in the United States in 1920, about 225 thousand in 1941, 650 thousand in 1950, and well over a million in 1959. The first combine reached England in 1928, but the machine did not come into common use until World War II. The windrow-pickup method of combining was developed by Thomas D. Campbell, a wheat grower of Hardin, Montana, about 1925. Commercial windrowers and swathers appeared on the market about 3 years later. Self-propelled swathers were developed in 1950 (Fig. 3-19). The windrow method is more expensive than direct combining; it requires 25–50 per cent more labor, but it facilitates the harvesting of weedy fields or those that ripen irregularly.

Early combines in California cut swaths 20–40 feet wide. Except for a few small types, the combines used in the Far West between 1900 and 1920 usually cut 18–24 feet. Most of the machines used in the Great Plains since 1918 have had cutter bars 12–16 feet long; those machines were self-powered. Most of the 8- and 10-foot machines, which first appeared during the middle 1920's were driven with a power takeoff from the tractor. Small tractor-powered combines with cuts of 3.3–6 feet were introduced into the eastern states in the early 1930's. Few combines cut a swath as wide as 20 feet at present; the average effective width for all machines in the United States is only about 10 feet.

The first combines were drawn by from 20 to 40 horses or mules usually hitched 6 abreast, except that the lead team was of 2, 3, or 4 horses. The team was driven by one man; lines reached only the lead team. Reins from the bridles connected all horses together, while eveners attached to equalizers compelled each animal to pull his share of the load. Two men in addition to the driver operated these machines; 2 or 3 additional men filled and sewed the sacks of grain and dropped them in piles on the ground. With a modern self-propelled combine and bulk threshing, one man does the work formerly done by 5. The cutting and threshing mechanisms of early combines were driven by a geared ground or bull wheel; threshing speed was rather unsteady. When auxiliary engines (first steam, later gasoline) were mounted on the combine, the number of horses needed to draw the larger machines was reduced from the usual 24–36 to 12–20. A steam tractor was first used to pull a combine in 1871, but it was expensive and feasible

FIGURE 3-17. Sectional view of small combine having rubber-faced flail bars on the cylinder and rubber block concaves.

(Courtesy International Harvester Company)

FIGURE 3-18. Side-hill combines with self-leveling devices are used on steep fields in the Pacific Northwest.

(Courtesy International Harvester Company)

FIGURE 3-19. (Top) Self-propelled swather. (Bottom) Combine with pickup attachment threshing from windrow.

(*Courtesy International Harvester Company and Deere and Company*)

only on level land. Gas tractors began to replace both horses and steam tractors before 1910. Crawler-type tractors, developed about 1905, were especially suited to loose soils and rolling land. The horse-drawn combine had practically disappeared by 1930.

The advantages of a push-type harvester—it avoids side draft and mashing down of the grain when opening a field—were appreciated as early as the first century AD. Some early reapers, grain headers, push binders, the Australian stripper, and a few early makes of combines were propelled from the rear. A self-propelled steam combine was operated in 1886, and a few commercial self-propelled combines with gasoline motors were used in the Pacific Northwest during World War I. A small combine (the Gleaner) mounted on a Fordson tractor was marketed from about 1926 to 1928. The modern self-propelled or push combine with rubber tires was developed in 1938. Twenty years later, a fifth of the combines in use and more than half the new machines being produced in the United States were self-propelled. The push combines cut a 7–16 foot swath. A large self-propelled combine requires 95 per cent less time to harvest an acre than the horse-drawn binder.

The labor shortage during and after World War II gave great impetus to the spread of combine harvesting. Only 20–25 per cent of the labor required to bind and thresh is required to combine [16] (Fig. 3-20). Custom combining became the vogue in areas where combining was not universal before the war. Often these machines were moved hundreds of miles across the Great Plains to participate in the harvest. The "Harvest Brigade," a special group of 500 self-propelled combines sold for custom use in the war effort, cut an average of 2500 acres each per season. Many of them followed the wheat harvest from south Texas to the Canadian border, then moved back to Texas to harvest grain sorghum. By 1950, about 90 per cent of the wheat, grain sorghum, and rice; 75 per cent of the barley, rye, and flaxseed; and 60 per cent of the oats in the United States were harvested with the combine. By 1960, nearly all grain was threshed with a combine.

Despite great progress in harvester development since 1930, hand harvesting of grain still prevails in many countries of the world. Even in the United States about 200 thousand acres of small grain on small or mountainous farms were cut with a cradle as late as 1946.

Corn Harvesting Machines

Husking by hand from the standing stalk was generally considered to be the most economical method of harvesting corn from the beginning of primitive Indian culture until the wide adoption of the mechanical picker shortly before 1940. When stalks were to be saved for feed, they were cut by hand with a large corn knife and placed in shocks to cure. A man could

FIGURE 3-20. **Harvesting and threshing with a binder, separator and steam tractor required large crews of itinerant workers who often traveled to the northwest on freight trains.**

(Courtesy US Department of Agriculture)

harvest an acre of stalks in 7–10 hours. Cutting sleds, drawn by a horse between 2 rows, were devised in the late 19th century. Usually, two men rode on the sled to grasp the upright stalks until an armful accumulated; the sled was then stopped while the gathering was set in a shock. This method was too laborious to be widely popular. The corn binder drawn by 2 to 4 horses, developed in 1892, cuts 5–7 acres in 10 hours but it requires at least one and usually two additional men to shock the bundles. Husking from the shock, loading, and cribbing the ears from an acre of 40-bushel corn requires about 10.5 hours; husking 40 bushels of corn from the standing stalks while throwing the ears in a moving wagon requires an average of only 8 hours (Fig. 3-21). Hand husking consumes much more time when done improperly. For example, in some countries the ears are snapped and thrown into baskets or bags which are carried to the end of the field and dumped—the ears are husked, piled, loaded, and hauled later. An acre of corn stalks can be hauled and stacked in about 4 hours. With the husker-shredder, an acre of corn can be husked and the stalks shredded and blown into the barn with about 6.5 hours of man labor.

Husking or picking from the standing stalk prevailed in the western and central Corn Belt for many years, whereas binding and shocking, was formerly common in the Northeastern States when winter wheat was to be sown on cornstubble land. Most of the corn in the Southeastern States is snapped from the stalk without husking, either by hand or with a mechanical snapper. The husks offer some protection from stored-grain insects.

Corn pickers of some promise were invented in 1874 and 1880, but successful horse-drawn machines were not manufactured until 1909. Appreciable numbers of 1-row horse- or tractor-drawn machines were sold during World War I. Power takeoff machines were available shortly thereafter, and a 2-row picker was built in 1928. Tractor-mounted machines were available at about that time. Hand husking still prevailed on many farms in the Corn Belt until World War II, when labor shortages stimulated wide use of the picker. Approximately 120 thousand mechanical pickers were used on farms in the United States in 1941, about 410 thousand in 1950, and 760 thousand in 1959. By 1956, 78 per cent of the United States corn crop harvested for grain was gathered with mechanical pickers. The modern 2-row picker drawn by or mounted on and powered from a tractor harvests about 12–15 acres in 10 hours. The picker-husker gathers and husks the ears; the picker-sheller (Fig. 3-22) also shells the grain; the picker-snapper gathers the ears still enclosed in the husk. Some of the corn combines harvest and shell a 4-row strip of corn.

FIGURE 3-21. **Husking and pulling ears of corn from the standing stalk by hand, and throwing the ears against the "bump board" at the far side of the wagon. The horses kept the wagon moving slowly down the row.**

(*Courtesy US Department of Agriculture*)

FIGURE 3-22. **Self-propelled picker-sheller or corn combine harvesting corn.**
(*Courtesy J. I. Case Company*)

THE AIRPLANE AS A FARM IMPLEMENT

The airplane first became an agricultural implement when it was used to spread insecticidal dusts on cotton fields in 1921 [12]. By 1930 the airplane was being used for sowing rice in flooded fields. Later it was used for dusting wheat fields. More recently it has been used for spraying or dusting crops with herbicides, insecticides, fungicides, defoliants, and dessicants, and for spreading fertilizer on rice fields [20]. The airplane is advantageous because it covers large acreages quickly, passes over muddy fields, and does not mash down the crop.

An airplane seeder flying 75 miles an hour covers a strip 1 mile long and 30 feet wide in 48 seconds, a rate of 270 acres an hour. Even though as much as from 65-75 per cent of the total time may be spent in loading the plane and in landing and taking off, from 600 to 900 acres may be seeded in 10 hours. The pilot, 2 flagmen stationed on opposite sides of the field, and 1 or 2 men to load the plane constitute the crew.

POWER FOR FIELD OPERATIONS

Humans, often slaves, supplied power for plowing before the discovery, perhaps about 4000 BC, that oxen could be made to draw a load. Horses, asses, and mules were of little use for the heavy work of plowing until the horse collar was invented, about AD 1000. Oxen, asses, horses, mules, water buffaloes, camels, and human slaves furnished the power for field work until late in the 19th century, when a few steam tractors were put into use. The latter were effective for plowing large tracts of prairie sod, but were more costly than animal power for most field operations.

A tractor with an internal combustion motor was built in 1889 and other models followed, but factory production began only in 1903. They were called gasoline traction engines until 1906, when the name "tractor" was coined. Early gas tractors had 1 or 2 cylinders and weighed as much as 1100 pounds per drawbar horsepower. Modern tractors weigh about 200 pounds per horsepower—indeed, modern rubber-tired tractors are so light that the wheels or tires often are weighted to increase traction. Other tractor improvements include additional cylinders, better motors, enclosed gears, easier starting, adjustable spacing of wheels, and better weight distribution. Tractors did not come into common use for plowing until about 1910 after improvements had made them an economical power unit. The crawler tractor was first built in 1905. The diesel tractor appeared about 1929. The development in 1924 of the "tricycle" type general purpose tractor, with low-pressure rubber tires added in 1932, furnished a machine suitable for the cultivation of row crops. Nearly 5 million tractors were in use on American farms in 1959.

Early tractors with steel wheels and lugs delivered a drawbar horsepower of about 50 per cent of the belt horsepower of the motor. The more efficient modern rubber-tired and crawler type tractors deliver 70–80 per cent of belt horsepower at the drawbar. The wheeled tractors on various grain farms in the United States in 1948 averaged from 15–20 drawbar horsepower; the crawler tractors, 24 drawbar horsepower. At average loads, these gasoline-powered tractors used about 0.1 gallon of motor fuel per rated drawbar horsepower per hour. Diesel tractors are more economical of fuel. From 2.25 to 2.90 gallons of motor oil are used per 100 gallons of motor fuel.

For most field operations, the tractor used has a drawbar-horsepower rating 2–3 times the number of horses required to pull the same implement. Most tractors travel at higher speeds and cover 1.5–3 times the area covered in an hour with horse-drawn implements of the same width.

Tractors often are operated at 50–75 per cent of rated load in order to allow for ample power in difficult spots. For this reason, tractors seem to be somewhat less efficient than animals or men on the basis of rated power. However, they are more efficient than animal power in hot weather, at high speeds, and through a long workday. Tractors are particularly valuable for saving losses by around-the-clock operation to complete seeding or harvesting on time.

For any field implement, 2.2 net horsepower hours for each 100 pounds of draft per foot of width are required to cover an acre [7]. Thus, a 12-inch moldboard plow with a draft of 500 pounds requires 11 horsepower-hours per acre. Pulled by 2 horses, it can turn an acre in 5.5 hours net time. Additional time would be required for turning at the ends of the field and for cleaning or adjusting the equipment. A spiketooth harrow with a draft of 40 pounds per foot of width would require only 0.88 net horsepower hours per acre foot of width. A tractor of 10 drawbar horsepower, drawing a harrow of 30–35 feet might cover an acre in 0.088 hour, more than 110 acres in 10 hours net time.

PERFORMANCE OF MACHINES

The performance and power requirements of the principal implements used in grain production are shown in Appendix Table A-12.

Draft requirements for tillage operations vary with soil type. The draft per square inch of furrow slice of moldboard plows averages about 3 pounds in sandy soils, 3–6 pounds in sandy loams, 5–7 pounds in silt loams, 6–8 pounds in clay loams, 7–10 pounds in clays, and 15–20 pounds in heavy gumbos. The draft is 15–35 per cent greater for plowing most dry soils than for the same soils moist. Sod land requires about 10 per cent more power than does stubble land of the same texture. Plowing virgin prairie sod on heavy clay soil requires about 50 per cent more power than does clay stubble land. Disc plows have about 5–10 per cent less draft than moldboard plows in hard dry soils, but otherwise the draft is about the same. The average depth of fall plowing in the United States in 1918 was 5.45 inches and of spring plowing 5.12 inches, but these depths may have increased somewhat since tractors have come into general use.

In moldboard plowing, more than 50 per cent of the power is used in cutting the furrow slice, about 30 per cent in turning the slice; less than 20 per cent is wasted in friction between the plow bottom and the soil. The draft increases about 15 per cent for each additional inch of plowing depth below 5 inches. Most soils, except deep sands, become harder as depth increases, but since the friction of the plow does not increase appreciably with greater depths of plowing—increased draft is nearly proportional to increased depth. Compared with a plowing speed of one mile per hour, the average draft is increased one-seventh for each mile-per-hour higher speed.

Since the draft of a grain drill is about 6 pounds per inch of width for each furrow opener, its total draft varies with the spacing of the furrow openers as well as with its effective width. Openers on semifurrow and furrow drills are 10–16 inches apart, as compared with 6, 7, or 8 inches on the common drill, but the draft per foot of width of the furrow drill is about 50 per cent greater because of the greater depth of the furrows.

The area covered per hour by any field implement depends upon speed travelled; effective width; and time lost in turning, in servicing the machine, and in loading, unloading, or cleaning. The rate of travel varies with the power available for a given amount of draft (Fig. 3-23). The effective width of combines and binders is about 6–9 inches more than the length of the sickle, because the points of the dividers spread beyond the ends of the cutter bar and draw in a wider swath. The time lost in field operations is greatest in small fields, but usually ranges from 10–40 per cent of the total time, 15–20 per cent under highly favorable conditions. With an average of 17.5 per cent lost time, the acreage covered in 10 hours equals the effective width of the machine in feet multiplied by the speed in miles per hour.

The draft and performance of various implements shown in Appendix Table A-12 was compiled from the Extension Service Handbook [7] and various other sources. The power requirements of some implements not listed include the subsoiler with a draft of 80 to 160 pounds per inch of depth, and the tractor-drawn corn picker which uses from 2 to 5 horsepower from the power takeoff for a 1-row picker.

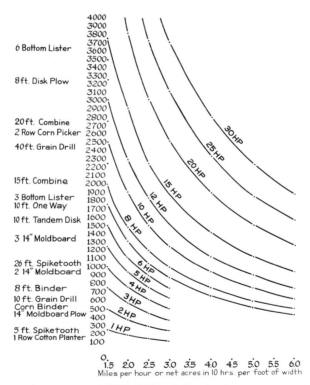

FIGURE 3-23. **Draft in pounds of typical farm implements (column near left), with power required and acreage covered per foot of width of the machine at indicated speeds.**

EFFECTIVE USE OF FARM MACHINES

The equipment typically used for the production of grain in any country depends chiefly upon the size and contour of fields, wage rates, labor supply, crop yields, economic levels, fuel costs, tariff rates, and the availability of repair parts and service facilities. Dependence upon any power implement or machine is hazardous in a country where needed major repair parts must be ordered from another country and shipments received one to three months later. Such a delay may mean the total loss of a crop. Primitive tools are used by necessity rather than by ignorance. Power implements cannot navigate steep slopes. The small farms of 5 acres or less that prevail in many countries are worked largely by hand labor because the maintenance of draft animals or tractors is too costly for such small areas. Grain farms of less than 40 acres might be operated more cheaply with animal power than with tractors in countries where such machines and fuel are expensive.

Tractors and other large machines are more advantageous where wages are high than where wages are low and farm laborers numerous.

Most expensive farm machines can be operated economically only when used for a minimum of 80–100 hours a year; overhead cost is materially reduced when they are used up to 300 hours a year. The minimum desirable annual use of a 1- to 3-plow tractor is 400–550 hours for economical operation. The annual cost for depreciation, interest, supplies, repairs, and replacements for many farm machines is then roughly 16–20 per cent of the original cost. Thus, $1000–1200 could well be spent for a machine that saves 200 hours of labor a year where wages are a dollar an hour, but an investment of only $50–60 dollars would be justified where wages are 5 cents an hour. A harvester with an expected life of 15 years that costs $3000 costs $200 a year for depreciation. Average annual interest charges are $75 at the rate of 5 per cent on one-half the original cost. Such a machine is uneconomic unless it is used on more than 100 acres yearly. The average combine in the United States harvests about 125 acres of grain a year, while those in Montana average nearly 300 acres each. Even a 6-foot combine should be used on about 140 acres annually, a 1-row corn picker on 70–80 acres, and a 2-row corn picker on 120–140 acres for economical operation.

FACTORS IN CHOICE OF FARM IMPLEMENTS

The objects of tillage are to loosen the soil, prepare suitable seedbeds, and destroy weeds, the soil surface to be left in condition to absorb water and resist wind and water erosion. These objectives may be achieved by many different types of implements. Stirring of the seedbed to a depth greater than 6–7 inches seldom is advantageous to any grain crop. A seedbed for different grains should be loose enough to place the seed 1–3 inches deep, but with somewhat more compact soil below that depth. The soil structure should be fine enough to provide close contact with the seed for quick germination, but not so fine as to favor puddling, crusting, or drifting of the soil. Weeds and weed seedlings in the field preferably should be killed by tillage shortly before planting. Vegetative residues, except when they would interfere with later intertillage, need to be cut up or turned under only to the extent necessary to permit placing the seed in friable soil. Turning the soil to bury weed seeds, which prevents their germination, is currently helpful, but such seeds may germinate later when brought to the surface.

Implements for Seedbed Preparation

Suitable seedbeds might be prepared with moldboard plows, wooden or disc plows, or with listers, chisels, sweeps, spades, or hoes, when properly used. Clods interfere with seeding as well as seedling emergence, but they may be broken with discs, harrows, rollers, tillers, floats, or hand tools, with similar beneficial results.

The moldboard plow, disc harrow, and spiketooth harrow are the basic tillage implements for seedbed preparation in the humid and irrigated areas of the United States. Two-way plows are used on irrigated land in order to avoid dead furrows which would interfere with the distribution of irrigation water. One-way disc plows, blade or sweep tillers, and the rotary rod weeder are used chiefly on semiarid grain farms, because they leave crop residues and clods on the soil surface to check soil blowing [25].

Implements for Small-grain Production

Disc drills, especially helpful on compact soils or on fields in which crop residues are on or near the surface, are used almost universally for sowing all small grains, except for some spring oats that are broadcast on disced cornstubble land. Furrow drills are used for fall sowing small grains in semiarid regions, particularly where the winters are cold. Furrow drills place the seed deeper where the soil is more moist to facilitate germination. The furrows check soil blowing, catch more snow, and protect the crop against winter killing.

Combines are used for harvesting nearly all of the small grains and grain sorghum in the United States, except in small fields or where it is desired to save all of the straw. The acre cost of combining is about the same as for binding and shocking, but the threshing of bound grain is an extra expense. In the southeastern states, a considerable acreage of oats is cut with a binder, the bundles fed whole without threshing.

Implements for Row-Planted Cereals

The row crops—corn and grain sorghum—usually are planted in lister furrows in semiarid areas; with surface planters in subhumid, humid, and irrigated areas; and on elevated beds where the rainfall exceeds 45–50 inches annually. Elevated beds protect the crop in wet fields. The lister method places the seed down in moist soil and requires one or two fewer cultivations of the crop than does surface planting. Check-row surface planting is advantageous in humid regions where weeds are abundant, unless thick planting is practiced or preemergence herbicides are used.

Special implements for intertillage are required for each planting method. Lister rows are intertilled with cultivators that have discs, sweep blades, or both. Lister disc cultivators turn the soil toward the ridge in the initial cultivation. In a later cultivation when the plants are larger, the discs are reversed to cut down the ridge, fill the furrow, and thus level the field. A third cultivation may require a surface implement. Surface cultivators are equipped with either sweeps or small shovels for tilling level fields or elevated beds. In any case, the chief object of intertillage is to control weeds. Sweep blades are often the most effective in cutting off weeds. The rotary hoe and similar implements are most effective in killing weed seedlings while the corn plants are small or not yet emerged.

Corn harvesters may merely snap off the ears, snap and husk them, or else snap, husk and shell in one operation. The latter method is popular where grain-drying facilities are available.

Diversity in Use of Implements

In the more primitive areas of Asia, Africa, southern Europe, Central America, and South America, a heavy short-handled hand hoe often replaces the plow and disc harrow in small fields. A lighter weight hoe may be used for intertillage. Small fields of the small grains are cut with a sickle or occasionally with a scythe. The stalks of corn or sorghum are cut with a sickle or machete. Corn is husked and shelled by hand in these areas. Other grains are threshed by flailing or trampling, rolling, or small foot-powered or motorized threshers are used.

On medium-sized farms, 10–80 acres in size in many countries, implements drawn by either small tractors or draft animals are used. On such farms, the single bottom moldboard plow is popular, while small disc, spike-tooth, or springtooth harrows usually are used for seedbed preparation. Seeding may be done with a drill or planter or by broadcasting. Intertillage is done with cultivators or by hand hoeing. Harvesting of grain may be done with a binder, reaper, scythe or sickle, or occasionally with a combine. Small threshers still prevail in such farming areas.

REFERENCES

1. Barger, E. L., *et al.*, *Tractors and their power units.* New York: Wiley. pp 1–496. 1952.
2. Cooper, M. R., G. T. Barton, and A. P. Brodell, "Progress of farm mechanization." USDA *Misc. Pub. 630.* pp 1–101. 1947.
3. "Crop machinery use data." *Ag. Eng. Data 2.* Am. Soc. Ag. Eng. 1949.
4. Davis, L. L., "California rice production," Cal. Ag. Ext. *Cir. 163.* pp 1–55. 1950.
5. Elwood, R. B., *et al.*, "Changes in technology and labor requirements in crop production—wheat, and oats." WPA Natl. Res. Proj. *Rpt. A-10.* pp 1–182. 1939.
6. Gittins, B. S., *Land of plenty,* 2d ed. Chicago: Farm Equip. Inst. pp 1–63. 1959.
7. Harvey, T. W., *Extension Service Handbook on Agriculture and Home Economics.* USDA. pp 1–951. 1927.
8. Holbrook, S. H., *Machines of plenty.* New York: Macmillan. pp 1–246. 1955.
9. Hopfen, H. J., and E. Biesalaski, "Small farm implements." New York: Columbia U. Press, Int. Doc. Serv. pp 1–79. 1953.
10. Hurst, W. M., and L. M. Church, "Power and machinery in agriculture." USDA *Misc. Pub. 157.* pp 1–39. 1933.
11. Hutchinson, W. T., *Cyrus Hall McCormick—seed-time, 1809–1856.* New York and London: Century. pp 1–493. 1960.
12. Isler, D. A., "Aircraft in agriculture," in *Power to Produce.* USDA Yrbk. of Ag. pp 157–163. 1960.
13. Macy, L. K., *et al.*, "Changes in technology and labor requirements in crop production—corn." WPA Natl. Res. Proj. *Rpt. A-5.* pp 1–81. 1938.
14. McKibben, E. G., and R. A. Griffin, "Changes in farm power and equipment—tractors, trucks, and automobiles." WPA Natl. Res. Proj. *Rpt. A-9.* pp 1–114. 1938.
15. ———, J. A. Hopkins, and R. A. Griffin, "Changes in farm power and equipment—field implements." WPA Natl. Res. Proj. *Rpt. A-11.* pp 1–111. 1939.
16. Miller, F., Q. W. Lindsey, and A. G. George, "Cost of operating machinery on Nebraska farms." Nebr. Ag. Exp. Sta. *Bul. 391.* pp 1–35. 1948.
17. Miller, W. F., "The evolution of reaping machines." USDA Off. Exp. Sta. *Bul. 103.* pp 1–43. 1902.
18. Minneman, P. G., and E. B. Hill, "A farm management study of crop production practices." Mich. Ag. Exp. Sta. *Spec. Bul. 241.* pp 1–58. 1933.
19. Mullins, T., and M. W. Slusher, "Comparison of farming systems for small rice farms in Arkansas." Ark. Ag. Exp. *Sta. Bul. 498.* 1950.
20. Shafer, N. E., J. D. Furrer, and J. W. Lomax, "Aircraft in agriculture." Nebr. Ag. Exp. *Sta. Cir. 88.* 1950.
21. Smith, H. P., *Farm machinery and equipment,* 4th ed. New York: McGraw-Hill. pp 514. 1955.
22. Stone, A. A., and H. E. Gulvin, *Machines for power farming.* New York: Wiley. pp 1–616. 1957.
23. Turner, A. W., and E. J. Johnson, *Machines for the farm, ranch, and plantation.* New York: McGraw-Hill. pp 1–793. 1948.
24. Wik, R. M., "Steam power on the American farm, 1830–1880." *Ag. Hist.*, **25**(4): 181–186. 1951.
25. Zingg, A. W., and C. J. Whitfield, "Stubble-mulch farming." USDA *Tech. Bul. 1166.* 1957.

4. STORAGE, DRYING, MARKETING, AND GRADING OF GRAIN

GRAIN STORAGE

Since prehistoric times, grain has been stored to save seed, to provide food between harvest seasons, and in advanced agricultural areas, to supply feed grain. Only one crop of a particular kind of grain is harvested each year in most temperate zone areas. Two grain crops a year sometimes are grown in subtropical or cool tropical areas, while two or three crops of rice can be grown in one year in the tropics when water is available. Thus, in most areas, considerable grain is stored for six months to a year, if not longer.

Storage Facilities

In primitive countries grain is stored in small buildings, underground pits, outdoor piles, or in woven bags and baskets [24]. In commercial grain areas, grain is stored in bulk bins, bagged grain in warehouses. However, in dry areas some bulk grain may be temporarily piled outdoors during the rush of the harvest period. Most of the storage bins on farms of the United States are constructed of sheet metal or wood and range 500–2000 bushels in capacity [33]. Storage bins in commercial grain elevators are constructed of concrete, wood, or steel, and usually range 1000–50,000 bushels in capacity; some hold 100,000 bushels or more. Considerable grain also is being stored in steel Quonset huts both on farms and at local markets [3, 20].

Formerly, cereal grain stored on farms was placed in the bin by hand. Now, deep farm bins or corn cribs can be filled with bulk grain or ear corn readily while unloading a truck or wagon, with a portable elevating device

FIGURE 4-1. **Unloading ear corn into a crib with a portable elevator.**

(Courtesy US Department of Agriculture)

(Fig. 4-1). More than a million farms in the United States had grain elevating devices in 1959. Such equipment moves the grain upward with augers, or by cups or cleats on an endless chain. In commercial grain storage elevators, grain usually is lifted to the top in dipperlike buckets attached to an endless belt. On most farms and in country elevators, grain is moved laterally with auger conveyers [4]. In large terminal elevators, grain is moved horizontally on wide endless belts.

More recently, grain is being moved pneumatically in some elevators, although 9–20 times more power is required than to move the same amount of grain in an auger conveyer. The minimum air velocity required to move grain horizontally through a pipe is 2000–3000 feet per minute. With an air velocity of 4000 feet per minute it is possible to move 6–12,000 pounds of grain sorghum per hour [29] through a 6-inch metal pipe. In a pneumatic system, a fan draws air past a stream of falling grain, forcing it through a pipe to a cyclone-type collector where the grain is dropped (Fig. 4-2).

Because spots of wet grain in a bin usually spoil, outer walls of bins must be tight enough to exclude rain or snow [36]. Outer bin walls of metal permit a rapid movement of heat from the grain near the walls when the temperature is cool, but they likewise absorb heat quickly in hot weather. Metal bins should be anchored to the ground to avoid wind damage when they are empty. Deep bins must have strong walls or be crossbraced to withstand heavy pressure. The lateral pressure of the wheat on the walls at the bottom of a full 2000-bushel round bin 16 feet in diameter and 12 feet deep is nearly 300 pounds per square foot [37].

A bushel is approximately 1.25 cubic feet (1 cu ft = 0.803 bu). The capacity of a round bin, in bushels, is computed thus: Square of diameter in feet $\times$ 0.7854 $\times$ height in feet $\times$ 0.803, or approximately $D^2 \times H \times 5/8$. For rectangular bins the formula is: width $\times$ length $\times$ height in feet $\times$ 0.8.

Length of Time in Storage

Dry grain that contains 11–12 per cent moisture, or less, can be stored

FIGURE 4-2. **Typical farm bins built of corrugated steel. Grain is being moved from one bin to another by a pneumatic system.**

(Courtesy US Department of Agriculture)

in weatherproof bins for many years in most climates without appreciable deterioration, provided it is protected from insects, rodents, external moisture, and high humidity. The composition of sound dry grain remains almost unchanged except for some increase in fatty acids and a slight loss of energy from respiration. At average air temperatures, a weight loss in dry matter of perhaps one per cent from respiration might be expected during 20 years of storage.

Milling and baking tests were made on samples of Marquis and Kanred varieties of wheat stored in a dry unheated room for 19 to 33 years in Colorado. Prolonged storage had no consistent effect on the protein content of the grain, but about 60 per cent of the samples showed a slight apparent loss of protein during storage. The ash content of the wheat remained unchanged, but the bran coat became more brittle during storage, and more of it pulverized and was carried over into the flour during milling. This increased the ash content of the flour. Diastatic activity also increased with longer storage. Thiamine differences were no greater than those that commonly occur among samples from different crop years. There was a fairly regular increase in fat acidity with storage, but satisfactory bread of good loaf volume was produced from all lots of flour. The bread made from wheat stored for 33 years was somewhat lacking in grain and texture despite the satisfactory loaf volume [15]. Kanred wheat stored for 19 years showed 47.2 per cent germination, but both wheats failed to germinate after storage for 27 years. Good bread was made from flour of the wheat that had lost its viability [14].

Moisture Content of Stored Grain

A ripening grain reaches its maximum weight of dry matter when its moisture content drops to 35–40 per cent. Since grains never ripen uniformly, some increase in dry matter may continue until the average moisture content of a field sample has dropped to 26–30 per cent. The individual grains in a single head or ear usually ripen over a period of 3–10 days; late heads, ears, and plants in a field extend the ripening period even more. Grain that is to be cured in the shock may be safely cut when the moisture content is 30 per cent or less. Corn that contains 26 per cent moisture, or less, is dry enough to be husked and stored in pressure-ventilated cribs, or to be shelled and dried artificially. Rice that is to be dried artificially may be cut and threshed with a combine at a moisture content of 16–26 per cent.

All shelled or threshed grain that contains more than 15 per cent moisture must be dried in some fashion before it can be stored in bulk for extended periods without spoilage. Grain that contains 15 per cent moisture usually will keep during a cold winter, provided it has been cooled by aeration or by moving it to another bin during a cold period. In most parts of northern United States, 14 per cent moisture is the maximum for safe winter storage. A moisture content of 13 per cent may be allowable for the central latitudes; 11–12 per cent moisture is the maximum for safe winter storage in the warmer Coastal Plain and Gulf Coast areas. Grain stored through the warm summer months should contain not more than 13 per cent moisture in the northern states, 12 per cent in central latitudes, and 11 per cent in the southern coastal areas.

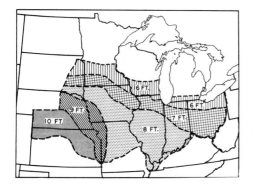

FIGURE 4-3. **Maximum widths of corn cribs recommended for safe storage in the Corn Belt states.**

(*Courtesy US Department of Agriculture*)

Ear corn that contains 20–21 per cent moisture, or less, in the grain can be preserved over winter in cribs (Figs. 4-1, 4-4) where natural drying in the fall will reduce the moisture content to perhaps 17 to 18 per cent. Further drying in the spring reduces the moisture content to 15 per cent or less. The suitable width of the crib for satisfactory drying ranges from 6 feet in the Great Lakes region to 10 feet in the warmer drier portions of the central Great Plains States [31] (Figs. 4-3, 4-4). Cribs only 3 feet wide are used in the cool humid areas of northwestern Europe.

Spoilage of Grain in Storage

Stored grain suffers damage when its moisture content and temperature are sufficiently high to permit organisms (insects included) to thrive. Grain-infesting insects usually are inactive when the moisture content of the grain is below 9 per cent and the temperature is 40°F or less. At moisture contents above 13 per cent and temperatures above 70°F insects are very active; the dry grain they consume is converted into growth energy and heat. Respiration releases heat, and produces carbon dioxide and water by breaking down carbohydrates, fats, and proteins. The released water raises the moisture content of the mass of grain. Spoilage by heating, molding, and decay ensue, in addition to the direct damage by the insects.

The chief damage to stored grain protected from insects and rodents results from the activities of microorganisms, chiefly fungi. The outer coat of

FIGURE 4-4. "Snapped" (unhusked) corn stored in a temporary snow-fence crib.

(*Courtesy US Department of Agriculture*)

each shelled grain may bear several thousand spores of fungi and bacteria that were present in the air, on the plants, or in the field. The fungi present are mostly species of *Aspergillus* (chiefly *A. glaucus, A. candidus,* and *A. flavus*), *Penicillium, Alternaria, Cladisporium, Helminthosporium,* and *Fusarium.* Some of these fungi are able to grow and multiply when the moisture content of the grain is as low as 13.5–15 per cent. Other species of fungi grow at 16–23 per cent moisture. Most aerobic bacteria do not multiply unless the moisture content of the grain is as high as about 20 per cent. Respiration releases heat and water vapor, which stimulates additional microbial activity at increasing rates.

All sound cereal grains that are able to germinate are living organisms in which respiration occurs. However, the rate of respiration is so low that the heat and moisture produced in dry grain is readily dissipated. Freshly harvested grain formerly was reputed to always go through a "sweat" because it frequently showed increases in temperature and moisture. However, no one seems to have detected sweating in grain that was well dried when stored. For many years it was assumed that the respiration of the grain itself was responsible for heating and spoilage when the moisture content exceeded 14–15 per cent. Numerous measurements showed rapidly increasing respiration rates as the moisture content and temperature of the grain increased (Fig. 4-5); often, moldiness or mustiness also increased. Despite this, the possibility that fungi were chiefly involved in these respiration measurements usually was ignored, until evidence was obtained by E. P. Carter [5, 6]. Wheat grain in which the viability and fungi had been killed by heat sterilization showed very little respiration or heat production even at moisture contents in excess of 16 per cent. When such "dead" wheat was reinfected with dust from unsterilized grain that obviously contained fungus spores, the respiration rate was similar to that of viable unsterilized grain of the same moisture content. These observations on the role of fungi in the respiration and heating of stored grain were fully confirmed soon thereafter [7, 16, 30]. It was found that sterilized but viable grain showed

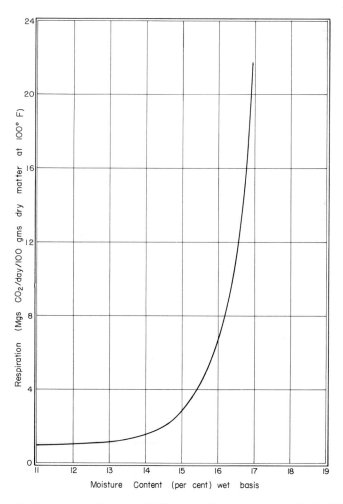

FIGURE 4-5. **Respiration of wheat of different moisture contents held at 100° F.**

little respiration at moisture contents at which rapid heating occurred in unsterilized grain.

Hard Red Spring wheat at 30°C (86°F) held at a relative humidity of 74–75 per cent and moisture content below 14.5 per cent yielded low but constant respiratory rates over an extended time. There was no significant increase in mold population or in chemical deterioration of the grain. At higher moisture contents respiratory rates increased with time. Respiratory increases were accompanied by mold growth, chemical deterioration of the grain, lowered viability, and increases in the moisture content of the wheat [27]. Experiments with a western white wheat free from internal molds provided direct evidence on the role of molds in the deterioration of stored grain [23].

Species of *Alternaria* and *Helminthosporium* were the principal molds (fungi) that infested the interior of sound, dry, hard spring wheat. At moisture contents above the critical level, the predominant fungi, in order of increased moisture content, were: *Aspergillus glaucus, A. Candidus, A. flavus,* and *Penicillium* species. The extent of mold proliferation with time was directly related to the respiratory activity, increased fat acidity, and reduced germination of the wheat. Increases in mold growth, heating, and respiration in damp wheat samples continued until a temperature of 52–55°C (125.6–131.0°F) was reached. Then the molds were killed, respiration dropped, and heating ceased. At high moisture contents of 26–30 per cent (equivalent to 95 per cent humidity), bacterial growth may cause wheat to heat to the bacterial thermal death range of 68–70°C (154.4–158.0°F). Under strictly controlled adiabatic conditions, wheat may continue to heat spontaneously due to nonbiological oxidation [27].

In the soft winter wheat area, species of *Aspergillus* and *Penicillium* usually predominated on the surface of wheat kernels, whereas species of *Alternaria* and *Aspergillus* were commonly found in the interior of the kernel. Samples of sound No. 1 grade of Soft Red Winter wheat carried from 3,000–57,000 spores per kernel. *Aspergillus candidus* usually was involved in actively heating wheat. Temperature increments of 20–26°C (68–78.8°F) were attained in wheat infested with this fungus. *Aspergillus glaucus* predominated in wheat samples that heated only moderately [6].

Keeping Quality of Treated Grain

Numerous compounds were tested for fungistatic ability on wheat stored with a moisture content of 16–25 per cent in Minnesota. The most effective moldicides were somewhat toxic to wheat. Wheat treated with one part of thiourea to 100 parts by weight of moist seed respired at a nearly constant rate over a 10-day period before molds began to increase. Sound untreated wheat stored at 30°C (86°F) and moisture contents above 16.1 per cent was rapidly overgrown by molds. The increase in respiration and decrease in viability of the seed, as the moisture content increased, was proportional to the increase in molds [28]. High moisture wheat failed to heat when treated with New Improved Ceresan or a heavy application of chloropicrin, or when stored in sealed vacuum containers. Fungi were absent or negligible in all cases. It was concluded that heating of moist wheat in storage could be entirely accounted for by the energy released in the respiration of fungi present on or in the kernels [6].

Wheat samples stored in nitrogen or in sealed containers deteriorated more slowly, retained their germinating ability longer, and suffered less germ damage than when stored in air. This indicates the role of oxygen in deterioration [18].

Types of Spoilage in Cereal Grain

The type of spoilage in cereal grain is determined largely by its moisture content. Grain that contains somewhat more than 20 per cent moisture usually sours due to the fermentation of soluble carbohydrates. Alcohol and organic acids are formed; heat is generated by the subsequent oxidation of carbon and hydrogen. When shelled and binned without drying, corn that contains 25 per cent moisture or more usually sours and heats in a few days. The souring is followed by rotting when oxygen is available, but wet grain placed in an airtight silo ferments until the oxygen is exhausted. Soon after, the fungi and enzymes present are destroyed by the heat. Ensiled grain is not usable for food or milling, but it makes good livestock feed. Some wet corn and grain sorghum is ensiled as a method of storage in the central states of the United States. Like ensiled forage, it must be fed promptly when it is taken from the silo; the several inches of grain near the surface exposed to the air must be removed from the silo and fed each day.

Grain that contains from 16–20 per cent moisture usually heats and becomes moldy as the result of fungus growth and respiration. In large bins, mold growth often is restricted by lack of oxygen, but the heating causes the grains to turn a dark brown ("bin burnt") color. Grain that contains approximately 14–15.5 per cent moisture often becomes musty due to limited fungus growth, unless it is cooled then stored in a cold climate.

Grain with 14–16 per cent of moisture, stored in terminal elevators in large bins where oxygen is limited, often develops darkened dead germs. Wheat so damaged is called "sick." The dead germs have a high content of fatty acids which gives a rancid flavor; they also contain fungus mycelia. Mold growth usually is evident on such grain which also is characterized by low viability and high fat acidity. Samples have been found to be infected

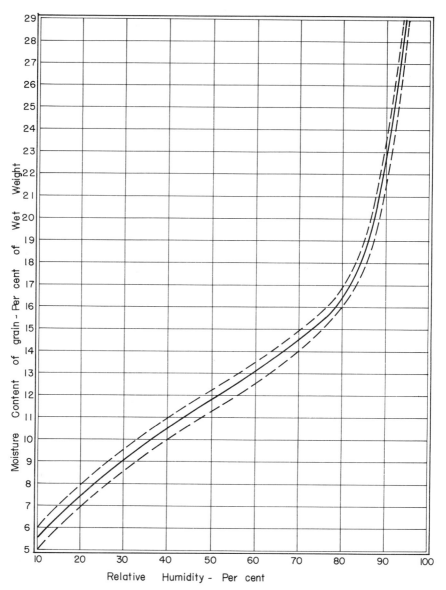

FIGURE 4-6. Equilibrium moisture content of grain at different relative humidities. The broken lines show the approximate range of the moisture-humidity relationship resulting from differences in temperature, method of measuring moisture content, and grain characteristics.

principally with *Aspergillus glaucus, Penicillium* spp., and to a lesser extent with *A. candidus, A. niger,* and a few bacteria. Sick wheat was produced in the laboratory by storage in sealed containers at 18 per cent moisture in atmospheres of carbon dioxide, nitrogen, or oxygen. Molds developed only under oxygen. Fat acidity increased in all samples but was greatest under oxygen [26]. In other experiments, wheat at 15–21 per cent moisture showed high levels of mold infestation that markedly increased losses in viability, caused germ damage, and increased fat acidity during storage of only 5–15 days. Losses in viability that preceded the discoloration of the germ were indicative of incipient damage as well as poor storage properties [35]. Flour from sick wheat is unfit for making bread because the desired elastic properties of the gluten have been impaired or destroyed.

Moisture Movement in Grain

Well-mixed wet and dry grain often reaches a uniform moisture content within 24–48 hours. Thus, moisture exchange between adjacent grains is rapid, but moisture and air movement through a mass of bulk grain is extremely slow. Consequently, a small batch of damp grain in a bin may spoil when it is surrounded by a large bulk of dry grain. The moisture content of grain at the top surface of a pile quickly comes into equilibrium with the relative humidity or vapor pressure of the immediate atmosphere. Grain exposed to an atmosphere of 65 per cent relative humidity has a moisture content of about 14 per cent, but the moisture content rises rapidly at higher humidities, especially above 80 per cent (Fig. 4-6).

Grain takes up water rapidly when wetted, up to 1 per cent per minute initially. Much of the water enters the grain at the hilum, but water also is absorbed by the bran coat. The testa tends to retard the entrance of water. After water enters the grain, it is absorbed on the surface of the endosperm, scutellum, and embryo cells and on the starch grains. A pound of wheat has about 30 acres of surface area on the cells. The cells start to swell when they absorb water. The volume change nearly parallels the weight of water absorbed. The wheat grain has a density of 1.374 at 11.3 per cent moisture, 1.282 at 20.9 per cent moisture [13]. Completely dry grain has a density of about 1.41. Absorption of water (density 1.0) plus the swelling of the grain thus reduces the test weight. The grain shrinks upon drying, but not quite to its original density. Repeated wetting and drying may lower the test weight of wheat 4 or 5 pounds per bushel. The absorption of water increases with declining temperatures. At a given relative humidity, the moisture content of the grain may be 0.5–1.5 per cent higher for every 30°F drop in temperature [22]. Vapor pressure increases with temperature (Fig. 4-7).

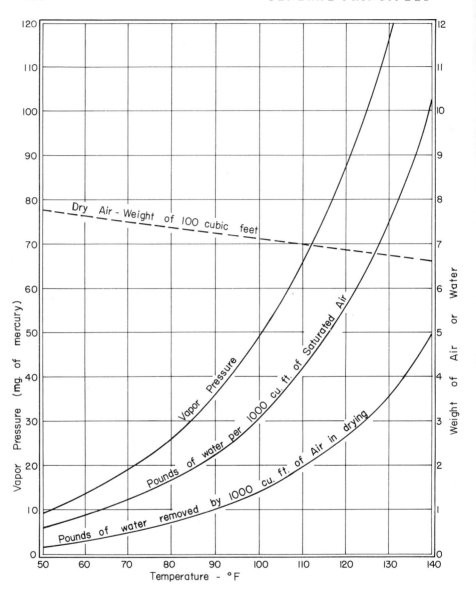

FIGURE 4-7. **Relation of vapor pressure to air temperature, to water in saturated air, and to pounds of water removed in drying grain computed at 50 per cent drying efficiency and assuming an initial 60 per cent relative humidity at 60° F.**

Heat Transfer in Grain

Heat transfer in cereal grain is very slow. The thermal conductivity of grain is only about 0.0003–0.0004 cgs units, about the same as that of dry soil or dry wood, one-tenth to one-sixth that of concrete. Daily fluctuations in air temperatures do not affect grain deeper than 6 inches below surface. There is very little direct heat transfer, over a 6-month period, in grain that is 10 feet from the top or sides of a bin. However, convection currents often develop during cold winter weather—warm air rises to the surface of the grain in the center of the bin, replaced by cool air that moves downward along the outer walls of the bin. The warm air may absorb moisture from the grain as it moves upward, and then the moisture may condense upon the cool grain at the surface. This sometimes results in spoilage of the upper layers of grain in a bin after the return of warm weather. Hot weather may induce upward convection currents just inside the heated bin walls. This creates a downward movement of air in the center of the bin, and moisture may condense on the colder lower layers of grain.

Aeration of Grain in Storage

The cooling of grain by aeration is an established practice in modern elevators [21]. When the air temperature is 10°F or more below the temperature of the grain, air is withdrawn from the bottom of the bin at the rate of 0.05–0.10 cubic feet per minute per bushel of grain. Outside cool air drawn down through the grain prevents moisture migration, reduces mold and insect activity, and helps to cool hot spots in the bin. Grain in a bin can be cooled down almost to air temperature in 80–160 hours of aeration. Aeration accomplishes very little drying of the grain. A perforated duct laid across the bottom of the bin is connected to a pipe that passes through the bin wall to an exhaust fan. Farm bins can be aerated by placing a vertical pipe, with perforations at the lower end, in the center of the bin. A 50–60-watt electric fan on top of the pipe above the grain will draw 50–100 cubic feet of air per minute and exhaust it through an outlet pipe. A one-horsepower exhaust fan will aerate up to 20,000 bushels of shelled corn or 5000 bushels of wheat in a bin 100 feet deep, with an air flow of 0.05 cubic feet per minute per bushel. The system also is useful in drawing fumigants down through the grain for insect control.

Formerly it was the practice to "turn" grain during cold weather by moving it from one bin to another. This moving also served to mix any spots of damp or hot grain in the bin with cooler and drier grain. Power and labor costs for turning grain four times a year range from 0.5–1.5 cent a bushel. Aeration costs only 0.1–0.5 cent per bushel yearly for power and labor, while the installed cost of aeration systems is only 1–5 cents per

FIGURE 4-8. **Drying rice on the ground in Taiwan.**

(Courtesy US Department of Agriculture)

bushel of bin capacity. Grain is exposed to cold air for only a few minutes during turning and the operation causes some shrinkage losses and breakage of grain. Also it is necessary to maintain one or more empty bins into which the grain can be moved. Elevator bins are regularly equipped with thermocouples at levels 4–7 feet apart to permit the reading or recording of temperatures at each level. A temperature of 90°F or higher warns the operator to aerate or turn the grain in the bin.

DRYING GRAIN[1]

Grain is dried most economically in the natural way of allowing it to stand in the field on the stalk or in shocks. Low humidity, heat of the sun, and gentle breezes carry away the water. A substantial portion of the world small grain crop receives no other form of drying. Corn seldom dries sufficiently on the standing stalk and often not in the shock because the husks cover the ears and the cobs are wetter than the grain. Grain threshed in wet or humid seasons or climates often requires special drying. Much grain dried by artificial methods has been harvested with a combine or field sheller. In hot dry climates, rice dry enough for combining and bin storage usually shows severe checking of the kernels. The checked kernels break during milling. This is avoided by combine harvesting of the rice while the

[1] See also [17].

grain is still damp. The rice is dried artificially [1, 25]. Grain sorghum often is harvested with a combine during cool autumn weather, when natural drying is slow. It may require artificial drying, especially when ripening has not been uniform, as often happens.

Natural Air Drying

Since early times, harvested grain has been air-dried before threshing by placing cut bundles in shocks or stooks on the ground. In some countries, rice and other grains are dried by hanging the bundles on fences, walls, or racks. When harvesting with combines in most countries, it is usually feasible to allow grain except corn and rice to stand in the field until dry enough for threshing and storage.

In many countries damp grain is dried by spreading it 4–6 inches deep on an outdoor floor or yard (Fig. 4-8). Often this grain is pushed up into piles each night to retard the absorption of moisture when the humidity is high, then spread out again next morning. This procedure is effective in warm, dry seasons. In semiarid sections of the United States, damp wheat or grain sorghum sometimes is dumped on the ground in long piles. The angle of repose of the damp grain pile is about 27 degrees. A pile 2.5 feet high slopes down gradually to a width of about 8.5 feet at the base. The small amount of grain in the deepest part of the pile then is only slightly more than 2 feet from the air surface. More than 70 per cent of it is within one foot of the surface; more than 40 per cent of it is within 6 inches of the open air. Grain that contains 15–18 per cent moisture usually dries down to a moisture content of less than 14 per cent within 3 weeks when it is so piled on dry ground, provided drying weather prevails.

FIGURE 4-9. **Bins with perforated walls for ventilation equipped with a suction cowl (left) and a wind pressure cowl (right).**

(Courtesy US Department of Agriculture)

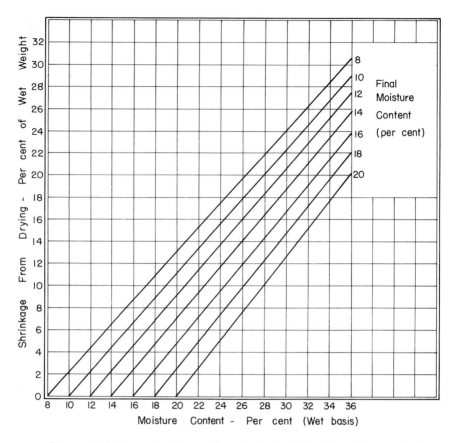

FIGURE 4-10. **Per cent shrinkage from drying to indicated moisture contents.**

Grain bins that are ventilated merely through perforations in the walls or floor of the bin, or by perforated tubes or screened flues inserted through holes in the sides and across the bin at 4-foot intervals, have proved inadequate. They dry only the grain that is within a few inches of the openings. Bins with perforations in the floors and cowl ventilators at the peak of the roof are adequate in semiarid areas for drying grain that is not more than about 2 per cent higher in moisture content than what is essential for safe storage. The wind pressure cowl is superior to the exhaust wind cowl in forcing air through the grain (Fig. 4-9). A disadvantage of such ventilated bins is that the grain absorbs moisture during damp periods. Rain or snow may enter the bins, unless the cowls and other openings are closed in some manner [32].

Drying With Forced Unheated Air

Grain that contains more than 15 per cent moisture will become drier when force-ventilated with air having a relative humidity of 70–75 per cent [12, 10]. Humidities not higher than 50–60 per cent are required to reduce the moisture content to less than 13 per cent. Thus, ventilation with unheated air should be intermittent, being operated only when the humidity is below 70 per cent after the grain has dried down to 15–17 per cent moisture. Such humidities often occur on clear days, especially between 10 AM and 6 PM.

The number of pounds of water in a bushel of grain of different moisture contents is shown in Table 4-1. For example, a lot of shelled corn that contains 30 per cent moisture contains 20.0 pounds of water per bushel. Thus, 67.5 pounds of such grain is the equivalent of one bushel (56 pounds) of corn that contains 15.5 per cent moisture. The drying of wheat from 20 per cent down to 14 per cent moisture involves the removal of 4.5 pounds (12.9 less 8.4) of water per bushel. This reduction of 6 per cent in moisture content is equivalent to a shrinkage in weight of about 7 per cent, as shown in Fig. 4-10.

Mechanical drying of binned grain with unheated air requires power that costs 2–4 cents per bushel just to operate the fan; labor and equipment add to the cost. The bins for drying must be provided with perforated ducts or false floors to permit the air to be drawn or forced through all parts of the bin by the ventilating fan. Trash, dust, and broken grains retard the flow of air through the mass of grain. Such material should be cleaned out before the bin is filled, or at least it should be distributed through the grain mass so as not to form pockets in the bin that are difficult to ventilate.

The requirements for drying grain with forced unheated air are shown in Table 4-2. A suitable size of fan of a propeller or centrifugal type, driven by a one-horsepower motor, delivers about 3000 cubic feet per minute at a one-inch static pressure. Such a fan delivering 3 cubic feet of air per minute per bushel through grain 4–6 feet deep in the bin might dry 700 bushels of wheat, 1500 bushels of oats, or 1250 bushels of corn that contain 20 per cent moisture, within 4 weeks or less. The drying of most grain requires an air flow of 1–6 cubic feet per minute per bushel of grain. Grain of high moisture content necessitates the greatest flow of air, especially when the air humidity is relatively high. Wheat offers about 50 per cent more resistance to air flow than oats and 2.5 times that of shelled corn because of smaller air spaces between the grains; the resistance of grain sorghum is slightly less than wheat. Also, a bushel of wheat contains more pounds of water at a given moisture percentage than do other grains, all of which have a lower bushel weight. Thus, the depth of wheat in the bin must be less than for other grains in order to achieve the same rate of drying. Resistance to air flow increases disproportionally with the increased thickness of

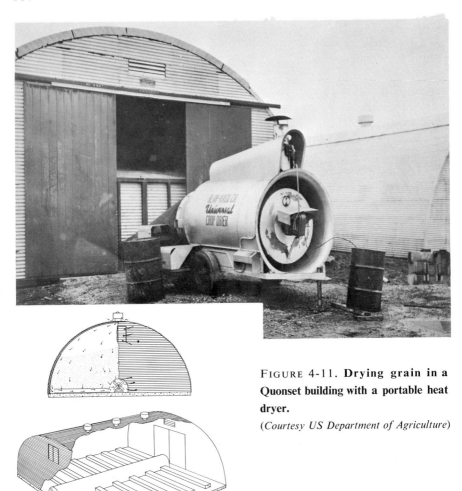

FIGURE 4-11. **Drying grain in a Quonset building with a portable heat dryer.**
(Courtesy US Department of Agriculture)

the layer of grain in the drying bin. The resistance to air flow through 4-foot depth of grain is about one-third as much as through 8 feet of grain, and half that through a 6-foot depth.

Drying Grain With Heated Air

Drying grain with heated air (Fig. 4-11) is more costly but more rapid and dependable than with unheated air [11, 9]. The heating of air in grain driers usually is done by burning either natural gas or petroleum fuels. The heat from each gallon of fuel will evaporate from 50–85 pounds of water from the grain with a direct-heat drier, 35–60 pounds with indirect heat.

Indirect heat requires about 40 per cent more fuel, but the fire hazard is greatly reduced. A higher drying efficiency is possible in summer weather than in winter, which accounts for the differences shown above for a given type of drier. A 400-bushel batch of wheat distributed 2 feet deep in a drying bin in summer could be dried from 20 per cent down to 13 per cent moisture content in slightly more than 5 hours with 7500 cubic feet per minute of air at 150°F temperature. Nearly 2100 pounds of water would be evaporated by the 25.5 gallons of fuel used. A direct-heat drier of this capacity requires a 5-horsepower motor to drive the fan and a burner consuming 5 gallons of fuel per hour. The air temperature for drying wet grain that is to be used for seed should not exceed 110°F; this also is about the maximum safe temperature for drying wet malting barley and rice [1, 25]. Corn, wheat, or grain sorghum for processing for starch or food products should be dried at a temperature not exceeding 130°F, because grain that has been overheated gives a low starch separation. Grain for feed can be dried at temperatures up to 170°F, but some loss in protein digestibility may occur from higher temperatures. Higher temperatures than those indicated are permissible when the grain is nearly dry.

The combine has created a serious problem in the harvesting of grain sorghums in areas of high humidity because it necessitates artificial drying to get the grain dry enough for storage [34]. Sorghum grain of more than 13 per cent moisture when threshed must be dried to prevent damage in storage [32]. Some Texas experiments indicate that sorghum grain sometimes can be artificially dried to a moisture content of 12 per cent most efficiently with air temperatures as follows: 150°F for grain with 14–16 per cent moisture; 175°F for grain with a moisture range 17–20 per cent; and 200°F for grain exceeding 20 per cent moisture. The Martin variety with a moisture content up to 20 per cent was dried with air temperatures as high as 175°F without a detrimental effect on germination. The wet-milling characteristics of Martin and Early Hegari were unimpaired by artificial drying to 11–13 per cent moisture with an air temperature of 125–200°F [34].

Commercial grain driers (Fig. 4-12) are mostly of column construction in which the grain moves downward slowly through perforated columns only a few inches thick. Heated air forced into chambers between these columns passes through the streams of grain to the outside, or it is recirculated through the upper and wetter layers of grain. Some farm driers also are of the column type (Fig. 4-13). Many farm driers have bins with tight sidewalls and perforated false bottom floors through which hot air is forced up through the grain. Other drying bins have perforated ducts across the bottom of the bin, or perforated inlet and exhaust ducts through the mass of grain. The heat for farm driers is supplied by burners, usually of a portable type, from which the hot air is blown into the bin.

Batch drying of grain in a bin or crib does not produce uniform drying. The grain nearest the hot air intake often is dried to a moisture content below the desired percentage before grain at the remote part of the pile has dried at all. Drying then proceeds upward and outward. After drying, the grain is moved from the drying bin to the storage bin, which mixes the drier and damper portions of the batch and thus largely equalizes the moisture content in a short time. Cooling the grain after drying, by blowing unheated air through it for an hour or less, is advisable.

Ear corn in storage cribs can be dried, provided the ends of the crib are sealed off with panels, canvas, or heavy paper, and hot air is blown in

FIGURE 4-12. A column-type rice drier. (1) cleaning machinery; (2) drying columns; (3) dump pit; (4) hot-air fans.

(Courtesy US Department of Agriculture)

through a canvas tube that enters or covers one side of the bin (Fig. 4-14). The air passes through the crib and escapes at the slotted uncovered side and at the top of the crib. With a 10-gallon-per-hour heater and a 5 hp. fan it is possible to dry large batches of ear corn (1200–11,000 bushels) before mold growth starts, because air flows freely through the mass (Appendix Table A-13). It may not be necessary to dry the cribbed ear corn below 17 per cent moisture because further natural drying will occur [31].

FIGURE 4-13. **A column-type farm drier.**
(*Courtesy US Department of Agriculture*)

FIGURE 4-14. **Drying ear corn in the crib with a portable drier.**
(*Courtesy US Department of Agriculture*)

INSECT DAMAGE TO STORED GRAIN

Insects destroy perhaps as much as 10 per cent of the world supply of stored grain each year. In the United States alone, more than 50 species of insects devour stored grain or grain products. Some of these pests, such as the rice weevil, granary weevil, lesser grain borer, and Angoumois grain moth, bore into the grain, consume its interior, and pupate there [38]. Other insects eat the germ or the germ and endosperm. Still others consume only spoiling grain, broken grains, or grain products.

The more destructive insects that infest grain and grain products in the United States are as follows:

Granary weevil (*Sitophilus granarious* (L.)
Rice weevil (*S. oryza* (L.)
Saw-toothed grain beetle (*Oryzaephilus surinamensis* (L.)
Confused flour beetle (*Tribolium confusum* (Duv.)
Red flour beetle (*T. castaneum* (Hbst.)
Square-necked grain beetle (*Cathartus quadricollis* (Guer.)
Larger black flour beetle (*Cynaeus augustus* (Lec.)
Broad-horned flour beetle (*Gnathocerus cornutus* (F.)
Angoumois grain moth (*Sitotrage cerealella* (Oliv.)
Khapra beetle (*Trogoderma granarium* (Everts.)
Lesser grain borer (*Rhizopertha dominica* (F.)
Long headed flour beetle (*Latheticus oryzae* (Waterh.)
Cadelle (*Tenebroides mauritanicus* (L.)

In warm climates, grain standing in the field may become infested with winged insects, such as the rice weevil and Angoumois grain moth, which continue their destruction after the grain is stored. Such infested grain should be fumigated before it is put in the bin or crib. Where storage insects are prevalent (Fig. 4-15), the bins should be cleaned thoroughly about a month before they will be filled with grain. Any waste grain in or near the bin or in cracks or air spaces in a bin wall serve as a source of insect infestation. The walls and floor of a cleaned bin should be sprayed at the rate of 2 gallons per 1000 square feet with a 2.5 per cent concentration of methoxychlor or 0.5 per cent concentration of pyrethrins in combination with a synergist, piperonyl butoxide. The pyrethrum mixture also is useful as a protectant for spraying on the grain as it is placed in the bin. Stored grain that is infested with insects must be fumigated unless it is very dry (9 per cent moisture or less) or is to be cooled and stored in a cold climate. The fumigants should be sprayed on the grain at the top of the bin, after the surface of the grain has been smoothed. Fumigation is effective only in tight bins, or in bins that are enveloped in a tight cover during fumigation.

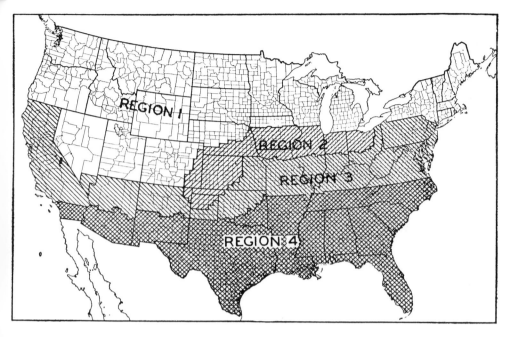

FIGURE 4-15. **Regional map of the United States, indicating relative hazard to farm-stored grain from insect attack. Region 1: best adapted for safe farm storage for first season. Region 2: insects troublesome in some years — frequent inspection and occasional fumigation necessary. Region 3: insects troublesome every year — frequent inspection and fumigation necessary. Region 4: insect control difficult; special precautions must be taken if grain is stored on the farm in this region.**

(Courtesy US Department of Agriculture)

Some recommendations for the fumigation of farm-stored grain are as follows:

| | *Gallons per 1000 Bushels* | |
| | *Wooden* | *Metal or* |
Fumigant	*Bin*	*Concrete Bin*
Carbon tetrachloride (100%)	6	3
Carbon tetrachloride-carbon disulfide (80–20%)	4	2
Ethylene dichloride-carbon tetrachloride (75–25%)	6	3
Carbon tetrachloride-ethylene dichloride- ethylene dibromide (60–35–5%)	4	2

Mills and warehouses can also be fumigated with hydrocyanic acid gas. Hydrocyanic acid is obtained either in liquid form or as granular calcium cyanide, both of which release the gas. The granular material may be metered into a stream of grain passing through a spout that drops the

FIGURE 4-16. A typical country elevator of crib construction, covered with sheet metal.
(*Courtesy US Department of Agriculture*)

FIGURE 4-17. Dumping grain into the receiving pit of a country elevator.
(*Courtesy US Department of Agriculture*)

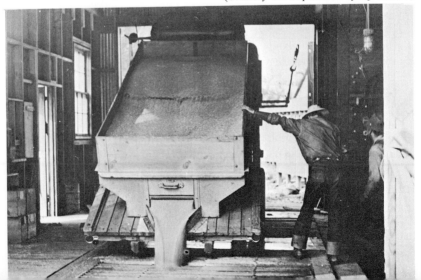

grain into a bin. A dosage of 15–24 pounds of calcium cyanide per 1000 bushels or 10–15 pounds per 1000 cubic feet is satisfactory. Liquid hydrocyanic acid can be piped under pressure to nozzles in the bins where it is forced out as gas. The pressure is supplied by an air compressor or from bottled nitrogen.

Since chemicals that kill insects are also poisonous to man, the precautions given on the labels of the chemical containers should always be followed. Gas masks should be worn when applying any of the chemicals. Bins and buildings that have been fumigated should be opened for ventilation for a few hours or days before they are entered.

MARKETING CEREAL GRAIN

More than nine-tenths of the rice, nearly nine-tenths of the wheat and grain sorghum, two-thirds of the rye and barley, one-third of the corn, and one-fourth of the oats produced in the United States is sold off the farm on which it is grown. Some of it goes directly to local millers or feeders, but a large proportion is trucked to local elevators.

Country Elevators

The older country elevators are mostly of wood crib construction with a storage capacity of 30,000 bushels (Fig. 4-16). Nearly all elevators built since 1940 are much larger and are of concrete construction with silo-type bins. These elevators usually receive and handle a yearly volume of grain at least 3–5 times their bin capacity, unless they are operated chiefly for storage [2]. A truckload (50–150 bushels) of grain from the farm is driven onto the scale in the elevator driveway, where it is weighed. The grain is sampled, usually as it is being dumped into a pit (Fig. 4-17). The grain is carried up to the top, the cupola, of the elevator building, usually by means of buckets on an endless belt, then spouted into a bin.

The grain sample is graded by testing for bushel weight, usually also for dockage or foreign material, and often for other qualities. The local price for each grade of grain is posted daily. The local price is the price for that grade at the terminal market, plus any premium for superior quality less the freight to that point, less handling charges, commissions, and inspection fees. Grain not sold at that price is placed in storage. Local elevator handling charges range 3–8 cents per bushel. Some of the grain purchased by the elevator may be sold locally, but most of it is soon shipped by rail to terminal markets [8].

Country elevators in the United States are of 3 types, each operated by a local manager. *Line* elevators are owned or leased by a company operating several or many elevators in different towns. *Independent* elevators are owned by individuals or partnerships. *Cooperative* (or "Co-Op") elevators are owned by organized groups or associations of farmers. Line elevators usually ship to their company headquarters or branches at the terminal markets. Independent elevators consign grain to commission merchants or brokers who sell the grain on the market at the terminal grain exchange. Cooperative elevators ship to commission merchants, or to cooperative associations holding memberships in the grain exchange. The leading terminal grain markets in the United States are in Chicago, Kansas City, Minneapolis, and Omaha.

When a local elevator consigns a carload of grain to a commission merchant at a terminal market he draws a sight draft on that dealer for a substantial portion of the value of the grain. This can be cashed immediately to provide working capital. When the grain arrives at the terminal market and is sold, the broker refunds the balance due the local elevator after deduction of freight, commissions, and fees.

Terminal Markets

All grain received at terminal markets is sampled and graded. All inspectors at a particular market are employees of a State Grain Inspection Department or the Grain Exchange, or are private inspectors working on a fee basis; all are licensed by the United States Department of Agriculture, which also supervises grain grading by checking occasional samples [19]. For each lot of grain, the inspectors issue certificates showing grade and test weight, and any important factor that determined the grade, such as moisture content or damage.

Grain that arrives at the market also is sampled by private sampling agencies for delivery to the commission firm or other consignee. The samples, each with a label showing the test weight, grade, and the grading factors, are placed on tables on the trading floor where the grain is being offered for sale. Bids and offers are based upon premiums above the posted price for contract grain of the particular grade, because most lots of grain received from country elevators exceed the minimum standards for the grade—say, higher in test weight; below maximum allowance for moisture content, foreign material, or other grains; the lots may consist largely of varieties superior for processing; or the wheat may be high in protein content. Contract grain usually has been mixed so that it just meets the requirements for the grade in several grading factors; for example, its test weight is unlikely to be more than one-half pound above the grade requirement. When a grade permits 2 per cent of other grains, contract grain frequently contains 1.8 per cent of other, cheaper grains.

Purchasers of grain at the terminal markets may be processors, dealers, or exporters, or a Government agency that is maintaining price supports or storing surplus grain. The purchaser informs the seller as to the mill or storage elevator where the grain shipment is to be delivered.

The terminal elevator (Fig. 4-18) or mill is located along a railroad siding from which carloads of grain can be unloaded. The car may be tipped up and emptied mechanically, or the grain may be pushed up to the door by a manually guided dragline scoop attached to a cable wound over a revolving drum (Fig. 4-19). The emptied grain slides down a chute into a pit, from which it is elevated, weighed, and transported to a bin.

Bulk handling of grain replaced bagging in the grain producing areas of the middle west before 1890, and then spread to the Pacific coast and eastern States after 1918. Tied bags held 1.5 bushels; sewed bags, 2.25–2.50 bushels.

Grain handling in Canada and to some extent in other countries follows procedures similar to those just described (Fig. 4-20). In many parts of the world, however, much grain is still handled in bags. Often it is sold in small lots to local dealers at village markets, after a customary haggling over the price.

The price of grain follows a typical seasonal fluctuation during most years, being lowest during the month after harvest when receipts at the market are at a maximum. The low-price months for oats and corn usually are August and November, respectively [8]. Prices are highest a month or two before the new crop begins to reach the market. In most years, seasonal differences in price are only slightly more than the cost of storage, together with possible shrinkage, risk of loss in farm storage, and interest rates on the value of the unsold grain.

Futures Trading

The purpose of futures trading is to permit speculation on grain prices, and yet to enable the buyer, seller, and processor of market grain to hedge their transactions and thus avoid great risk of loss from changes in price. The Chicago Board of Trade, organized in 1848 to facilitate grain market-ing, adopted in 1865 a special set of rules governing dealing in futures contracts by its members [39]. Trading in futures later was established by the grain exchanges in other important grain markets. The volume in bushels of futures trading greatly exceeds that of the grain actually marketed during a particular year because of hedging procedures as well as speculation. Hedg-ing consists of selling futures when grain is purchased and buying back the futures ("closing the hedge") when the grain or grain products are sold. Thus, a lot of grain bought in turn by a country elevator, terminal grain dealer, and flour miller involves six futures transactions—a purchase and a sale by each of the three grain handlers. A country elevator operator usually

FIGURE 4-18. **A terminal elevator with concrete silo-type bins.**

(Courtesy US Department of Agriculture)

FIGURE 4-19. **Unloading grain from a boxcar with a dragline scoop.**

(Courtesy US Department of Agriculture)

FIGURE 4-20. **A large terminal elevator in Canada loading barge steamboats for ship-ment through the Great Lakes.**

(Courtesy US Department of Agriculture)

hedges each day's grain purchases by wiring to his broker or representative at the terminal market to sell futures of a similar amount. The hedge is closed by the broker when the grain is sold at the terminal market. The futures price at the time of sale determines the actual selling price of the cash grain because the cash sale is based upon an agreed margin over the future price. The buyer immediately sells futures in the approximate amount of his grain purchase.

Most grain dealers are not speculators, but some who speculated soon went bankrupt. The operations of speculators help to keep the market fluid, softening the effects of fluctuations in the amounts of cash grain that are sold. Without speculators it might be difficult to hedge large sales of grain for export or processing. A speculator is in a "long" position when his purchases of futures exceed those that he has sold in the expectation that prices will go higher. He sells "short" when he expects that prices will drop. All future sales of grain are contracts to deliver the grain on or before the end of the month (May, July, September, or December) indicated in the transaction. Only occasionally is actual grain delivery called for, cash settlements being much more simple. Grain delivered is the contract grade, usually of a mixed lot stored in a terminal elevator, often varieties of inferior quality for processing.

Futures transactions are conducted in a separate "pit" for each grain, located in the same room as that in which cash grain is sold (Fig. 4-21). The smallest unit for futures trading of grain usually is 5000 bushels. With two motions of the arm accompanied by hand signals, a dealer may offer to buy or sell as much as 25 thousand bushels of grain at an indi-

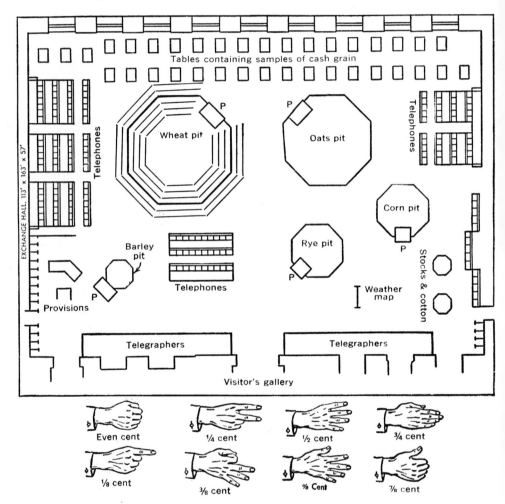

FIGURE 4-21. **Diagram of grain trading floor at Chicago, Ill., showing the tables for displaying samples of "cash grain" offered for sale, and the step-bordered pits for futures transactions. Changes in price are recorded at the platforms marked "P." Below are shown the hand signals used to indicate the fractional prices in futures transactions.**

(*Courtesy Chicago Board of Trade*)

cated price; a signal accompanied by a nod indicates acceptance. The shouting that goes on around a pit merely helps attract the attention of a buyer or seller. Transactions are conducted under strict rules established by the Grain Exchanges or Board of Trade. The exchanges, which operate the marketing facilities, are subject to federal regulations under the Commodity Exchange Act. Only members of the particular exchange may directly engage in futures trading operations, but members may act as brokers for others. Speculators as well as grain dealers may trade in futures through their brokers. Prices of grain futures fluctuate constantly with changes in present and prospective supplies, demands for the different cash grains, and changes in the volume and trends in trading. The prices of cash grain roughly follow the futures prices.

GRADING GRAIN

In the United States and Canada, at least, grain grades are firmly fixed except when, after public hearings, they are revised and the changes announced some months in advance. Grades and changes in grades are established by the Secretary of Agriculture after open hearings, under the authority of the United States Grain Standards Act of 1916. In some countries authorities promulgate a "Fair Average Quality" for each season with specified grades above and below that quality.

Collection of Samples

In the United States, samples of grain in a boxcar or truck are taken with a brass probe made of two concentric tubes with slots on one side of each (Fig. 4-22). The inner tube (core) with partitions between the slots is rotated within the outer shell after the probe has been inserted into the grain so that the slots of both tubes are congruent, allowing the grain to flow into the core. The core is then turned to close the slots, and the probe withdrawn. Five or more probe samples are taken from each carload and emptied on a canvas. Each sample is emptied separately so that each section of the sample can be examined for appearance and odors of the grain in each part of the car. If the quality of grain in different parts is not the same, the parts of the sample are kept separate and the proportion represented by each part is roughly estimated. Otherwise the entire sample on the canvas is bulked together and poured into a bag. Bagged lots are sampled by inserting a pointed sack trier into each of several bags and drawing out some grain. A stream of grain falling from an elevator spout or from the rear of a truck can be sampled with a pail or a "pelican."

FIGURE 4-22. (Top) Probing a car of grain. Each probe full is emptied on a canvas and each portion is examined for quality, uniformity and odor before the sample is thrown together. (Bottom) Grain inspection laboratory equipment consisting of dockage tester, weight per bushel tester, Boerner Divider, and moisture tester.

(*Courtesy US Department of Agriculture*)

The latter is a dipperlike device on a long handle that cuts through the stream of falling grain at intervals.

Grading Procedure

The bags from which the official samples were taken are removed to the inspection laboratory, where the grain is cut down to a size suitable for grading by pouring through a Boerner sampler. The market class and test weight of all samples is determined, and "dockage" is measured except in corn and oat samples (Fig. 4-23). Dockage is foreign material in the grain that can be separated readily by passing the grain over or through a set of specified sieves, and often also a wild-oat separator. The total dockage is weighed, and the test weight of the dockage-free sample is determined. The weight of the dockage is deducted from the total weight in computing the quantity of actual grain in a market lot. Impurities such as other grains, weed seeds, and stem fragments left in the grain after the dockage is removed are separated, weighed, and recorded as "foreign material." Foreign material is separated from samples of corn and oats, but dockage is not determined on these grains. Damaged kernels and such other factors as might affect the grade are then determined.

Moisture content is determined on any grain sample that feels slightly damp or even tough. Moisture determinations are made on samples that still contain dockage.

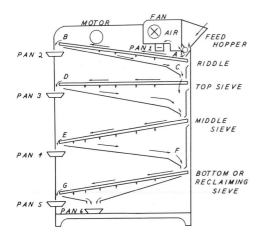

FIGURE 4-23. **Sectional view of a Carter Dockage Tester. This machine is used in determining dockage in wheat, barley, rye, grain sorghum, and flaxseed and broken corn and foreign material in corn.**
(*Courtesy US Department of Agriculture*)

The moisture content of the grain may be measured by any device that gives results comparable to methods used in establishing the standards. Most determinations are made with electric moisture meters (Fig. 4-24), which give a quick reading but may be inaccurate when the sample is a mixture of wet and dry grain that has not reached a moisture equilibrium.

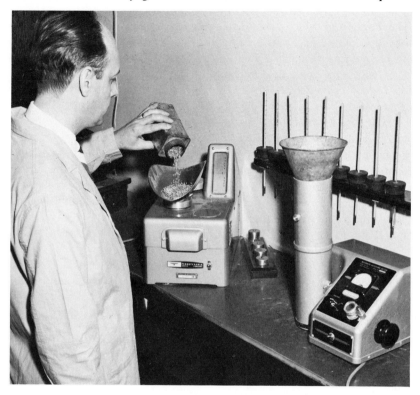

FIGURE 4-24. **Sample is weighed in preparation for the moisture test. At right is an electric moisture meter used by official graders to determine moisture content.**

(Courtesy US Department of Agriculture)

Such mixed lots can be measured with a Brown-Duvel moisture tester which distills the water from a 100-gram sample of grain immersed in a 150-milliliter bath of heated oil. This test is completed in less than 30 minutes; other methods, such as the drying oven and vacuum oven, require several hours.

TABLE 4-1. **Pounds of Water Per Bushel[1] of Grain at Different Moisture Content Percentages.[2]**

	Pounds of Water per Bushel		
Grain Moisture Content, Per cent	Shelled Corn and Grain Sorghum (Pounds of Dry Matter per Bushel =47.32)	Wheat (Pounds of Dry Matter per Bushel =51.6)	Oats (Pounds of Dry Matter per Bushel =27.4)
35	25.4	27.8	14.6
30	20.2	22.1	11.7
28	18.4	20.1	10.6
26	16.6	18.2	9.6
24	14.9	16.4	8.6
22	13.3	14.6	7.7
20	11.8	12.9	6.8
18	10.4	11.4	6.0
17	9.7	10.6	5.6
16	9.0	9.8	5.2
15	8.3	9.1	4.8
14	7.7	8.4	4.4
13	7.1	7.7	4.1
12	6.5	7.0	3.7
11	5.9	6.4	3.4
10	5.3	5.8	3.0
9	4.7	5.1	2.7
8	4.1	4.5	2.3

[1] A bushel is defined here as the amount of grain required to yield 56 pounds of shelled corn or grain sorghum at 15.5 per cent moisture, 60 pounds of wheat at 14 per cent, and 32 pounds of oats at 14.5 per cent.

[2] To determine the number of pounds of grain required to make a bushel at a given moisture percentage, add the pounds of water to the pounds of dry matter (shown at head of column). For example: to obtain the weight of corn at 28 per cent moisture content required to make a bushel, add the pounds of water (18.4) to the pounds of dry matter per bushel (47.32). This totals 65.7 pounds: it requires 65.7 pounds of corn of 28 per cent moisture content to make a bushel (56 pounds) of 15.5 per cent corn.

TABLE 4-2. **Fan Requirements for Drying Oats, Shelled Corn, and Wheat with Unheated Air from Different Percentages of Moisture Content and at Various Practical Depths.**

WHEAT

Grain Moisture Content, Per cent	Recommended Minimum Air-flow Rate per Bushel, cfm	Practical Grain Depths, ft	Static Pressure,[1] in., Water Gage	Maximum Quantity that Can be Dried per Fan Horsepower,[2] Bushels
20	3	4	1.2	830
		6	2.3	440
18	2	4	0.8	1880
		8	2.5	600
16	1	8	1.3	2300
		10	2.0	1500

OATS

25	3	4	0.8	1250
		6	1.7	590
20	2	6	1.1	1360
		8	1.8	830
18	1½	8	1.4	1430
		10	2.0	1000
16	1	8	0.9	3330
		12	1.9	1580

SHELLED CORN

25	5	4	0.7	860
		6	1.6	380
20	3	6	0.9	1120
		8	1.5	670
18	2	6	0.6	2500
		8	0.9	1670
		12	2.2	680
16	1	8	0.5	6000
		12	1.0	3000
		16	1.6	1880

[1] Static pressure includes 0.25 inch allowance for loss from duct friction.

[2] Air flow (cfm) per horsepower based on 3000 cfm of air at 1-inch static pressure.

TABLE 4-3. **Physical Properties of Cereal Kernels.**[1]

Grain	Wt. per Bushel, lb	Bulk Grain Air Space, Per cent	Kernel Specific Gravity	Coefficient of Friction	Angle of Repose in Pile (Degrees)		Resistance to Air Flow[2]	Thermal Conductivity[3]
					Filling	Emptying		
Corn, shelled	56	40	1.19	0.52	16	27	0.065	1.22
Oats	32	47–55	0.95–1.06	0.53	18	32	0.15	0.90
Barley	48	44–58	1.13–1.26	0.59	16	28	0.13	
Barley, hull-less	60	40	1.33					
Rye	56	41	1.23		17	26		
Grain sorghum	56	37	1.22–1.26		20	33	0.19	
Rice, rough	45	46–50	1.12	0.68–0.73	20	36	0.15	
Wheat[4]	60	39–43	1.29–1.32	0.47	16	27	0.23	0.89–1.13

[1] Adapted from *Agricultural Engineers Yearbook* (2nd ed., pp 97–106, 1955)

[2] Pressure drop in inches of water per foot of depth of grain under an air flow through the grain of 10 cubic feet per minute per square foot.

[3] Btu inch per sq. ft. per hour per degree F. The thermal conductivity increases with increases in temperature and moisture content.

[4] The specific heat of wheat is 0.39 to 0.51, wheat flour 0.40 and wheat starch 0.32 to 0.38.
The specific heat increases with an increase in moisture content.
Wt. per cu. ft. of grain is bushel weight × 0.8.

REFERENCES

1. Alred, F. L., "Recent research on drying and storage of rough rice." South. Coop. Ser. *Bul. 29.* 1953.

2. Anderson, N., *et al.*, "Economic aspects of grain storage in the Northern Great Plains." Mont. Ag. Exp. Sta. *Bul. 523.* 1956.

3. Anderson, J. A., and A. W. Alcock, Eds., "Storage of cereal grains and their products." Vol. II. St. Paul, Minn.: Amer. Assn. Cer. Chem. Monograph Series. pp 515. 1954.

4. Bruce, W. M., *et al.*, "Planning grain storage elevators." U. Georgia *Bul. 51 (7d).* 1951.

5. Carter, E. P., and G. Y. Young, "Effect of moisture content, temperature, and length of storage on the development of sick wheat in sealed containers." *Cer. Chem., 22*(5): 418–428. 1945.

6. ———, and G. Y. Young, "Role of fungi in the heating of moist wheat." USDA *Cir. 838.* pp 1–26. 1950.

7. Christensen, C. M., "Deterioration of stored grain by fungi." *Bot. Rev.,* **23**(2): 108–134. 1957.

8. Clough, M., and J. W. Browning, "Feed grains," in *Marketing.* USDA Yrbk. of Ag. pp 403–413. 1954.

9. "Drying ear corn with heated air." USDA *Leaflet 333.* 1952.

10. "Drying ear corn with unheated air." USDA *Leaflet 334.* 1952.

11. "Drying shelled corn and small grain with heated air." USDA *Leaflet 331.* 1952.

12. "Drying shelled corn and small grain with unheated air." USDA *Leaflet 332.* 1952.

13. Dubois, M., W. F. Geddes, and T. Smith, "The carbohydrates of the Gramineae. X: A quantitative study of the carbohydrates of the wheat germ." *Cer. Chem.,* **37**(4): 557–568. 1960.

14. Fifield, C. C., and D. W. Robertson, "Milling, baking, and chemical properties of Marquis and Kanred wheat grown in Colorado and stored 19 to 27 years." *Agron. J.,* **44**(11): 555–559. 1952.

15. ———, and D. W. Robertson, "Milling, baking, and chemical properties of Marquis and Kanred wheat grown in Colorado and stored 25 to 33 years." *Cer. Sci. Today,* **4**: 170–183. 1959.

16. Geddes, W. F., "The chemistry, microbiology, and physics of grain storage." *Food Tech.,* **12**(11): 7–14. 1958.

17. Gerzhoi, A. P., and V. F. Samochetov, "Grain drying and grain driers." (Eng. trans.) Office Tech. Serv., U.S. Dept. Comm. pp 1–304. 1960.

18. Glass, R. L., *et al.*, "Grain storage studies. XXVIII: The influence of temperature and moisture level on the behavior of wheat stored in air or nitrogen." *Cer. Chem.,* **36**: 341–356. 1959.

19. "Grain grading primer." USDA *Misc. Publ. 742.* 1957.

20. Hall, C. W., *Drying Farm Crops.* Reynoldsburg, Ohio: Agricultural Consulting Associates, Inc. pp 1–336. 1957.

21. Holman, L. E., "Aeration of grain in commercial storages." USDA *Mktg. Rpt. 178.* pp 1–46. 1960.

22. Haynes, Jr., B. C., "Vapor pressure determination of seed hygroscopicity." USDA *Tech. Bul. 1229.* 1961.

23. Hummel, B. C. W., *et al.*, "Grain storage studies. VIII: Comparative changes in respiration, viability, and chemical composition of mold-free and mold-contaminated wheat upon storage." *Cer. Chem.*, **31**: 143–150. 1954.
24. Kirk, L. E., *et al.*, "Storing and Drying Grain." FAO Ag. Studies, *No. 6.* 1948.
25. McNeal, X., "Artificial drying of combined rice." Ark. Ag. Exp. Sta. *Bul. 487.* 1949.
26. Milner, M., C. M. Christensen, and W. F. Geddes, "Grain storage studies. V: Chemical and microbiological studies on 'sick' wheat." *Cer. Chem.*, **24**: 23–38. 1947.
27. ———, C. M. Christensen, and W. F. Geddes, "Grain storage studies. VI: Wheat respiration in relation to moisture content, mold growth, chemical deterioration, and heating." *Cer. Chem.*, **24**: 182–199. 1947.
28. ———, C. M. Christensen, and W. F. Geddes, "Grain storage studies. VII: Influence of certain mold inhibitors on respiration of moist wheat." *Cer. Chem.*, **24**: 507–517. 1947.
29. Person, Jr., N. K., and J. W. Sorenson, Jr., "Design data for the pneumatic conveying of sorghum seed." Tex. Ag. Exp. Sta. *Misc. Publ. 507.* pp 1–8. 1961.
30. Semeniuk, G., J. S. Anderson, and A. W. Alcock, "Microflora in storage of cereal grains and their products." Am. Assn. Cereal Chem. Monograph Series *No. 2.* pp. 77–151. 1945.
31. Shedd, C. K., "Storage of ear corn on the farm." USDA *Farmers Bul. 2010.* 1949.
32. ———, and H. H. Walkden, "Grain sorghum storage." USDA *Cir. 760.* 1947.
33. Simons, J. W., "How to dry and store grain and seed on Georgia farms." Ga. Ag. Exp. Sta. *Bul. N.S. 33* (rev.). 1958.
34. Sorenson, J. W., Jr., *et al.*, "Drying and its effects on the milling characteristics of sorghum." Tex. Ag. Exp. Sta. *Bul. 710.* pp 1–144. 1949.
35. Sorger-Dominegg, H., *et al.*, "Grain storage studies. XVII: Effect of mold growth during temporary exposure of wheat to high moisture contents upon the development of germ damage and other indices of deterioration during subsequent storage." *Cer. Chem.*, **32**: 270–285. 1955.
36. Stahl, B. M., "Grain bin requirements." USDA *Cir. 835.* 1950.
37. ———, "Engineering data on grain storage," in *Agricultural Engineers Yearbook*, 2d. ed. pp 97–106. 1955.
38. "Stored-grain pests." USDA *Farmers Bul. 1260* (rev.). 1958.
39. White, B. S., and W. E. Beach, "Selling: The transfer of ownership," in *Marketing.* USDA Yrbk. of Ag. pp 302–309. 1954.

PART II Indian Corn or Maize

Corn

5. IMPORTANCE, HISTORY, AND ADAPTATION

ECONOMIC IMPORTANCE

Indian corn or maize (*Zea mays,* L.) ranks as one of the four principal cereal crops of the world. More than half the total world corn crop is grown in the United States, where it is a basic crop. In fact, corn has had a dominant influence on American economics, politics, history, literature, even art [7].

Corn as a World Crop

As a world crop, corn is grown on all continents in many countries (Fig. 5-1). The average annual harvested area in the world from 1950 to 1954 was 222.17 million acres with a grain production of 5.645 billion bushels, or 158.06 million short tons. The average yield per acre was 25.4 bushels. The countries that led in corn production were the United States, Brazil, Soviet Russia, Mexico, Yugoslavia, Rumania, Argentina, Union of South Africa, and Italy [1].

Corn is unable to compete with rice in the Orient, except possibly with upland rice. Corn is competitive with rice only under conditions of insufficient heat or moisture for the rice crop. The corn crop also is in competition with other cereals in most foreign countries as a choice for foods, feed, or industrial uses [10].

Corn in the United States

In the United States, corn is more widely grown than any other crop. It occupies approximately 25 per cent of the crop land in the country. It is raised in every state (Fig. 5-2), but about 75 per cent of the average annual harvest of the country is produced in the Corn Belt; *i.e.,* most of the

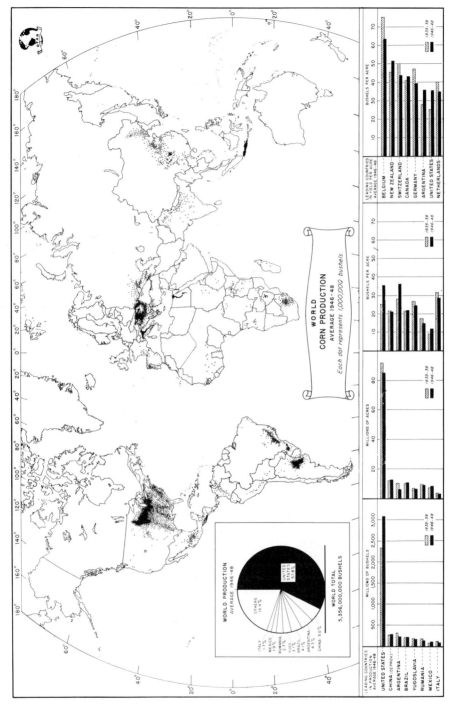

FIGURE 5-1. **Average world production of corn, 1946-1948. Each dot represents 1,000,000 bushels.**

(*Courtesy US Department of Agriculture*)

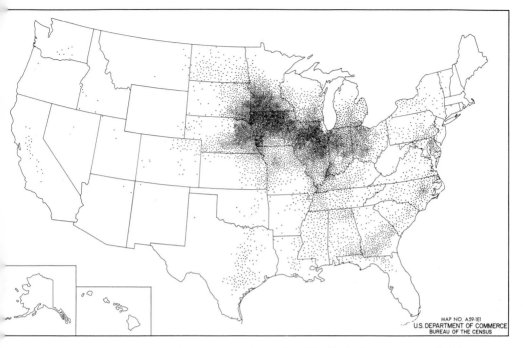

FIGURE 5-2. **Acreage of corn in the United States in 1959. Each dot represents 10,000 acres. The US total was 79,616,031 acres.**

(*Courtesy US Department of Commerce*)

north central states [7]. During the 10-year period 1952–1961, the average annual harvested acreage was 77.4 million acres with a production of 3.6 billion bushels. The average yield was 46.3 bushels per acre; the average yield for 1960 and 1961 exceeded 57 bushels. Iowa, Illinois, Minnesota, Indiana, Nebraska, and Ohio led in corn production [1].

More than three-fourths of the American corn crop is fed to livestock as grain, silage, or fodder on the farms where it is produced. Some is shipped for use as feed; the remainder is processed into food or industrial products. Corn contributes more to the diet of the American people than any other crop, when one includes its indirect presence in the form of meat, dairy products, and eggs [7].

Corn production in the United States increased markedly because of increases of more than 90 per cent in acre yield between 1940 and 1961 (Fig. 5-3), due largely to extensive use of hybrid seed, mineral fertilizers, closer spacing, more effective pest control, supplemental irrigation, and timelier field operations as a result of extensive mechanization [7]. The average increase in acre yields of hybrids over open-pollinated corn grown under identical conditions formerly was estimated at 20 per cent, but better hybrids

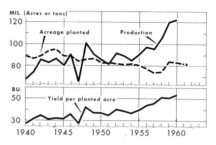

FIGURE 5-3. **Acreage, yield, and pro-**
duction of corn in the United States
from 1940 to 1960.

(*Courtesy US Department of Agriculture*)

have raised this to about 25 per cent. The total national corn acreage planted
to hybrid seed increased from 0.1 per cent in 1933 to 94.9 per cent in 1959.

HISTORY OF MAIZE CULTURE

The history of Indian corn or maize in western civilization began in
1492, less than a month after Columbus discovered the New World. Apparently, the first permanent contact of Europeans with Indian corn came
when an exploratory party sent to inland Cuba returned with reports that
they had seen large quantities of a grain which the Indians called *maiz*.
A note on maize was made in the log of the voyage on November 6, although Columbus may have observed maize in Haiti as early as October
16 [34, 35, 36].

Records of the 16th century show that early explorers found maize to
be cultivated by the most advanced Indian races everywhere from what is
now southern Canada to southern Chile. All evidence indicated that the Indians had grown corn for a long time. Numerous types showed wide ranges
of adaptation to latitude, altitude, climate, and soil conditions. A great body
of religious ceremony, folklore, and art had grown up about the culture and
uses of the maize plant [31, 34, 35].

Maize, introduced into Europe by the Spaniards, was known in Spain
in 1494, sometime after Columbus returned from his second voyage. The first
importations were made from the West Indies, but others soon followed
from Mexico and Peru. The plant was first grown in Europe as a garden
curiosity. Within a few years, Indian corn had spread from Spain to southern
France, Italy, the Balkans, and North Africa. The first accounts of maize
were published in Europe by Nicolo Syllacio in 1494, by Peter Martyr in
1511 and 1516, and by Jerome Bock in 1532. It was described and illustrated in the great European herbals from sometime in the 1530's until
after 1700. The first maize type described was similar to the flints of eastern
North America, but a type similar to present-day corn of the Caribbean area
was described late in the 16th century. The herbals present a wide divergence of opinion about the food value of maize [33, 35, 36, 8].

The Portuguese distributed maize along the west coast of Africa early in the 16th century, and probably introduced it into India at about the same time. Maize had reached western China by about 1575. In the meantime, as a result of Magellan's voyage, New World maize was introduced into the East Indies and the Philippines from whence it soon spread to the mainland of eastern Asia [31, 35]. Corn first reached Japan in 1573.

The Spanish conquerors depended on corn for food and feed during their expeditions. Wherever they settled, they adopted corn culture from the Indians. Early explorers observed large fields of corn being grown by the Indians in what is now the United States. The Jamestown colony, established in 1607, probably was saved from starvation by corn obtained from the Indians. The Indians also showed the early colonists how to raise the crop. Along the New England coast, corn was commonly fertilized with fish placed in each hill at planting time. The white man took over corn from the Indians during the 16th and 17th centuries [30].

The modern Corn Belt dents were developed in the United States during the 19th century from crosses of the northern flints with the old southern dents. The northern flints, which had predominated in northeastern United States before the discovery of America, are very similar to the common yellow flints now grown in the highlands of Guatemala. The old southern dents, undoubtedly derived largely from Mexican sources, were being grown as far north as Virginia by 1700. These dents are characterized by high kernel-row numbers, tapered ears, soft texture, and pointed kernels. Mixtures of southern dent and northern flint corn, intended to encourage cross pollination, were widely planted between 1780 and 1850. Selection eventually produced the distinctive cylindrical dent corns of the Corn Belt [6, 3, 30].

PRE-COLUMBIAN CORN

Corn was a highly developed cultivated crop in the New World long before its discovery by the white man. The three principal centers of intensive corn culture were the Mexican Plateau, the Yucatan-Guatemala region, and Peru. These centers corresponded, respectively, to the three great pre-Columbian civilizations of the Aztecs, the Mayas, and the Incas. The only records on pre-Columbian corn, on parchment paper and in pictorial inscriptions, mostly from the Aztec area, merely emphasize its importance in Indian culture [35].

Fossil evidence of corn comprises a number of pollen grains obtained from more than 200 feet below the present site of Mexico City. Although estimated to be at least 80 thousand years old, this pollen appears to be almost identical with that of modern corn in point of morphological characteristics. It indicates that wild corn was indigenous to Mexico many thousands of years ago [35, 17].

Archaeological studies in the Americas have resulted in the recovery of many preserved specimens of corn as well as artifacts associated with the plant. Numerous specimens of cobs, ears, tassels, or stalks of corn have been excavated from prehistoric tombs, campsites, trash heaps, and caves. They indicate the presence of corn as a cultivated plant in the New World for 5600 years or more [2, 35, 17]. Stone and pottery artifacts also picture maize. Most of the specimens come from the drier climates, particularly along the coast of Chile and Peru, in the southwestern United States, and in parts of Mexico [2].

The oldest known remains of cultivated corn come from a rock shelter in New Mexico known as Bat Cave. This cave had an accumulation of debris to a depth of 6 feet at the bottom of which some small cobs of ancient corn were found, dated by radiocarbon as about 5600 years old. This small-eared corn is assumed to be popcorn with each kernel partly enclosed in the floral bracts or husks. The ears are 0.75-inch long and have only about 50 kernels [19, 17].

All of the major endosperm types of corn—flint, flour, dent, sweet, and popcorn—have been known in the Americas since early times [2]. The great variability of the corn plant led to the selection of varieties adapted to a wide range of soil and climatic conditions. Large late varieties grown in the tropical lowlands required 11–12 months to mature. Small early varieties grown by the Mandans of North Dakota and by the Quechuas in the Andes highlands could be matured in about 2 months. The deep-rooted Navajo and Hopi varieties of the southwestern United States were grown in areas with almost no summer rainfall [36].

ORIGIN OF CORN

The origin of maize is unknown, since the plant has been found only under cultivation. Corn is now dependent on man for its survival.

Geographical Origin

The likeliest primary center of origin of maize is considered by most authorities to be Central America and Mexico, where many diverse types of corn are found. Its relatives, teosinte and several species of tripsacum, also are found in this region [29, 32, 34, 35, 22]. The discovery of fossil corn pollen with other archaeological evidence in Mexico points to Mexico as an early center of domestication [20].

Figure 5-4. Teosinte (Euchlaena mexicana): (1) Plant, (2) branch with staminate and pistillate inflorescences, (3) ear, (4) grains with attached stigmas, (5) and (6) mature grains.

(*Courtesy US Department of Agriculture*)

A possible secondary center of origin of maize is South America in the Andean region of Bolivia, Ecuador, and Peru. A great diversity of corn occurs in the highlands of Peru, while pod corn is found frequently in valleys on the eastern slopes of the Andes [29]. Moreover, there are at least three primitive races of maize in Peru today [20].

An Asiatic origin for corn, or at least its appearance in Asia in pre-Columbian times, has been proposed several times. The European herbalists of the 16th and 17th centuries generally regarded corn as an Asiatic plant. Recently, the theory has been applied to some collections of peculiar varieties of corn grown for centuries by the hill tribes of Assam in northern India [28]. However, there is no record of the existence of the corn plant in the Old World before 1492 in the form of plant material, artifact, or written report [36, 20].

Theories of Botanical Origin

A satisfactory explanation of the botanical origin of maize also must account for its close relationship with teosinte (Fig. 5-4). The two genera can be hybridized readily; they produce fertile progeny. Four more-or-less distinct hypotheses have been advanced during the past century to account for the origin of maize [16]:

1. Maize originated from pod corn, which differs from normal maize primarily in that the seeds are enclosed in glumes.
2. Maize originated from teosinte, its closest relative, by direct selection, by large-scale mutations, or by hybridization of teosinte with another grass, now unknown.
3. Maize, teosinte, and the more distantly related gama grass (*Tripsacum* spp.) have descended along independent lines from a common ancestor.
4. Present-day maize arose from a primitive maize-tripsacum hybrid. This is the so-called tripartite hypothesis.

The pod corn hypothesis has been advocated as plausible on the basis of several facts—it was known in Peru in ancient times, its repeated discovery in South America in the 18th and 19th centuries, and the recent development of pod corn that breeds true [16]. Some of the oldest-known specimens of corn found in Bat Cave have long glumes which indicate a form of pod corn [19]. When pod corn was crossed with popcorn, a reconstructed corn was obtained which had numerous characteristics regarded as primitive [17]. Some authorities discount pod corn as wild corn on the grounds that the general effect of the tunicate gene on the plant places pod corn in the category of an anomaly [35, 36].

Teosinte often has been thought of as wild corn because of its superficial appearance, its present occurrence as a wild plant, and the fact that it produces fertile hybrids with practically all varieties of corn. Reports that teosinte has been changed to corn by a few generations of selection are based on corn-teosinte hybrids rather than on teosinte alone. Teosinte also has a highly specialized morphological structure that tends to rule it out as a wild corn [36]. Another reason for rejection of teosinte is the lack of evidence that the American Indians used it as a food plant [16]. Moreover, the earliest Bat Cave corn apparently was not derived from teosinte [19].

One of the currently favored hypotheses for the origin of corn is the view that corn, teosinte, and tripsacum have arisen directly from some common ancestor by divergent evolution [31, 34, 35, 36, 22]. Proponents of this hypothesis believe that the visible morphological differences among the three genera are due to differential abortion of the various organs during development.

The tripartite hypothesis for the origin of maize was based on the successful hybridization of corn and tripsacum, followed by an analysis of gene differences between corn, tripsacum, and teosinte. The essentials of the hypothesis are as follows: 1. Cultivated maize originated from a wild form of pod corn once indigenous to the lowlands of South America; 2. teosinte, the closest relative of maize, is the product of natural hybridization of *Zea* and *Tripsacum* which occurred after cultivated maize had been introduced by man into Central America; and 3. new types of corn, originating directly or indirectly from this cross and exhibiting admixtures with tripsacum or teosinte, comprise the majority of modern Central American and North American varieties [18, 16].

Numerous criticisms have been leveled at this hypothesis. Interfertility of tripsacum with corn or teosinte are unknown in the wild. Corn and tripsacum hybrids have been produced artificially by shortening the corn silks, facilitated by embryo-culture techniques. The degree of fertility with these artificial procedures is so low that the probability of hybridization of corn with any species of tripsacum in nature is remote. The degree of fertility of tripsacum-teosinte hybrids is still lower. There is little or no support from cytogenetics for the hypothesis. Corn and annual teosinte have 20 diploid chromosomes while tripsacum has 36 or 72 [34, 22, 36].

ADAPTATION[1]

Corn has such a remarkable diversity of vegetative types that sorts adapted to nearly all environmental conditions are in cultivation; corn is now more widely distributed over the world than any other cereal crop. Corn is grown from latitude 58°N in Canada and the Soviet Union to latitude 40°S in the Southern Hemisphere. It is produced from below sea level in

[1] For a survey of the literature on climatic requirements of corn, see [25].

the Caspian Plain to altitudes of more than 12,000 feet in the Peruvian
Andes [11].

Temperature

Corn is a warm-weather plant that requires high temperatures day and
night during the growing season. The crop is seldom grown where the mean
summer temperature is less than 66°F, or where the average night temperature for the three summer months falls below 55°F. The Corn Belt of
the United States has a mean summer temperature of 70–80°F, a mean
night temperature above 58°F, and a frost-free season of more than 140
days [11].

Few corn strains or varieties are able to germinate satisfactorily at
temperatures below 50°F. Warm weather after planting hastens germination
as well as early growth. The average temperature, at the time planting
begins, varies 54–57°F in most areas where corn is grown in the United
States. Low temperatures, 46–54°F, retard germination of corn kernels
and predispose them to attack by various soil-borne organisms [24]. But
extremely high temperatures may be injurious, especially when accompanied
by deficient moisture. The plants are most susceptible to injury from high
temperatures at the tasseling stage. Inbred lines and hybrids among them
exhibit great differences in injury from heat and drought. Some strains are
able to produce viable pollen at temperatures at which the pollen of other
strains is nonviable [11].

The corn plant is injured by freezing temperatures any time during the
growing season. However, most strains are able to recover from freezes
that occur before the plants are six inches tall. Frosts early in the fall before the grain is mature kill the leaf tissue and reduce yields as well as
quality.

Precipitation

Annual precipitation in the regions of the world where corn is grown
without irrigation ranges from only 10 inches in the semiarid plains of Russia to more than 200 inches in tropical Hindustan. The annual precipitation
in the Corn Belt is 25–50 inches. The areas in the United States which
have well-distributed rains during June, July, and August, that average 3–6
inches per month, have the highest average yields. The western limit of
corn production in the United States coincides approximately with the line
of mean summer (June, July, and August) precipitation of 8 inches [11].

Other Climatic Factors

The progressively longer photoperiod proceeding north and south of the equator during the season of early growth is an important factor in the latitudinal adaptation of corn. As a short-day species, flowering is accelerated by shorter photoperiods. A standard Nebraska variety flowered in an average of 13 days less time when planted in three southern states than it did in Nebraska. Three southern varieties required an average of 18 days longer to tassel in Nebraska than in their native states [13]. Two Wisconsin corn hybrids reached the maximum stage of maturity 6 weeks later in the Netherlands than in Wisconsin, probably due chiefly to the longer photoperiod in the Netherlands [4].

Hail often causes severe yield reductions in corn. Hailstorms are most harmful between the periods of jointing and silking. Severe losses occur when defoliation is over 50 per cent [25]. When hail damage occurs early in plant growth, corn may recover from complete defoliation.

Along the Gulf coast corn suffers severe lodging as a result of occasional tropical hurricanes. Wind also contributes to water loss from corn plants, and also lacerates the leaves.

FIGURE 5-5. **Profiles of 4 soil types: (A) Chestnut soil in semiarid Great Plains showing carbonate zone at the 2-foot depth; (B) Prairie loess soil in eastern Nebraska with black soil high in organic matter to a depth of 1.5 feet; (C) Brown podsolic soil suitable for corn production; and (D) Podsol soil of low fertility.**

Soil Conditions

Corn makes its best growth on fertile, well-drained, loam soils. Of the zonal or great soil groups in America, the Prairie soils are the best suited to the crop. These soils, high in organic matter and exchangeable bases, extend from western Indiana to eastern Nebraska (Fig. 5-5). Probably the best soils of the Corn Belt are the Wabash, Webster, Brookston, and Clyde series. Other suitable prairie soils are the Marshall, Tama, Clarion, Carrington, and Waukesha series. In the Chernozem region to the west, the Moody soils of Nebraska and South Dakota are productive for corn. Other important corn soils are silt loams of the Clinton, Miami, Hagerstown, Mawry, and Bladen series [21].

The corn plant is sensitive to deficient soil aeration, particularly that resulting from excessive soil water, poor tilth, or impervious subsoil. Corn is grown successfully over a range of soil reactions from pH 5–8. However, yields usually are affected adversely by a soil acidity of less than pH 5.5. Alkaline soils may produce good yields under irrigation [21].

Adjustment to Environment

Some strains of corn grow less than 2 feet tall, have only 8 or 9 leaves, and require 60–70 days to mature. Other strains grow more than 20 feet tall, bear 42–44 leaves, and need 300–330 days to reach maturity [15]. There are characteristic varieties in each climate. In the northern United States, varieties are 5–8 feet tall, bear 12–16 leaves, mature in 90–120 days, and may develop several tillers. In the Corn Belt, adapted varieties are 8–10 feet tall, bear 18–21 leaves, mature in 130–150 days, and usually have few or no tillers. Varieties in the Gulf States may grow to a height of 10–12 feet, bear 23–25 leaves, require 170–190 days to mature, and produce two or more ears per plant. These widely divergent types have been developed by selection over a very long period of time by the American Indian [11].

In most cases, open-pollinated corn grown for a period of years becomes adjusted to the local conditions of moisture supply, temperature, and length of frost-free season [9]. This self-adaptation is brought about by natural selection in the mixed or heterozygous population of an open-pollinated corn variety. Adaptation of corn to a region of moisture shortage consists of a reduction in vegetative development with a consequent reduction in the amount of water used by the individual plant [14]. When grown together at Lincoln, Nebraska, adapted corn obtained from the southeastern section of the state ripened 30 days later than did that from the extreme western section. Data on types adapted to different Nebraska conditions are as follows:

Nebraska Source	Period from Planting to		Plant Height	Yield per Acre
	Ripening	*Silking*		
	(Days)	(Days)	(In.)	(Bu)
Richardson County (eastern)	128	76	90	31.8
Kimball County (western)	97	53	61	26.5

From east to west in Nebraska, the altitude increases, the rainfall and mean temperature decrease, and the growing season becomes shorter. Adapted varieties respond to these western conditions by a reduction in vegetative development. As climatic conditions become more adverse, stalks of adapted varieties are shorter, leaf area less, ears shorter, kernels more shallow, and yields lower. Similar results have been obtained in other states [26, 12].

Corn hybrids are subject to the same adaptation problem as are open-pollinated varieties. However, nearly identical hybrid seed is produced each year, since inbred lines are fixed genetically so that natural selection is inoperative. Performance tests merely reveal whether or not a hybrid is adapted to the conditions under which it is grown. Unadapted hybrids must be replaced by others that prove to be more suitable for production in a particular area.

Weather Effects on Yields

Continuous experimental records for 47 years in Nebraska show an average grain yield of 41 bushels per acre, with annual yields that range from complete failures to 75 bushels. Combinations of high temperature, low rainfall, low relative humidity, and high evaporation were conducive to low yields [13]. Some Nebraska data for the period from 1902–1948 are as follows:

Years Averaged	Yield of Grain per Acre		Summer weather factors[1]				
	Range	*Mean*	*Mean Temperature*	*Mean Relative Humidity*	*Precipitation*	*Evaporation Free Water Surface*	*Precipitation Crop Year[2]*
(No.)	(Bu)	(Bu)	(°F.)	(%)	(In.)	(In.)	(In.)
12	0–20	6.2	78.3	58.8	7.1	31.5	20.9
8	21–40	32.8	75.9	66.3	12.4	26.4	27.9
15	41–60	51.3	75.1	66.4	12.1	23.4	29.0
12	61–75	68.2	73.1	70.2	13.3	20.0	31.7

[1] Three summer months: June, July, and August.
[2] Crop Year: October 1 to September 30.

In Illinois, precipitation and maximum daily temperatures 50–74 days before and 14–30 days after tasseling accounted for up to 67 per cent of the corn yield variability during the period from 1903 through 1956 [23].

Results for a 38-year span in Georgia indicate that high temperatures near the end of the growing season are beneficial to corn when rainfall is adequate. High temperatures, when no rainfall occurs, cause the greatest damage in the first half of June [27].

In addition to occasional deficient seasonal rainfall, corn yields in the Blackland Prairie of Texas were limited by high temperatures and low humidity during the 41-year period 1913–1953. Rainfall in June, when pollination normally occurs, was correlated more closely with yields ($r = 0.55$) than total rainfall during any other period. There was a negative correlation ($r = -0.79$) between yield and maximum June temperature, but a positive correlation ($r = 0.79$) between yield and mean relative humidity in June. When rainfall during more than one month was considered, that for the period October 1–August 1 showed the highest correlation with yield ($r = 0.55$). Hot winds were particularly detrimental to good yields [5].

REFERENCES

1. "Agricultural Statistics, 1960." USDA. pp 632. 1961.
2. Anderson, E., "Corn before Columbus." Des Moines: Pioneer Hi-Bred Corn Co. pp 1–24. 1947.
3. ———, and W. L. Brown, "Origin of Corn Belt maize and its genetic significance," in *Heterosis*, Ames: Ia. St. Coll. Press. pp 124–148. 1952.
4. Andrew, R. H., F. P. Ferwerda, and A. M. Strommen, "Maturation and yield of corn as influenced by climate and production technique." *Agron. J.*, **48**: 231–236. 1956.
5. Bates, R. P., "Climatic factors and corn yields in Texas Blacklands." *Agron. J.*, **47**: 367–369. 1955.
6. Brown, W. L., and E. Anderson, "The southern dent corns." Mo. Bot. Garden *Ann.*, **35**: 255–268. 1948.
7. "Corn facts and figures," 6th ed. New York: Corn Ind. Res. Found. pp 1–48. 1954.
8. Finan, J. J., "Maize in the Herbals." Waltham, Mass.: *Chronica Botanica*. pp 1–191. 1950.
9. Goodding, T. H., and T. A. Kiesselbach, "The adaptation of corn to upland and bottom land soils." *J. Am. Soc. Agron.*, **23**: 928–937. 1931.
10. Jasny, N., "Competition among the grains." Stanford U. Food Res. Inst., pp 1–606. 1940.
11. Jenkins, M. T., "Influence of climate and weather on growth of corn," in *Climate and Man*. USDA Yrbk. of Ag. pp 308–320. 1941.
12. Jones, D. F., and E. Huntington, "The adaptation of corn to climate." *J. Am. Soc. Agron.*, **27**: 261–270. 1935.
13. Kiesselbach, T. A., "Progressive development and seasonal variations of the corn crop." Nebr. Ag. Exp. Sta. *Res. Bul. 166*. 1950.
14. ———, and F. D. Keim, "Regional adaptation of corn in Nebraska." Nebr. Ag. Exp. Sta. *Res. Bul. 19*. 1921.

15. Kuleshov, N. N., "World's diversity of phenotypes of maize." *J. Am. Soc. Agron.*, **25**: 688–700. 1933.
16. Mangelsdorf, P. C., "The origin and evolution of maize," in *Advances in Genetics*, Vol. I. New York: Academic Press. pp 161–207. 1947.
17. ———, "Ancestor of corn." *Science*, **128**(3335): 1313–1320. 1958.
18. ———, and R. G. Reeves, *The Origin of Indian Corn and its Relatives.* (monograph) Tex. Ag. Exp. Sta. *Bul. 574.* 1939.
19. ———, and C. E. Smith, Jr., "New archaeological evidence on evolution of maize." Harvard U. Bot. Mus. Leaflets, **13**(8): 213–247. 1949.
20. ———, and R. G. Reeves, "The origin of corn. IV: Place and time of origin." Harvard Univ. Bot. Mus. Leaflets, **18**(10). 1959.
21. Morgan, M. F., J. H. Gourley, and J. K. Ableiter, "The soil requirements of economic plants, in *Soils and Men.* USDA Yrbk. of Ag. pp 753–776. 1938.
22. Randolph, L. F., "New evidence on the origin of maize." *Am. Nat.*, **86**: 193–202. 1952.
23. Runge, E. C. A., and R. T. Odell, "The relation between precipitation, temperature, and the yield of corn on the Agronomy South Farm, Urbana, Illinois." *Agron. J.*, **50**: 448–454. 1958.
24. Rush, G. E., and N. P. Neal, "The effect of maturity and other factors on stands of corn at low temperatures." *Agron. J.*, **43**: 112–116. 1951.
25. Shaw, R. H., "Climatic requirement," in *Corn and Corn Improvement.* New York: Academic Press. pp 315–341. 1955.
26. Sprague, H. B., "The adaptation of corn to climate." *J. Am. Soc. Agron.*, **27**: 680–681. 1935.
27. Stacy, S. V., *et al.*, "Joint effects of maximum temperatures and rainfall on corn yields, Experiment, Georgia." *Agron. J.*, **49**: 26–28. 1957.
28. Stonor, C. R., and E. Anderson, "Maize among the hill peoples of Assam." Mo. Bot. Garden *Ann.*, **36**: 355–404. 1949.
29. Vavilov, N. I., "The origin, variation, immunity and, breeding of cultivated plants." (Trans. K. Starr Chester.) *Chron. Bot.*, **13**(1–6): 1–364. 1949–50.
30. Wallace, H. A., and W. L. Brown, *Corn and its Early Fathers.* Lansing: Mich. St. U. Press. pp 134. 1956.
31. Weatherwax, P., *The Story of the Maize Plant.* Chicago: U. of Chicago Press. pp 99–114. 1923.
32. ———, "The origin of the maize plant and maize agriculture in ancient America." U. N. Mex. *Bul.* pp 1–8. 1936.
33. ———, "Early contacts of European science with the Indian corn plant." Ind. Acad. Sci. *Proc.*, **54**: 169–178. 1945.
34. ———, "The history of corn." *Sci. Mo.*, **71**(1): 50–60. 1950.
35. ———, *Indian Corn in Old America.* New York: Macmillan. pp 1–253. 1954.
36. ———, and L. F. Randolph, "History and origin of maize," in *Corn and Corn Improvement.* New York: Academic Press. pp 1–61. 1955.

Corn

6. BOTANY

CLASSIFICATION OF CORN

Indian corn or maize (*Zea mays*, L.) is a member of the tribe Tripsaceae or Maydeae of the grass family, Gramineae.

Maize is a monoecious plant with functional staminate flowers borne in tassels located terminally on the stems. Functional pistillate flowers are borne in the ears, which terminate the lateral branches. Structurally, the ear branches are similar to the main stem, except that they are much shortened and covered with modified leaves or husks. Basal branches or tillers may form roots and develop stems similar to the main stem. All types of corn have 10 pairs of chromosomes [47, 48, 23].

RELATIVES OF CORN

The nearest relative of corn is teosinte, *Euchlaena,* which is found wild from central Mexico southward into Honduras. Two species have been described, the annual *E. mexicana,* and the perennial *E. perennis.* Teosinte resembles maize, except that 10–60 branches arise from the base of the plant; they grow as tall as the main stem. The stems are terminated by staminate tassels; short lateral branches bear the pistillate spikelets. The female inflorescence is usually a single spike enclosed in the sheath of a single leaf, similar to a small maize ear. The perennial species is similar to the annual form, except that the stems arise from long-lived rhizomes. The annual teosinte has 10 chromosome pairs; the perennial form, 20 pairs [43, 47, 48].

Maize is more remotely related to *Tripsacum*. This genus includes 7 to 9 species, scattered from the east central United States southward into Brazil and Paraguay. The most widely known species is *T. dactyloides* L.,

146

FIGURE 6-1. **The roots of a corn plant in the silking stage that penetrated more than 3 feet deep. The swollen parts of the stem above are nodes.**

(*Courtesy US Department of Agriculture*)

or gama grass. The plants bear several upright stems which grow from short rhizomes. The stems tend to branch at all nodes, but each may be terminated by an inflorescence. The flowers are borne either in single spikes or in a panicle of spikes. The staminate spikelets are arranged in pairs in the upper portion of each spike; the single pistillate spikelets appear alternately along the axis imbedded in it. There is a rudimentary second female spikelet with each fertile one. All species of Tripsacum are perennial. Some species have 18 chromosome pairs, others 36 pairs [43, 47, 48].

Job's tears (*Coix lacryma-jobi*), an annual from southern Asia, is grown in the United States as an ornamental. The fruits, enclosed in a corneus to stony beadlike bract, are used for beads. Thin-hulled strains, grown for food in the Philippine Islands and in South America, are known as "adlay," a species that has 10 pairs of chromosomes.

MORPHOLOGY OF THE VEGETATIVE ORGANS

The vegetative parts of the corn plant consist of a fibrous root system (Fig. 6-1), stems with conspicuous nodes, and alternate two-ranked (distichous) leaves. Branches are formed at many of the nodes, while adventitious roots may develop at the base of the internodes. Branches that arise from nodes below the soil surface, known as tillers or suckers, resemble the main stem. The aerial branches develop as rudimentary or functional ear shoots. All stems and branches normally form terminal inflorescences [16, 23, 34].

Stalks

The culm, stem, or stalk of maize varies in length from 2 to 20 or more feet in different regional types. A leaf is attached to each node, and often a bud or branch arises at a node.

The upper internodes are nearly cylindrical; the lower ones are alternately grooved, often with buds in the base of the groove. The buds that develop produce ear shoots. The length of the ear-shoot internode often is associated with the internode length of the main stalk [1]. The internode consists of a pithy interior comprised mainly of parenchyma with vascular bundles distributed throughout, surrounded by a hard rind or shell which includes the epidermis [23] (Fig. 6-2). The base of the internode contains

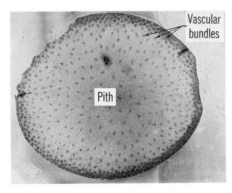

FIGURE 6-2. **Cross section of corn internode showing vascular bundles distributed throughout the pith.**

(*Courtesy Nebraska Agricultural Experiment Station*)

a growth ring in which cell division elongates the internode. Aerial root primordia also are evident in this growth ring.

The node contains cross-connections between the vascular bundles.

Leaf

One parallel-veined leaf is formed at each node in corn. The successive leaves alternate on opposite sides of the stalk, at right angles to the face of a kernel that is planted in a vertical position with the tip downward. The fully formed leaf consists of a blade connected to the sheath by a collar-like ligule. The blade is thin, flat, expanded, and has a definite midrib. The sheath is thicker, more rigid, and has a less conspicuous midrib than the blade. The sheath clasps the internode above the node to which it is attached. In plants with short internodes, and in young plants before the internodes elongate, the lower sheath encloses the sheaths of the leaves from the higher nodes. The ligule consists of a thin hyaline membrane without green color. The blade tapers from the widest portion toward the tip, and also slightly toward the base until it abruptly narrows to join the sheath [23].

From 60–100 thousand stomata per square inch occur on the lower leaf surface, with from 50–60 thousand stomata per square inch on the upper surface [45] (Fig. 6-3).

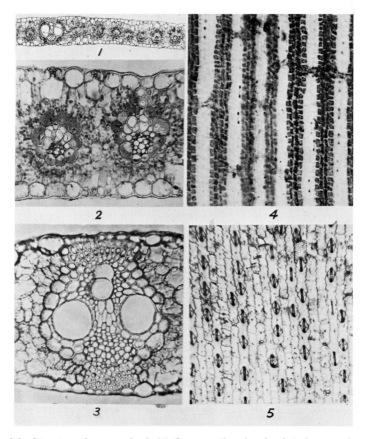

FIGURE 6-3. **Structures in a corn leaf: (1) Cross section showing interior vascular strands, parenchyma cells, and outer epidermis; (2) enlarged small vascular strands; (3) enlarged large vascular strand; (4) veins beneath epidermis; and (5) epidermis showing stomata.**
(*Courtesy Nebraska Agricultural Experiment Station*)

Root System

The root system of corn consists of the seminal roots, which grow downward at the time of seed germination; coronal roots, which arise from stem tissue shortly after the plumule has emerged; and aerial or brace roots, which arise from nodes above the soil surface.

The seminal roots consist of the radicle or primary root plus a variable number of pairs of lateral roots which arise adventitiously at the base of the first node of the stem just above the scutellar node. The usual number of seminal roots is 3–5, but it varies from 1–13 per plant [23].

The coronal roots arise from the basal portion of the stem. The first whorl of four or five crown roots appears at the base of the second internode about as soon as the tip of the coleoptile reaches the soil surface (Fig. 6-4). A few of the higher internodes may have approximately the

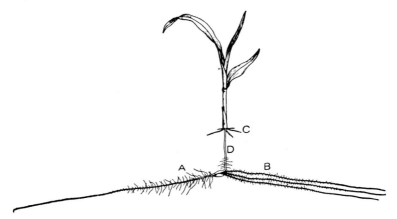

FIGURE 6-4. **Corn plant 2 weeks after planting: (A) Primary seminal root, (B) lateral seminal roots, (C) coronal or crown roots, and (D) subcrown internode.**
(*Courtesy Nebraska Agricultural Experiment Station*)

same number. Under Nebraska conditions, an average of nine internodes bear functional roots, eight bearing them below the surface of the soil, the other just above the surface. The functional crown roots averaged about 85 per stalk, all of which branched and rebranched [50].

Brace roots that grow out from second, third, and sometimes higher nodes above the soil surface may or may not enter the soil and become functional.

MORPHOLOGY OF THE INFLORESCENCE

The main stem and tillers terminate in staminate inflorescences or tassels. The branches that arise from nodes above the soil surface terminate in a pistillate inflorescence or ear (Fig. 6-5), but usually all ear buds degenerate except the upper one or two located about midway on the stalk [23] except on prolific types.

Staminate Inflorescence

The branches of the panicle or tassel are spirally arranged around the axis [2]. The spikelets are usually arranged in pairs, one sessile the other pedicellate (Fig. 6-6). Groups of three or four spikelets may be found occasionally. Each spikelet is enclosed by two glumes. There are two florets per spikelet, each with a lemma, a palea, three stamens, two lodicules, and a rudimentary pistil. The upper floret is more advanced in development than the lower one. The lemmas and paleas are thinner and more abruptly pointed than are the glumes. These are all protective organs for the stamens. The lodicules swell, prying the lemma and palea apart so that the stamens can be pushed out by elongation of the filaments when the pollen is mature.

Each apparent node in the tassel may bear 1-4 pairs of spikelets. The average number is roughly proportional to the number of kernel rows on the ear [2, 51].

Pistillate Inflorescence

The branch or shank that bears the pistillate inflorescence (ear) is

FIGURE 6-5. **(Left) Pistillate inflorescences — young ears in silking stage; and (right) staminate inflorescence or tassel of the corn plant.**

(Courtesy Nebraska Agricultural Experiment Station)

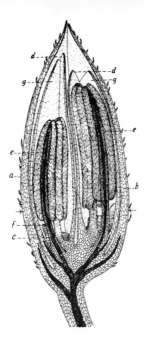

FIGURE 6-6. Staminate spikelet showing upper flower (right) and lower flower (left) with 1.5 anthers removed from each flower: (a) Lower or outer glume, (b) upper or inner glume, (c) lodicule, (d) palea, (e) anther, (f) filament of anther, and (g) lemma.

(*Courtesy Nebraska Agricultural Experiment Station*)

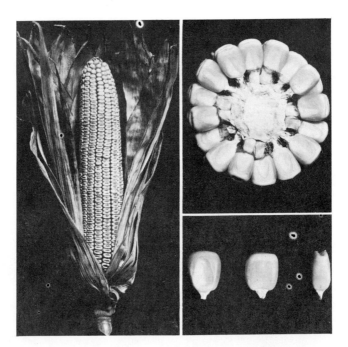

FIGURE 6-7. (Left) Ear with husks. (Upper right) Cross-section of ear showing kernel attachment to cob. (Lower right) Kernels; the germ side of the kernel faces the tip of the ear except in those that develop from the lower floret of the spikelet.

(*Courtesy Nebraska Agricultural Experiment Station*)

more slender and has shorter internodes than the culm. The husks that surround the ear are modified sheaths that bear short leaflike structures in most sorts of dent corn [23].

The ear is a spike with a thickened axis (Fig. 6-7). The paired pistillate spikelets on the ear ordinarily are borne in several longitudinal rows. Both spikelets in the pair are usually sessile. The individual spikelet is two-flowered, but usually only one floret is fertile. This paired arrangement explains the customary even number of rows of grain on the ear. When the second floret in a spikelet develops, the kernels are so crowded that the appearance of rows is destroyed as, for example, in the Country Gentleman variety of sweet corn (Fig. 6-8).

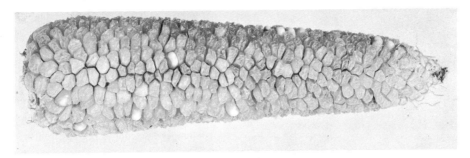

FIGURE 6-8. **Ear of Country Gentleman sweet corn which develops kernels in both florets of the spikelet; the resultant crowding prevents the kernels from forming straight rows. The smooth white-capped kernels resulted from outcrossing by pollen from field corn.**

(Courtesy US Department of Agriculture)

The thick fleshy glumes are too short to cover the other parts of the spikelet, while the lemmas and paleas (chaff) are thinner and shorter than the glumes.

KERNEL OR CARYOPSIS

The corn kernel is a one-seeded fruit, or caryopsis. The seed, enclosed within the pericarp, consists of the embryo, endosperm, and remnants of the seed coats and nucellus.

In the mature kernel (Fig. 6-9), the pericarp forms the tough protective cover. The integuments or seed coats beneath the pericarp are scattered noncellular remnants. The outer wall of the nucellular epidermis forms a continuous semipermeable membrane between the pericarp and aleurone.

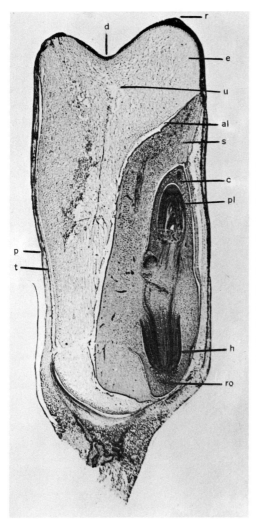

FIGURE 6-9. **Half of nearly mature dent corn kernel showing dent (d), remnant of style (r), endosperm (e), unfilled portion of immature endosperm (u), aleurone (al), scutellum (s), plumule (pl), hypocotyl and radicle (h), testa or true seed coat (t), and pericarp (p). The germ comprises the entire darker area including the scutellum (s), coleoptile (c), and rootcap (ro).**

(*Courtesy US Department of Agriculture*)

There is a silk scar on the pericarp at the apical end of the kernel; at the lower end, the pericarp connects with the pedicel or tip cap.

The endosperm, beneath the pericarp and its adherent parts, consists of cells filled primarily with starch grains. It is surrounded by a layer of aleurone cells, except for a layer of conducting cells where the endosperm joins the embryo.

At the base of the kernel, the embryo is embedded near one of the faces of the endosperm. The embryo consists of the plumule, radicle, and scutellum. The scutellum, sometimes considered the first leaf, is attached to the scutellar node of the central axis. It is a modified cotyledon that serves as a food storage organ. The second leaflike structure is the coleoptile or

FIGURE 6-10. **Ears of (left to right) pop, sweet, flour, flint, dent, and pod corn.**
(*Courtesy US Department of Agriculture*)

plumule sheath. The plumule consists of four or five small foliage leaves each rolled up inside those below it to form a cone within the coleoptile. The primary root or radicle is enclosed by the coleorhiza or root sheath. Initials of two or more adventitious seminal roots arise at the base of the first internode of the stem [23].

The relative proportions of the kernel parts are approximately as follows: endosperm, 85 per cent; embryo and scutellum, 10 per cent; and the pericarp with remnants of the nucellus, seed coats, and pedicel, 5 per cent [23].

CORN GROUPS OR TYPES

Corn grown under cultivation is commonly classified into six groups based on kernel characteristics; pod corn, grown occasionally as a botanical curiosity, usually is included as a seventh group. The groups commonly recognized in the United States are dent, flint, flour, sweet, pop, waxy, and pod corns [45, 41] (Fig. 6-10). Except for waxy corn, these groups often have been regarded as botanical varieties or subspecies designated by trinomials. At present this seems unwarranted because inheritance studies show that the subspecies are fully interfertile, and the group characteristics differentiated by one or only a few genetic factors.

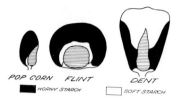 

POP CORN   FLINT   DENT   FLOUR

■ HORNY STARCH   □ SOFT STARCH   ▤ GERM

FIGURE 6-11. **Typical proportions of horny and soft starch in 4 corn groups** (*Courtesy US Department of Agriculture*)

The *dent corn* kernel is characterized by a depression or dent in the crown which is caused by shrinkage during ripening in a deposit of soft starch at the crown. This soft starch is surrounded on the sides by hard or corneous starch which shrinks less. The kernels of different dent corn varieties vary in shape from narrow, deep, so-called shoe-peg types to wide, shallow, square types. Most of the corn grown commercially in the United States is of the dent type.

In the *flint corn* kernel, the hard starch layer extends over the crown but soft starch is deposited in the center. Flint corn kernels shrink uniformly as they mature. Many flint corns tiller profusely. Adapted varieties yield well.

Flour or soft corn kernels consist almost entirely of soft starch (Fig. 6-11), with a very thin layer of hard starch on the sides. The kernels show little or no denting. Flour corns resemble the flints in plant as well as in ear characteristics. Flour corns are seldom grown in the United States, except by American Indians for home use.

Flint and flour corns with variegated kernel color (Fig. 6-12) are now being grown for ornamental uses. Formerly the growing of these mixed types by American Indians reduced the degree of inbreeding, which resulted in some degree of hybrid vigor.

Sweet corn kernels have such a large proportion of sugar to starch that they are wrinkled and translucent when dry. Sweet corns appear to have lost the ability to produce abundant, full-developed starch grains. Sweetness can be determined by a single recessive genetic factor. Most of the sweet corn varieties grown in the United States are transformed flint corns as, for example, Golden Bantam [41]. A few varieties, such as Evergreen, are derived from dent corn. Most of the sweet corn grown in the United States is harvested while immature, tender, and sweet and then cut from the cob for canning or freezing. Much of the remainder is eaten fresh on the cob

FIGURE 6-12. **"Indian corn" — flour corn with colored kernels.**

after boiling. Some of the ears are frozen directly. Small quantities of the cut fresh grains also are dried in the sun.

Popcorn is characterized by a higher percentage of hard endosperm starch than flint corn, which makes it burst open upon heating. The popping results from a rapid expansion of moisture in each individual starch grain, after partial hydrolysis during heating. The confinement of this pressure for a time, followed by its sudden release, is the role of the flinty matrix of protein. The average increase in volume of the older open-pollinated varieties was about 15–20 times the original volume of shelled corn [45], but improved hybrids may give an expansion of 30–35 volumes. It is often difficult to distinguish between some varieties of pop and flint corn [12]. Most varieties of popcorn have small hard kernels, but some popcorns native to South America have larger, softer kernels. Popcorn has been grown in the New World since prehistoric times, but it is rather rare in the eastern hemisphere. The Spanish variety is a typical flint corn with a long slender ear and a stalk of medium height, but the kernel pops readily. Popcorn may have arisen by mutation from flint corn, but the only character it has in common with popcorns is the ability to pop.

The endosperm starch in *waxy corn* consists entirely of amylopectin, whereas ordinary corn starch is a mixture of 71–72 per cent amylopectin and 28–29 per cent amylose. The kernels have a uniformly dull rather soft endosperm. The term waxy refers to the waxlike appearance of the endosperm of the grain when it is cut or broken. Waxy starch stains red when treated with iodine. Waxy corn was discovered in China sometime before 1908 when samples were first sent to the United States. About 32,000 acres of waxy corn were grown in this country in 1949. Waxy starch is adaptable to many special industrial and food uses, but particularly for the manufacture of adhesives.

Each *pod corn* kernel is enclosed in a pod or husk. The ear also is covered by a husk, like the corn of the other groups. Pod corn may have the endosperm characteristics of the dent, flint, flour, pop, sweet, or waxy types. Typical present-day pod corn is heterozygous. When planted, it segregates into a 1:2:1 ratio of 1 normal type without pods to 2 of pod corn to 1 of a long-podded sterile ear type that sometimes has fertile seeds in the tassel. The podded (tunicate) characteristic is dominant and controlled by a single genetic factor. Some of the primitive corns may have been podded. Pod corn is never grown commercially.

OPEN-POLLINATED VARIETIES

Open-pollinated varieties of corn have been almost entirely replaced by hybrids in the United States since 1940. Some varieties were grown under widely different environmental conditions, which often resulted in innumerable strains within a single named variety that had been adapted by natural or manual selection to meet local conditions. Open-pollinated varieties (Fig. 6-13) now are chiefly of historic interest because the inbred lines used in hybrids were derived directly or indirectly from them. Since these varieties now face extinction, concerted efforts have been made to preserve some of the better ones as basic sources of germ plasm for future corn improvement.

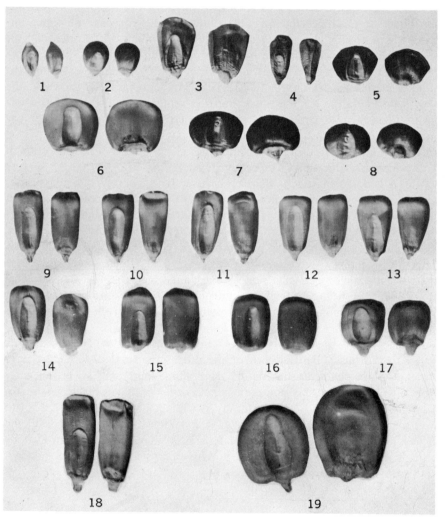

FIGURE 6-13. **Paired kernels of 19 varieties of corn: (1) Rice popcorn, (2) Pearl popcorn, (3) Stowell Evergreen sweet corn, (4) Country Gentleman sweet corn, (5) Black Mexican sweet corn, (6) (7) (8) 3 varieties of flint corn, (9 to 17) 9 varieties of dent corn, (18) horsetooth or shoepeg dent corn, and (19) Cuzco corn from Peru.**

(*Courtesy US Department of Agriculture*)

A large number of open-pollinated dent varieties were grown in the Corn Belt before the advent of hybrids. Well known varieties included Johnson County White, Reid Yellow Dent, Krug, Silver King, Clarage, and Leaming. In the southern states, prolific dent varieties that produce more than one ear per stalk were commonly grown, but a few flint varieties also were popular. These were usually large, long-season varieties.

Early dent varieties were common under short-season conditions in the northern, northeastern, and western states, such as Golden Glow, Minnesota 13, and Northwestern Dent. Popular early flint varieties included King Phillip, Longfellow, Gehu Yellow, and Dakota White.

HYBRID CORN

Hybrid corn constitutes one of the most important advances in American agriculture in the past 100 years.

Hybrid corn is defined as the first generation of a cross that involves two or more inbred lines. These inbred lines are developed by controlled self-pollination of adapted strains for 5–7 generations. The yields of inbreds are reduced as the result of the inbreeding process, in some cases to 50 per cent of that of the parent varieties. The principal value of inbred lines is that the plants within a particular line are essentially alike in their inheritance. Vigor is restored when suitable genetically different inbred lines are crossed. Good first-generation hybrids between inbreds produce 20–30 per cent more corn than the original open-pollinated parent varieties from which the inbred lines were obtained. These results are applicable only for the first hybrid generation. Seed from first generation (F_1) plants when planted the next year will be characterized by lower yields, less uniform plants, and other undesirable traits. Thus, first generation seed must be produced each season from inbred parents maintained solely for that purpose [18].

Several kinds of hybrids are possible on the basis of the number of inbred lines involved. The simplest hybrid, known as a single cross (A×B), is made from a cross between two inbred lines. A three-way cross (A×B)×C, is a cross between a single cross and a third inbred. A cross between two single crosses is known as a double cross (A×B)(C×D). A synthetic variety is one that results from a combination of many inbred lines. A topcross is a cross between an inbred line and an open-pollinated strain. Nearly all of the commercial field corn crop is produced from double-cross seed. Single crosses often are uneconomical because the seed is produced on inbred plants which are relatively low yielders. Double-cross seed is produced on single-cross plants that are highly productive of quality seed.

Yield tests in many Corn Belt states have demonstrated the superiority of certain hybrids over the best of the former open-pollinated varieties. Hybrids often have outyielded these varieties by 15–35 per cent. Corn hybrids are as specific in adaptation to environmental conditions as are open-pollinated varieties. Some hybrids are more able to withstand drought, wind, diseases, insects, and other unfavorable conditions. In addition, they are uniform in plant characters, ripen uniformly, and generally possess lodging resistance.

New corn hybrids are being developed by state agricultural experiment stations, the U.S. Department of Agriculture, and numerous commercial companies to meet specific environmental conditions. Hundreds of different corn hybrids are now being grown on a commercial scale. Hybrid corn also has expanded rapidly in other countries, particularly in Mexico, Yugoslavia, Italy, the Soviet Union, and Egypt. Many countries are now developing their own inbred lines and hybrids, but American lines and hybrids also have been used where they are adapted.

PROGRESSIVE PLANT DEVELOPMENT

Germination

The optimum temperature for the germination of the corn kernel is about 86°F (30°C). When the seed is planted in the field, emergence of the seedling occurs in 5–10 days under favorable conditions [23]. Germination is slower as the temperature decreases, but some germination may occur at temperatures as low as 40°F.

In germination the organs of the embryo, which remained dry in the dormant seed, resume growth. The primary root, enclosed in its sheath or coleorhiza, elongates until it breaks through the pericarp, later breaks out of the coleorhiza, and then makes its way downward. This development occurs in 35–55 hours. The plumule, enclosed by its sheath or coleoptile, begins to elongate and also breaks through the pericarp of the kernel. At first the coleoptile grows faster than the plumule, but when it is exposed to light at the soil surface it ceases to grow. The plumule then breaks out through the tip of the coleoptile. About the time that the coleoptile reaches the soil surface, the first crown roots appear immediately above the coleoptilar node. Later, an additional whorl of roots forms at the base of each of the successive 6–10 basal underground internodes of the stem. These crown roots soon form the major part of the root system of the plant [23].

In germination, enzymes in the embryo, chiefly in the scutellum, digest the cells of the endosperm, since there is always a layer of partially disorganized cells in contact with it. The aleurone layer also produces enzymes during germination [46].

Vegetative Growth

Seedling growth has been described in detail [23] as follows. As the stem elongates, its growing point continues to form additional leaf initials, one at each node, which later develop into leaves. After all the leaves are started, but before many of them are unrolled, the growing point of the stem elongates, becomes branched, and starts to differentiate into the young tassel. Before the tassel has differentiated, while the growing point of the stem is still giving rise to additional leaf initials, branch buds have formed in some of the lowermost leaf axils. Those in some of the lower axils may develop tillers, while the rest form ear shoots, most of which soon degenerate with only the upper one or two developing functional ears (Fig. 6-14). At the stage of tassel differentiation, reached in approximately three weeks, the initials have been laid down for all of the nodes and internodes of the stem as well as for all of the leaves, tillers, and ear branches.

The stem tip becomes evident very early in the development of the embryo. Soon after the meristematic tissues are formed, the vascular bundles become evident, being extended through both nodes and internodes. In the nodes, all the longitudinal bundles become united by small cross bundles which form the nodal network. Bundles extend from each node into the leaf that arises from that node. When buds for branches form at the nodes, their vascular bundles also become united to the network of bundles in the node. The internodes are very short at first, but begin to elongate through the formation of new cells by an intercalary meristem that is located near the base of each internode except the first one. In the first internode, this region

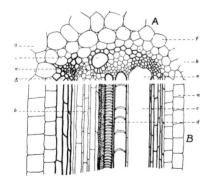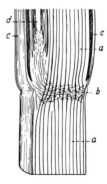

FIGURE 6-14. Left, Vascular bundle of corn culm: A. Cross section, (a and b) sides of bundles, (c) pitted vessel, (d) supportive tissue, (e) lacuna, (f) parenchyma cells of pith, (g) compressed protophloem. B. Longitudinal section, (a) parenchyma cells of pith, (b) phloem cells of bundle, (c) lacuna and, (d) xylem. Right, Section of culm including ear node and rudimentary ear: (a) internodes, (b) node, (c) leaf sheath, and (d) ear shoot.
(*Courtesy Nebraska Agricultural Experiment Station*)

of new cell formation occurs at the upper end. The cells later elongate until the internodes comprise most of the length of the stem [23].

Upon germination the leaves already formed in the embryo resume growth. The formation of leaf initials is resumed, and continues until all the leaves have started. Finally the growing point of the stem begins to differentiate to form the tassel. The total number of leaves formed varies with the vegetative type. The part of the leaf that is formed first is the tip of the blade. The growing region where new cells are formed remains at the base of each leaf. After the blade is formed the ligule is differentiated near the leaf base. The formation of new cells at the base of the leaf continues, now forming the tissues of the sheath [23]. Later increase in leaf blade size is due largely to a rapid increase in size of the small meristematic cells which had previously been formed at its base. When the blade is almost fully grown it is still only partially rolled. Full display is brought about partly by elongation of the internode beneath it and partly by elongation of the sheath.

The seminal roots function in early seedling growth before the later developing but more extensive coronal roots of the higher internodes assume the major uptake of water and mineral nutrients. Under ordinary field conditions, all seminal roots except the first grow nearly horizontally for a short distance before they turn downward. The coronal roots from about the lower five internodes likewise grow horizontally for some distance before turning downward. Those from the higher internodes, which appear later in the season, grow downward at once. This peculiar behavior of the earlier roots may be due to the low temperature of the deeper soil at the time the roots form. So-called brace roots, which often develop from the lower 1–4 aerial internodes on the stalk become functional whenever they enter the soil.

Corn varieties grouped into small, medium, and large vegetative types that averaged 55, 87, and 92 inches tall, respectively, had correspondingly greater root systems [50]. Compared with the small type, the medium and large types had, respectively, 33 and 50 per cent greater maximum spread; 9 and 10 per cent deeper maximum penetration; 42 and 65 per cent more functional main roots per plant; 22 and 92 per cent greater combined length of main roots per plant; 115 and 311 per cent greater root weight; 86 and 268 per cent greater root volume; and 10 and 29 per cent larger diameter of main roots. The rate of growth of roots and tops was approximately the same for all types until the tassel stage of the small varieties. Rapid root and top growth continued in the medium and large types until they produced tassels. There is a rather high correlation between root and top growth, which in turn is associated with the length of the vegetative period of the plant.

Growth of Reproductive Organs

The morphological development of the maize staminate and pistillate inflorescences has been described by several investigators [42, 45, 49, 6, 7, 8, 23].

Development of Staminate Inflorescence. Differentiation of the tassel begins with elongation of the growing point of the stem which may take place 2–3 weeks after seedling emergence. Outgrowths soon appear on the central axis as well as on the branches of the tassel. A spikelet with two flowers finally arises from each lobe. The two glumes are formed in the same manner as ordinary leaves. In the axil of the lower glume a growing ing point forms from which develops the lower flower, while the original growing point of the spikelet gives rise to the upper or terminal flower. The flower initials then give rise to lemmas and paleas for each flower. Finally, each growing point forms three stamens, two lodicules, and a rudimentary pistil for each flower. The stamen begins as a lobe but the terminal part differentiates into an anther while the lower part forms the filament. Within each of the four chambers of an anther, spore mother cells are finally formed. The spore mother cells undergo meiosis to form the microspores or pollen grains with the haploid number of 10 chromosomes. At the time of maturity, the pollen grain is trinucleate. One of the nuclei remains as the vegetative nucleus while the other two become crescent-shaped sperm cells. At anthesis, the lodicules swell so that the anthers are pushed out of the floral bracts by the elongation of the filaments. The anthers soon break open near the tip for release of the pollen. Since the pollen is carried by the wind, cross pollination generally occurs. A tassel may shed pollen for a week or more.

Development of Pistillate Inflorescence. Early stages of ear development are similar to those of tassel formation [23]. At first the ear is smooth, but protuberances soon form in rows. The basal protuberances form first and development advances toward the tip of the ears. Each one becomes bilobed, each lobe developing a spikelet with two flowers, only one of which commonly persists. The growing point of the upper flower is differentiated to form the functional pistil or silk. A single sessile ovule is developed which consists of a nucellus with two integuments or rudimentary seed coats. The united carpels, which will form the ovary wall or pericarp of the mature kernel, grow upward until they completely enclose the ovule. As a result of meiosis, the embryo sac is formed with a content of eight nuclei. The fully organized embryo sac has at the micropylar end one egg cell with two synergids beside it. A little nearer the middle are two polar nuclei, while at the opposite end are three antipodal cells [27].

The formation of floral organs in maize is not prevented by dense planting; that is, 24,000 plants as compared with 12,000 plants per acre. Competitive pressure does not produce a marked retardation of ear elongation, ovary development, or silk elongation until approximately 74 days after planting. Barrenness is the result of failure of silk emergence during the pollen-shedding period [35].

Prolific corn hybrids and varieties, widely grown in the southern states, usually produce two ears per plant. In Georgia studies, the first-ear yield was relatively unaffected by environment unless the crop was so poor that few second ears developed. Variations in second-ear yields resulted primarily from differences in number rather than size. The plants tended to develop a full-sized first ear, while additional yield came from second ears. Total yield per plant was reduced 53 per cent when the first ear shoot was bagged to prevent pollination, but only 28 per cent when the second ear-shoot was bagged. The plants were able to shift 24 per cent of the potential first-ear yield to the second ear, but only 9 per cent of the second-ear yield to the first ear [5].

Fertilization

Pollen grains shed by the tassels germinate when they lodge on fresh silks. The germinated pollen grain sends out a pollen tube which grows in the sheath of cells that surrounds the vascular tissue until it reaches the base of the silk where it enters the cavity of the ovary through the micropyle [23]. Several pollen grains may germinate and send down pollen tubes on a single silk, but usually only one functions in fertilization. The others cease growth when the first pollen tube reaches the ovary. Each silk must be penetrated and each ovary must be fertilized to produce a grain. Only one in several thousand pollen grains shed from the tassel is able to perform its prescribed function.

When the pollen tube reaches the micropyle, it grows between the cells of the nucellar tissue until it reaches the embryo sac. Rupture of the end of the pollen tube releases two sperms. The nucleus of one sperm fuses with the egg nucleus to form the embryo or new sporophyte which has the diploid number of 20 chromosomes. The other sperm nucleus fuses with one of the two polar nuclei, which in turn fuses with the other polar nucleus to establish the primary endosperm nucleus with 30 chromosomes. The endosperm is triploid (3X) tissue [44]. This double fertilization explains how characters of the male parent may appear in the endosperm as well as in the embryo. The immediate observable effect of foreign pollen on the endosperm is known as xenia [23].

Corn is normally a cross-pollinated plant, but some self-pollination may occur. When 40 plants of white corn were distributed in a field of yellow dent corn, kernels on the white ear were yellow after being fertilized by pollen from yellow plants due to xenia. Only 0.70 per cent of verified self-fertilization was found [22], partly because of the predominance of pollen from the yellow corn plants. Ordinarily, less than 5 per cent of self-pollination occurs in open-pollinated corn plants under field conditions.

Kernel Development

The primary endosperm nucleus undergoes division prior to that of the zygote. The first division of the fertilized egg occurs 28–34 hours after pollination; the endosperm may have 8–32 nuclei by this time. Approximately 128 free endosperm nuclei may be formed three days after pollination. The embryo sac enlarges with a central vacuole being formed surrounded by a layer of cytoplasm. Shortly afterwards, cell walls are formed between the free nuclei. Through further divisions the central vacuole or cavity becomes filled with cellular tissue. Thereafter, the cells of the outer layer of the endosperm become differentiated into tissue that functions in food conduction [31]. For some time after the endosperm becomes cellular, cell divisions occur throughout, but soon cease in the interior. Divisions are then confined to the peripheral zone which later becomes differentiated into the aleurone layer.

Except for the surface layers, all cells of the endosperm consist largely of starch grains. Starch formation begins two weeks or less after fertilization. The first cells to show starch grains are in the upper or crown part of the kernel. Starch formation progresses towards the base of the kernel. Persistence of antipodal tissue (haploid) until the maturity of the kernel has been observed [31]. In early development, this tissue is near the micropyle, but it is finally crowded into the crown of the kernel as the endosperm enlarges. The antipodal cells are filled with starch at maturity.

The early stages of development show an irregular arrangement of cells, lacking conformity to a definite pattern. Growth is restricted to the apical region from about the fourth to the ninth days. The proembryo soon becomes a club-shaped mass of cells. The basal cells form the suspensor. The first sign of further differentiation of the embryo is the appearance of a region of small cells on the anterior side of the embyro, slightly below the tip. The stem tip, which develops from this region, soon becomes evident by the formation of a slight protuberance. The rapid development of tissues of the scutellum (first modified leaf) pushes the original tip of the proembryo aside, making the stem tip appear lateral in early development [23]. A ring of tissue forms around the stem tip which develops into the coleoptile (second modified leaf). The growing point of the stem next begins to form leaf initials, the first being on the side opposite from the scutellum. The number varies from four to six before the embryo becomes dormant in the mature seed. These leaves remain rolled inside the coleoptile until emergence at the time of germination. Tissues in the lower part of the embryo begin differentiation to form the initial of the primary root at about the same time that the stem tip begins to differentiate. A number of lateral seminal root initials form just above the scutellar node. The embryo is morphologically mature in about 45 days.

SEED VIABILITY

Healthy, well-preserved seed corn usually has a viability of 95 to 100 per cent. The chief cause of low germination is injury from freezing [22, 23]. This results from exposure to low temperatures while the moisture content of the seed is still high. Seed that contains 14 per cent or less of moisture will endure, without injury, almost any amount of freezing to which it is likely to be exposed. Another cause of reduced viability is infection with seed-borne organisms that cause seed decay or the death of young seedlings. Seed treatment with commercial disinfectants or protectants, such as Arasan or Spergon, may increase seedling emergence by about 5–20 per cent.

Soil-borne pathogens, particularly *Pythium* species, also cause seed rots and seedling blights that reduce seedling emergence, especially in cold wet soil. Seed treatment provides some protection from soil-borne pathogens [14].

Corn may retain its viability for several years under favorable storage conditions when properly mature and dried to a safe moisture content. Under subhumid Nebraska conditions, seed up to four years old can be planted in the field without serious stand reduction, but germination usually begins to drop rapidly after six years [23]. Under semiarid conditions in Colorado, the average germination of corn was 32 per cent after 21 years of air-dry storage [32]. Under warm humid conditions of the Gulf States the seed often loses its viability in one year, unless it is well dried and then kept in sealed or cold storage. Each increase of one per cent moisture content and each 10°F higher temperature reduces the seed life by about half.

PHOTOSYNTHESIS

The rate of photosynthesis in corn, as measured by carbon-dioxide absorption under field conditions, was highest at air temperatures of 77–86°F. Visibily wilted corn plants showed a lower rate of photosynthesis [39]. As normally grown, field corn usually receives sufficient carbon dioxide and sunlight for maximum production, except in the absence of air movement or in very thick stands.

In the young corn plant, some carbohydrates are translocated downward from the lower leaves to the crown and roots. After fertilization, translocation is towards the ear [26].

Intensity of solar radiation had a predominant effect on the rate of photosynthesis in corn in New York experiments. Net absorption of carbon dioxide by the plant was highly correlated with solar radiation ($r = 0.95$). Within limits, a warmer temperature also increased carbon dioxide assimilation. Respiration, with a loss of carbon dioxide, increased as night temperature increased, but its magnitude was only 5–15 per cent of that of midday assimilation. An increase in carbon dioxide concentration also increased the assimilation in closed chambers, especially at high light intensities. Small increases in the concentration of carbon dioxide caused large decreases in the stomatal openings and in transpiration, without any decrease in assimilation. Drought reduced assimilation. Rates of assimilation were about the same early or late in the day, with midday values much less for corn on dry soil than on soil kept moist at field capacity, even though the dry corn showed no visible wilting or leaf-curling [29].

WATER UTILIZATION

Corn requires a plentiful supply of moisture, distributed throughout the growing season, but especially during rapid growth, pollination, and grain development. In Nebraska experiments, the transpiration ratio; that is, the number of pounds of water used by the plant in the production of one pound of dry matter varied from 261–445 in different seasons. Fully half the total water was transpired during a period of about five weeks after the plants developed their maximum leaf area. The water requirements in the different seasons were closely associated with the amount of evaporation [21].

Evapotranspiration, which includes evaporation from the soil surface as well as water loss from the plants by transpiration, measures the total water utilization. For the entire growing season, May 1–September 9, it has been estimated that evapotranspiration consisted of 56 per cent evaporation from the soil and 44 per cent transpiration by the corn plant [15]. An actively growing corn crop in Iowa completely shades the ground for a period of only 2–3 weeks during the growing season. In this period, the ratio of evapotranspiration to open-pan evaporation was 0.81. Before this period, the ratio increased as the leaf area increased, but afterwards it declined with a decline in physiological activity of the plants. The ratio at planting time was 0.36 [10]. In western Minnesota, 40–50 per cent of the water losses during the growing season could be accounted for by evaporation from the soil surface [17].

Corn utilized water to a depth of five feet or more in a deep, permeable, and well-drained Brunizem soil in Illinois. Rainfall and irrigation affected the soil-moisture profile to a depth of only two feet on corn and fallow plots [33]. Corn utilized moisture down to the fifth foot at kernel formation. The period of highest water requirement appears to be from tasseling to kernel formation.

Nutrient element uptake by corn plants may be limited by soil productivity and environmental factors, chiefly soil moisture supply. Phosphorus, dry matter, nitrogen, magnesium, potassium, and calcium accumulation by mature corn plants grown under conditions of decreased moisture supply were 40, 44, 50, 65, 71, and 93 per cent, respectively, of the values obtained for the mature corn plants produced with adequate moisture throughout the growing season [20].

Corn yields often are closely related to the soil moisture reserves at the beginning of the growing season, as well as to moisture stress to which the plant is subjected during the season, especially in areas of limited rainfall. The efficiency of water use was strongly conditioned by soil temperature. Supplemental irrigation in Illinois was desirable for deep-rooted crops only when there was serious moisture depletion in the upper two feet of soil [25].

Moisture stress prior to silking reduced corn grain yields by 25 per cent, at silking by 50 per cent, and after silking by 21 per cent [11].

Root growth in small corn seedlings decreases as soil-moisture tension increases from 1 to 12 atmospheres. Increases in radicle elongation, fresh weight, dry weight, and degree of seedling hydration gradually diminish as soil tension increases. Growth differences are most evident in the range 1–3 atmospheres [13].

The manner in which corn plants respond to drought depends upon the stage of growth when the moisture deficiency occurs. Severe early drought results in stunting as well as delayed silking in relation to time of tasseling. Many plants may fail to silk, whereas the tassels may be partially or completely sterile. Partially or completely barren plants are the result. The leaves may wilt and some of them "fire" (turn yellow) and die. Drought after favorable fertilization of the ear shoots may cause the ears to shorten by dying back from the tips. Fired leaves may cause the kernels to remain small and chaffy [24]. Drought periods in the northwestern corner of the Corn Belt definitely reduce crop yields in the year of the drought, and sometimes in the subsequent year [4]. Corn varieties adapted to extremely droughty conditions are grown by the Hopi, Zuni, and Navajo Indians in the semiarid sections of Arizona and New Mexico [19].

MINERAL NUTRITION

Nutrient Absorption

The corn plant requires large amounts of nitrogen, phosphorus, potassium, calcium, magnesium, and sulfur for maximum yields. Minor elements needed are manganese, iron, boron, copper, zinc, and molybdenum [30]. Accessory elements found in corn include silicon, aluminum, nickel, cobalt, chromium, tin, lead, silver, barium, strontium, chlorine, and sodium [31, 32].

Many factors influence the absorption of nutrients. These include the chemical form, environment, and the effects of certain ions on the absorption of others.

The corn plant apparently is able to utilize nitrogen as nitrates, ammonium salts, nitrites, and certain organic forms. A considerable portion of the nitrogen absorbed by corn in the field is in the form of nitrates because nitrification occurs at a fairly rapid rate in most soils. Corn also can absorb appreciable amounts of ammonium nitrogen in the form of ammonium sulfate. Some nitrate nitrogen may be necessary for the synthesis of protein [40]. It is generally held that relatively high pH levels of the substrate are conducive to high rates of ammonium absorption, while relatively low pH levels favor high rates of nitrate absorption. Nitrite absorption by corn plants also has been demonstrated. There is some evidence that corn is able to assimilate organic forms of nitrogen directly; in order of availability, these forms are as follows: asparagin, casein, cottonseed meal, hemoglobin, linseed meal, uric acid, peptone, guanin, alanin, urea, creatin, malt, and glycocoll [9]. Thus, it appears that the plant might be able to supplement the inorganic sources of nitrogen by direct utilization of some of the organic nitrogen compounds that occur in manure or in plant decomposition products. Nitrogen uptake by the corn plant continues throughout the growing season, although the rate of increase diminishes towards plant maturity [52]. After nitrogen enters the corn plant, most of it is converted into amino acids, amides, proteins, and cholorophyll. More than half of the nitrogen accumulates in the grain [38].

Phosphorus is generally absorbed by the corn plant in the form of inorganic phosphates. The plant seems unable to obtain much of its phosphorous from relatively insoluble phosphorus carriers, such as rock phosphate. After phosphorus enters the corn plant, it is rapidly transported to live tissues. It is found in the plant in the form of phytin, lecithin, hexose phosphates, nucleic acid, phosphoproteins, and as inorganic forms associated mostly with magnesium, potassium, sodium, and calcium. Phosphorus appears to accumulate in the corn plant at a fairly continuous rate up to the time of maturity [36]. Approximately 75 per cent of the total phosphorus in the corn plant at maturity is in the grain, of which about three-fourths or more occurs in the form of phytin.

Potassium is absorbed in large quantities by the corn plant from soluble inorganic sources. It appears to remain in the plant tissue entirely in solution in the cell sap. There is no evidence of insoluble or fixed or un-ionizable forms, except possibly in the cob tissue [28]. Potassium accumulation reaches a maximum about three weeks after the corn plant silks. Thereafter, an actual loss of potassium occurs, largely from the leaves and stems of the plant [36].

Calcium is found largely in the stems and leaves, with only a small amount in the grain. Magnesium is absorbed throughout plant growth but it usually accumulates in the grain or in the leaves. The leaf margins accumulate boron, manganese, and silica [37, 38].

Dry Matter Accumulation

The accumulation of dry matter in corn tends to follow the characteristic sigmoid curve representative of the grand period of growth. Dry matter production is slow immediately after seedling emergence. During the first 40–50 days the leaf area, photosynthetic activity, and total dry matter increase at an accelerated rate. Throughout the next 50–60 days the dry matter tends to accumulate rather uniformly. As maturity is approached, dry matter production drops rapidly [3, 30]. In Ohio experiments the maximum dry matter production occurred between July 26 and August 4, which coincided with the stages of tasseling, silking, and cessation of growth in height [36].

At maturity, nearly half the dry matter of the corn plant is contained in the grain, largely in the form of starch [38].

REFERENCES

1. Anderson, E., "The corn plant today." Des Moines: Pioneer Hi-Bred Corn Co. pp 1–20. 1949.
2. ———, "The sacred plume." Des Moines: Pioneer Hi-Bred Corn Co. pp 1–24. 1951.
3. Bair, R. A., "Growth rate of maize under field conditions." *Pl. Phys.*, **17**: 619–631. 1942.
4. Basile, R. W., "Drought in relation to corn yield in the northwestern corner of the Corn Belt." *Agron. J.*, **46**: 4–7. 1954.
5. Bauman, L. F., "Relative yields of first (apical) and second ears of semi-prolific southern corn hybrids." *Agron. J.*, **52**: 220–222. 1960.
6. Bonnett, O. T., "Development of the staminate and pistillate inflorescences of sweet corn." *J. Ag. Res.*, **60**(1): 25–38. 1940.
7. ———, "Ear and tassel development in maize." Mo. Bot. Garden *Ann.*, **35**: 269–287. 1948.
8. ———, "Developmental morphology of the vegetative and floral shoots of maize." Ill. Ag. Exp. Sta. *Bul. 568*. 1953.
9. Brigham, R. O., "Assimilation of organic nitrogen by *Zea mays* and the influence of *Bacillus subtilis* on such assimilation." *Soil Sci.*, **3**: 155–195. 1917.
10. Denmead, O. T., and R. H. Shaw, "Evapotranspiration in relation to the development of the corn crop." *Agron. J.*, **51**: 725–726. 1959.
11. ———, and R. H. Shaw, "The effects of soil moisture stress at different stages of growth on the development and yield of corn." *Agron. J.*, **52**: 272–274. 1960.
12. Erwin, A. T., "The origin and history of pop corn, *Zea mays* L. var. *indurata* (Sturt.) Bailey, mut. *everta* (Sturt.) Erwin." *Agron. J.*, **41**: 53–56. 1949.

13. Gingrich, J. R., and M. B. Russell, "Effect of soil moisture tension and oxygen concentration on the growth of corn roots." *Agron. J.*, **48**: 517–520. 1956.

14. Goodsell, S. F., G. Huey, and R. Royce, "The effect of moisture and temperature during storage on cold test reaction of *Zea mays* seed stored in the air, carbon dioxide, or nitrogen." *Agron. J.*, **47**: 61–64. 1955.

15. Harrold, L. J., *et al.*, "Transpiration evaluation of corn grown on a plastic covered lysimeter." Soil Sci. Soc. Amer. *Proc.*, **23**: 174–178. 1959.

16. Hector, J. M., *Introduction to the Botany of Field Crops*, Vol. I, *Cereals*. Johannesberg, S. Africa: Central News Agency, Ltd. pp 392–478. 1936.

17. Holt, R. F., and C. A. Van Doren, "Water utilization of field corn in western Minnesota." *Agron. J.*, **53**: 43–45. 1961.

18. Jenkins, M. T., "Corn improvement," in USDA Yrbk. of Ag., pp 455–495. 1936.

19. ———, "Influence of climate and weather on growth of corn," in *Climate and Man*. USDA Yrbk. of Ag. pp 308–320. 1941.

20. Jenne, E. A., *et al.*, "Change in nutrient element accumulation by corn with depletion of soil moisture." *Agron. J.*, **50**: 71–74. 1958.

21. Kiesselbach, T. A., "Transpiration as a factor in crop production." Nebr. Ag. Exp. Sta. *Res. Bul. 6.* 1916.

22. ———, "Corn investigations." Nebr. Ag. Exp. Sta. *Res. Bul. 20.* 1922.

23. ———, "The structure and reproduction of corn." Nebr. Ag. Exp. Sta. *Res. Bul. 161.* 1949.

24. ———, "Progressive development and seasonal variations of the corn crop." Nebr. Ag. Exp. Sta. *Res. Bul. 166.* 1950.

25. Letey, J., and D. B. Peters, "Influence of soil moisture levels and seasonal weather on efficiency of water use by corn." *Agron. J.*, **49**: 362–365. 1957.

26. Loomis, W. E., "The translocation of carbohydrates in maize." Contrib. Ia. Corn Res. Inst., **1**(1): 101–112. 1935.

27. Miller, E. C., "Development of the pistillate spikelet and fertilization in maize." *J. Ag. Res.*, **18**: 225–266. 1919.

28. Morris, V. H., and J. D. Sayre, "Solubility of potassium in corn tissues." *Pl. Phys.*, **10**: 565–568. 1935.

29. Moss, D. N., R. B. Musgrave, and E. R. Lemon, "Photosynthesis under field conditions. III: Some effects of light, carbon dioxide, temperature, and soil moisture on photosynthesis, respiration, and transpiration of corn." *Crop Sci.*, **1**: 83–87. 1961.

30. Nelson, L. B., "The mineral nutrition of corn as related to its growth and culture," in *Advances in Agronomy*, Vol. VIII. New York: Academic Press. pp 321–375. 1956.

31. Randolph, L. F., "Developmental morphology of the caryopsis of maize." *J. Ag. Res.*, **53**: 881–916. 1936.

32. Robertson, D. W., A. M. Lute, and H. Kroeger, "Germination of 20-year-old wheat, oats, barley, corn, rye, sorghum, and soybeans." *J. Am. Soc. Agron.*, **35**: 786–795. 1943.

33. Russell, M. B., and R. E. Danielson, "Time and depth patterns of water use by corn." *Agron. J.*, **48**: 163–165. 1956.

34. Sass, J. E., "Vegetative morphology," in *Corn and Corn Improvement*. New York: Academic Press. pp 63–87. 1955.

35. ———, and F. A. Loeffel, "Development of axillary buds in relation to barrenness." *Agron. J.*, **51**: 484–486. 1959.

36. Sayre, J. D., "Mineral accumulation in corn." *Pl. Phys.*, **23**: 267–281. 1948.
37. ———, "Accumulation of radioisotopes in corn leaves." Ohio Ag. Exp. Sta. *Res. Bul. 723*. 1952.
38. ———, "Mineral nutrition of corn," in *Corn and Corn Improvement*. New York: Academic Press. pp 293–314. 1955.
39. Verduin, J., and W. E. Loomis, "Absorption of carbon dioxide by maize." *Pl. Phys.*, **19**: 278–293. 1944.
40. Viets, F. G., A. L. Moson, and M. I. Whitehead, "Nitrogen metabolism of corn (*Zea mays*) as influenced by ammonium nutrition." *Pl. Phys.*, **21**: 271–289. 1946.
41. Wallace, H. A., and E. N. Bressman, *Corn and corn growing*, 5th ed. New York: Wiley. pp 1–424. 1949.
42. Weatherwax, P., "The development of the spikelets of *Zea mays*." Torr. Bot. Club, *Bul.*, **43**: 483–496. 1917.
43. ———, "The evolution of maize." Torr. Bot. Club Bul., **45**: 309–342. 1918.
44. ———, "Gametogenesis and fecundation in *Zea mays* as the basis of xenia and heredity of the endosperm." Torr. Bot. Club Bul., **46**: 73–90. 1919.
45. ———, *The story of the maize plant*. Chicago: U. of Chicago Press. pp 99–114. 1923.
46. ———, "The endosperm of *Zea* and *Coix*." *Am. J. Bot.*, **17**: 371–380. 1930.
47. ———, "The phylogeny of *Zea mays*." *Am. Mid. Nat.*, **16**(1): 1–71. 1935.
48. ———, *Indian corn in Old America*. New York: Macmillan. pp 1–253. 1954.
49. ———, "Structure and development of reproductive organs," in *Corn and Corn Improvement*. New York: Academic Press. pp 89–121. 1955.
50. Weihing, R. M., "The comparative root development of regional types of corn." *J. Am. Soc. Agron.*, **27**: 526–537. 1935.
51. Wellhausen, E. J., L. M. Roberts, and L. W. Leng, "Relation between tassel condensation and ear row number in maize." *Agron. J.*, **46**: 284–286. 1954.
52. Whitehead, E. I., F. G. Viets, and A. L. Hexon, "Nitrogen distribution in the corn plant." S. Dak. Ag. Exp. Sta. *Bul. 7*. 1948.

Corn

7. CULTURAL PRACTICES

CROP ROTATIONS

In order to maintain corn yields, corn usually is grown in rotation with other crops. A good rotation that includes legumes and grasses contributes to improved soil structure. Corn rotations usually include a small grain, and a legume or legume-grass mixture as a sod crop. Few rotations provide for more than two successive corn crops.

In the Corn Belt, corn generally fits well into rotations with such crops as small grains, soybeans, and sod crops. Corn usually follows a legume or legume-grass mixture. Deep-rooted legumes such as alfalfa, sweetclover, and sericea lespedeza are particularly effective in rotations with corn. Spring oats often are grown after corn, especially in the northwestern part of the Corn Belt. A common four-year rotation is corn, corn, oats, and clover (red clover or sweetclover). Second-year corn should receive a substantial application of manure, commercial fertilizer, or both. Soybeans also may be substituted for one of the corn crops. A two-year rotation sometimes grown is corn, and oats seeded with sweetclover. The sweetclover is plowed under for green manure. In some areas, a popular three-year rotation is corn, winter wheat, and mixed hay. Rotations may be extended two years or more to include alfalfa—where it can be grown—instead of clover [68, 61]. The alfalfa may be grown in a mixture with brome grass. Sweetclover is being grown less extensively because of sweetclover weevil damage. The present trend in the Corn Belt is to grow corn continuously, with heavy applications of nitrogen fertilizer to replace that which would have been supplied by a legume grown in rotation. The corn stalk residues from a high-yielding crop supply an abundance of organic matter to the soil.

In the Southern states, corn ranks second only to cotton in acreage. Since these two crops do not supplement each other well, it is advisable to grow soybeans with corn, followed by some fall-seeded crop such as rye or winter peas to be turned under for green manure as a preparation for cotton

[40]. Yields of continuous corn at the Arkansas Station over a 12-year period averaged 19.6 bushels per acre; corn in a three-year rotation (corn-oats-red clover) averaged 28.7 bushels [3]. A Kentucky experiment conducted over a 27-year period included various legumes in a three-year rotation of a legume, corn, and wheat. Yields of corn and wheat were much lower after soybeans than after clovers and lespedeza. Except for a decrease where soybeans were grown for hay, soil nitrogen was maintained at or near the original level [10]. Corn in the South is sometimes rotated with grasses or grass-legume mixtures which remain on the land 2–5 years or more [61].

In the Western states, most rotations in the irrigated areas include a small grain, alfalfa for 2–4 years, and a cultivated crop such as corn, sugar beets, or potatoes. Under dryland conditions, alternate corn and wheat crops are a widely used sequence, particularly in regions where the annual precipitation is 18 inches or more. Occasionally, barley or oats may be used instead of wheat. Corn usually shows a relatively small response to the extra moisture provided by fallow.

MANURES

Any barnyard manure available usually is applied to land to be planted to corn. Manures vary widely in chemical composition, but usually consist of 50–70 per cent water as hauled to the field. In this condition, one ton of manure ordinarily contains fertilizer constituents equivalent to that of 100 pounds of a 10–5–10 commercial fertilizer. Additional fertilizer values come from some of the minor elements as well as from the organic matter in the manure [61]. Phosphorus fertilizers should often be used to supplement the manure to provide the mineral balance needed for maximum yields.

Commonly, manure is applied at rates of 8–12 tons per acre. In Ohio, 8 tons of manure increased the yield of corn about 12 bushels an acre on land that produced 30 bushels without manure [48]. In an Iowa experiment, 8 tons of manure were applied on clover sod that preceded two crops of corn in a four-year rotation of corn, corn, oats, and clover. A similar set of plots received no manure during the 24-year period, 1915–38 (inclusive). The average increased yield from the plots to which manure had been applied was 11.8 bushels per acre (21.1 per cent) for the first corn crop, and 9.7 bushels (19.1 per cent) for the second [66].

Corn will respond to large applications of manure so long as the soil is moist enough to promote decay of the manure as well as to maintain the heavier plant growth that results from the heavy manuring. Manure may be applied in the fall or spring, except on sandy land where spring applications are preferable to avoid undue losses from leaching [40].

COMMERCIAL FERTILIZERS

Even productive soils cropped for a generation or more usually require the addition of chemical nutrients in order to produce corn crops of 80 or more bushels per acre. Nutrients most often deficient are nitrogen, phosphorus, and potassium. A corn crop of 100 bushels per acre usually removes from each acre of soil about 160 pounds of nitrogen (N), 50 pounds of phosphoric oxide (P_2O_5), and 80 pounds of potash (K_2O). Appreciable quantities of calcium, magnesium, and sulfur also are removed, but these nutrients are usually sufficient in well-limed soils in the Corn Belt [61].

Effects of Fertilizer Applications

Frequently, 50 per cent or more of the nitrogen required by the corn crop must be supplied through fertilizers. Common nitrogen fertilizers include ammonium sulfate, ammonium nitrate, ammonium phosphate, ammonia, calcium cyanamid, and urea. The need for nitrogen is greatest on sandy, eroded soils low in organic matter. Nitrogen deficiencies also are likely to occur under cropping systems that involve few legumes, limited applications of manure, and second-year corn [37]. Corn response to nitrogen fertilizer (Fig. 7-1) is greater with ample moisture than under drier conditions [61].

In a North Carolina experiment, average corn yields over a nine-year period were 26, 54, 74, 85, and 91 bushels per acre for 0, 40, 80, 120, and 160 pounds of nitrogen per acre, respectively. Corn yields were increased about one bushel for each two pounds of nitrogen applied [29]. Corn also

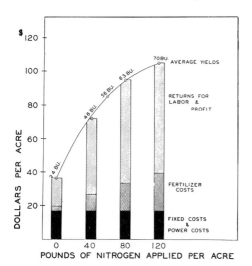

FIGURE 7-1. **Typical response of corn to nitrogen on soils of medium-low fertility. Average of 25 experiments.**

(*Courtesy US Department of Agriculture*)

has shown large yield responses to heavy nitrogen fertilizer applications on highly productive irrigated soils in the State of Washington. The average yield of 18 hybrids grown in thick stands (17,400 plants per acre) were 43, 110, and 136 bushels per acre when 0, 90, and 148 pounds of nitrogen per acre, respectively, were applied [64]. In the irrigated Republican Valley of Nebraska, applications of 80–120 pounds of nitrogen per acre usually were needed for maximum yields [39]. In Iowa, applications of 40–100 pounds of nitrogen increased corn yields after a grass sod, whereas 20–60 pounds were generally effective on second-year corn. There was little or no response to nitrogen on corn the first year after a legume [12].

Phosphorus usually is applied to corn in the form of superphosphate. Most fertilizer formulas for this crop specify a fairly large percentage of phosphorus (as P_2O_5), such as 2–12–6, 3–18–9, or 3–12–12 at planting time [66]. This then is supplemented with side dressings of nitrogen after the corn is growing. On a phosphorus-deficient soil in Arkansas, corn in a three-year rotation (small grain, legume, corn) yielded 14.7 bushels per acre, whereas corn in the same rotation plus 100 pounds of superphosphate (20 per cent P_2O_5) per acre yielded 30.1 bushels [3].

Potash fertilizer usually is applied in the form of either potassium chloride (muriate of potash) or potassium sulfate. Corn response to potassium fertilizer is practically nonexistent in the subhumid or in the arid regions of the Western states. However, potassium deficiencies are widespread throughout much of the humid region in the Eastern states, particularly on sandy soils [37]. Corn on muck and peat soils usually benefits from potash applications. A deficiency may be suspected on land that has been tile-drained for corn production. Corn Belt soils high in lime also are likely to be deficient [66].

Nutrient Deficiency Symptoms

The leaves of well-fertilized corn remain green until the crop is practically mature. The lower leaves are first to show certain deficiency symptoms. Potassium deficiency is indicated by early dying along the leaf edges toward the tip. Phosphorus deficiency is indicated by the purpling of the leaves of young corn plants, which usually is accompanied by slow growth. Yellowing and dying along the midribs of the leaves in a widening band toward the tips is typical of serious nitrogen deficiency. Nitrogen hunger in young plants is shown by an anemic yellow-green color of all leaves [61].

Deficiency symptoms of many minor elements also have been described [18]. Zinc deficiencies of irrigated corn have been observed on exposed subsoils after the removal of the surface soil to facilitate gravity irrigation. The most common zinc deficiency symptom of corn is light interveinal chlorosis of the older leaves, which rapidly develops into a broad bleached stripe.

FIGURE 7-2. **Planting corn on ridges while side-banding fertilizers (from white hoppers).**
(*Courtesy J. I. Case Company*)

Applications of zinc sulfate or manure will remedy the zinc deficiency [65, 17].

Fertilizer Practices

Corn fertilizer practices vary in different parts of the country. In the Northern states, a widespread practice is to apply 100–200 pounds of a low-nitrogen mixed fertilizer, such as 3–12–12 or 3–18–9, in bands near the seed at planting time. A separate application of 40–80 pounds of nitrogen is made either before or after planting. In the Southern states, from 200–600 pounds per acre of a mixed fertilizer often is broadcast to be plowed under or otherwise incorporated in the soil before the corn is planted. A 12–12–12 grade may be used where manure is in short supply. A supplemental nitrogen application usually is made after the plants begin active growth. In the Western states, nitrogen often is the only nutrient applied [37].

The placement of comparatively small amounts of fertilizer in bands along the row near the seed during planting is a widespread practice. It places the nutrients within the early absorptive range of the roots [35], but also limits the binding of phosphorus by clays in the soil. The bands of fertilizers are best placed from 1.5–2 inches to the side and 1–2 inches deeper than the seed (Fig. 7-2). When placed too near the seed, the soluble salts may delay germination or reduce stands. Potash and nitrogen are especially injurious when applied heavily too near the seed. There is also more danger to the corn when the soil is dry than when it is moist [57, 61].

A heavy application of nitrogen before or during planting may be lost by leaching, or cause excessive early vegetative growth. Application of nitrogen as a side dressing at the second or third cultivation generally has increased yields over those obtained from applications only at planting time. This practice makes nitrogen available when large amounts are needed: at the critical fruiting stage of corn development [41, 4]. Results in North Carolina indicate that a single side-dressed application when corn was two feet high was better than pretassel applications and as good as any of the split applications [29]. However, some irrigated corn that received 120 pounds of nitrogen per acre as ammonium nitrate produced about the same yields when the fertilizer was broadcast and plowed under as from side-dressed or split applications [36]. When ammonium nitrate was applied with the seed, marked reductions in plant populations occurred on highly calcareous soils in Texas [8].

Soluble phosphates usually are applied as a part of the localized application when the corn is planted. Where moisture in the surface soil is limited, phosphorus is sometimes applied deeper in the soil. Insoluble phosphates usually are applied ahead of alfalfa or clovers in the rotation.

Applications of potassium usually are made as a part of the hill or row fertilizer at planting time, applied broadcast or banded at deeper layers in the soil before corn is planted, or side-dressed while corn is growing. High concentrations of chloride in row applications of potassium chloride fertilizer depress plant growth, delay maturity, and decrease yields [71].

Effects on Different Plant Populations

The rate of planting generally has little influence on corn grain yields at low levels of soil fertility, but successively higher rates of planting—up to 16–18 thousand plants per acre for single-ear hybrids—are needed to obtain the maximum response from increased fertility levels. The maximum rate of planting for multiple-ear (prolific) hybrids with increased fertility is around 10–12 thousand plants per acre. Under dryland conditions on the Great Plains, where soil moisture is limited, maximum populations are about 8 thousand plants per acre for single-ear hybrids [37].

In Pennsylvania, the highest yield was obtained with 11 thousand plants per acre when 150 pounds of a 10–10–10 fertilizer was applied at planting time. When the population was increased to 16 thousand plants per acre, the yield was substantially increased with a broadcast application of 600 pounds of the same fertilizer [49]. At four soil fertility levels in Ohio, maximum yields were obtained with progressively higher planting rates with increased fertility [58].

In North Carolina, optimum stands for prolific hybrids appeared to be 4, 7, and 10–13 thousand plants per acre for low, medium, and adequate nitrogen levels, respectively. The nitrogen applications for the three levels were 20, 70, and 120 to 170 pounds per acre, respectively [29]. In Alabama, 12 thousand corn plants per acre produced higher average yields than did either 6 or 18 thousand plants, for nitrogen fertilizer applications that ranged from 0–160 pounds per acre. There was little or no increase in grain yield from applications of more than 40 pounds of nitrogen per acre for any plant population [63]. For high yields of a Texas hybrid, a soil nutrient balance had to be maintained along with at least 10 thousand plants per acre. Lodging was increased by nitrogen fertilization, but decreased by potassium [15].

SEEDBED PREPARATION

A seedbed suitable for efficient corn production must be sufficiently mellow for seed germination. It may also need to be protected from erosion hazards.

Plowing

The moldboard plow is still the most widely used implement for corn seedbed preparation on comparatively level land east of the 30-inch rainfall line [57], and on irrigated lands. In drier regions, the one-way plow, Noble blade, lister, and other implements are generally used.

The best time for plowing depends upon the local conditions. Some clay soils become mellow only when plowed in the fall; some injurious insects can be partly controlled by fall plowing. However, fall plowing is inadvisable on land subject to winter erosion, and on silt loam soils subject to winter compaction [61]. In the Corn Belt, and on irrigated lands in the Western states, fields that have been in clover, alfalfa, or pasture, usually are plowed in the fall so that the sod will be partly broken down during the winter months [40]. In an experiment with corn following wheat at the Nebraska Station, early spring-plowed land produced 5 per cent more corn than late spring-plowed land, and 18 per cent more than fall-plowed land [27]. Similar results were obtained in Missouri [24]. Spring plowing is practiced in the Southern states to avoid water erosion, as well as to permit the growing of a winter cover crop. In the Great Plains, the yield of corn after small grain stubble may be slightly higher from spring plowing than from fall plowing.

When growing corn after corn in the Great Plains, it may be necessary to blank-list in the fall to roughen the soil surface as protection against wind erosion.

Land for corn usually is plowed deep enough (6–8 inches) to turn under crop residues, plant growth, and manures [67]. In Nebraska, plowing early in the spring to depths of 4.0, 5.5, 7.0, and 10.0 inches for surface-planted corn yielded 11-year averages, respectively, 30.5, 31.5, 33.3, and 33.5 bushels per acre. Plowing deeper than 7 inches was regarded as impractical [27]. There has been little or no benefit in corn yields from subsoiling 12–24 inches deep in the North Central states, where soils regularly freeze to a considerable depth [31]. Results from subsoiling on the Great Plains also have been negative. Occasional benefits have been reported in the South, Southwest, and West, where little or no freezing occurs.

Final Preparation

Final preparation of the seedbed for planting corn usually is accomplished with combinations of the disc, spiketooth harrow, springtooth harrow, cultipacker, and rotary hoe. Seedbeds should be fine and loose, and deep enough to provide good contact between the seed and moist soil. There is no advantage in working plowed land more than necessary to obtain a good stand. A slightly lumpy surface is superior to a fine powdery surface because it reduces runoff as well as soil losses [61, 67].

In the drier areas, final preparation of the seedbed may begin as much as 3–4 weeks before planting. The implements may be the one-way disc plow, the field cultivator, or the lister ridge buster. The land may be tilled again just before planting to kill newly germinated weeds.

In the humid areas, where plowing often is delayed by wet soils, seedbed preparation usually follows soon thereafter. The disk and the springtooth harrow followed by the spiketooth harrow and sometimes by the cultipacker are the commonly used implements.

Plowed soil often is overworked, which results in the destruction of tilth by compaction, chiefly from the tractor wheels. A minimum of tillage is most desirable, provided that weeds are properly controlled and the seed placed under conditions suitable for quick germination.

Mulch Tillage

Stubble-mulch tillage leaves most of the surface residues above ground as the soil is being prepared for a seedbed. This method is used to some extent in dry regions, particularly in the Great Plains, to protect the soil surface from wind and water erosion. The method is especially effective on porous soils or on sloping land. The tillage may be accomplished with a one-way disc followed by a rod weeder, or by a field cultivator with V-shaped blades drawn a few inches below the soil surface; thus the soil is loosened but not turned over. Special furrow openers have been devised so that corn can be planted through the residues. In Nebraska, yields of corn during three dry years were 60 per cent higher on stubble-mulched land than where all residues were plowed under. There was a slight decrease in yield on mulched land during three wet years [11].

In the more humid areas, crop residues left in the surface 3 inches of soil on corn land greatly reduced erosion losses. In Ohio, plowed land on a 15 per cent slope lost 16 tons of soil per acre, compared with only 0.2 tons for mulch-tilled land [61]. In the Corn Belt, unfortunately, stubble-mulch tillage has failed to produce corn yields equal to those on plowed land. In Ohio, corn grown on mulch-tilled soil averaged approximately 4 bushels per acre less than that on conventionally plowed land [5].

An alternative to stubble-mulch tillage in the humid areas is a manure mulch applied to the corn field at the rate of 6–8 tons per acre after the plants are 10–15 inches tall. In Ohio experiments, significantly higher corn yields were obtained on manure-mulched land than on land where the same quantity of manure was plowed under. Moreover, the average loss of runoff water on 10–12 per cent slopes was 4.1 inches on nonmulched soil and 1.8 inches on manure-mulched soil. Erosion was reduced from 12.2 tons to 0.5 ton per acre by the manure mulch [5, 57].

PLANTING PRACTICES

Corn planting practices have changed markedly since 1940 because of the widespread use of hybrids, commercial fertilizers, and modern tractor-drawn machinery. Planting rates are higher, the rows are closer together, drill planting is replacing hill planting, fertilizer placement often accompanies planting, and herbicides often are applied during or immediately after planting.

Time of Planting

Commercial field corn planting in the United States (Fig. 7-3) begins in late January in the extreme South and progresses northward at an average rate of 13 miles per day. Planting ends in early June in the extreme North [57]. Corn is usually planted 10–14 days after the average date of the last killing frost. It may be planted earlier in warm dry weather, but later in cold wet weather. The daytime temperature of the soil in which the seed is placed should be 60°F or higher. Over a 20-year period at the Ohio Station, the highest yields were obtained by planting between May 7–12. Plantings delayed one, two, and three weeks resulted in yield reductions of 2, 7, and 14 bushels per acre, respectively [61].

Corn kernels planted abnormally early in Wisconsin, and thus exposed

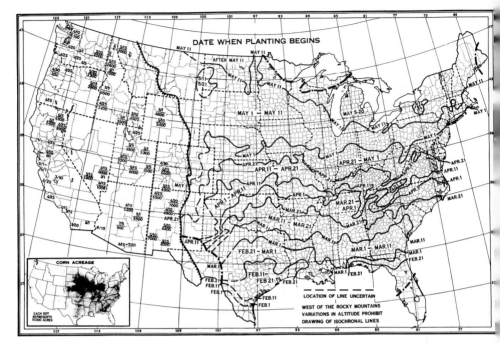

FIGURE 7-3. **Dates for planting corn in the United States.**

(Courtesy US Department of Agriculture)

to temperatures of 46°–54°F, are predisposed to attack by various soil organisms, particularly *Pythium* species [46]. In northern Colorado, corn planted in cold wet soil on April 20 usually emerged about the same time as that planted on May 1 [32].

Planting dates apparently are less critical in the Southern states. In Louisiana, the differences in yield for corn plantings made between February 25 and May 15 were not significant, but plantings made in June or July consistently produced lower yields. The data indicated that corn should be planted in April, which was early enough to produce maximum yields but late enough to avoid maximum infestations of the Southern corn root worm [23].

Rate of Planting

Corn planting rates are much heavier in the Corn Belt than formerly [13]. Before the widespread use of adapted hybrids together with heavy nitrogen application, it was customary to plant three seeds per hill in hills 3.5 feet apart, or roughly 10,666 seeds per acre. A good stand from such a rate was about 9000 plants per acre. In Ohio, optimum stands for adapted

After the final cultivation of corn, a lay-by spray application from drop nozzles may be directed at the ground for the destruction of late-season weeds. The spray should be directed so as to affect only the lower 12 inches of the corn stalks [44]. Applications of 1–2 pounds of 2,4-D usually are recommended for maximum weed control with a minimum of injury to the corn crop [61].

Among the cereals, corn seems to be the most sensitive to injury by 2,4-D as postemergence sprays, but it is the least injured by preemergence treatments because the seeds are planted deeper. Excessive application causes serious damage to corn, particularly at the tasseling and silking stage. Results of experiments also indicate that applications of 2,4-D to the foliage of corn in early growth stages (6–8 leaves) may reduce yields [51, 45].

IRRIGATION

Corn produces high yields under irrigation in regions of low rainfall in the Western states. Adequate moisture to prevent wilting of the corn plant is essential throughout the growing season. The amount of water used in a season is ordinarily 16–25 inches [43]. Corn makes its maximum demand

FIGURE 7-7. **The two tanks contain a liquid herbicide which is applied behind the planter.**
(*Courtesy J. I. Case Company*)

for moisture during the silking and tasseling period. In Washington, soil moisture depletion to the wilting point for periods of 1–2 days at the tasseling stage resulted in a yield reduction of as much as 22 per cent, while such deficits for 6–8 days at this stage reduced yields about 50 per cent. Later irrigations failed to make up these losses [42].

Frequency of irrigation depends primarily on the moisture retentiveness of the soil. In western Nebraska, three irrigations applied to corn during the period from just before tasseling through silking produced 119 bushels per acre. Stands of 17–19 thousand plants per acre in conjunction with 80–120 pounds of nitrogen were regarded as essential for high corn yields [39]. A preplanting irrigation is sometimes necessary, but the added soil moisture may reduce irrigation necessary during the period of heavy water usage when irrigation capacity may be limited. In Colorado, two irrigations usually are sufficient to produce a corn crop, although three may be necessary on the more sandy soils [30]. In Oregon, 11–15 irrigations were required to produce yields of 107–132 bushels per acre on a shallow sandy loam soil with heavy nitrogen fertilization [31].

Corn in the Western states usually is irrigated by the furrow method, that is, in the cultivator furrows between the rows (Fig. 7-8). The length of run for efficient irrigation is estimated at 125 feet for sandy soils to 850

FIGURE 7-8. **Irrigation of corn rows by the use of syphon tubes.**

(Courtesy US Department of Agriculture)

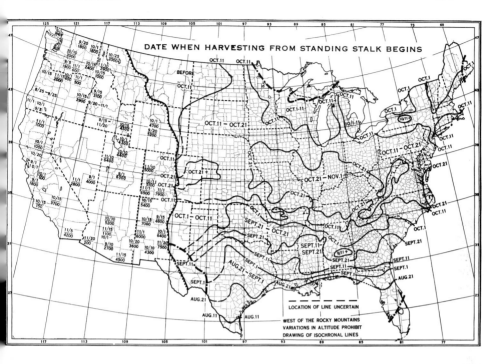

FIGURE 7-9. **Dates for harvesting corn for crib storage without artificial drying.**

(*Courtesy US Department of Agriculture*)

feet for heavy clay soils [16]. Sprinkler irrigation may be preferable on slopes steeper than 2 per cent.

Supplemental irrigation of corn has become more common in the humid Eastern states where drought occurs occasionally during the growing season. It often is applied between the tasseling and early dent stages. The sprinkler method is widely used on deep sandy soils of high water intake rate, on hilly land, and on steep slopes. The furrow method is adaptable to slopes of less than 0.5 per cent, or where the rows are laid out on the contour. High yields are possible with about 15 thousand plants per acre along with 100–150 pounds of nitrogen fertilizer, provided phosphorous and potash in the soil also are adequate [21].

HARVEST

Corn is harvested for grain, silage, and occasionally as fodder. About 4 per cent of the crop is consumed in the field by livestock.

Grain

Ear corn at maturity contains approximately 38 per cent of moisture while the grain contains about 34 per cent, the difference being due to a 20 per cent higher moisture content of the cobs. Such corn is unsafe for crib storage until the kernel moisture has declined to about 20 per cent, or unless the crop is artificially dried [53] (Fig. 7-9).

About 78 per cent of the American acreage of corn for grain was harvested by mechanical pickers in 1956 [54]. Mechanical harvesting has increased since that year. Extensive use of pickers resulted from farm labor shortages, high wages, and the development of corn hybrids which usually have much stronger stalks than do the old open-pollinated varieties. A mechanical harvester requires about 2.5 man-hours to harvest an acre, compared with about 9 hours for hand harvest [50]. Both one-row and two-row pickers are used, while corn combines may gather four rows at a time. The picker-husker snaps the ears from the standing stalks, removes most of the husks, and delivers the ears to a wagon or truck (Fig. 7-10).

In Nebraska experiments, the mechanical picker operated most efficiently at a kernel moisture content of 22–24 per cent, or above the limit of moisture for corn to be cribbed safely. Prolonged delay in harvest after the 17–20 per cent moisture stage subjects the corn to excessive ear droppage, stalk breakage, and shellage by the picker [53]. The losses by shellage were less than 2 per cent at a kernel moisture content of 22 per

FIGURE 7-10. **Two-row tractor-mounted corn picker harvesting and husking corn.**
(Courtesy Allis-Chalmers Mfg. Co.)

cent, ranged from 2–6 per cent when the kernel moisture was reduced to 15–17 per cent, and the loss was 9–13 per cent when the corn stood in the field until the kernel moisture was down to 14–15 per cent [61]. Texas experiments indicate an average machine efficiency for successive harvest dates as follows: August 97.1 per cent, September 92.4 per cent, and October 87.1 per cent. Lodged stalk percentages, the most important factor in lowering machine efficiency, were 12.1, 24.5, and 54.5 in August, September, and October, respectively [52]. In Michigan experiments, total picker losses—*i.e.,* gleaned ear corn and shelled corn—averaged 6.0, 6.9, 10.3, and 13.4 per cent of the total yield for average plant populations of 10,300, 14,900, 18,900, and 22,900 plants per acre, respectively. Lodging is more general in thick stands. In Michigan, within the recommended plant populations—*i.e.,* up to 16 thousand plants per acre—there were no significant increases in either ear or shelled corn losses as population was increased [69].

Combination picker-shellers (Fig. 7-11) or corn combines (Fig. 3-26 and 7-12) are the latest machines for corn harvest. They pick, husk, shell (or thresh), and deliver corn into hoppers in one operation. They will harvest grain with a moisture content of 27 per cent or less. The grain is then dried artificially [61].

Almost 20 per cent of the United States acreage of corn for grain was harvested by hand in 1956, mainly from standing stalks [56] (Fig. 3-24).

Silage

Corn for silage should be harvested when about one-fourth of the kernels have begun to dent. However, earlier harvest is advocated when the plants begin to dry because of drought or freezing [61]. Most of the crop for silage is now harvested with field silage cutters or forage harvesters (Fig. 7-13).

HYBRID CORN SEED PRODUCTION

Since the general adoption of hybrid corn in American agriculture, hybrid corn seed production has become a specialized industry largely operated by commercial firms. Both open-pedigree and closed-pedigree hybrids are produced and certified in many states. Agronomic practices for the production of hybrid corn seed are similar to those for growing corn for feed, except for certain special measures necessary to assure high quality seed [1].

FIGURE 7-11. **Two-row, tractor-mounted picker-sheller delivering the grain into a trailer.**
(*Courtesy International Harvester Company*)

FIGURE 7-12. **Two-row, self-propelled corn combine conveying the shelled grain from the grain tank to a truck.**
(*Courtesy International Harvester Company*)

Planting

Seed fields usually are isolated a minimum distance of 40 rods from other corn. The distance occasionally is modified by the use of border rows on the sides of the seed field exposed to pollen from other corn. Isolation of at least 80 rods is preferred for seed fields of yellow corn grown near white corn, sweet corn, or popcorn [1].

FIGURE 7-13. **One-row tractor-drawn field silage cutter.**
(Courtesy International Harvester Company)

Inbred lines or single crosses are grown in seed fields in alternate rows or groups of rows for the production of hybrid corn seed. In fields for the production of single-cross seed, the row ratio usually is two rows of the female or seed inbred parent to one row of the male or pollen inbred parent, or a combination of four female rows to two male rows. Double-cross seed fields generally are planted in a ratio of six or eight rows of the female single-cross parent to two rows of the male single cross (Fig. 7-14).

Detasseling Seed Fields

Prompt detasseling before pollen is shed is necessary in single-cross or

FIGURE 7-14. **Six seed parent (detasseled) rows, between paired rows of the pollen parent.**
(Courtesy US Department of Agriculture)

double-cross seed fields to assure cross-pollination for the seed grown on the female plants, unless male-sterile lines are used. All tassels are pulled from the stalks by hand. Sometimes each detasseler occupies a high seat on a motorized carrier (detasseling machine) which moves the workers over the rows while they pull out tassels. Detasseling is started as soon as the tassel has emerged, but prior to the emergence of silks on the female plants. Tassel removal for a particular field usually spreads over 5–10 days. The field is gone over daily while the tassels are emerging rapidly, but intervals of 2–3 days may suffice later in the season. State seed certification standards generally prescribe a low percentage of pollen-shedding tassels tolerated on female rows, usually a maximum of 1 per cent at any one time.

Cytoplasmic male sterility now has come into wide use as a means to eliminate the large crews of workers that are required for detasseling. A mixture of seed produced by the male-sterile and normal stocks assures pollination in the double-cross field. Often a ratio of two-thirds of the female corn rows in the double-cross seed field are planted to the male-sterile single cross, to one-third of the female corn planted to the normal single-cross that requires detasseling [1].

Seed Harvest

Commercial producers of hybrid corn seed usually begin harvest when the crop is physiologically mature—*i.e.,* when the grain contains about 35 per cent moisture. Most of the seed crop is harvested at a 25–35 per cent moisture level. In some seasons, immature corn is harvested with a moisture content of 40–45 per cent in order to avoid freezing.

Small seed fields or patches usually are hand-harvested. Most commercial hybrid corn seed fields now are harvested with mechanical corn pickers. The seed ears are then husked, sorted, and dried.

Seed Drying

It is critical in seed production to dry high-moisture ears down to a safe moisture level before seed viability is damaged by freezing temperatures, heating in storage, or fungus growths. Small lots may be dried on hangers or racks designed so that the ears do not touch each other. Many large commercial lots are dried artificially by driers that use forced drafts of heated air.

When corn seed is mature at the time of harvest, it can be dried artificially at a temperature range of 105°–110°F without loss of viability. The moisture content generally is reduced from 34–35 per cent to 12–13 per cent for safe storage [26, 9]. At high grain-moisture levels up to 50 per cent, 105°F is a safer temperature to use for drying [34].

In experiments in Nebraska, the emergence of corn seedlings from untreated artificially dried seed was lower than that from untreated naturally dried seed when the seedlings were exposed to a cold soil temperature of 41°F for 7–14 days. Prior seed treatment with Arasan eliminated the effect of soil pathogens that largely were responsible for the reduced seedling emergence [33]. Mechanical damage to kernels by commercial processing of corn seed also has been suggested as a cause for poor seedling emergence in cold wet years [70].

Seed Processing

After the seed ears are dried, they usually are shelled with a cylinder sheller. The shelled seed often is sized or mechanically sorted for size and shape of kernels. Most of the commercial hybrid corn seed is sorted mechanically into flat and round kernels of three sizes each. Medium flat kernels usually are preferred by farmers. A different corn planter plate is required for each size or shape of kernel to assure uniform seed distribution in the row.

The sized and cleaned seed usually is treated with organic fungicides that contain Thiram, Phygon, Spergon, or Captan. These fungicides are applied in dust or slurry form at rates of application that vary from 0.5–1.0 ounce of active ingredient per bushel [1]. The seed is then bagged for market.

REFERENCES

1. Airy, J. M., "Production of hybrid corn seed," in *Corn and Corn Improvement* (G. F. Sprague, ed.). New York: Academic Press. pp 379–422. 1955.
2. Andrew, R. H., "The influence of depth of planting and temperature upon stand and seedling vigor of sweet corn strains." *Agron. J.*, **45**: 32–35. 1953.
3. Bartholomew, R. P., "Increasing corn yields in Arkansas." Ark. Ag. Exp. Sta. *Bul. 473.* 1948.
4. Bennett, W. F., G. Stanford, and L. Dumenil, "Nitrogen, phosphorus, and potassium content of the corn leaf and grain as related to nitrogen fertilization and yield." Soil. Sci. Soc. Am. *Proc.*, **17**: 252–258. 1953.
5. Borst, H. L., and H. J. Mederski, "Surface mulches and mulch tillage for corn production." Ohio Ag. Exp. Sta. *Res. Bul. 796.* 1957.
6. Boswell, F. C., O. E. Anderson, and S. V. Stacey, "Some effects of irrigation, nitrogen, and plant population on corn." Ga. Ag. Exp. Sta. *Bul. N.S. 60.* 1959.
7. Brown, H. B., and H. C. Lovett, "Comparative effects of furrow, level, and ridge culture on corn production at Baton Rouge, Louisiana." La. Ag. Exp. Sta. *Bul. 302.* 1938.
8. Collier, J. W., "Effect of fertilizers applied with seed corn on plant population and yields on highly calcareous clay soils." *Agron. J.*, **46**: 118–120. 1954.
9. Dimmock, F., "The effects of immaturity and artificial drying upon the quality of seed corn." Can. Dep. Ag. Tech. *Bul. 58.* 1947.
10. Doll, E. C., and L. A. Link, "Influence of various legumes on the yields of succeeding corn and wheat and nitrogen content of the soil." *Agron. J.*, **49**: 307–309. 1957.
11. Duley, F. L., and J. C. Russel, "Stubble-mulch farming." USDA *Farmers Bul. 1997.* 1948.
12. Dumenil, L., "Nitrogen fertilizers for corn." Ia. Ag. Exp. Sta. *Bul. P114.* 1952.
13. Dungan, G. H., "Response of corn to extremely deep planting." *Agron. J.*, **42**: 256–257. 1950.
14. ———, A. L. Lang, and J. W. Pendleton, "Corn plant population in relation to soil productivity, in *Advances in Agronomy*, Vol. X. New York: Academic Press. pp 435–473. 1958.
15. Fisher, F. L., and O. E. Smith, "The influence of nutrient balance on yield and lodging of Texas hybrid corn No. 28." *Agron. J.*, **52**: 201–204. 1960.
16. Francis, C. J., and J. W. Turelle, "Irrigating corn." USDA *Farmers Bul. 2059.* 1953.
17. Grunes, D. L., *et al.*, "Zinc deficiency of corn and potatoes as related to soil and plant analyses." *Agron. J.*, **53**: 68–71. 1961.
18. Hambridge, G. (ed.), *Hunger Signs in Crops.* Washington, D.C.: Am. Soc. Agron.— Ntl. Fert. Assn. 1941.

19. *Handbook of Ohio experiments in agronomy*. Ohio Ag. Exp. Sta. Book Series *B-1*. 1951.

20. Hinkle, D. A., and J. D. Garrett, "Corn fertilizer and spacing experiments." Ark. Ag. Exp. Sta. *Bul. 635*. 1961.

21. Jamison, V. C., and O. W. Beale, "Irrigation of corn in the eastern United States." USDA *Agricultural Handbook No. 148*. 1958.

22. Jenkins, M. T., "A comparison of the surface, furrow, and listed methods of planting corn." *J. Am. Soc. Agron.*, **26**: 734–737. 1934.

23. Jones, D. M., and H. B. Brown, "Effect of date of planting on corn yields, insect infestation, and fungus diseases." La. Ag. Exp. Sta. *Bul. 327*. 1941.

24. Jones, M. M., and R. P. Beasley, "Corn tillage studies on rolling Putnam silt loam." Mo. Ag. Exp. Sta. *Bul. 475*. 1943.

25. Jordan, H. V., K. D. Laird, and D. D. Ferguson, "Growth rates and nutrient uptake by corn in a fertilizer spacing experiment." *Agron. J.*, **42**: 261–268. 1950.

26. Kiesselbach, T. A., and J. A. Ratcliffe, "Freezing injury to seed corn." Nebr. Ag. Exp. Sta. *Res. Bul. 16*. 1918.

27. ———, A. Anderson, and W. E. Lyness, "Cultural practices in corn production." Nebr. Ag. Exp. Sta. *Bul. 293*. 1935.

28. Kohnke, H., and S. R. Miles, "Rates and patterns of seeding corn on high-fertility land." *Agron. J.*, **43**: 488–493. 1951.

29. Krantz, B. A., and W. V. Chandler, "Fertilize corn for higher yields." N.C. Ag. Exp. Sta. *Bul. 366*. 1954.

30. Larson, C. A., F. S. Viets, and R. W. Leamer, "Field corn production on the Umatilla irrigation project." Ore. Ag. Exp. Sta. *Bul. 480*. 1950.

31. Larson, W. E., *et al.*, "Effect of subsoiling and deep fertilizer placement on yields of corn in Iowa and Illinois." *Agron. J.*, **52**: 185–189. 1960.

32. Leonard, W. H., J. F. Brandon, and J. J. Curtis, "Corn production in Colorado." Colo. Ag. Exp. Sta. *Bul. 463*. 1940.

33. Livingston, J. E., "Effect of low temperature on the germination of artificially dried seed corn." Nebr. Ag. Exp. Sta. *Res. Bul. 169*. 1951.

34. McRostrie, G. P., "Some factors influencing artificial drying of mature grain corn." *Agron. J.*, **41**: 425–429. 1949.

35. Millar, C. E., "Root systems of young corn plants in relation to fertilizer applications." *J. Am. Soc. Agron.*, **22**: 868–873. 1930.

36. Nelson, C. E., "Methods of applying ammonium nitrate fertilizer on field corn, and a study of the movement of NH_4 and NO_3 nitrogen on the soil under irrigation." *Agron. J.*, **45**: 154–157. 1953.

37. Nelson, L. B., "The mineral nutrition of corn as related to its growth and culture," in *Advances in Agronomy*, Vol. VIII. New York: Academic Press. pp 321–375. 1956.

38. Pumphrey, F. V., and A. F. Dreier, "Grain, silage, and plant population experiments with corn hybrids at the Scottsbluff Experiment Station." Nebr. Ag. Exp. Sta. *Bul. 449*. 1959.

39. Rhoades, H. F., *et al.*, "Fertilization and irrigation practice on newly irrigated land in the Republican Valley." Nebr. Ag. Exp. Sta. *Bul. 424*. 1954.

40. Richey, F. D., "Corn culture." USDA *Farmers Bul. 1714*. 1933.

41. Robertson, W. K., and A. J. Ohlrogge, "An evaluation of methods of side-dressing corn with nitrogen." *Agron. J.*, **44**: 170–172. 1952.

42. Robins, J. S., and C. E. Domingo, "Some effects of severe soil moisture deficits at specific growth stages in corn." *Agron. J.*, **45**: 618–621. 1953.
43. ———, and H. F. Rhoades, "Irrigation of field corn in the West." USDA *Lflt. 440*. 1958.
44. Robinson, R. G., and R. S. Dunham, "Spray placement in corn after layby." *Agron. J.*, **48**: 35–37. 1956.
45. Rossman, E. C., and D. W. Staniforth, "Effects of 2,4-D on inbred lines and a single cross of maize." *Pl. Phys.*, **24**: 60–74. 1949.
46. Rush, G. E., and N. P. Neal, "The effect of maturity and other factors on stands of corn at low temperatures." *Agron. J.*, **43**: 112–116. 1951.
47. Salmon, S. C., "Corn production in Kansas." Kans. Ag. Exp. Sta. *Bul. 238*. 1926.
48. Salter, R. M., and C. J. Schollenberger, "Farm manure," in *Soils and Men*. USDA Yrbk. of Ag. pp 445–461. 1938.
49. Seems, B. L., and L. L. Huber, "Corn planting rates, soil productivity, and yield." Pa. Ag. Exp. Sta. *Bul. 480*. 1947.
50. Shedd, C. K., E. V. Collins, and J. B. Davidson, "Labor, power, and machinery in corn production." Ia. Ag. Exp. Sta. *Bul. 365*. 1937.
51. Slife, F. W., *et al.*, "Controlling weeds in corn with 2,4-D." Ill. Ag. Exten. *Cir. 652*. 1950.
52. Smith, H. P., and J. W. Sorenson, "Mechanical harvesting of corn." Tex. Ag. Exp. Sta. *Bul. 706*. 1948.
53. Smith, C. W., W. E. Lyness, and T. A. Kiesselbach, "Factors affecting the efficiency of the mechanical corn picker." Nebr. Ag. Exp. Sta. *Bul. 394*. 1949.
54. Stickler, F. C., and H. H. Laude, "Effect of row spacing and plant population on performance of corn, grain sorghum, and forage sorghum." *Agron. J.*, **52**: 275–277. 1960.
55. Stinson, H. T., and D. N. Moss, "Some effects of shade upon corn hybrids tolerant and intolerant of dense planting." *Agron. J.*, **52**: 482–484. 1960.
56. Strickler, P. E., J. D. Ahalt, and R. S. McCauley, "Harvesting the 1956 corn crop." USDA *ARS 43-19*. 1959.
57. Stringfield, G. H., "Corn culture," in *Corn and Corn Improvement* (G. F. Sprague, ed.). New York: Academic Press. pp 343–378. 1955.
58. ———, and L. E. Thatcher, "Stands and methods of planting corn hybrids." *J. Am. Soc. Agron.*, **39**: 995–1010. 1947.
59. ———, and L. E. Thatcher, "Corn row spaces and crop sequences." *Agron. J.*, **43**: 276–281. 1951.
60. ———, and J. L. Haynes, "Wide corn-row spaces and wheat interseedings." *Agron. J.*, **51**: 390–391. 1959.
61. ———, and M. S. Anderson, "Corn production." USDA *Farmers Bul. 2073*. 1960.
62. Suggested guide for chemical control of weeds. USDA ARS *Special Report 22-27*. 1961.
63. Thomas, W., "Effect of plant population and rates of fertilizer nitrogen on average weight of ears and yield of corn in the South." *Agron. J.*, **48**: 228–230. 1956.
64. Viets, Jr., F. G., and C. E. Domingo, "Yields and nitrogen content of corn hybrids as affected by nitrogen supply." Soil Sci. Soc. Am. *Proc.*, **13**: 303–306. 1948.
65. ———, *et al.*, "Zinc deficiency in corn in central Washington." *Agron. J.*, **45**(11): 559–565. 1953.

66. Wallace, H. A., and E. N. Bressman, *Corn and corn growing*, 5th ed. New York: Wiley. pp 1–424. 1949.

67. Willard, C. J., G. S. Taylor, and W. H. Johnson, "Tillage principles in preparing land for corn." Ohio Ag. Exp. Sta. *Res. Cir. 30.* 1956.

68. Williams, C. G., and F. A. Welton, "Corn experiments." Ohio Ag. Exp. Sta. *Bul.* 282. 1915.

69. Woods, D. J., and E. C. Rossman, "Mechanical harvest of corn at different plant populations." *Agron. J.*, **48**: 394–397. 1956.

70. Wortman, L. S., and E. H. Rinke, "Seed corn injury in various stages of processing and its effect upon cold test performance." *Agron. J.*, **43**: 299–305. 1951.

71. Younts, S. E., and R. B. Musgrave, "Growth, maturity, and yield of corn as affected by chloride in potassium fertilizer." *Agron. J.*, **50**: 423–429. 1958.

Corn

8. COMPOSITION, PROCESSED PRODUCTS, AND UTILIZATION

MARKET GRADES FOR CORN

Market grades for corn have been established by the United States Department of Agriculture under the Grain Standards Act of 1916. Under these standards corn is defined as a grain that consists of 50 per cent or more of whole kernels of shelled corn of the dent or flint varieties. It may not contain more than 10 per cent of other grains for which standards have been established.

Corn Classes

Color of corn has become increasingly important because many food products are made from the grain. In the manufacture of white corn meal, or white corn grits, or toasted corn flakes, a very small percentage of non-white kernels will affect the attractiveness of the product.

Classes of corn are based entirely on color, namely, Yellow Corn, White Corn, and Mixed Corn. A slight tinge of red on otherwise yellow kernels does not affect their classification as Yellow Corn, nor does a slight tinge of light straw color or of pink kernels that are otherwise white affect their classification as White Corn. Kernels that are deep red, blue, purple, striped, or variegated in color are classified as Mixed Corn. A mixture of more than 5.0 per cent of kernels other than yellow in Yellow Corn, or a mixture of more than 2.0 per cent of kernels other than white in White Corn, cause the corn to be classified as Mixed Corn. White-capped yellow kernels are classed as Mixed Corn [35, 15, 31].

Corn Grades

Corn is graded in accordance with the respective grade requirements for the numerical grades, sample grade, and special grades when applicable. The official grades are given in Table 8-1.

TABLE 8-1. **Grade Requirements for Yellow, White, and Mixed Corn.**

Grade	Minimum Test Weight per Bushel	Moisture	Maximum Limits of Cracked Corn and Foreign Material	Damaged Kernels	
				Total	Heat-Damaged
(No.)	(Lb)	(Per cent)	(Per cent)	(Per cent)	(Per cent)
1	56	14.0	2	3	0.1
2	54	15.5	3	5	0.2
3	52	17.5	4	7	0.5
4	49	20.0	5	10	1.0
5	46	23.0	7	15	3.0

Sample Grade: Sample grade shall be corn which does not meet the requirements of any of the grades from No. 1 to No. 5, inclusive; or which contains stones; or which is musty, or sour, or heating; or which has any commercially objectionable foreign odor; or which is otherwise of distinctly low quality.

There are three special grades for corn, namely, flint corn, flint and dent corn, and weevily corn. Most of the corn in commerce is of the dent type, but some flint types are on the market. Flint corn is defined as corn of any class that consists of 95 per cent or more of corn of the flint varieties. An example of a grade designation for flint corn is "No. 1 Yellow Corn, Flint." Flint and dent corn is defined as corn of any class which consists of a mixture of the flint and dent varieties with a content of more than 5 per cent but less than 95 per cent of corn of the flint varieties. Weevily corn is corn that is infested with live weevils or other insects injurious to stored grain.

Damaged kernels of corn are those kernels or pieces of kernels which are heat-damaged, sprouted, frosted, badly ground damaged, badly weather damaged, moldy, diseased, or otherwise materially damaged. Heat-damaged kernels are those that have been materially discolored and damaged by external heat or as a result of heating caused by fermentation.

Determinations of class, damaged kernels, and heat-damaged kernels are on the basis of the grain after the removal of the broken corn and foreign material. All other determinations are made on the basis of the grain as a whole.

Determination of Soundness

Corn grain that has undergone severe heating or fermentation, or has been attacked by fungi or by certain types of bacteria, will have suffered a degree of irreparable damage. The outward evidence of such damage may be obscured, but the actual deterioration that has taken place ultimately will be manifest in the inferior quality of products derived from the processed grain [41].

When grain is graded, condition and damage are appraised by odor and by the percentage by weight of damaged kernels present in the grain. Heat damage is considered separately from other forms of damage. The damaged-kernel index of soundness is subject to several inherent weaknesses: it fails to take into consideration the degree of damage in the damaged portion; it is based on visual inspection; and it is subject to the errors of personal judgment [41].

Deterioration of the corn kernel is associated with chemical changes in several of its components. The quantities of free fatty acids, amino acids, and acid phosphates in the kernel tend to increase as deterioration progresses. Fat acidity, which increases with incipient deterioration, appears to be a reliable index of soundness in corn [41].

Drying in Relation to Grade and Use

In Nebraska experiments, mature ear corn was reduced in kernel moisture from 27 per cent or more to a safe storage value of about 14 per cent by heated air under forced draft at temperatures that ranged from 120°–240°F in 4–49 hours. The market grade of corn was unaffected by drying temperatures up to 180°F, but higher temperatures often resulted in lower grades. Nutritive value was significantly reduced by 140°F, or higher temperatures [17].

On the basis of quality as well as recovery of the starch, acceptable processing of corn was obtained when the grain had reached a temperature of 160°F during drying. The initial moisture content of the corn, harvested at 30 and 20 per cent moisture, was relatively unimportant. However, since corn oil is an important by-product, commercial processing requires the separation of a high yield of high quality oil. Corn with a dead germ is difficult to process, with the result that the subsequent yield and quality of the oil are low. Corn that had reached temperatures above 140°F during drying showed a definite decrease in viability, which lowered its quality for use in starch production [27].

CHEMICAL COMPOSITION

The chemical composition of the corn plant, or of the grain, reflects its value for feed, food, and industrial uses.

Composition of the Corn Plant

Chemical compositions of the green corn fodder, dried forage, and silage are given in Table 8-2 [12].

TABLE 8-2. **Percentage Composition of Corn Plant—Green Fodder, Dried Forage, and Silage.**

Item	Moisture	Ash	Crude Protein	Ether Extract	Crude Fiber	Nitrogen-Free Extract
Green corn fodder:						
Dent, immature	79.0	1.2	1.7	0.5	5.6	12.0
Dent, mature	73.4	1.5	2.0	0.9	6.7	15.5
Flint, immature	79.8	1.1	2.0	0.7	4.3	12.1
Flint, mature	77.1	1.1	2.1	0.8	4.3	14.6
Dried forage:						
Corn cobs	10.7	1.4	2.4	0.5	30.1	54.9
Corn fodder	11.8	5.8	7.4	2.4	23.0	49.6
Corn husks	9.8	2.9	2.9	0.7	30.7	53.0
Corn leaves	11.8	8.5	8.1	2.2	24.4	45.0
Corn stalks	11.7	4.6	4.8	1.8	32.7	44.0
Corn stover	10.7	6.1	5.7	1.5	30.3	45.7
Silage:						
Corn silage	73.8	1.7	2.1	0.8	6.3	15.3
Immature corn	79.1	1.4	1.7	0.8	6.0	11.0
Mature corn	70.9	1.4	2.4	0.9	6.9	17.5
Corn stover silage	80.7	1.8	1.8	0.6	5.6	9.5

The sucrose (cane sugar) content of corn stalks varies in different inbred lines. These differences are independent of grain yield [38].

In Iowa experiments with severely drought-injured corn, the weight per plant was only 19 per cent of that of normal plants. Failure to form starch in the vegetative organs make drought-injured or barren stalks low in feeding value. Sucrose, which is the principal storage form in the stalk, is readily lost in curing and storage. High sugar, together with high soluble nitrogen, favors heating of the stover as well as formation of a poor-quality silage [25].

Kernel Composition

The average composition of the corn kernel is approximately as follows: water, 13.5 per cent; protein, 10.0 per cent; oil, 4.0 per cent; starch 61.0 per cent; sugars, 1.4 per cent; pentosans, 6.0 per cent; crude fiber, 2.3 per cent; ash, 1.4 per cent; and other substances, 0.4 per cent. Those substances generally grouped as carbohydrates include starch, sugars, pentosans, and crude fiber. The ash includes minerals as follows: Potassium, 0.40 per cent; phosphorus, 0.43 per cent; magnesium, 0.16 per cent; sulfur, 0.14 per cent; and other minerals, 0.27 per cent.

In yellow dent corn, the pericarp constitutes about 5.5 per cent of the kernel, the tip cap 0.8 per cent, the endosperm about 82 per cent, and the germ (with scutellum included) about 11.6 per cent. The chemical composition of the component parts of the kernel on a moisture-free basis is given in Table 8-3 [9]. About 70 per cent of the protein in flint corn is in the endosperm. A concentration gradient exists from the outer to the inner layers. The aleurone layer of corn contains less of the total protein than in wheat, but the scutellum contains more [18].

TABLE 8-3. **Percentage Composition of the Component Parts of the Yellow Dent Corn Kernel.**

Chemical Analysis	Portion of Kernel			
	Endosperm	Embryo	Pericarp	Tip Cap
Protein	73.1	23.9	2.2	0.8
Oil	15.0	83.2	1.2	0.6
Sugar	28.2	70.0	1.1	0.7
Starch	98.0	1.3	0.6	0.1
Ash	18.2	78.5	2.5	0.8

The protein in the germ of the corn kernel is biologically balanced. Zein, the principal protein in the endosperm, is deficient in tryptophane and lysine, two amino acids essential in animal nutrition [20]. A linear relationship has been reported between zein content and total protein [16]. The proteins in corn, in contrast to those in wheat, are unable to form a glutenous substance. Consequently, corn breads are of the unleavened type. There appears to be little difference between frosted and normal corn in total crude protein. Soft corn is high in amide, albumen, and globulin nitrogen. It is low in glutelin, with a zein content which is variable [2].

Ordinary corn starch is composed of about 78 per cent amylopectin and 22 per cent amylose. Waxy corn is 100 per cent amylopectin [20].

Ash constitutes about 1.3 per cent of the kernel of yellow dent corn. The kernel contains about 0.018 per cent calcium, and 0.30 per cent phosphorus. The average iron content is 24.6 (range: 19.0–34.8) milligrams per kilogram, while that of manganese is 5.5 (range: 3.4–7.4) milligrams per kilogram. The grain averages 472 calories per 100 grams [8].

The percentage composition of feedstuffs made from the corn kernel is shown in Table 8-4 [12].

TABLE 8-4. **Percentage Composition of Ear-corn and Shelled Corn Feedstuffs.**

Corn Product	Mois-ture	Ash	Crude Protein	Ether Ex-tract	Crude Fiber	Nitrogen-Free Extract	Cal-cium	Phos-phorus
Corn, shelled	12.9	1.3	9.3	4.3	1.9	70.3	0.01	0.26
Corn bran	10.0	2.1	10.0	6.6	8.8	62.5	0.03	0.14
Corn chop	11.3	1.4	9.8	4.1	2.1	71.3	0.01	0.26
Corn (ear) chop	10.7	2.0	8.2	3.4	9.2	66.5	——	——
Corn-feed meal	10.8	1.9	10.5	5.3	2.9	68.6	0.04	0.38
Corn-germ meal	7.0	3.8	20.8	9.6	7.3	51.5	0.05	0.59
Corn-gluten feed	9.5	6.0	27.6	3.0	7.5	46.4	0.11	0.78
Corn-gluten meal	8.0	2.2	43.0	2.7	3.7	40.4	0.10	0.47
Corn oil meal	8.7	2.2	22.1	6.8	10.8	49.4	0.06	0.62

As the starch is being deposited in the developing grain between fertilization and maturity, there is a gradual reduction in the percentages of mineral matter, protein, and crude fiber in the grain. However, the percentage of fat increases during grain development, while the total protein per plant also is high in immature stages [21].

Vitamins in Corn Grain

The vitamin content of corn is important because of its large use as livestock feed. Corn furnishes significant quantities of Vitamin A, nicotinic acid, riboflavin, pantothenic acid, Vitamin E, and certain other nutritional factors [35]. Vitamin content of corn is given in Table 8-5 [13].

TABLE 8-5. **Average Vitamin Content of Corn.**

Vitamin	Content per Pound, mg	
	Yellow Corn	White Corn
Carotene	2.20	——
Vitamin A	1990.00	——
Thiamine	2.06	2.22
Riboflavin	0.60	0.61
Niacin	6.40	6.04
Pantothenic acid	3.36	——
Vitamin E	11.21	13.93

The endosperm and germ of yellow corn contain precursors of Vitamin A (pro-vitamin A) which are converted to vitamin A by animals. The Vitamin A potency varies with yellow kernel color. Corn with white kernels contains practically no pro-vitamin A.

The water-soluble Vitamin B complex in corn includes thiamin (Vitamin B_1), riboflavin (Vitamin B_2), biotin, pantothenic acid, pyridoxin, and nicotinic acid (niacin) [35]. However, the thiamin, riboflavin, and nicotinic acid contents are insufficient to satisfy the high requirements of most livestock. The differences in riboflavin and thiamin contents of white and yellow corn are similar, as indicated in Table 8-6 [4].

TABLE 8-6. **Average Contents of Specified B-Complex Vitamins in Corn Grain.**

Type of Corn	Riboflavin	Specified Vitamins, Milligrams per Kilogram[1]		Biotin	Pyridoxin
		Nicotinic Acid	Pantothenic Acid		
Dent, yellow					
Hybrid	0.93	25.9	4.6	0.092	6.9
Open-pollinated	1.11	15.1	3.6	0.053	5.0
Dent, white	0.97	18.6	3.5	0.075	6.8
Flint	0.75	16.3	5.1	0.074	6.3
Flour	1.03	24.5	6.4	0.097	6.9
Sweet	1.69	30.0	8.2	0.101	7.0
Popcorn	1.03	17.2	3.4	0.065	4.9

[1] USDA Northern Regional Research Laboratory.

Corn grown in widely separated areas of the United States had average contents of thiamin, riboflavin, niacin, and pantothenic acid of 4.90, 1.02, 28.08, and 6.42 milligrams per kilogram, respectively. The content of these vitamins was independent of each other and of fat content of the grain [33]. Niacin content might be correlated with protein content [33], but this seems doubtful [29], particularly since niacin is not correlated with the contents of lysine, zein, tryptophane, valine, leucine, or isoleucine, the principal amino acid components of corn protein [29].

Corn varieties or lines may differ in niacin content. Inbred lines of dent corn have ranged from 13.9–53.3 micrograms per gram (1 microgram = 0.000,001g.) in niacin content. Hybrids tend to be intermediate between their parent lines in concentration of this vitamin. The seed parent exerted more influence on niacin content than did the pollen parent [32]. In mature corn kernels, nicotinic acid content and starch content appear to be negatively correlated. Mature corn kernels with a surgery endosperm are high in niacin content [3, 37]. The average niacin content of sugary kernels was about 23 per cent higher than that of waxy kernels, while waxy kernels in turn were about 18 per cent higher in niacin than dent kernels [22]. The niacin content may be essentially equal in sugary (su_1) and starchy (Su_1) kernels in the early stages of development, but it builds up in the sugary kernels as they approach maturity [37].

FACTORS THAT AFFECT KERNEL COMPOSITION

It is generally assumed that environmental factors, as well as inherited characteristics, influence the chemical composition of corn.

Protein Content

Protein, the principal nitrogenous substance in the corn kernel, varies in content as a result of a complex interaction between genetic, environmental, and physiological factors. Many years ago, C. G. Hopkins of the Illinois Station demonstrated that the protein content could be altered by selection [19]. He began selection for high and low protein content in the Burr White variety in 1896. Ear-to-row selection was practiced for the first 28 generations, while mass selection with intrastrain controlled cross-pollination was employed for the last 22 generations. The original variety had an average protein content of 10.92 per cent in 1896. After 50 generations of selection in 1949, the average protein content of Illinois High Protein was 19.45 per cent, while that of Illinois Low Protein was 4.91 per cent. Grain yields of these selected strains were approximately 50 per cent of those of adapted hybrids [40].

Direct effects of the pollen parent on the total protein content of the corn kernel were tested by pollinating the silks of the Illinois High Protein and Illinois Low Protein strains with mixtures of pollen from white and yellow types of corn that differed in protein content. Kernels produced on the same ear but with different pollen parents were separated by sorting for endosperm color. The direct effects of pollen on protein content were so small (the greatest difference was 0.36 per cent) that they were considered to be of no practical importance [23].

Commercial hybrids differ in their relative protein and starch contents [10]. Hybrids with a high protein content are low in starch, and vice versa. Illinois Hybrid 200 averaged high in both protein and oil, but lowest in starch [7]. Genetic differences are relatively more important than stage of maturity, locational differences in weather conditions, or soil type in the determination of protein content. Hybrids high in protein tend to be high even though the protein content varies with environment [30].

Probably the two most important environmental factors that affect the protein content of a particular hybrid are the thickness of stand and the nitrogen supply in the soil. A general decrease in corn protein, observed by the feed industry, is attributed to a deficiency of available soil nitrogen, particularly when growing a high-yielding hybrid at a thick rate of planting [10]. In Colorado tests, corn drilled in 42-inch rows with 12, 9, 6, and 3 inches between single plants in the row contained 9.9, 9.4, 9.0, and 8.9 per cent protein, respectively [24]. In Missouri, an increase in plant population caused only a slight decrease in crude protein content [42]. Highest protein yields per acre in Virginia occurred with the heaviest stand (16 thousand plants per acre) and heaviest nitrogen application. Protein content was significantly higher under droughty conditions than under good growing conditions [14]. When the total nitrogen of the kernel is increased by breeding or nitrogen fertilization, all nitrogen fractions of the whole kernel usually are increased. Zein, a relatively low-quality protein, increases at the fastest rate [34].

In two-year tests in Michigan, the protein content of 8 hybrids varied from 7.44–12.88 per cent, depending upon season, location, stage of maturity, and hybrid. Soil nitrogen appeared to be the critical environmental factor affecting protein percentage. Corn was higher in protein when it followed alfalfa in a rotation than when it followed other crops. The soil nitrogen supply may be adequate for good yields but inadequate for maximum protein content. Excess nitrogen beyond that required for maximum growth may increase the protein content of the grain. Seasonal differences in weather conditions had a comparatively smaller effect on protein content than did crop sequence. In these tests there was no relationship between corn yield and the protein content of the grain [30].

Oil Content

On a per-unit of weight basis, corn oil is the most valuable major product of the corn milling industry. Only the oil in the germ is commercially extractable. Oil content is largely a characteristic of the particular hybrid, but some differences may be attributed to environment [7].

Selection at the Illinois Agricultural Experiment Station produced strains with high and low oil contents. The original variety had an oil content of 4.70 per cent in 1896. After 50 generations of selection, the mean oil content of the Illinois high oil strain was 15.36 per cent, whereas that of the low oil strain was 1.01 per cent. The high oil strain has small ears and kernels, but with relatively large germs. The low oil strain has a large ear with a low row number, and large deeply dented kernels with small germs [40]. Another investigation revealed that the genotype of the ear parent has a predominant influence on the oil content of the grain. The oil content may be increased as much as 3 per cent without loss of yield [28].

Other Constituents

Extreme differences in production practices, such as fertilizer applications or green manures, failed to produce significant differences in niacin content at reasonable corn yield levels [32]. However, heavy applications of nitrogen and phosphorus increased the thiamin, but decreased the nicotinic acid in corn kernels [11].

INDUSTRIAL PROCESSING OF CORN

About 280 million bushels, or 8–10 per cent of the annual corn grain domestic utilization in the United States goes into industrial products. Corn yields more industrial products than any other grain. While every part of the plant has commercial value, the kernels are by far the most important because of their high carbohydrate content. Wet milling, dry milling, and the distillery operations are the most important corn industries [5, 6, 26, 36].

Wet Milling

The wet millers produce starch, starch derivatives, oil, and feed from corn. Yellow corn is generally used. It can be of fairly high moisture content, when processed immediately, because the corn is steeped in water. The starch, protein, and oil-rich fractions are separated while still wet [26]. Wet milling utilizes about 150 million bushels of corn annually.

FIGURE 8-1. **Corn starch is being flushed from these starch tables after the protein has been floated off.**

(Courtesy US Department of Agriculture)

Starch is obtained from the fully softened, degermed, and finely ground shelled corn [5]. In this process, cleaned shelled corn, after being steeped in warm water from about 40–60 hours, is coarsely ground to release the germ which is separated by flotation. The remainder is more finely ground, the hulls and fibers being separated from the starch and gluten by screens. This starch-gluten mixture is then pumped to high-speed centrifugal ma-

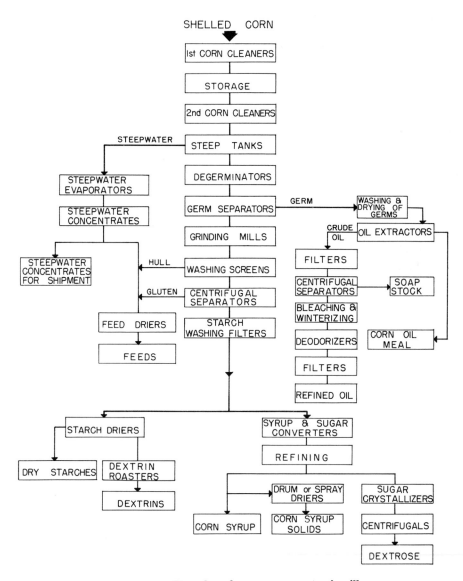

FIGURE 8-2. **Flow sheet for wet-process starch mill.**

(Courtesy Corn Industries Research Foundation, Inc.)

chines, where the relatively heavier starch is separated from the lighter gluten by centrifugal force. These machines have largely replaced the long flat-bottomed starch tables formerly used [6] (Fig. 8-1). Dried starch is sold for food, laundry, or industrial purposes. Dried starch is also processed by heat, pressure, and chemicals into various types of adhesives. Wet starch is hydrolized into syrups or sugars, chiefly dextrose (Fig. 8-2).

The by-products include oil which is extracted from the germs by pressure or solvents. Gluten feed contains proteins, corn solubles, and parts of the hull. Oil cake or oil-cake meal remain after the extraction of the oil from the germ. Zein, an alcohol-soluble protein, is used in making lacquer, as a basic plastic material, a carrier for textile colors or for printing inks, a binder of abrasives, and as a laminating glue. Corn steepwater, in which the corn is soaked prior to processing, provides a medium for the culture of fungi that produce penicillin and other antibiotics [6].

A bushel of average-quality corn with 16 per cent moisture yields by the wet process about 35 pounds of pearl starch, 1.6 pounds of oil, with the remainder as feed. About 40 pounds of syrup or 27.5 pounds of refined corn sugar (dextrose) may be obtained from the 35 pounds of starch separated from a bushel of corn.

Dry Milling

Products of dry milling are meal, grits, hominy, flour, flakes, feed, and oil. Corn meal may be made by the so-called "old process," or the "new process." Old-process meal is made by grinding the whole kernel between closely rotating stones. The germ is usually ground with the meal. New-process meal is made from degermed hulled corn kernels by the use of steel rolls, cylinders, and other modern equipment. Corn flour is the fine granules separated and bolted from the coarser meal grits or hominy after grinding. It may be as fine as wheat flour [5].

Hominy, or grits, is the coarsely ground endosperm of the corn kernel from which most of the hull and germ have been separated. Corn flakes are made by rolling grits after they have been flavored with malt, sugar, and other ingredients, and then roasting the flakes.

About two bushels of corn (56 pounds per bushel) are required to make 100 pounds of old-process meal, but nearly three bushels are necessary to make the same quantity of degermed or new-process meal. The new process yields the dry miller about 29 pounds of grits or meal, and four pounds of corn flour from each bushel of corn. About 100 million bushels annually are used in making the above products. Ground corn is used as an adjunct to barley malt in the brewing industry.

Distilling

The distillation and fermentation industries include the manufacturers

FIGURE 8-3. **The production and uses of corn on small subsistence farms of the 19th century.**

(*Courtesy US Department of Agriculture*)

of ethyl alcohol, butyl alcohol, acetone, and whiskey. About 30 million bushels annually are used in these industries. Corn is the major raw material used in the production of distilled spirits for beverage purposes in the United States, particularly whiskey [5, 26].

In the production of alcohol from corn for beverages or industrial uses, the grain is cleaned, degermed, ground into meal, and then cooked into a mash. The starch is converted into sugar by the action of diastatic enzymes present in barley malt that is added to the mash. Yeast is added to the converted mash to induce the fermentation of the sugar into alcohol and carbon dioxide. The by-product grain residue from the fermented mash is used for feed. Other by-products of the distilling industry include corn oil, corn-oil cake, corn-oil meal, fusel oil, vitamin concentrates, protein concentrates, grain germ mixtures, and alcohols other than ethyl alcohol.

Butyl alcohol and acetone are produced by bacterial fermentation of corn. The corn is first degermed, then ground to a coarse meal, cooked, inoculated with a certain bacterial culture, fermented, and finally distilled. The bacterial fermentation yields mixed solvents that consist of about 60 per cent butyl alcohol, 30 per cent acetone, and 10 per cent of ethyl alcohol. Among the by-products of this process are methanol, carbon dioxide, and livestock feed from the germs and from the processed material left after fermentation.

UTILIZATION OF CORN AND ITS PRODUCTS

Some of the uses of corn, together with former methods of corn production, are shown in Fig. 8-3. From 85–90 per cent of the acreage of corn harvested in the United States is for grain. About 8–9 per cent is cut for silage, while 3–4 per cent is used for fodder or pastured down. Nearly 140 million bushels of corn is used for food.

Livestock Feed

Nearly 90 per cent of the corn grain harvested is used directly as livestock feed; at least two-thirds is used on the farms where it is produced.

By-products of corn industries used for livestock feed include gluten feed, gluten meal, oil cake, oil meal, corn-sugar molasses, germ cake or meal, dried distillers grains, and dried brewers grains. Corn is an important ingredient in mixed manufactured feeds.

Industrial Use

Corn has numerous industrial uses. Corn stalks or leaves have been used for making paper, paperboard, and wallboard. The cobs are utilized for a cork substitute, fuel, furfural, pipe bowls, xylose, and many other products. Corn meal, flour, or grits are used in such products as adhesives, explosives, textile sizing, core binders, and soaps. Corn starch has a wide variety of uses which include asbestos, ceramics, dyes, plastics, oil cloth, and linoleum. Dextrins are used in soaps, ink, dyes, mucilage, pastes, and in many other products. Corn syrup is used in shoe polish, glassine paper, rayon, and in tobacco. Corn sugars are used in the manufacture of chemicals, leather preparations, dyes, cold process rubbers, and explosives. Corn oil is important in paint, varnish, and rubber substitutes.

Recent experiments indicate that concrete made from corn cob fragments, sand, and cement may be successfully used for farm building construction. The high moisture absorption of such concrete necessitates some method of waterproofing the wall surfaces [1].

Human Uses

The simplest and probably the first method of cooking corn was to place it on hot stones or in hot sand or ashes for parching. The corn was regarded as better when it popped during the process [39]. At present, corn usually is parched in hot oil.

There is a long list of modern human foods made from corn. These include hominy, grits, corn flakes, malt syrup, and bakery products. Corn syrup is used directly for food or in various bakery products. Corn sugar is used in numerous foods, while corn oil is used in cooking oils, oleomargarine, mayonnaise, and in lecithin. The Indians learned to make fresh hominy by soaking the grain in potash lye that was leached from wood ashes. This treatment separated the hulls from the endosperm and germ. The United States produces about 300 million pounds of popcorn annually, most of which is consumed as food.

Nonfood products that contain some corn ingredients are streptomycin, perfumes, nail-polish removers, liniments, and cosmetics.

REFERENCES

1. Boyd, J. S., and T. J. Brevik, "Use of corn cobs as a filler for concrete used in farm construction." Mich. Ag. Exp. Sta. *Quart. Bul.*, **35**:(1): 87–94. 1952.
2. Bushey, A., "Some chemical characteristics of soft corn." S.Dak. Ag. Exp. Sta. *Bul. 210.* 1924.
3. Cameron, J. W., and H. J. Teas, "The relation between nicotinic acid and carbohydrates in a series of maize endosperm genotypes." Natl. Acad. Sci. *Proc.* **34**: 390–398. 1948.
4. Conner, R. T., and G. J. Straub, "The thiamin and riboflavin contents of wheat and corn." *Cer. Chem.*, **18**: 671–677. 1941.
5. *Corn facts and figures*, 5th ed. New York: Corn Industries Research Foundation. pp 1–48. 1949.

6. *Corn in industry*, 5th ed. New York: Corn Ind. Res. Found. pp 63. 1960.

7. Curtis, J. J., and F. R. Earle, "Analyses of double-cross hybrid corn varieties produced on farms." *Cer. Chem.*, 23(1): 88–96. 1946.

8. Duncan, C. W., *et al.*, "The chemical composition and nutritive value of yellow dent corn grain. I: The iron, manganese, and gross calorie content." Mich. Ag. Exp. Sta. *Quart. Bul.*, 33(4): 351–360. 1951.

9. Earle, F. R., J. J. Curtis, and J. E. Hubbard, "Composition of the component parts of the corn kernel." *Cer. Chem.*, 23: 504–511. 1946.

10. Earley, E. B., and E. E. DeTurk, "Corn protein and soil fertility." In *What's new in the production, storage, and utilization of hybrid seed corn*, 3rd Ann. Ind. Res. Conf. Chicago: Am. Seed Trade Assn. pp 84–95. 1948.

11. ———, J. N. Carter, and B. C. Johnson, "Nicotinic acid, thiamine, and carotene content of kernels of medium and high protein corn." *Agron. J.*, 44(6): 326–328. 1952.

12. Ellis, N. R., W. R. Kauffman, and C. O. Miller, "Composition of the principal feedstuffs used for livestock," in *Food and Life*. USDA Yrbk. of Ag. pp 1065–74. 1939.

13. ———, and L. L. Madsen, "The vitamin content of animal feedstuffs." USDA Bur. An. Ind. *AHD Pub. 61*. 1943.

14. Genter, C. F., J. F. Eheart, and W. N. Linkous, "Effects of location, hybrid, fertilizer, and rate of planting on the oil and protein contents of corn grain." *Agron. J.*, 48: 63–67. 1956.

15. "Grain grading primer." USDA *Misc. Pub. No. 740*. 1957.

16. Hansen, D. W., B. Brimhall, and G. F. Sprague, "Relationship of zein to the total protein in corn." *Cer. Chem.*, 23(3): 329–335. 1946.

17. Hathaway, I. L., F. D. Yung, and T. A. Kiesselbach, "The effect of drying temperature upon the nutritive value and commercial grade of corn." *J. An. Sci.*, 11(2): 430–440. 1952.

18. Hinton, J. J. C., "The distribution of protein in the maize kernel in comparison with that in wheat." *Cer. Chem.*, 30:(5): 441–445. 1953.

19. Hopkins, C. G., "Improvement in the chemical content of the corn kernel." Ill. Ag. Exp. Sta. *Bul. 55*. 1899.

20. Jenkins, M. T., "The hybrid corn of tomorrow," in *Crops and Soils*, Vol. 1, No. 2. Madison, Wisc.: Am. Soc. of Agron. 1948.

21. Kiesselbach, T. A., "Progressive development and seasonal variations of the corn crop." Nebr. Ag. Exp. Sta. Res. *Bul. 166*. 1950.

22. Leng, E. R., J. J. Curtis, and M. C. Shekleton, "Niacin content of waxy, sugary, and dent F_2 segregating kernels in corn." *Sci.*, 111(2894): 665–666. 1950.

23. ———, F. R. Earle, and J. J. Curtis, "Direct effect of pollen parent on protein content of the corn kernel." *Cer. Chem.*, 28(6): 479–482. 1951.

24. Leonard, W. H., and A. Clark, "Protein content of corn as influenced by laboratory samples and field replication." Colo. Ag. Exp. Sta. *Tech. Bul. 19*. 1936.

25. Loomis, W. E., "The chemical composition of drouth-injured corn plants." *J. Am. Soc. Agron.*, 29(8): 697–702. 1937.

26. Majors, K. R., "Cereal grains as food and feed," in *Crops in Peace and War*. USDA Yrbk. of Ag. pp 331–340. 1950–51.

27. McMasters, M. M., *et al.*, "A study of the effect of drying conditions on the suitability for starch production of corn artificially dried after shelling." *Cer. Chem.*, 36: 247–260. 1959.

28. Miller, P. A., and B. Brimhall, "Factors influencing the oil and protein content of corn grain." *Agron. J.*, **43**(7): 305–311. 1951.

29. ———, T. L. Hurst, and B. Brimhall, "Relationships of lysine and niacin with the crude protein and certain protein components in corn grain." *Agron. J.*, **44**(7): 343–345. 1952.

30. Norden, A. J., E. C. Rossman, and E. J. Benne, "Some factors that affect protein content of corn." Mich. Ag. Exp. Sta. *Quart. Bul.*, **35**(3): 210–225. 1952.

31. "Official grain standards of the United States." USDA *SRA-AMS-177*, pp 93. 1960.

32. Richey, F. D., and R. F. Dawson, "A survey of the possibilities and methods of breeding high-niacin corn (maize)." *Pl. Phys.*, **23**: 238–254. 1948.

33. Sarkar, B. C. R., R. W. Luecke, C. F. Huffman, and C. W. Duncan, "The chemical composition and nutritive value of yellow dent corn grain. II: The thiamin, riboflavin, niacin, and pantothenic acid content." Mich. Ag. Exp. Sta. *Quart. Bul.* **33**(4): 361–371. 1951.

34. Schneider, E. O., E. B. Earley, and E. E. DeTurk, "Nitrogen fractions of the component parts of the corn kernel as affected by selection and soil nitrogen." *Agron. J.*, **44**(4): 161–169. 1952.

35. Shollenberger, J. H., and C. M. Jaeger, "Corn, its products and uses." USDA Nor. Reg. Res. Lab. *ACE-121.* 1943 (rev. 1947).

36. Sprague, G. F., "Industrial utilization," in *Corn and Corn Improvement*. New York: Academic Press. pp 613–636. 1955.

37. Teas, H. J., J. W. Cameron, and A. C. Newton, "Tryptophan, niacin, indoleacetic acid, and carbohydrates in developing sugary and starchy maize kernels." *Agron. J.*, **44**: 434–438. 1952.

38. Van Reen, R., and W. R. Singleton, "Sucrose content in stalks of maize inbreds." *Agron. J.*, **44**(12): 610–614. 1952.

39. Weatherwax, P., *Indian Corn in Old America*. New York: Macmillan. pp 253. 1954.

40. Woodworth, C. M., E. R. Leng, and R. W. Jugenheimer, "Fifty generations of selection for protein and oil in corn." *Agron. J.*, **44**(2): 60–64. 1952.

41. Zeleny, L., and D. A. Coleman, "The chemical determination of soundness in corn." USDA *Tech. Bul. 644.* 1939.

42. Zuber, M. S., G. E. Smith, and C. W. Gehrke, "Crude protein of corn grain and stover as influenced by different hybrids, plant populations and nitrogen levels." *Agron. J.*, **46**: 257–261. 1954.

Corn

9. DISEASES AND INSECT PESTS[1]

INTRODUCTION

Corn grown in the United States is subject to about 25 diseases which reduce production by many million bushels annually [63]. Foliage and ear rot diseases generally are most abundant in moist seasons. Seedling blights are most destructive at low soil temperatures. Highly productive soils produce strong plants which may resist stalk and ear rots but succumb to smuts. Hybrids differ in their ability to resist certain diseases [63, 65, 69].

Almost 400 species of insects also attack the corn plant, but only a few cause serious damage. Hybrids differ in their tolerance to insect attack.

A. Corn Diseases

SEED ROTS AND SEEDLING BLIGHTS

The organisms that cause seedling blights are carried on the seed or in the soil, and often are severe when corn is planted in cold wet soil or when cold wet weather prevails after planting. The seed may be attacked before or during germination, and the seedling attacked soon thereafter. The seeds may rot or the seedlings die before emergence. The shoots and roots of seedlings that do emerge in warm soils are usually stunted, or partly decayed [65 69, 30].

Fungi that cause ear rot and also seedling blight include *Diplodia zeae,*

[1] Helpful suggestions were made by Dr. Arnold J. Ullstrup, Department of Botany, Purdue Agricultural Experiment Station, Lafayette, Indiana, on corn diseases, and by Dr. F. F. Dicke, Federal Corn Borer Laboratory, Ankeny, Iowa, on corn insects.

219

Gibberella zeae, Fusarium moniliforme, Nigrospora oryzae, Penicillium species, and *Aspergillus* species. Diplodia seedling blight is less prevalent than the Gibberella or Fusarium seedling blights. Affected seedlings are characterized by a brown dry rot on the stem below the soil surface. Seedlings infected with *Gibberella zeae* have discolored kernel remnants, brownish areas on the subcrown internode, and yellowed leaves. When infected kernels are planted, the disease spreads to the seedling. Strictly soil-borne fungi, such as *Pythium* species, may also cause seedling blight [63, 65, 30].

Seed treatment is the most practical method of controlling seedling diseases. Mercurial compounds have been replaced largely by organic non-mercurial compounds such as Arasan, Thiram, Phygon, and Orthocide. When applied as dusts or slurries, these fungicides will generally protect the seed as well as the seedling from attack by fungi [30]. Seed treatment is particularly effective for the protection of kernels with cracked or injured seed coats [63, 65]. Seed treatment with Spergon or Arasan produced 5–10 per cent better stands and yields than did untreated seed in Arkansas [9]. Seedling diseases may be restricted by planting sound, well-matured, disease-free seed that contains a minimum of kernels with cracked or injured seed coats in warm soil. The use of resistant hybrids is another effective control [65].

ROOT, STALK, AND EAR ROT DISEASES

Some of the parasitic organisms that cause diseases on the roots, stalks, or ears of the corn plant also may cause seed rots and seedling blights.

Diplodia Rots

The Diplodia rots occur wherever corn is grown intensively, especially in the Corn Belt. They include a seedling blight, a stalk rot, and an ear rot [18, 63, 65, 68].

Diplodia stalk rot, which causes much stalk breakage in corn (Fig. 9-1) before and during the harvest season, is increased by abundant late seasonal rainfall. Affected plants suddenly show a wilted appearance similar to frost injury, followed by a brownish discoloration of the lower part of the stalk, and a softening of the tissues. As the disease progresses, the pith is destroyed so that only the vascular bundles are left within the partly hollow stalk. Plants affected as early as mid-August produce chaffy ears and stalks that usually break over before harvest [43].

Diplodia ear rot is prevalent in the principal corn-growing areas of the United States, and is found in most other countries where corn is grown. It is serious in seasons of excessive moisture. Heavy infection reduces yields and lowers the market grade. This ear rot usually develops after the kernels have reached the soft-dough stage. The first field symptom is bleached husks. The ear may be completely rotted or mummified when infection occurs early and progresses rapidly. Otherwise the kernels appear grayish-brown, usually with black fungus bodies on the grain, husks, and cobs. Ears infected somewhat later are covered with a whitish mold (Fig. 9-1),

FIGURE 9-1. (A) **Diplodia stalk rot,** (B) **Helminthosporium blight,** (C) **Diplodia ear rot, and** (D) **corn leaf rust.**

(*Courtesy US Department of Agriculture*)

whereas those infected still later appear disease-free until the ear is broken or the kernels removed. Mold then will be seen between the kernels, and the kernel tips will be discolored. Infection usually begins at the base of the ear, but sometimes it starts at the tip. Fungus penetration at the butt is largely due to local infections on the shank [37].

Diplodia zeae fungus enters the stalk from the crown of the plant or through the nodes. Spores may lodge at the base of the ear shank or on the silks where they germinate and penetrate the tissues. The fungus lives on from one season to another on old stalks in the field or on the seed. The spore sacs appear on the stalks as small black specks. In moist warm weather, spores are released from the pycnidia or small black fruiting bodies of the fungus and carried by wind currents to corn plants. Infection of seedlings from Diplodia-infected kernels usually takes place in the natural wounds at the points of production of the secondary radicles near the attachment of the mesocotyl to the scutellum [53].

Diplodia rots are best controlled by growing resistant hybrids, but even the most resistant types may develop some infection. Long-season hybrids are less susceptible to stalk rot than those that mature early. There is no positive evidence that crop rotation is very effective in controlling the disease. Arasan and Orthocide treatments control seed infection, but are ineffective against the stalk and ear rots.

Gibberella Rots

The fungi, *Gibberella zeae* (or *G. saubinettii*) and *G. fujikuroi* (conidial stage: *Fusarium moniliforme*), are responsible for widespread stalk and ear rots [38].

Gibberella stalk rot, caused by *Gibberella zeae,* occurs in the northern areas of the Corn Belt, but causes severe damage only occasionally. The rot usually is confined to the crown or lower internodes. The decayed pith is reddened, and the stalks often break over as the plants mature. Stalk rot caused by *G. fujikuroi* seldom has been a serious problem in the United States [63].

Gibberella ear rot, also caused by *G. zeae,* is sometimes troublesome in the northern part of the Corn Belt [38]. Infected portions of the ears, husks, and kernels become reddened. Infection almost always starts at the tip of the ear, and proceeds downward through the kernels. The ear is seldom wholly rotted. The husks, usually reddish pink, are stuck together by the fungus growth between them.

Fusarium kernel rot, or pink kernel rot, caused by *Gibberella fujikuroi,* is more common in the drier parts of the Corn Belt and in some of the Western states. In California, high relative humidity at silking time and during the maturation period favors infection [59]. The symptom, a pink coloration on the kernel caps, usually is seen first after the kernels are well dented. Infected kernels later become powdery pink. This rot frequently enters injured kernels, often those attacked by the corn earworm, but seldom involves most of the ear. Starchy, rough-kerneled ears appear to be somewhat more susceptible to this disease than are smooth hard-kerneled ears [63, 65, 68].

Gibberella rot fungi overwinter on old corn stalks in the field or on the seed. The sexual spores occur in perithecia on the surface of the old stalks from the previous year as small bluish-black globular structures that are especially abundant about the nodes. The spores are released in mild moist weather of the growing season. They are blown to corn fields where they infect susceptible plants. Initial infection is reduced by plowing under all corn refuse, and by rotating corn with crops other than wheat or barley. Severity of these rots increases with increased plant vigor as well as with increased applications of nitrogen fertilizers, but decreases with increased potash applications [46, 49]. The Gibberella rots can be reduced to a considerable extent by growing adapted hybrids of minimum susceptibility.

Seed infection by fungi that cause stalk rots is more likely to occur in starchy than horny seeds (Fig. 9-2).

Nigrospora Rots

Nigrospora cob rot, sometimes known as basisporium cob rot, is prevalent in the northwestern part of the Corn Belt, but has been found in most corn areas of the United States. Severe infections, when they occur, reduce both the yield and market quality of the grain [63].

The disease is seldom conspicuous before harvest. Badly infected ears are chaffy and break easily. The cobs, and often the shanks, have a shredded appearance. Severely infected ears show a gray discoloration of the internal cob tissues. The pith may be completely disintegrated. Chaff on normally red-cobbed hybrids is brown instead of red as in healthy ears. Diseased kernels are often dull and bleached in color. Black spores may be observed on the butt of the ear as well as on the tips of the kernels. A white mycelial growth is visible in the cob or between the kernels when moisture is abundant [63, 65, 68].

Nigrospora ear rot is caused by a fungus *Nigrospora oryzae* (*Basisporium gallarum*). It lives from one season to another on plant refuse in the field. Corn plants in a vigorous state of growth usually evade the disease, but plants that are retarded by poor soils, root injury, cold, or stalk rot may be attacked.

Nigrospora ear rot can be limited by growing adapted full-season hybrids. Corn is more susceptible to infection when it matures too early, or is frosted before fully mature [63].

Pythium Rots

Pythium root rot of corn is seldom a serious disease in the Corn Belt. It usually attacks young plants that are subjected to extended cold wet weather. The disease is characterized by an embryo rot which prevents germination, or by a rot of the secondary rootlets that stunts the seedlings. Seedlings that survive are reduced in vigor. Older plants suffer weak roots, stunting, lodging, and premature death. The fungus attacks the root hairs as well as the finer rootlets. Light-brown water-soaked lesions develop on infected roots in the early stages. Saprophytic organisms soon complete the destruction of the tissues. In the advanced stages of the disease, much of the root system is destroyed, with the result that the plants can be pulled readily. The disease is caused by the fungus *Pythium arrhenomanes* which lives in the soil, but probably several other species of *Pythium* also are involved [63, 10]. These fungi are present in many soils, in decayed kernels, and in diseased seedlings resulting from planting in cold soils when corn was germinated at low temperatures (48°–50°F) [30]. Some Pythium species may stunt corn seedlings without conspicuous lesions on the shoots or roots in warm (68°–77°F) soils favorable for growth of the corn plant [29]. Where the disease causes serious losses, a practical control is to follow a crop rotation that includes legumes, which are immune to the fungus. Inbred lines and single crosses of dent corn differ widely in their reaction to pythium root rot [20, 28].

FIGURE 9-2. **The corn at left was planted with corneous (horny) seed; the lodged stalks at right grew from starchy seeds.**

(*Courtesy US Department of Agriculture*)

A Pythium stalk rot occurs occasionally in the Corn Belt after periods of very hot humid weather. It appears to be most severe in bottom lands where poor air drainage prevents the surface soil from drying out. The rot of the stalk is usually limited to one internode above the brace roots. Severely rotted stalks fall over but seldom break off completely. The rotted area is brown, soft, and only the strands of the fibrovascular bundles are left. Sometimes furlike tufts of the fungus may be observed on the rotted area. The disease is caused by a fungus known as *Pythium butleri* (*P. aphanidermatum*). This organism lives in the soil and becomes actively parasitic on corn only when the temperature and humidity are high. There is no control known for the disease, but crop rotation may reduce infection in the Corn Belt where the organism primarily attacks corn. Some inbred lines of corn are resistant to the fungus [21, 65].

Rhizoctonia Rots

Rhizoctonia ear rot, caused by the fungus *Rhizoctonia zeae,* is known to occur only in Florida. In early stages of infection the husks and kernels are covered with a pink mycelial growth of the fungus which later becomes dull gray. Small salmon-colored to brown sclerotia are seen in the fungus growth as the disease advances. The ears seem to be susceptible primarily in the early stages of growth. The fungus is carried over from one season to the next as dormant mycelium and sclerotia on the seed as well as on plant refuse. The distribution of the disease indicates that it is favored by warm humid weather. There is no control known for the disease [68, 70].

Black Bundle Disease

Black bundle disease usually is of minor importance, but has been reported from all parts of the United States where corn is grown, as well as from Kenya. The symptoms, which usually appear when the kernels begin to dent, include the development of nubbin ears, multiple ears at a single node, excessive suckering, barren stalks, dwarfing, and purple discoloration of the plant. The vascular bundles of the stalk are light brown to black. The disease has been reported as caused by the fungus, *Cephalosporium acramonium* [38]. The fungus is present in the blackened vascular bundles that contain a deposit of a gumlike material in the cells and vessels of the bundle after the stalks have tasseled out and after severe root injury. The fungus is not an active pathogen when it invades normal vascular bundles through uninjured root systems [27].

Physalospora Ear Rots

Gray ear rot has been found in most of the Eastern states, but it has been serious only in restricted areas. The early symptoms of the disease closely resemble those of diplodia ear rot. The husks are bleached and adhere to each other as a result of the growth of the fungus. The ear often remains upright until harvest. Infected ears show small black specks scattered through the pith of the cob. Severely infected ears are slate gray in color as well as light in weight. Kernels from infected ears show dark gray streaks or small black specks beneath the seed coat. Gray ear rot is caused by the fungus, *Physalospora zeae.* The fungus causes large lesions on the leaves as well as attacking the ears. The spores are produced on infected leaves, and are carried by the wind to leaves or ears where they germinate to start an infection. The disease overwinters on the leaves. Wet weather at silking time or later favors the development of the disease. Hybrids with poor husk protection, or those that hold ears in an upright position for a relatively long time, tend to be susceptible to the disease [64, 65, 68].

Physalospora ear rot, caused by *Physalospora zeicola,* is confined to the Gulf States. The symptoms are similar to those for gray ear rot, except that the leaves are not attacked. Perithecia as well as pycnidia are produced on corn stalks in the field.

Bacterial Stalk Rot

Bacterial stalk rot is generally confined to the southern areas of the Corn Belt, but it is seldom a serious disease. It seems to be most abundant in hot weather, especially in fields that have been flooded. The disease may attack young as well as old plants. The principal symptom is a brown discolored area near the base of the stalk which develops a soft rot. The rot appears to pass transversely through the stalk rather than vertically. Weakened stalks may break over.

Bacterial stalk rot is caused by a bacterium, *Phytomonas dissolvens.* It enters the corn plant through wounds, insect injuries, or stomata. The bacterium appears to live over from year to year on infected corn stubble. Definite control measures are unknown, but rotation probably minimizes losses because corn is the only known host [63].

LEAF BLIGHTS OR SPOTS

Leaf blights of field corn have increased in importance since 1940, when heavy epidemics of one or another of these diseases have occurred. The increase in leaf blight seems to be associated with the increase in the acreage planted to hybrid corn because most corn hybrids are uniformly susceptible to one or more of these diseases. Open-pollinated varieties may

FIGURE 9-3. **Golden Bantam sweet corn. Left: Healthy plant; Right: Plant attacked by bacterial wilt.**

(Courtesy US Department of Agriculture)

contain plants that are partly tolerant to the diseases. Humid weather favors the spread of the leaf diseases. Leaf diseases reduce grain yields when appreciable amounts of leaf tissue are killed [66].

Bacterial Wilt

Bacterial wilt, or Stewart's disease, primarily affects sweet corn, popcorn, and flint corn (Fig. 9-3). Dent corn is heavily attacked occasionally, especially by the so-called late infection. The disease is more prevalent in the Corn Belt and the Eastern states than in the South.

In early infection, conspicuous longitudinal light-green or yellow stripes

FIGURE 9-4. **Lesions of northern leaf blight of corn.**

(*Courtesy US Department of Agriculture*)

appear on the leaves. Infected tissues die, turn brown, and dry out. Diseased plants may die or remain stunted. Late infection is characterized by long irregular dead streaks which run along the veins of the leaves, particularly on the lower leaves. A lesion develops where an infested corn flea beetle has fed on the leaf. Exudate may ooze from the veins that border the lesions. In severe epidemics as much as one-half of the leaf area may be killed [19, 63, 65, 56].

Bacterial wilt is caused by a bacterial organism known as *Bacterium stewarti*. The bacteria develop in abundance in the leaf veins as well as in the vascular bundles of the stalks. It is generally believed that all infection is initiated by the feeding of infested corn flea beetles. The bacteria overwinter in the bodies of hibernating flea beetles and are carried to corn plants by the beetles during the next crop season [54, 22].

Probably the best control for bacterial wilt is growing resistant hybrids. Dent corn is generally more resistant than sweet corn. The Evergreen and Country Gentleman types of sweet corn are more resistant than the Golden

Bantam types. Tall or late-planted hybrids generally are more resistant than short or early hybrids [66].

Helminthosporium Leaf Diseases

Three Helminthosporium leaf diseases attack corn, and may cause considerable damage to susceptible hybrids in wet seasons.

Northern corn leaf blight is widely distributed over the world and attacks all kinds of corn. It is most common in the eastern half of the Corn Belt to the Atlantic coast and southward. The most severe damage occurs under conditions of abundant rainfall, heavy dews, and warm summer weather which afford ideal conditions for the development of the disease. Losses may amount to as much as 50 per cent of the grain yield. The disease usually occurs first on the lower leaves of the corn plant and progresses upward. Small elliptical spots first appear as dark, grayish-green, water-soaked areas. Later they turn greenish-tan. The spots become larger and spindle-shaped. The lesions are elliptical and may range up to 6 × 1.5 inches in size (Fig. 9-4). Spores develop abundantly on both surfaces of the spots after rain or heavy dews to give a dark-green velvety appearance to the lesions. Several lesions may combine to form larger areas that may kill entire leaves or even the plant. Heavily infected fields may appear dry and fired [66, 55]. Northern corn leaf blight is caused by the fungus *Helminthosporium turcicum*. It lives through the winter on old infected leaves in the field, produces spores the next spring, and infects corn again. The most effective control lies in the development of resistant hybrids. Resistance is controlled by a large number of genetic factors [66, 33]. Several resistant inbred lines have been developed [34, 35]. Dithane or Parzate dusts or sprays have been used to control the disease on sweet-corn fields in Florida. These fungicides have also been used in the Corn Belt to control the disease in hybrid dent corn seed fields. For effective control, spray chemicals should be applied soon after corn silks. A total of 6–8 applications was necessary for control [66, 55].

Southern corn leaf blight occurs wherever corn is grown under warm humid conditions. In the United States, it is found primarily in the Southeastern states, but it reaches northward into the southern parts of the Corn Belt states, and eastward from there to the Atlantic coast. This disease thrives at somewhat higher temperatures than does the northern corn leaf blight. It may cause reduced yields, weakened stalks, and fodder damage through destruction of green leaf tissue. The disease symptoms consist of grayish-tan to straw-colored spots which may extend over most of the leaf surface. The spots may range up to 1.5 × 0.25 inches. In contrast to northern corn leaf blight, the lesions are smaller, oblong rather than elliptical in shape, and lighter in color. Southern corn leaf blight is caused by

Helminthosporium maydis. The spores which spread the fungus overwinter on dead corn leaves. The only known control for the disease is the use of resistant hybrids. Resistance to this disease appears to be governed by a number of genetic factors, different from those that determine resistance to northern corn leaf blight [65, 66, 55].

Helminthosporium leaf spot is found over the eastern half of the United States and in a few other countries. The disease is not widespread, and is of minor economic importance in the United States. Helminthosporium leaf spot is caused by the fungus, *Helminthosporium carbonum.* Race I of this fungus produces circular or oval spots up to 1 inch in diameter on the leaves. They are yellowish-green at first, but later become tan or straw-colored with a profuse cover of dark velvety spores. Spore production is especially abundant on leaf sheaths. This disease also attacks the ears, where it causes a black rot that imparts a charred appearance to the kernels. All above-ground parts of plants are susceptible. Race II produces leaf symptoms that are easily confused with southern corn leaf blight. The spots are tan or light-brown and angular, 0.125–0.25 inch wide and up to one inch long. In heavy infection, they coalesce to form large deadened areas. Race II also causes blackened ears. The disease overwinters on old infected leaves in the field. It can be controlled only by the use of resistant inbreds in hybrids. Resistance to Race I is determined by a single dominant gene, hence the progeny from a cross of a susceptible inbred with a resistant inbred is completely resistant. It is believed that several genes are involved in the inheritance of resistance to Race II [63, 65, 66, 55].

Corn Rusts

Both common corn rust and southern corn rust attack corn in the United States, but seldom cause serious damage to the crop because they usually attack late in the growing season. Corn rust is abundant in some seasons, usually after moist weather. Severe infection at silking time probably causes some loss in grain yield. A third rust, tropical corn rust, is found only in the American tropics. Corn rusts frequently are severe in Mexico and Central America [63, 67].

Common corn rust, caused by the fungus, *Puccinia sorghi,* produces small pustules (Fig. 9-1) that rupture the epidermis of the leaves to expose rusty-brown uredospores. Dark brown to black winter spores (teliospores) develop toward the end of the season. The summer spores may overwinter in some Corn Belt areas to infect corn directly. Teliospores, which overwinter in old corn leaves, germinate in the spring to produce basidiospores (sporidia). These infect wood-sorrel (*Oxalis* spp.) to produce pycnospores, and later aeciospores form in aecia on the lower surface of the Oxalis leaves. The aeciospores infect corn leaves. Moderate temperatures, frequent heavy dews, and succulent growth of the host as on high-nitrogen soils favor the development of common corn rust. Resistance is due to one dominant gene in each of six inbred lines studied [57]. Control measures are seldom necessary in the United States, but inbred lines of corn differ in resistance to the rust [63, 67].

Southern corn rust, caused by *Puccinia polyspora,* is found from Massachusetts westward to southern Indiana and southward to the Gulf of Mexico. It has been found in Mexico, Central America, South America, and Africa. The cinnamon-brown pustules tend to be smaller and more circular in outline than those of common corn rust. Pustules of the telial stage are chocolate brown to black, but they remain covered by the leaf epidermis for a long time. Southern corn rust requires somewhat higher temperatures for optimum development than does common corn rust. There is no known alternate host for southern corn rust. Inoculum in the southern part of the Corn Belt may be carried northward by wind currents [67].

Bacterial Leaf Blight

Bacterial leaf blight has occurred sporadically in several Central and Southern states since 1928. The disease affects some varieties of dent, sweet, and popcorn. It is distinct from bacterial wilt.

The symptoms are long, narrow, sharply delimited stripes or streaks on the leaves. The streaks are water-soaked and olive-green in early stages, but later they turn brown or tan with reddish-brown margins. The streaks, often most abundant near the midrib, may extend almost the entire length of the leaf. They are narrower, more regular in outline, and more oily in appearance than those caused by bacterial wilt. Seriously diseased leaves shred readily when exposed to wind or rain [66, 55].

The organism also causes a dark brown or black rot of the stalk pith. Stalk infection usually occurs at or just above the ear node. The outside of the stalk may show reddish-brown streaks. The tops of the corn plants fade and die as the rot progresses. Many infected plants are dwarfed, show bleached tops, and produce sterile multiple ears [55].

Dent corn appears to be more resistant to infection than sweet corn; popcorn is most susceptible [66].

Brown Spot

Brown spot, caused by the fungus, *Physoderma zeae-maydis,* is found primarily in the Southeastern states where temperatures, humidity, and rainfall are high, but also occurs occasionally in the southern part of the Corn Belt. This disease is of relatively little economic importance in the United

States, except possibly in the Gulf States. Golden-brown circular spots occur on the leaf blades and sheaths, but the spots at the base of the leaf tend to be purple. Brown spot lesions are smooth and seldom break the epidermis, whereas rust pustules are rough and powdery and break the epidermis. The spots contain many spores that spread the disease when temperatures are high and free moisture is present on the leaves. Severe stalk infection may cause stalk breakage. Definite control measures are unknown [63, 65].

Other Leaf Diseases

Gray leaf spot of corn occurs throughout the Southern states. The spots caused by this disease may be confused with those of southern corn leaf blight, but the spots are narrower. Some are less than 0.0625 inch wide and 0.25–1.5 inches long. Their color is light-sepia at first, but with age they bleach to ashen gray with narrow light-sepia borders. The disease is caused by two fungi, *Cercospora sorghi* and *C. zeae-maydis,* which sometimes occur on the same leaf [55].

Bacterial leaf spot of corn, caused by *Pseudomonas syringae* (or *Bacterium holci*), is seldom a serious disease. The round, elliptical, or irregular water-soaked lesions on the lower leaves of the plant range in size from 0.125–0.5 inch in diameter. The spots are dark-green and water-soaked in appearance at first, but later become light brown with a darker brown or reddish-brown narrow border. A yellow halo may occur around some of the larger spots. In extremely wet weather infection may occur on the margins as well as on the tips of the lower leaves, which causes them to turn brown and die [55].

Crazy top, caused by a fungus, *Sclerospora macrospora,* occurs sporadically, especially in corn on low water-logged areas. The most conspicuous symptom of the disease is the bunchy appearance of the tassel due to replacement of the normal floral parts by numerous small leaves. Other symptoms include stunting, excessive tillering, narrow-streaked leaves, and barrenness. The most practical means of control is land drainage [65].

Purple sheath spot occurs in many corn fields late in the season, but the damage caused is negligible. Symptoms are purple or brownish irregular blotches on the leaf sheaths. The outer epidermis of the sheath remains intact, but the inside becomes cracked and partly rotted. A number of fungi and bacteria may cause the condition when they lodge between the sheath and the stalk. Marked differences among strains in susceptibility are evident [63].

CORN SMUTS

Common Smut

Common smut, caused by the fungus *Ustilago maydis* or *U. zeae,* is found wherever corn is grown, and is one of the most destructive of all corn diseases [67]. Average annual yield losses in Illinois ranged from less than 0.5 per cent to 8.0 per cent in 21 years [39, 63]. Smut causes many plants to be barren and reduces the size of ears in others.

Smut galls may occur on the leaves, tassels, ears, or stalks, and range in size from minute pustules to six inches or more in diameter (Fig. 9-5). Damage depends on size as well as on the number of galls present. Galls on the ear are usually the most destructive. Tassel smut, or galls two inches or more in diameter on the stalk above the ear, may reduce the yield of infected plants from 30–100 per cent. Galls of the same size below the ear cause about half of that damage [32, 36]. At first, the galls

FIGURE 9-5. **Galls of common corn smut.**

(Courtesy US Department of Agriculture)

have a silvery-white appearance, but soon the interior is converted into a black powdery mass of smut spores which are exposed upon the rupture of the membrane [63].

The black spores overwinter in the soil or in manure, and germinate to cause infection directly or to produce secondary spores which infect the corn plant. Infection is particularly likely to enter young succulent (meristematic) tissues or wounds. The more vigorous plants are likely to be most smutted. The galls are the result of a local rather than a systemic infection.

Dry weather, late planting, infertile soil, or soil especially high in nitrogen, tend to increase smut [39]. The disease frequently is more severe in the semiarid Great Plains than in the more humid Corn Belt to the east [6, 63].

Smut-resistant hybrids offer the most effective means for control. While none is completely immune, most hybrids have moderate resistance because the more susceptible inbred lines were discarded by breeders. Breeding for smut resistance is complicated by the existence of different physiologic races of the pathogen that attack different inbred lines. Inheritance of resistance to common smut is determined by a relatively large number of genetic factors [67]. Crop rotation and the destruction of smut galls may reduce the disease somewhat, but are not a practical means of control [40]. Thicker planting may reduce the incidence of smut [73].

Head Smut

Head smut of corn, caused by the fungus, *Sphacelotheca reiliana,* is of minor importance in the United States, except in some localized areas of the West. It is far more prevalent in Asia, Africa, Europe, and Australia [67].

The tassels and ears may be completely or partially converted into smut galls as they emerge. Occasionally, the tip of the stalk is affected. The bracts of partly smutted floral structures often develop leafy proliferations.

The chlamydospores of the head smut fungus live in soil or on the seed. Relatively dry soil seems to be favorable for causing infection. The spores germinate in the spring to form secondary spores or sporidia which penetrate the young seedlings. The mycelium develops systemically in the tissues of the young corn plant, and forms galls which contain the chlamydospores. The physiologic races that attack sorghum are unable to parasitize corn, and vice versa [67].

Head smut of corn can be controlled somewhat by growing other crops in infested fields for at least two years. Seed treatment will reduce seedling infection, and prevent the disease from being carried to new fields.

OTHER CORN DISEASES

In the United States, sugarcane mosaic may attack corn grown in the vicinity of sugar cane fields infected with the same disease. It reduces corn yields to a slight extent. The symptoms appear as a mottling or striping of light green surrounded by the normal dark-green tissues, especially on the younger leaves. The disease is caused by a virus spread by the corn aphid and certain other insects. It can be controlled by isolating the corn from sugarcane and by eradication of susceptible wild grass hosts and volunteer sugarcane sprouts [63].

Three other virus diseases are known on corn in this country: Stunt in California and Texas, leaf fleck in California, and celery stripe in Florida. Stunt is potentially important, but so far none of the virus diseases has caused serious damage to corn.

B. Insect Pests

SOIL-INHABITING INSECTS

Insects that live either on or beneath the soil surface at some time in their growing or feeding stages include rootworms, cutworms, wireworms, billbugs, seedcorn beetles, seedcorn maggots, white grubs, and corn root aphid [26].

The Corn Rootworms

The northern corn rootworm (*Diabratica longicornis*) is prevalent in the Corn Belt, where it may cause considerable damage. It has caused yield reductions that range from 10–30 per cent in Iowa [26]. The adult beetle is yellowish-green with prominent black bars or longitudinal stripes on the back. It is about one-fifth inch long, and may feed on the pollen, silks, and exposed kernels of the corn plant. The larva, a slender white worm about a half-inch long with a brownish-yellow head, tunnels through the roots. Corn with heavy root damage often falls over, especially after a rain accompanied by wind. The adults lay their eggs in the fall in old corn fields. The larvae hatch in the spring, feed on the roots of the newly planted corn, grow to maturity, pupate, and then emerge as adults to complete the life cycle [62]. This pest is relatively easy to control by crop rotations in which one or two years of corn are followed by two years in a legume or grass crop. Corn yields, on infested soils in Iowa, also have been increased by an additional application of 40, 60, or 80 pounds of nitrogen per acre at the last cultivation. Soil applications of 0.5–1.0 pound per acre (actual chemical) of aldrin, chlordane, gamma BHC, heptachlor, or dieldrin have reduced rootworm populations. These chemicals may be applied as a spray either on plowed land and immediately disked under before the crop is planted, or just behind the planter shoes with a planter-mounted sprayer; or in insecticide-fertilizer mixtures broadcast before planting or banded during planting [26].

The western corn rootworm (*Diabratica virgifera*) periodically causes serious damage in Colorado, Nebraska, Kansas, and New Mexico, especially where corn is grown after corn under conditions of favorable soil moisture. Its distribution now overlaps that of *D. longicornis* in the Corn Belt. The western corn rootworm is similar to the northern corn rootworm in general appearance, habits, life history, and in damage caused to the corn plant. The adult is yellowish-green in color with either a large dark area or three dark stripes separated by yellow lines on the back. The wing covers always have yellow margins. The adult sometimes feeds on the interveinal areas of the leaves. Control measures are the same as for the northern corn rootworm [62, 26].

The southern corn rootworm (*Diabratica duodecimpunctata*) is particularly injurious to corn in the Southern States, but it is found as far north as the central Corn Belt. The adult, which is the 12-spotted cucumber beetle, is yellow with 12 black spots arranged in four rows down the back. The larvae are slightly larger than those of the northern corn rootworm, but otherwise very similar in appearance. They feed on the young roots of the corn plant, but also tunnel in the underground portions of the stalk to some extent (Fig. 9-6). The adults commonly feed on the leaves as well as the silks. Southern corn rootworm overwinters in the adult stage in the Southern states and as far north as Missouri. The adults fly north in the early spring where they deposit eggs at the base of young corn plants. These eggs hatch into larvae which tunnel into the roots. The worms mature in midsummer, pupate, and emerge as adult beetles [26]. There usually is one generation per year in the northern areas, but two or more farther south. This insect is difficult to control because the eggs are laid in the spring, often after the corn plants have emerged. Control through crop rotation has been ineffective in Iowa. Cultural practices advocated to reduce rootworm injury include early plowing, fertilization, green manuring, and clean cultivation to destroy weeds that may provide early food for the larvae. Special planting dates also are recommended for corn in the Southern states. Tests with soil insecticides indicate that chlordane reduces rootworm injury when applied in the drill rows at planting time at the rate of 1–2 pounds per acre. Gamma BHC at the rate of one pound per acre also has been recommended.

Cutworms

Important species of cutworms that attack corn are the black cutworm (*Agrotis ypsilon*), glassy cutworm (*Crymodes devastator*), dingy cutworm

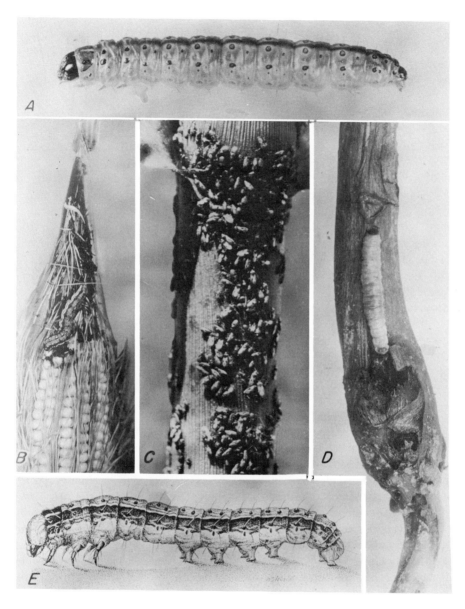

FIGURE 9-6. Insects that attack corn: (A) European corn borer, (B) corn earworm, (C) chinch bugs, (D) corn rootworm, and (E) fall armyworm.

(*Courtesy US Department of Agriculture*)

(*Feltis subgothica*), and the clay-backed cutworm (*Agrotis gladiaria*). These cutworms are widely distributed throughout North America, but different species predominate in different areas. They destroy young plants to thin the stand [13].

The cutworm larvae vary in color from a light-glassy to a grayish-black or brown. The moths also vary in color, but usually are gray or brown. Common cutworms are nocturnal feeders. Their presence is indicated by young plants severed at or near the soil surface.

Cutworm moths deposit eggs in grass or sod lands in the early fall. The larvae of many species hatch the same fall, overwinter in the soil, and are present when the corn is planted the next spring. They feed on the young emerging plants. In late June or early July, the mature larva forms a loose cell in the soil where it pupates. A few days later the adult moth emerges. There usually is one generation per year, except in the South, where the black cutworm overwinters in the pupal stage and has two or more generations annually.

Fall plowing long has been advocated for the destruction of cutworm larvae. It is moderately effective, but should be avoided on erodable land. Most farmers replant when stands have been depleted by cutworms. Recently, effective control has been obtained by the application of two pounds of toxaphene per acre, banded along the rows as soon as the first seedling damage is noted. When these bands are 12–18 inches wide, the resistant glassy cutworms also are killed [41].

Wireworms

Wireworms damage corn through loss of stands. They are small, shiny, yellowish or brownish worms about one inch long. The adults, click beetles, are brown or black. The larvae generally feed on the seeds or roots of young plants. Wireworms also are injurious to many other crops. Many species attack corn, some of the important being *Melanotus cribulosus, M. communis, Agriotes mancus,* and *Aeolus mellillus.*

A generation may require one or more years, depending upon the species. In the Corn Belt, wireworms usually pupate in July or early August. After 15–20 days, the pupae turn into beetles which overwinter in the pupal cells. The beetles deposit their eggs in the soil in the spring. The larvae hatch in a few days and feed on the corn plant.

Cultural practices advocated for the control of wireworms include soil drainage, crop rotation, clean cultivation, and summer plowing. Seed treatment with lindane (25 per cent wettable powder), applied at the rate of 4.5 ounces per bushel of corn, has been fairly effective except on peat soils or under conditions of heavy infestation. A field application of two pounds of aldrin or chlordane per acre has been recommended for high levels of infestation [41].

Billbugs

Several species, particularly the maize billbug (*Calendra maidis*), injure corn in the United States. They are snout beetles which are usually brown in color. They vary from 0.25–1 inch in length. The larvae are white with brown head, plump, and legless. The adult beetles make oblong or round holes in the leaves, or cause bud injury, in young corn plants. The larvae may tunnel in the lower part of the stem. The primary damage is loss of stands or stunted plants.

Infestations are likely to occur on corn planted on sodland or in moist soil. One generation per year occurs in species commonly found on corn. The beetles deposit their eggs early in the summer. Young grubs soon hatch from the eggs, pupate for a short period in the fall, and finally emerge as beetles. The adults overwinter in the roots or stubble of host plants, and attack corn seedlings in the spring.

Drainage of swampy areas near where corn is grown will reduce billbug damage. Other cultural controls include crop rotation, early planting, and fertilization. Application of toxaphene, at the rate of two pounds per acre sprayed over the rows, has been recommended to reduce infestation [41].

Corn Root Aphid

Serious injury is caused to corn each year by the corn root aphid (*Anuraphis maidi-radicis*). It is a small soft-bodied, bluish-green insect, almost spherical when full-grown. This aphid is distributed widely throughout the United States east of the Rocky Mountains, but it is especially destructive in the Corn Belt. The corn root aphids cluster on the corn roots where they suck the plant juices. Infested plants are dwarfed, the leaves brown or otherwise discolored. The injury is most obvious in the spring when the plants are 6–18 inches high [11].

The corn root aphid appears to depend for survival on the small brown corn field ant or related ants. In the fall the aphid eggs are stored by the ants in their nests, where they overwinter. When the eggs hatch in the spring, the ants place the young aphids on the roots of corn or other plants. Successive generations of wingless aphids are produced in the summer by unfertilized females. Summer spread of the aphids is accomplished by winged females which fly to other fields where they are again cared for by ants. A sexual generation of winged males and females is produced in the fall. After mating, the females lay the eggs that overwinter [45].

Control measures include rotation with other crops for one or two years in order to starve out the aphids. Reduced aphid infestations were obtained in western Illinois when spring plowing was delayed until just prior to corn planting. A more desirable practice, however, appears to be early deep spring plowing followed by several deep diskings to disorganize the aphid colonies, as well as to prevent the growth of weeds on which the aphids live before they attack corn. Fertilizers stimulate the production of vigorous plants that resist damage [3, 11]. Chlordane applied at the rate of one pound per acre has been recommended for the control of both the corn root aphid and related ants [41].

Sugarcane Beetle

The sugarcane beetle (*Euetheola rugiceps*), sometimes called the rough-headed cornstalk beetle, damages corn seriously in some areas. It is found only in the Southern states of the United States. In Louisiana it has long been a pest of sugarcane and rice. The adult beetle is black, stout, hard-shelled, and about a half-inch long. The beetles injure corn seedlings upon emergence. They chew into the stems of young plants, which often destroys the growing point [61].

The sugarcane beetle develops in low, poorly drained soils. The beetles overwinter in the soil, and become active in late April or early May about the time the corn plants appear above ground. The beetles lay their eggs in the ground from spring to early summer. The larvae appear in about two weeks, mature in about two months, and then pupate for about two weeks. The beetles emerge in late summer or early fall [61].

An important control measure is to crop low, poorly drained fields or pastures that have been out of cultivation for some time. Such lands should be plowed in late August or early September in Virginia, but earlier in areas farther south. Crops other than corn, sugarcane, or rice should be planted in the first year of cultivation to avoid beetle damage. Other control measures include frequent crop rotation, clean cultivation, and soil drainage. Corn planted in late April in Virginia is injured less than that planted in May. So far, the application of chemicals has proved ineffective or impractical [61].

Other Soil-Inhabiting Insects

Several other soil-inhabiting insects that attack corn are: sod webworms (*Crambus* spp.), particularly the corn root webworm (*C. caliginosellus*); white grubs (*Phyllophaga* spp.); seed corn maggot (*Hylemiyia cilicrura*); and seed corn beetles (*Agonoderus lecontei* and *Clivia impressifrons*).

LEAF, STALK, AND EAR INSECTS

Corn Earworm

The corn earworm (*Heliothis armigera*) occurs throughout the United States. It is most destructive in the Southern states. Field corn is injured less severely than sweet corn, but an estimated 2 per cent of the crop is destroyed annually [4]. Cotton, sorghum, and other crops are also susceptible.

Full-grown larvae of the corn earworm are about 1.5 inches long, and they vary in color from shades of brown to green with conspicuous stripes of various shades of cream, yellow, brown, slate, and black. The moth varies in color from a light olive green to dark reddish-brown [4].

The worms feed on the buds or central shoots and tender folded leaves of young plants. Such leaves present a ragged appearance when they unfold. The worms also attack the tassels, but usually go to the silks as soon as they appear. After the silks dry out, the larvae devour or destroy the developing kernels. As the kernels harden, the larvae bore under them to feed on the soft germs [4]. Severe infestations may cause a grain loss of 50 per cent.

The corn earworm moth, which does not eat corn, lays its eggs on the silks, or occasionally on the corn leaves. The larvae hatch in 2–8 days, and feed downward along the silks into the ear tip (Fig. 9-6). The newly-hatched larvae are whitish with a black head. They grow rapidly and change color through a series of molts. The full-grown larva leaves the ear, drops to the ground, and bores into the soil to a depth of 1–9 inches where it pupates. Finally, the moth emerges. The development from egg to adult takes about 30 days in midsummer. Pupae produced in late summer or early fall may pass the winter in the soil and emerge as moths in the next spring or early summer. There usually is only one generation annually in the extreme north, three or four generations in the Corn Belt, and as many as seven generations in the South [4].

Some southern hybrids, including Dixie 11, Dixie 18, Georgia 281, Louisiana 521, and Texas hybrids 9W, 11W, 24, and 30, have some resistance to the corn earworm. These hybrids are characterized by a tight husk that extends at least two inches beyond the tip of the ear, and helps to keep out some of the earworms. It usually is impractical to control earworms in field corn by the use of fungicides, except in the case of valuable seed corn. Large acreages may be protected by the use of three gallons of 25 per cent DDT emulsion and seven gallons of white mineral oil with a viscosity of 65–95 seconds Saybolt at 100°F with enough water added to make 100 gallons. Two or more applications should be made at the rate of 25 gallons per acre. The first application should be made about two days after the silks appear with additional applications at two-day intervals [4]. Reduction of corn earworm infestation by the use of DDT in California was accompanied by a reduction in kernel damage caused by Fusarium ear rot [59].

European Corn Borer

The European corn borer (*Pyrausta nubilalis*), one of the most serious pests of corn, was first observed in the United States in 1917. First established in Massachusetts, it spread to the 37 states east of the Rocky Mountains.

The larva is characterized by a dark brown or black head, while the body color ranges from light brown to dark brown or to pink. The body divisions each bear a row of small dark brown spots (Fig. 9-6). The borer is about three-fourths inch long.

The European corn borer attacks over 200 species of plants, but is most injurious to corn. The larva tunnels within the stalks, ears, tassels, leaf midribs, brace roots, and stubble. Second-generation borers may cause extensive stalk breakage and ear droppage [5, 25]. The larvae also feed to some extent on the surfaces of leaf blades, tassel buds, ear husks, silks, and leaf sheaths. In the Eastern states, the losses in corn yields average about 3 per cent per borer per stalk up to about 20 borers per stalk. Increases in stalk breakage of up to 6 per cent have been observed for each borer per stalk [48].

The single-generation strain of the borer passes the winter in burrows in corn stalks, ears, stubble, or other plant material. They generally become active in May, and after a pupal period of 10–14 days, emerge as moths from late May to early July. The females soon lay their eggs, usually in masses of 15–20, generally near the midrib on the underside of the corn leaves. The eggs hatch in from 5–7 days. The newly hatched borers crawl down into the leaf whorl to feed. After they are about half-grown or larger, they bore into the stalk and continue to feed. They overwinter in the stalk in a dormant condition [1, 5, 24].

The multiple-generation strain of the borer occurs throughout the infested area. Two or more generations may develop, but the number of second-generation borers is reduced in a cool season. Moths of the second generation, which, in Kansas, emerge from late July to early August, lay their eggs on the corn leaves near the ear. The hatched borers commonly feed on the ear. The mature borer of this or later generations passes the winter within the corn plant or in nearby weeds [13].

Cultural methods for corn borer control include the plowing under of all crop or weed residues. The plowing may be done in the fall or spring before May 1 in the southern Corn Belt or May 15 in the northern part [31, 7, 24]. The land should be plowed to a depth of 6 inches or more to

FIGURE 9-7. **Field sprayer for use in controlling the European corn borer.**
(*Courtesy US Department of Agriculture*)

assure deep coverage of infested material. An average of 77 per cent of the winter borer population in Illinois fields was killed by mechanical corn pickers, adverse weather, pasturing of stalk fields, and other causes [3]. Tight corn-picker rolls killed about 36 per cent of the borers during harvest. Infested plants may be chopped or shredded and fed to livestock as silage or fodder.

Strong-stalked adapted hybrids should be planted at the optimum time for the locality. Some hybrid varieties are resistant or tolerant to corn-borer infestation. Inbred lines resistant to leaf-feeding by first-brood borers, include L317, B2, Oh7, Oh40B, Oh41, Oh43, Oh45, Oh51A, W10, W22, W23, A392, R4, R61, Hy, and Wr3. Leaf-feeding resistance is controlled by 1–3 or more genes [51, 52]. A double-cross hybrid should contain at least three resistant lines for effective resistance. Good stalk strength increases the tolerance to second-brood borers. Single-cross combinations that include inbred lines B14, Wf9, B15, and B30, have a low percentage of stalk breakage [15].

Insecticides may be used profitably to control the borers in sweet corn or seed production fields. It may be advisable to spray for first-generation larvae control in field corn when more than 50 egg masses per 100 stalks are found on plants less than 3 feet tall. At least 100 egg masses per 100 stalks should be present before spraying to control second-generation borers is deemed practicable. The recommended dosage is 1.5 pounds of actual DDT per acre, applied as a spray or dust by ground equipment or aircraft [23]. Sprays have been more effective than dusts under Corn Belt conditions. Application of insecticides has been more effective with field sprayers (Fig. 9-7) than with aircraft [24]. Corn plants treated with DDT are unsafe to feed to animals. Ryania is very effective, but too expensive for general use on field corn.

Natural enemies, including certain birds and at least 29 insect parasites and predators, reduce corn-borer numbers but cannot be depended upon for complete control [1, 5, 24].

Southwestern Corn Borer

The southwestern corn borer (*Diatraea grandiosella*) crossed the Mexican border into Arizona, New Mexico, and Texas by 1913, and spread across Oklahoma and Kansas by 1942. It is destructive to corn but harms sorghum only slightly. Serious outbreaks of the pest occurred in Kansas between 1941 and 1945 [72].

The southwestern corn-borer larvae are a dull white color, with a regular pattern of conspicuous dark brown or black spots. The mature borers of the second generation are all white except for occasional faint spots. The white borers girdle the cornstalks in the fall. The female moths, about three-fourths inch long, are off-white to pale yellow in color. The males are slightly smaller but somewhat darker. The eggs are elliptical to oval in shape, but decidedly flattened with a slightly convex upper surface.

The mature borers of the second generation overwinter in the bases of corn stalks. In Kansas they pupate in June but emerge as moths within a few days. The moths deposit eggs on corn leaves in late June or early July. These first generation larvae infest the central bud within the leaf whorl or bore into the corn stalks. The borers then pupate and another generation of moths emerges in time to deposit eggs on the corn leaves about August 15–31. The larvae of this generation are well developed by September 15. They girdle the stalks and prepare cells in which to hibernate [72].

Control measures include substitution of sorghum for corn, early planting, late fall treatment of stubble to expose it to the surface, and plowing under of stalks or stubble to a depth of at least four inches before June 1 to prevent the escape of the moths from the cells.

Southern Cornstalk Borer

The southern cornstalk borer (*Diatraea crambidoides*) causes serious damage to corn in the South. It is found from northern Florida to Maryland, and as far west as Kansas, Oklahoma, and Texas.

The full-grown larva of the southern corn borer is a dirty-white worm, one inch long, and covered with many dark spots, each with a short dark bristle. The head and neck shield are brownish-yellow. It is similar to the southwestern corn borer (*D. grandiosella*) in many respects.

The larvae feed in the leaf whorl of young corn plants, and ragged holes appear in the leaves as they unroll. Later the borer tunnels in the stalks, which causes greater damage. Plants weakened by tunnels have reduced grain yields, and they break over readily in the wind.

The southern cornstalk borer overwinters in the corn root in the larval stage, and pupates from March 15 to April 30. After 10 or more days in the pupal stage the moth emerges, mates, and lays its eggs on the underside of the lower corn leaves. The larvae hatch in 7–10 days, and burrow into the stalks where growth is completed. The larvae finally pupates. After 7–10 days the moth emerges, mates, and lays eggs. The larvae of the second generation overwinter in corn stalks or stubble below the soil surface [60].

Plowing out and dragging the stubble exposes the borers to fatal winter temperatures above ground. In the deep South, where the winters are mild, the land should be plowed at some time before March to cover the stubble or roots with at least two inches of soil to prevent emergence of the moths. Crop rotations also are advocated [60].

Chinch Bugs

The chinch bug (*Blissus leucopterus*) is one of the most destructive insects of corn in the United States. It is distributed generally throughout the country but is most abundant in the Ohio, Missouri, and upper Mississippi valleys [47].

The adult chinch bug is about one-sixth inch in length with a black body with whitish markings (Fig. 9-8). The long-winged form prevails throughout the central states. The young nymphs are light red, but become darker red as they develop.

Corn is infested with chinch bugs most heavily when it is growing next to small grain fields. As the small grains ripen, the young bugs migrate on foot to the corn. They collect on the lower part of the cornstalks where they suck the sap. This causes the plant to turn yellow, wilt, and often die.

Chinch bugs overwinter in the adult stage in the tufts of perennial grasses, or in debris (Fig. 9-8). The bugs emerge from hibernation in the spring between February or March and late May. They fly to small grain fields, feed for several days, and deposit their eggs on the lower leaf sheaths of small grain plants. The eggs hatch in 7–14 days, and the young bugs feed on the small grain plants. When the small grain ripens, the bugs move on foot to corn, sorghum, or other nearby succulent grass hosts, where they complete their growth to the winged stage. Thereafter, they are able to fly over the entire field or to adjacent fields. The adults lay their eggs to start the second generation which develops before fall. A third brood has been observed in southern areas. During the fall, the adults of the last brood fly to grasses for hibernation [44, 47].

Chinch bug outbreaks accompany above-normal temperatures and below-normal rainfall between March and October. Cold winters do not kill the chinch bugs in the areas where they are abundant [58].

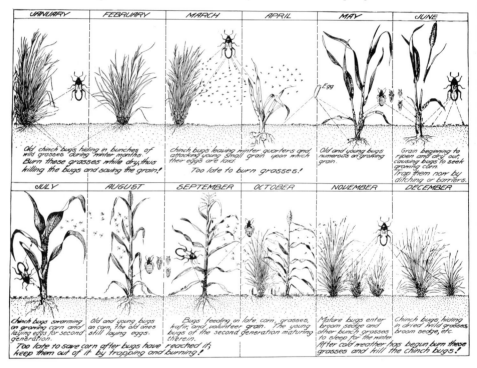

FIGURE 9-8. **The life cycle of the chinch bug.**

The on-foot migration of chinch bugs to corn fields can be checked with furrow barriers with the soil thrown towards the noninfested fields. A line of coal-tar creosote is poured along the top of the ridge. Since creosote is a repellant, the bugs will travel along the line rather than cross it. Postholes 20–30 feet apart are dug along the line to trap the bugs. Kerosene is sprinkled in these holes daily to kill the bugs. Other types of barriers are the creosote-treated paper fence, dinitro toxic dust, and DDT-pyrophylite dust. The materials are renewed when necessary [47].

Insecticidal chemicals, such as dieldrin, will prevent chinch bug migration for 10–14 days when applied as a spray at the rate of 0.5 pound per acre on strips 1–3 rods wide at the margins of the corn field [12].

Other Leaf, Stalk, and Ear Insects

The armyworm (*Cirphis unipuncta*) is widely distributed in the corn-growing areas of the United States. It feeds on corn leaves. The larvae are effectively destroyed with toxaphene aerial sprays at the rate of 1.5–2.0 pounds per acre. Dusts that contain 20 per cent of toxaphene, or 10 per cent of DDT, applied at the rate of 20 pounds per acre, also are effective in armyworm control [71].

The fall armyworm (*Laphygma frugiperda*) occurs generally in the southeastern states, but the moths frequently migrate far to the north where the larvae (Fig. 9-6) damage late-planted or late-maturing corn. It has been controlled by a spray prepared with two pounds of wettable powder containing 50 per cent of either DDT or TDE in 40 gallons of water applied to each acre [42].

The lesser cornstalk borer (*Elasmopalpus lignosellus*) attacks corn as well as sugarcane, sorghum, cowpeas, and beans in the Southern states. The principal control measure is the destruction of crop debris in which the larvae overwinter.

Many kinds of grasshoppers (*Melanoplus* spp., *Camnula pellucida*,

FIGURE 9-9. **Corn (left) was stripped by grasshoppers, but the grain sorghum (right) was scarcely damaged.**

(Courtesy US Department of Agriculture)

and *Schistocerca americana*) attack the corn plant. Grasshoppers are wide-ly spread over the United States, and cause serious damage in some years in the Dakotas, Iowa, Nebraska, Kansas, Missouri, and Oklahoma (Fig. 9-9). Poisoned bran bait was the standard control method for grasshoppers until 1947. Several newer insecticides are very effective. The recommended rates per acre of the actual chemical, are: aldrin, 1.5–2 ounces; chlordane, 0.5–1 pound; dieldrin, 0.75–1 ounce; heptachlor, 3–4 ounces; or toxaphene, 1–1.5 pounds. For dusts, the dosages should be increased 50 per cent [50].

Other insects that attack corn plants include the corn leaf aphid (*Aphis maidis*), corn flea beetle (*Chaetocnema pulicaria*), and the Japanese beetle (*Popillia japonica*).

STORED CORN GRAIN INSECTS

Rice Weevil

The rice or black weevil (*Sitophilus oryzae*) probably is the most de-structive insect pest in stored grain. It is a reddish-brown snout beetle about one-sixteenth inch long (Fig. 9-10). It is further characterized by four light-reddish or yellowish spots. The larvae, which feed in the grain, are

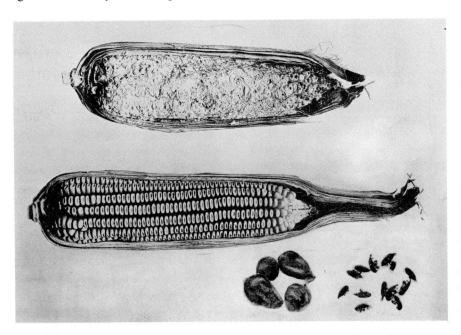

FIGURE 9-10. The grain in the upper ear of corn with the short husks was destroyed by weevils. The long husks on the lower ear protected the grain from the weevils. Below (left) popcorn kernels showing weevil borings. Below (right) adult rice weevils.

(*Courtesy US Department of Agriculture*)

white legless grubs. Field infestations occur in the Southern states when the grain becomes firm. The insect is prevalent in accumulations of old grain around granaries in the Northern states [8].

The adult rice weevils eat small cavities in the grain in order to deposit their eggs. The larvae hatch and burrow inside the kernel. The fully grown larvae transform to pupae, and then to adult weevils which bore their way out of the grain. The life cycle may be completed in as few as 26 days in warm summer weather [8]. There may be as many as 7 generations annually under favorable conditions, but the number is considerably less in the north.

Field infestations of the rice weevil in corn in Louisiana were controlled until harvest in November by three applications at three-day intervals of emulsion sprays that contained DDT and mineral oil. The first application was made when about 15 per cent of the silks had appeared [17].

Control practices include storage of corn in weather-tight, rodent-proof bins thoroughly cleaned before being filled. All carryover waste grain around storage bins should be destroyed. Surface fumigants may be applied to stored corn where there is evidence of infestation. An effective fumigant is a mixture of carbon tetrachloride (4 parts) and carbon disulfide (1 part) applied at the rate of 3–5 gallons per 1000 bushels. A mixture of ethylene dichloride (3 parts) and carbon tetrachloride (1 part) is another effective fumigant when applied at the same rate. Treatment should be repeated when bin inspections reveal further infestations [8].

Angoumois Grain Moth

The Angoumois grain moth (*Sitotroga cerealella*) is found all over the world. It infests grain in storage, but also in the field in the warm and tropical areas. It is particularly serious in the Southeastern states. Infestation is indicated by capped-over round holes in the kernels. The small white larva has a yellowish head. The adult is a grayish-brown moth with pointed hair-fringed wings about a half-inch wide when spread [8].

The moths deposit their eggs on grain in storage, but in warm climates, eggs also are laid on exposed ear tips before the corn is harvested. The larvae hatch, bore into the grain, feed, and grow. Pupation occurs within the grain, and moths emerge to deposit more eggs. A generation requires about 30 days in warm climates. Infestation is continuous in cribbed corn in the South.

Control consists in fumigation of the stored grain as for the rice weevil.

Other Stored Corn Insects

Other stored-grain insects that infest corn or corn products include the granary weevil (*Sitophilus granarius*), the flat grain beetle (*Laemophloeus pusillus*), saw-toothed grain beetle (*Oryzaephilus surinamensis*), cadelle (*Tenebroides mauritanicus*), flour beetle (*Tribolium* spp.), Indian-meal moth (*Plodia interpunctella*), and pink corn worm (*Pyroderces rileyi*).

Control measures consist of storage bin sanitation and fumigation as for the rice weevil.

REFERENCES

1. Baker, W. A., W. G. Bradley, and C. A. Clark, "Biological control of the European corn borer in the United States," USDA *Tech. Bul. 983.* 1949.
2. Bigger, J. H., and F. C. Bauer, "Plowing dates as they affected the abundance of corn root aphids at Clayton, Illinois, 1929–32," *J. Am. Soc. Agron.*, **31**: 695–697. 1939.
3. ———, and H. B. Petty, "Reduction of corn borer numbers from October to June, a ten-year study," Ill. Ag. Exp. Sta. *Bul. 566.* 1953.
4. Blanchard, R. A., and W. A. Douglas, "The corn earworm as an enemy of field corn in the Eastern States," USDA *Farmers Bul. 1651.* (rev.). 1953.
5. Bradley, W. G., "The European corn borer," in *Insects.* USDA Yrbk. of Ag. pp 614–621. 1952.
6. Coffman, F. A., W. H. Tisdale, and J. F. Brandon, "Observations on corn smut at Akron, Colorado." *J. Am. Soc. Agron.*, **18**(5): 403–411. 1926.
7. "Corn borer control in field corn," Ill. *Exten. Cir. 637.* 1949.
8. Cotton R. T., "Control of insects attacking grain in farm storage." USDA *Farmers Bul. 1811.* 1938.
9. Cralley, E. M., "Corn seed treatment." Ark. Ag. Exp. Sta. *Bul. 466.* 1947.
10. Crane, P. L., "Factors affecting resistance to Pythium seedling blight of maize incited by *Pythium ultimum.*" *Agron. J.*, **48**(8): 365–368. 1956.
11. Davis, J. J., "The corn root aphid and methods of controlling it." USDA *Farmers Bul. 891.* 1917. (rev. 1949).
12. Decker, O. C., J. H. Bigger, and C. J. Weinman, "Spraying the margins of fields as a substitute for barrier construction in chinch bug control." *J. Econ. Ent.*, **46**: 316–320. 1953.
13. Dicke, F. F., "The most important corn insects," in *Corn and Corn Improvement*, New York: Academic Press. pp 537–612. 1955.
14. ———, and M. T. Jenkins, "Susceptibility of certain strains of field corn in hybrid combinations to damage by corn ear-worms." USDA *Tech. Bul. 898.* 1945.
15. ———, and L. H. Penny, "Built-in resistance helps fight corn borers." *Crops and Soils*, **4**(9): 9–11. 1952.
16. Dickson, J. G., *Diseases of Field Crops*, 2d ed. New York: McGraw-Hill. pp 74–114. 1956.
17. Douglas, W. A., and C. E. Smith, "Control of corn earworm and rice weevil in dent corn with DDT—mineral oil emulsions." *J. Econ. Ent.*, **46**: 683–684. 1953.
18. Durrell, L. W., "Dry rot of corn." Ia. Ag. Exp. Sta. *Res. Bul. 77.* 1923.
19. Elliott, C., "Bacterial wilt of corn." USDA *Farmers Bul. 1878.* 1941.
20. ———, "Relative susceptibility to Pythium root rot of twelve dent corn inbreds." *J. Ag. Res.*, **64**(12): 711–723. 1942.
21. ———, "A Pythium stalk rot of corn." *J. Ag. Res.*, **66**(1): 21–39. 1943.
22. ———, and F. W. Poos, "Seasonal development, insect vectors, and host range of bacterial wilt of sweet corn." *J. Ag. Res.*, **60**(10): 645–686. 1940.

23. "European corn borer control for Nebraska," Nebr. Ag. Exp. Sta. *Ext. Cir. 1555*. 1950.

24. "The European corn borer and its control," Nor. Cent. Reg. *Publ. No. 22* (rev.). 1952.

25. "The European corn borer and its control," USDA *Farmers Bul. 2084*. 1955.

26. Gunderson, H., and J. H. Lilly, "Control corn rootworms." Ia. Ag. Exten. Serv. *Pamph. 178* (rev.). 1953.

27. Harris, M. R., "The relationship of *Cephalosporium acremonium* to the black-bundle disease of corn." *Phytopath.*, **26**: 965–980. 1936.

28. Hooker, A. L., and J. G. Dickson, "Resistance to Pythium manifest by excised corn embryos at low temperatures." *Agron. J.*, **44**(8): 443–447. 1952.

29. Hoppe, P. E., "Differences in Pythium injury to corn seedlings at high and low soil temperatures." *Phytopath.*, **39**: 77–84. 1949.

30. ———, "Infestations of corn seedlings," in *Plant Diseases*. USDA Yrbk. of Ag. pp 377–380. 1953.

31. Huber, L. L., C. R. Neiswander, and R. M. Salter, "The European corn borer and its environment." Ohio Ag. Exp. Sta. *Bul. 429*. 1928.

32. Immer, F. R., and J. J. Christensen, "Further studies on the reaction of corn to smut and the effect of smut on yield." *Phytopath.*, **21**: 661–674. 1931.

33. Jenkins, M. T., and A. L. Robert, "Inheritance of resistance to the leaf blight of corn caused by *Helminthosporium turcicum*." *Agron. J.*, **44**: 136–140. 1952.

34. ———, A. L. Robert, and W. R. Findley Jr., "Reaction of inbred lines of corn to *Helminthosporium turcicum* Pass. in different seasons." *Agron. J.*, **49**: 481–483. 1957.

35. ———, and A. L. Robert, "Evaluating the breeding potential of inbred lines of corn resistant to the leaf blight caused by *Helminthosporium turcicum*." *Agron. J.*, **51**: 93–96. 1959.

36. Johnson, I. J., and J. J. Christensen, "Relation between number, size, and location of smut infections to reduction in yield in corn." *Phytopath.*, **25**: 223–233. 1935.

37. Koehler, B., "Natural mode of entrance of fungi into corn ears and some symptoms that indicate infection." *J. Ag. Res.*, **64**(8): 421–442. 1942.

38. ———, and J. R. Holbert, "Corn diseases in Illinois." Ill. Ag. Exp. Sta. *Bul. 354*. 1930.

39. ———, and J. R. Holbert, "Combatting corn diseases." Ill. Ag. Exp. Sta. *Cir. 484*. 1938.

40. Leukel, R. W., and V. F. Tapke, "Cereal smuts and their control." USDA *Farmers Bul. 2069*. 1954.

41. Lilly, J. H., and H. Gunderson, "Insecticides for soil insects." *Iowa Farm Science*, **7**(9): 15–17. 1953.

42. Luginbill, P., "Habits and control of the fall armyworm." USDA *Farmers Bul. 1990*. 1950.

43. McNew, G. L., "Crown infection of corn by *Diplodia zeae*." Ia. Ag. Exp. Sta. *Res. Bul. 216*. 1937.

44. Mohler, J. G., *Corn in Knasas*. Rpt. of Kans. St. Bd. Ag., **48**(191): 1–283. 1929.

45. Muma, M. H., "Insects injurious to corn in Nebraska." Nebr. Ext. Serv. *Cir. 1537*. 1946.

46. Otto, H. J., and H. L. Everett, "Influence of nitrogen and potassium fertilization on the incidence of stalk rot of corn." *Agron. J.*, **48**: 301–305. 1956.

47. Packard, C. M., P. Luginbill, and C. Benton, "How to fight the chinch bug." USDA *Farmers Bul. 1780*. 1937 (rev. 1951).

48. Painter, R. H., and D. A. Wilbur, "The European corn borer in Kansas." Kans. Ag. Exp. Sta. *Cir. 262.* 1950.

49. Parker, D. T., and W. C. Burrows, "Root and stalk rot in corn as affected by fertilizers and tillage treatment." *Agron. J.*, **51**(7): 414–417. 1959.

50. Parker, J. R., "Grasshoppers: A new look at an ancient enemy." USDA *Farmers Bul. 2064.* 1954.

51. Penny, L. H., and F. F. Dicke, "Inheritance of resistance in corn to leaf feeding of the European corn borer." *Agron. J.*, **48**: 200–203. 1956.

52. ———, and F. F. Dicke, "A single gene-pair controlling segregation for European corn borer resistance." *Agron. J.*, **49**: 193–196. 1957.

53. Raleigh, W. P., "Infection studies of *Diplodia zeae* (Schw.) Lev. and control of seedling blights of corn." Ia. Ag. Exp. Sta. *Res. Bul. 124.* 1930.

54. Rand, F. V., and L. C. Cash, "Bacterial wilt in corn." USDA *Tech. Bul. 362.* 1933 (rev. 1937).

55. Robert, A. L., "Some of the leaf blights of corn," in *Plant Diseases.* USDA Yrbk. of Ag. pp 380–385. 1953.

56. ———, "Bacterial wilt and Stewarts leaf blight of corn." USDA *Farmers Bul. 2092.* 1955.

57. Russell, W. A., and A. L. Hooker, "Inheritance of resistance in corn to rust, *Puccinia sorghi* Schw., and genetic relationships among different sources of resistance." *Agron. J.*, **51**: 21–24. 1959.

58. Shelford, V. F., and W. P. Flint, "Populations of the chinch bug in the upper Mississippi Valley from 1823–1940." *Ecol.*, **24**: 435–455. 1943.

59. Smeltzer, D. G., "Relationship between Fusarium ear rot and corn earworm infestation." *Agron. J.*, **51**: 53–54. 1959.

60. "The southern cornstalk borer," USDA *Lflt. 363.* 1954.

61. "The sugarcane beetle on corn in the Southern States," USDA *Lflt. 362.* 1954.

62. Tate, H. D., and O. S. Bare, "Corn rootworms." Nebr. Ag. Exp. Sta. *Bul. 381.* 1946.

63. Ullstrup, A. J., "Diseases of dent corn in the United States." USDA *Cir. 674.* 1943.

64. ———, "An undescribed ear rot of corn caused by *Physalospora zeae*." *Phytopath.*, **36**: 201–212. 1946.

65. ———, "Diseases of dent corn in Indiana." Purdue Ag. Exp. Sta. *Cir. 359.* 1950.

66. ———, "Leaf blights of corn." Ind. Ag. Exp. Sta. *Bul. 572.* 1952.

67. ———, "Some smuts and rusts of corn," in *Plant Diseases.* USDA Yrbk. of Ag. pp 386–389. 1953.

68. ———, "Several ear rots of corn," in *Plant Diseases.* USDA Yrbk. of Ag. pp 390–392. 1953.

69. ———, "Diseases of corn," in *Corn and Corn Improvement.* New York: Academic press. pp 465–536. 1955.

70. Vorhees, R. K. "Sclerotial rot of corn caused by *Rhizoctonia zeae*, n. sp." *Phytopath.*, **24**: 1290–1303. 1934.

71. Walton, W. R. and C. M. Packard, "The armyworm and its control." USDA *Farmers Bul. 1850.* Revised 1951.

72. Wilbur, D. A. N. R. Bryson and R. H. Painter "Southwestern corn borer in Kansas." Kans. Ag. Exp. Sta. *Bul. 339.* 1950.

73. Wilcoxson, R. I., and R. P. Covey, "The relationship between corn plant populations and smut infection." *Agron. J.*, **52**(9): 545. 1960.

Corn

10. BREEDING[1]

NATURE OF CORN IMPROVEMENT

Before 1920, corn improvement in the United States was accomplished largely through selection within open-pollinated varieties. Since that time, more and more emphasis in research has been placed on corn hybrids.

New hybrid varieties of corn are sought that will be superior in yield as well as in other characteristics to those now in production. These hybrids must also be adapted to the area where they are to be grown. Improvements sought in hybrids may include lodging resistance, resistance to ear droppage, long ear husks to reduce insect damage, disease resistance, insect resistance, and special qualities. High protein, high oil, and high amylose content are included as quality factors.

CYTOGENETICS

Cytogenetics in maize involves the interpretation of genetic phenomena due to differences in chromosome morphology, polyploidy, and interspecific hybridization [62, 30, 61].

Chromosome Morphology

The 10 A-chromosomes that comprise the gametic number in maize can be recognized by their relative lengths, chromosome-arm ratios, and knob positions at the prophase of the first meiotic division.

[1] More detailed information on corn breeding is available in *Corn and Corn Improvement*, G. F. Sprague, ed., New York: Academic Press, 1955. See Chapter 5. Another excellent general reference is *Methods of Plant Breeding*, 2d ed., by H. K. Hayes, F. R. Immer, and D. C. Smith, New York: McGraw-Hill, 1955. See Chapters 14 and 15.

A special type of supernumerary chromosome is designated as a B-type. These B-chromosomes are not homologous with A-chromosomes. They appear to be genetically inert because they are not essential for normal growth. When there are more than 10 or 15 of them, several abnormalities appear which increase in intensity with increases in numbers. These abnormalities include reduction in fertility, decreased vigor, defective kernels, aborted pollen, and the like. Seed is rarely produced on plants having 25 or more B-chromosomes [43, 55, 57, 61].

Polyploidy

Corn has 10 regular chromosomes in the reproductive cells (haploid), 20 in the somatic cells (diploid), and 30 in the endosperm cells (triploid). There are from 1 to 8 chromosome sets in corn plants.

Monoploid or haploid plants, which have one set of chromosomes, arise spontaneously by the parthenogenetic development of unfertilized eggs. Androgenic (paternal) haploids have also been obtained in low frequency [26]. Monoploids are smaller and weaker plants than are the diploids. Homozygous diploid lines have been produced directly from monoploid maize plants as a result of occasional spontaneous doubling of the chromosome complement. Monoploid maize is useful as a possible source of homozygous diploid inbred lines [7, 8].

Triploid plants that arise in diploid populations usually come from the fertilization of a diploid or unreduced egg by a haploid sperm. Triploids also occur regularly in the hybridization of diploid with tetraploid lines [61]. When triploid plants are selfed, some plants are isolated with $2n + 1$ chromosomes known as trisomics. The supernumery chromosome is identical with its two homologues in primary trisomics.

Tetraploid maize plants have been produced artificially when the chromosome number is doubled by heat treatments applied to young ears at the time of the first divisions of the young embryo [56], or by use of the genetic marker, elongate (el) [1]. Tetraploids have been induced with a frequency of 2–5 per cent. Tetraploid corn resembles diploid in points of height and growth habit, but it has broader leaves, sturdier stalks, and larger tassels, ears, and kernels [61]. Tetraploid strains are not as fertile as the diploid lines from which they are derived. There are meiotic irregularities in tetraploid maize, with the result that the offspring do not always have 40 chromosomes [56, 62]. Doubling the number of chromosomes in pure yellow corn has been found to cause a 40 per cent increase in the content of carotenoid pigment [58].

Octoploids also have been obtained from tetraploids by heat treatment of the young ears.

Intergeneric Hybrids

Corn has been crossed with two related genera, teosinte (*Euchlaena* spp.) and gama grass (*Tripsacum* spp.). Teosinte is undoubtedly the closest relative of maize.

Corn crosses readily with each of three annual strains of teosinte, commonly called the Chalco, Durango, and Florida varieties. Chromosomes of the two genera are similar, except in the short arm of Chromosome 9 in the Durango and Florida hybrids with maize [3].

Gama grass (*Tripsacum dactyloides*) crosses much less readily with maize than does teosinte. By use of a special technique, it has been possible to cross both the diploid ($2n = 36$) and tetraploid ($2n = 72$) forms with maize ($2n = 20$). The F_1 hybrids in both cases are almost completely sterile. The F_1 hybrid of corn with diploid gama grass has been crossed with annual teosinte to produce a trigeneric hybrid that contains chromosomes of corn, teosinte, and gama grass [50].

GENETICS

Corn is well suited to genetic research because it is readily cultivated, produces a relatively large number of seeds per ear, affords an abundance of distinct hereditary variations, and because the sexes are separated on the plant. Consequently, the corn plant has occupied a prominent place in the development of genetic principles since 1910. This advance in theoretical knowledge has furnished the basic material on which modern corn breeding is based. Nearly 500 mutant genes, most of them simple recessives, have been listed [20, 82]. Mutations have been found that affect endosperm characters, chlorophyll development, plant colors, plant height, root development, strength of stalk, disease resistance, insect resistance, and many other characteristics [30, 61].

Endosperm Characters

Xenia may result when varieties that differ in a single visible endosperm character are crossed. When a character difference is dependent upon a single dominant factor carried by the male parent, xenia occurs. When dominance is incomplete, xenia occurs when either variety is the male.

Endosperm characters separate some of the major corn groups. Starchy endosperm is dominant over sweet with a 3:1 segregation of starchy to sweet in F_2. Starchy also is dominant over waxy as a single-factor difference. Moreover, yellow endosperm is dominant over colorless (white). Three pairs of factors for yellow color have been described [54]. Both starchy vs.

sugary kernel type and yellow vs. white endosperm color exhibit xenia effects.

Normally, a dominant character in the endosperm is not suppressed by two doses of the recessive character, but crosses between floury and flinty types afford an exception. In a flinty × floury cross, the endosperm of the F_1 is flinty in character (FFf). In the reciprocal cross, floury × flinty, the F_1 endosperm is floury (ffF). The dominance of F over f is insufficient to produce flintiness in the presence of two doses of the recessive factor for floury.

Some characters depend on the combined action of several different genes. For example, purple aleurone color develops only in the presence of five dominant genes. The genes which must be present as dominants are designated A_1, A_2, C, R, and Pr. There are several combinations that produce white kernels. Some crosses also will produce red or purple corn [41]. There is a series of allelic factors for the A-locus, R-locus, and C-locus that cause modifications of aleurone color.

Numerous characters cause incomplete development of the endosperm. A total of fourteen factors (de_1 . . . de_{14}) have been associated with endosperm deficiency. These factors, which are simple recessives to normal, produce different degrees of endosperm expression. Based on dry weight of the seeds, de_1 gives an endosperm that is 50.4 per cent of the normal, whereas de_{14} gives an endosperm that is only 2.4 per cent of the normal. The other factors in the series are intermediate in expression. It has been shown that waxy, floury, shrunken, brittle, and the fourteen defective endosperm types can be arranged in a series based on the percentage reduction from normal. Thus, at least 18 dominant factors appear to be necessary in maize to produce normal endosperm [49].

Chlorophyll Variations

Recessive heritable chlorophyll abnormalities that affect leaf colors are fairly common in maize. These may be expressed in either the seedling or the mature plant, or in both.

At least 86 genes affect normal chlorophyll development in seedlings. Chlorophyll-deficient seedlings are generally white, virescent, or luteus (yellow). There are eight or more white-seedling types or albinos, each due to a single gene in the homozygous recessive condition, which die when the endosperm reserves are depleted. In two cases, duplicate genes also are involved in white seedlings. At least seven genes exist for luteus seedlings. Most luteus types are lethal, but some give yellow seedlings and plants. There are twenty or more virescent seedling types. Some of these are lethal, whereas others develop into normal-appearing green plants. The amount of chlorophyll in different virescent types is influenced by environmental conditions, primarily temperature. There are at least ten genetic types of pale-green seedlings that produce a yellowish-green color in the seedling. Some are lethal, but others develop to maturity. About 37 other genes affect seedling chlorophyll color alone or in conjunction with mature-plant color [27].

At least seventeen mature-plant chlorophyll abnormalities also have been described; golden, green-striped, japonica variegated leaf, fine-striped, blotched leaf (with necrotic areas), and others [42, 9, 10].

The interaction of more than 100 genes is necessary for normal chlorophyll development.

Plant Colors

The interactions of the five nonallelic genes A_1, A_2, B, Pl, and R are known to be concerned with color in the corn plant [17]. These are described in Table 10-1 [18].

TABLE 10-1. **Interaction of the Plant Color Genes.**

Genes			With r^{rr} Plant Color	Anther Color	With R^{gg} Plant Color	Anther Color
A_1A_2	B	Pl	purple	purple	purple	green
"	B	pl	sunred	pink	sunred	green
"	b	Pl	dilute purple	purple	green	green
"	b	pl	dilute sunred	pink	green	green
$A_1a^*_2$	B	Pl	brown	green	brown	green
"	B	pl	green	green	green	green
a_1a_2	b	Pl	green	green	green	green
"	b	pl	green	green	green	green

* NOTE: A_1a_2 and a_1A_2 are equivalents.

Male Sterility

There are many known factors for genetic male sterility. A total of 20 genes (ms_1 . . . ms_{20}) have been listed [20], but numerous others also have been found. One group of genes causes pollen sterility due to incompletely developed pollen unable to effect fertilization. Cytologically, these male-steriles are characterized by degeneration of the microsporocytes, or of the microspore cells [4].

The first cytoplasmic male-sterile stock described in corn was obtained from a Peruvian variety. When crossed to the normal form, the F_1 plants were all male sterile. It was demonstrated that pollen sterility was controlled by the cytoplasm [60]. This stock has been lost. Another type of cytoplasmic male-sterility originated from a cross that involved the genetic type known as "Iojap" [76]. Certain lines also have the ability to restore fertility, which appears to be conditioned by a single dominant gene [38]. A cytoplasmic male-sterile stock has been reported from Texas where it was obtained from Mexican June strains. When inbreds were crossed on this sterile stock, the F_1 hybrids of some combinations were completely sterile, others exhibited partial or complete fertility [70].

In corn, cytoplasmic male sterile types can be utilized as seed parents to eliminate the cost of detasseling in the commercial production of hybrid seed. Fertility must be restored in the commercial crop where grain yield is the objective. Hybrids are now being produced with the Texas source of sterility in which one or both inbred lines of the male single cross carries the fertility-restoration factor [18]. This means that about half the plants in commercial seed fields are totally fertile. These plants usually produce sufficient pollen for a satisfactory seed set [76]. Pollen fertility restoration in cytoplasmic male-sterile crosses of corn that involves the Texas types of cytoplasm is due primarily to two dominant genes, Rf_1 and Rf_2 [11]. The Rf_1 gene is located on chromosome 3 [5]. The Rf_2 gene is almost universally present. The known exceptions include inbred WF9 and its backcross derivatives, most of which are $rf_1rf_1rf_2rf_2$.

Disease Reaction

In general, the resistance of a corn hybrid to any disease is proportional to the number of resistant inbreds that were combined to make the hybrid.

Resistance to the northern leaf blight (*Helminthosporium turcicum*) is controlled by numerous genes [33, 34]. Resistance to the southern leaf blight (*H. maydis*) also appears to be due to a large number of genes, but different ones than those that control resistance in the northern leaf blight [51]. There are two known physiologic races of Helminthosporium leaf spot (*H. carbonum*). Resistance to Race I is determined by a single dominant gene, Hm, located in chromosome 1 [81]. Inheritance of resistance to Race II probably includes a number of genes [40].

Resistance to bacterial wilt (*Bacterium stewarti*) is controlled by three independent dominant genes, Sw, Sw_2, and Sw_3. All three genes present in a dominant condition affords a high degree of resistance; the triple recessive condition results in a high degree of susceptibility to the disease [83].

There are at least seven physiologic races of leaf rust (*Puccinia sorghi*) on corn in the United States [80]. Resistance to Races I and III has been explained as a monogenic dominant [48]. A later study of six resistant maize lines adds confirmation, with the possibility that the genes involved are in an allelic series or the loci are closely linked with less than 5 per cent of cross-ing over [71]. Both dominant and recessive genes at additional loci may also condition resistance.

Inheritance of resistance to common smut of corn (*Ustilago maydis*) appears to be determined by a relatively large number of genes. Genes for smut resistance have been reported in chromosomes 6, 7, and 8 [72].

Insect Resistance

In general, resistance of corn to insect attacks appears to be controlled by a number of genes.

Resistance of corn to the European corn borer (*Pyrausta nubilalis*) appears to be conditioned by multiple factors in most instances. General observations indicate that resistance of double-cross hybrids is related to the resistance of the inbred parents [76]. Leaf-feeding ratings, in one cross between resistant and susceptible inbred lines, indicated the segregation of genes for borer resistance at three or more loci. In another cross, two or more genes appeared to be involved [52]. In a later study, a single dominant gene appeared to control resistance to leaf feeding by the borer [53].

Resistance of corn to the earworm (*Heliothis armigera*) appears to be conditioned by multiple factors. Resistant hybrids should have long, tight husks as well as hard-textured kernels over the tip of the ear.

Chemical Characters

A classical example of selection for chemical composition in corn is the long-range experiment started by C. G. Hopkins at the Illinois Station in 1896. The original Burr White variety had a mean oil content of 4.7 per cent and a mean protein content of 10.9 per cent. After 50 generations of selections, the mean oil content of Illinois High Oil was 15.4 per cent, while that of Illinois Low Oil was only 1.0 per cent. The mean protein content of Illinois High Protein was 19.5 per cent, while that of Illinois Low Protein was 4.9 per cent [84, 40]. The minimum number of genes involved in protein differences between Illinois high and low strains has been estimated as 22 pairs [22], but probably a similar number determines the minimum differ-ence between Illinois high and low oil strains [25]. A slight dominance of both high-oil and high-protein percentages is indicated.

Niacin content of the corn grain is inherited as a quantitative charac-ter. Hybrids tend to be intermediate between their parents, but the seed parent generally exercises more influence than does the pollen parent [68, 69].

High amylose content is controlled by the recessive gene, ae. Crosses between lines that involved this gene segregated in F_3 for amylose contents that ranged from 25.4 to 70.3 per cent. Ordinary maize contains about 27 per cent of amylose, a linear-type molecule, and 73 per cent amylopectin, large branched molecules. Starch of high amylose content can be used in the production of plastics [85].

Other Maize Characters

Kernel-row number is a quantitative character in maize, but it is less affected by environmental diversity than are most characters of this type. Crosses among practically homozygous inbreds of like row number most frequently produce F_1 progeny with more rows on the average than the mid-parent values. Crosses between 8- and 12-rowed inbreds most frequently gave F_1 progeny with fewer rows on the average than the mid-parent value. Results of crosses of 8-rowed with 16- and 18-rowed types indicated that selection of F_2 parents with different row numbers produced significantly different F_3 progeny [21].

LINKAGE GROUPS

Many genes for the different characters in maize have been located in the ten linkage groups that correspond to the ten morphologically distinguishable chromosomes. These chromosomes are numbered mainly in order of decreased length, from 1 . . . 10; that is, chromosome 1 is the longest, chromosome 10 the shortest. A few genes of economic importance are noted for each linkage group [27, 39]:

Chromosome 1: Resistance to grasshoppers (ag) from Maiz Amargo; resistance vs. susceptibility to leaf blight, *Helminthosporium carbonum* (Hm hm).

Chromosome 2: Plant color booster (B) that gives intense sun red, purple, or brown plant color in appropriate genotypes; floury endosperm (fl).

Chromosome 3: Barren stalk (ba); anthocyanin plant, aleurone, and pericarp color (A); shrunken endosperm-2 (sh₂). The long arm of this chromosome contains one of the genes for European corn borer resistance.

Chromosome 4: Starchy vs. sugary endosperm (Su su); tunicate vs. normal plants (Tu tu). This chromosome has 2 genes for resistance to leaf blight, *Helminthosporium turcicum*.

Chromosome 5: Purple vs. red aleurone (Pr pr); high amylose (ae); anthocyanin-2 (A₂), dominant allele complementary to A factor (Chromosome 3) in the production of plant and aleurone colors.

Chromosome 6: Yellow vs. white endosperm (Yy); plant color factor pair (Pl pl).

Chromosome 7: Hairy sheath (Hs), with leaf sheaths hairy throughout development; brown aleurone (Bn), shows only in absence of purple or red aleurone.

Chromosome 8: Virescent seedling-16 (v_{16}); japonica (j), variegated white stripes in leaves and sheaths.

Chromosome 9: Aleurone color (C), gives purple or red aleurone in appropriate genotypes; starchy vs. waxy endosperm (Wx wx).

Chromosome 10: Resistance to Race III of rust, *Puccinia sorghi* (Rp); colored aleurone and plant (R), gives purple or red aleurone in appropriate genotypes.

HETEROSIS OR HYBRID VIGOR

Heterosis is the phenomenon in which a cross of two stocks produces a hybrid that is superior in size, yield, or general vigor. In classical genetics, heterosis involves the increased vigor of the F_1 (first filial) generation over that of the greater parent. In statistical or quantitative genetics, the criterion of heterosis is the superiority of the F_1 over the average of the two parents. This is necessary because the common measures of variation are based on deviations from a mean.

Two different hypotheses have been advanced to account for heterosis: physiologic stimulation, and dominant favorable growth factors. Under either hypothesis, heterosis and inbreeding depression are different aspects of the same phenomenon. Under the first hypothesis, the loss in vigor upon inbreeding is due to a disappearance of stimulation as the strains become homozygous. Under the second hypothesis, the reduction in vigor is due to the uncovering of deleterious recessives as inbreeding progresses.

Physiologic stimulation attributes the vigor of the F_1 in maize to its heterozygous condition. Thus, the greater the number of genes for which the plant is heterozygous, the greater its heterosis. For example, a hybrid with a genetic constitution AaBbCcDd would be more vigorous than another hybrid with a genetic constitution of AABBccDd. Theoretically, it would be impossible to obtain an inbred line as vigorous as the F_1 hybrids, should this heterozygosity theory be responsible for heterosis. Diversity of germ plasm definitely affects the degree of heterosis [14, 15, 40].

A genetic mechanism, by which physiologic stimulation might arise, has been proposed by E. M. East [13]. This hypothesis involves a series of alleles at locus A, for example, such as A^1, A^2, A^3, and A^4. Each allele of a higher order is assumed to have a positive-action function, divergence being further and further from that of A^1. Thus, A^1A^4 would have a greater physiological efficiency than would A^1A^2 [66]. Another possible genetic mechanism was proposed by F. H. Hull [28]. The superiority of the heterozygote Aa, over either homozygote AA or aa, was defined as over-dominance.

The hypothesis of cumulative interactions of many favorable dominant, or partially dominant, linked genes assumes that dominant factors contributed by each parent are favorable while recessive factors are harmful. Thus, a hybrid is more vigorous than its parents because it has more dominant factors [6, 36]. Except for linkage and the large number of factors involved, it would be possible under this hypothesis to obtain inbred lines that were equal to the F_1 hybrid in yield.

The dominance hypothesis has considerable intuitive appeal because most of the genetic traits studied exhibit partial to complete dominance. A large amount of accumulated data indicate that partial to complete dominance also accounts for most of the observed heterosis. However, over-dominance has not been excluded [46], and it appears possible that both types of gene action may be involved. In that event, the relative importance of the two types of gene action becomes more pertinent than the matter of which hypothesis is correct.

IMPROVEMENT OF OPEN-POLLINATED CORN

Improvement of corn probably has taken place since the earliest date of its cultivation by primitive man. Many of the superior varieties of open-pollinated corn in the United States were developed by farmer-breeders before 1900. Mass selection was the most widely used method for corn improvement, although ear-to-row selection and variety hybridization received some attention [63, 65, 30, 75, 76, 77, 40]. The application of these breeding methods to corn in the United States is now primarily of historical interest: open-pollinated varieties represented only about 5 per cent of the total corn acreage in 1959.

Mass Selection

Mass selection in corn consists in the selection of desirable ears from the better plants, after which the selected seed is planted *en masse*. A certain amount of mass selection has been practiced by corn growers since the earliest times. This method has been important in the improvement of open-pollinated varieties by modification of maturity, ear type, plant type, and chemical composition. Until recently, mass selection was considered rather ineffective for the attainment of increased acre yields, due possibly to the fact that environmental effects completely overshadowed genetic effects in the early work. Most early American varieties were developed by mass selection—for example, Reid Yellow Dent. Due to the complex mixture of hybrids in open-pollinated varieties, mass selection has been almost completely dependent upon the accuracy of the visual identification [75, 76, 77]. Experience has shown that yields may be maintained, or even slightly increased, when selection for a specific type is not too close. Nebraska work on mass selection for grain yield in the Hays Golden open-pollinated variety indicates a 3.9 per cent gain per year over the original variety during a four-year period. This is in close agreement with genetic gain predicted from information obtained on additive genetic variance [23].

Ear-type selection became popular about 1900, with the advent of the corn show. Characteristics associated with show-type ears were assumed to be of value for the production of high yields, even though such selection usually was made without reference to the plant that produced the ear. Numerous experiments were conducted 1910–25 to measure the relationship between ear characters and yield performance in the field. In general, long smooth, heavy ears with less than the average number of kernel rows produced higher average yields than did other ear types [63]. Close selection for a particular ear type in the Boone County White variety resulted in decreased productiveness, comparable to the effects of inbreeding [24].

Varietal Hybridization

Varietal hybridization utilizes F_1 crosses between open-pollinated varieties of corn to obtain larger yields. American Indians probably utilized hybridization long before the advent of the white man. Their religious ceremonies resulted in semicontrolled mixtures of types characterized by different endosperm colors. The first controlled experiments on varietal hybridization, from which yield data were obtained, were reported by W. J. Beal of the Michigan Station in 1877. He states that hybrids outyielded their parent varieties by amounts that range from 10–50 per cent [76].

Results from 244 comparisons between parents and hybrids reveal that 82 per cent of the crosses yielded more than the average of the parents, while 18 per cent produced less. Approximately 56 per cent of the crosses produced yields in excess of the higher-yielding parent. In general, the highest-yielding crosses involved high-yielding parents that differed considerably in ear type. Crosses between flint or flour types and dents usually produced increased yields. Dent-by-dent crosses exhibited less superiority [63]. Some varietal hybrids have performed well in the Netherlands, Yugoslavia, and Mexico [40].

Ear-to-Row Selection

Ear-to-row selection—one form of the progeny test—was introduced by C. G. Hopkins at the Illinois Station about 1896 in experiments to modify the chemical composition of the corn kernel. The relative productiveness of different ears is evaluated by planting a portion of the seed from each ear in individual rows, from which performance of the plots is determined. Seed from the higher yielding ears is increased for commercial use.

The original ear-to-row procedures were modified by various investigators to overcome specific difficulties. Performance tests were improved by use of replications as well as by check rows. Inbreeding was lessened by detasseling plants in parts of the rows. Seed was composited from detasseled plants of high-yielding progenies. Seed of progenies that showed promise was increased.

Ear-to-row selection apparently is effective for plant or seed characteristics that can be evaluated accurately by visual observation. The method does not affect yield, except for relatively unselected varieties in the first few years of selection [30].

Ear-to-row selection was compared with mass selection at the Illinois Station [73]. Seed of 990 selected ears were planted ear-to-row. Composited seed of these same ears was planted in an isolated plot and maintained by mass selection. Selection was made for both high and low yield in the pedigree or ear-to-row type of selection. The Illinois Station strain of Reid Yellow Dent was used as a standard. The high-yielding strain, maintained by ear-to-row selection, yielded 108.3 per cent of Reid Yellow Dent, compared with 106.1 per cent for the nonpedigree strain maintained by mass selection as an average for the second five-year period. The low-yielding strain developed by ear-to-row selection averaged 85.7 per cent of Reid Yellow Dent. Selection for low yield by the ear-to-row method was more effective than selection for high yield [40].

HYBRIDS BETWEEN INBRED LINES

Hybrid corn is the F_1 progeny from a cross that involves inbred lines. The breeding of hybrid corn involves certain basic principles: development of inbred lines by controlled self-pollination, determination of the more productive lines in crosses, and the utilization of superior crosses in the commercial production of hybrid corn [30, 75, 76, 66] (Fig. 10-1). The types of hybrids generally grown are single crosses, three-way crosses, and double crosses (see Chap. 6).

History of Corn Hybrids

Hybrid corn was developed as a result of genetic research. Before 1900, corn had been self-fertilized occasionally by a few investigators.

W. J. Beal of the Michigan Station, who began to experiment with corn variety crosses in 1878, self-fertilized corn plants by controlled self-pollination methods. Inbreeding of corn was conducted between 1900 and 1908 by the U.S. Department of Agriculture, and also by the Illinois and Connecticut Agricultural Experiment Stations. The inbred lines were found to be inferior to open-pollinated varieties in vigor as well as in yield. These investigations were stimulated when G. H. Shull reported in 1908 and 1909 that a

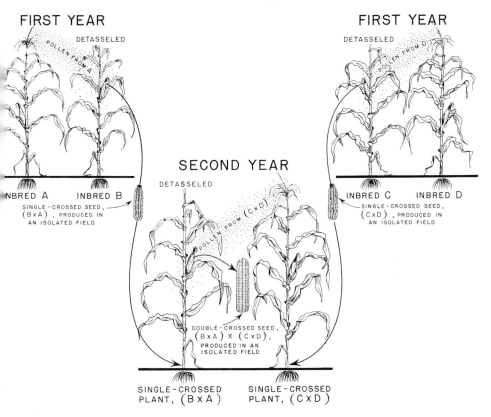

FIGURE 10-1. **Method for the production of double-cross hybrid seed from 4 inbred lines of corn.**

(*Courtesy US Department of Agriculture*)

large amount of vigor resulted from crosses between certain inbred lines. The first crosses were single crosses that generally proved to be unsatisfactory commercially because of low seed yields produced on inbred parents. This difficulty was overcome by the double cross developed by D. F. Jones at the Connecticut Station in 1917. The first hybrid for commercial growing was the Burr-Leaming double cross produced in Connecticut in 1920. Modern commercial production of corn hybrids began at Johnston, Iowa, in 1926.

Development of Inbred Lines

The development of inbred lines in corn necessitates artificially controlled pollination. In hand pollination, the uppermost ear shoot is covered to keep out foreign pollen before the silks emerge. Small glassine bags generally are used for this purpose. The appropriate tassel is enclosed with a large heavy paper bag after the silks have become visible within the ear-shoot bag. The tassel must have started to shed pollen by the time it is covered. A day or two later, pollen is collected in the tassel bag and dusted on the silks of the desired plant. The pollinated ear shoot is covered with the large tassel bag until harvest.

Most inbred lines involved in present-day hybrids were developed by either self-pollination (application of a plant's pollen to its own silks) or sib-pollination (the application of a plant's pollen to silks of a sister plant). Self-pollinated plants approach homozygosis approximately three times more rapidly than plants that are brother-sister mated [35].

Rigid selection should be practiced so as to isolate superior inbred lines. Plants are selected for desired traits such as vigor, yield, standability, maturity, low ears, dark green chlorophyll, good tassels, disease resistance, insect resistance, and freedom from abnormalities. Many recessive characters are uncovered when corn plants are self-fertilized. Some of these are undesirable seed, seedling, or mature plant abnormalities [49]. Such plants often fail to survive; others are eliminated in selection.

The purpose of inbreeding is to isolate superior lines that breed true for their characteristics. After 3–4 generations of self-fertilization, lines become distinct types that breed true. Inbreeding is accompanied by a reduction in vigor, more marked in earlier than later inbred generations. Uniformity for most characters is attained after 5–7 years of inbreeding [30]. Further reductions in vigor are small [75]. Reduction in plant height usually ceases after 5 generations, while reduction in yield ceases after 20 generations [37] (Fig. 10-2). There are various modifications of this standard method for the development of inbred lines.

Practically all of the inbreds produced before 1930 were isolated as new lines from open-pollinated varieties. A great majority of these lines were discarded on the basis of preliminary tests. Later, productive hybrids were inbred as a more intensive source of new lines [75].

Improvement of established inbred lines often is effected by the backcross method—*i.e.,* the cross of a hybrid to one of the parents. The backcross method is used chiefly for the transfer of one or two simply inherited characters to an otherwise satisfactory inbred line. Suppose A is such an inbred, and B is an inbred possessing the character (or characters) that A lacks. Inbred A is called the recurrent parent; inbred B is called the nonrecurrent parent. The method involves a series of backcrosses to the inbred line, $A,$ to be improved. The character (or characters) in which improvement is sought is maintained by selection. Selfing after the last backcross is necessary in order to obtain homozygosity of the character (or characters) transferred to the recurrent parent. Some corn inbreds have been improved for heat tolerance as well as yield by the addition of teosinte genes through use of the backcross method [59].

Convergent improvement utilizes double backcrossing in an effort to improve characters of the two parental inbreds of an otherwise desirable single cross [64, 67]. The F_1 is backcrossed to both parents through several generations. Selection attempts to retain plants with the desired traits from both parents. The desired genes are then fixed by several generations of self-fertilization, and the recovered lines are tested in field trials.

Evaluation Tests of Inbred Lines

Final evaluation of inbred lines can be determined best by hybrid performance. In earlier years of corn breeding programs, inbred lines usually were evaluated in hybrid combinations only after they had been inbred for

FIGURE 10-2. **Eight generations of self-fertilization of the Illinois Leaming variety.**
(*Courtesy Connecticut Agricultural Experiment Station, from Circular No. 198*)

several generations. Many of the inbreds were divided into groups of about 10 lines. These were combined into all possible single crosses, which were then tested in field trials. However, this procedure requires a large amount of work to test a relatively few lines.

Other early studies indicated that crosses of inbreds with standard open-pollinated varieties (topcrosses) provide an efficient method for the preliminary evaluation of inbred lines for later use in other types of hybrid combinations. It is possible to discard 50 per cent or more of the inbred lines on the basis of a preliminary test [32]. Testing of inbred lines in three-way crosses also is an efficient method where a desirable single-cross seed parent is available.

The type of tester for the evaluation of inbred lines in hybrid combination depends primarily on whether information is sought on general or specific combining ability. General combining ability is the average performance of an inbred line in a number of hybrid combinations. Because of their heterogeneity, open-pollinated varieties or synthetics usually are used for the determination of general combining ability. Specific combining ability is used to designate those cases in which certain combinations do relatively better or worse than would be expected on the basis of the average performance of the lines involved. Desirable single-cross seed parents make excellent testers for the determination of specific combining ability. General combining ability is assumed to be due to additive gene action, while specific combining ability is dependent on dominance, epistasis, and genotypic-environmental interactions [78].

Early versus Late Testing

There has been some diversity of opinion as to the best time for evaluation of inbred lines of corn. Proponents of late testing recommend that inbreds be self-fertilized for five years or more before evaluation in hybrid combinations. During this period, selection is practiced among or within lines for general vigor, strong stalks, resistance to diseases, and the like.

Early testing, now widely practiced in corn breeding, differs in two main respects from the usual procedures for testing inbred lines: The original selfed plants (S_0) are outcrossed to a tester at the time of the first selfing, after which the general performance of the topcross progeny is determined; lines are heavily discarded after this first test to permit a greater concentration of effort on the families of greatest promise in the S_1 and S_2 generations where selection usually is most effective [74]. This type of testing is the forerunner of the various types of recurrent selection now being used.

Prediction of Hybrid Performance

Single-cross data for various agronomic characters may be used to predict the performance of double-crossed combinations. First, a limited number of inbreds (up to about 15) with the highest general combining ability are crossed in all possible combinations. These are tested for performance to obtain specific combining ability. The formula for the determination of the number of single crosses possible from a given number (n) of lines is $(n-1)n/2$. Thus, for 10 lines, 45 distinct single crosses are possible.

The most efficient method for the estimation is based on the average performance of the four nonparental single-cross combinations [29]. For example, the performance of the single crosses A × C, A × D, B × C, and B × D, would be used to predict the performance of the double cross, (A × B) (C × D). This method has been found effective by several investigators. [10, 2].

The order in which the four component lines are paired may have a marked effect on variability as well as yield. In general, the highest-yielding double crosses are those that combine single crosses that differ most widely in parentage. Suppose lines A and B are obtained from one variety, lines Y and Z from another. The highest-yielding double cross would be (A × B) (Y × Z). In crosses of two early with two late lines, the highest yield with the lowest variability ordinarily will be obtained from the (E × E) (L × L) combination [10, 16, 17].

The use of single-cross performance data for the prediction of the best double crosses is now standard procedure. Such prediction eliminates needless expense for tests of many inferior hybrids. The formula to determine the number of double crosses possible from a given number (n) of inbred lines is: $n(n-1)(n-2)(n-3)/8$. Thus for 10 lines, 630 distinct double crosses are possible.

Next, seed is produced of those double crosses that have the best predicted performance. These hybrids are tested for yield preliminary to commercial production of the more desirable ones.

This method of prediction has one serious weakness from the commercial standpoint: it insures high-yielding hybrids, but it fails to insure that such hybrids will possess an acceptable seed parent. An alternate scheme, used to some extent, is to cross a series of lines to one or more single crosses selected for kernel sizing properties. Then the average of (A × B) × 1 and (A × B) × 2 is the predicted performance of (A × B) (1 × 2).

SYNTHETIC VARIETIES

A synthetic variety consists of advanced generations of a multiple hybrid increased by open pollination. The term usually is restricted to combinations that involve more than four inbred lines.

A type of recurrent selection has been suggested for the development of synthetic varieties from short-time inbreds. The essential steps of the procedure are as follows [31]:

1. The isolation of one-generation selfed lines.
2. Testing these lines in topcrosses for yield as well as other characters to determine their relative endowments with respect to genes that affect these characters.
3. Intercrossing of the better-endowed selfed lines to produce a synthetic variety.

Yields of synthetics, where the component lines were chosen for specific characteristics other than combining ability, were as high as those of local standard open-pollinated varieties [79].

A synthetic variety was formed in Nebraska from eight high first-generation selfed lines (S_1), as determined by a topcross yield test on Krug yellow dent, the original parent variety. The second and third generations of the high synthetics substantially outyielded the parent variety [45].

Synthetics have been developed that outyield adapted open-pollinated varieties, but seldom are they as productive as the best-adapted double crosses grown in the area. However, synthetics do offer possibilities for the development of inbred lines.

RECURRENT SELECTION

Recurrent selection is a general term used to designate a new system of breeding. The main types of recurrent selection are for general and specific combining ability. Reciprocal recurrent selection is still another type. These differ only in the choice of the tester parent. They are similar in that each involves self-pollination in some heterozygous population, outcrossing to some appropriate tester, yield trial evaluation of the test-cross progenies, and finally the formation of a new population by utilizing the selfed seed that gives rise to the superior test crosses. Where selection is for general combining ability, a tester that provides a broad genetic base is used—for example, an open-pollinated variety, a synthetic, or a double-cross hybrid. Where selection is to be based on specific combining ability, a more restricted genetic base tester, such as an inbred line or single cross, is employed [44, 47]. Populations that result from recurrent selection can be used in various ways to produce improved corn varieties. These populations can be inbred to produce homozygous lines to be used in the production of hybrid varieties, or used as sources of foundation stocks for synthetic varieties, or used directly as in reciprocal recurrent selection.

REFERENCES

1. Alexander, D. E., "The genetic induction of autotetraploidy: A proposal for its use in corn breeding." *Agron. J.*, **49**(1): 40–43. 1957.
2. Anderson, D. C., "The relation between single and double cross yields in corn." *J. Am. Soc. Agron.*, **30**: 209–211. 1938.
3. Beadle, G. W., "Studies of Euchlaena and its hybrids with Zea. I: Chromosome behavior in *Euchlaena mexicana* and its hybrids with *Zea mays*." *Zeits. Induk. Abst. Vererb.*, **62**: 291–304. 1932.
4. ———, "Genes in maize for pollen sterility." *Genetics*, **17**: 413–431. 1932.
5. Blickenstaff, J., D. L. Thompson, and P. H. Harvey, "Inheritance and linkage of pollen fertility restoration in cytoplasmic male-sterile crosses of corn." *Agron. J.*, **50**: 430–434. 1958.
6. Bruce, A. B., "The Mendelian theory of heredity and the augmentation of vigor." *Science*, **32**: 627–628. 1910.
7. Chase, S. S., "Monoploid frequencies in a commercial double cross maize, and in its component single cross hybrids and inbred lines." *Genetics*, **34**: 328–332. 1949.
8. ———, "Production of homozygous diploids of maize from monoploids." *Agron. J.*, **44**(5): 263–267. 1952.
9. Demerec, M., "Genetic relations of five factor pairs for virescent seedlings." Cornell U. Ag. Exp. Sta. *Memoir 84*. 1924.
10. Doxtator, C. W., and I. J. Johnson, "Prediction of double-cross yields in corn." *J. Am. Soc. Agron.*, **28**: 460–462. 1936.
11. Duvick, D. N., "Allelism and comparative genetics of fertility restoration of cytoplasmically pollen sterile maize." *Genetics*, **41**: 544–565. 1956.
12. ———, *Maize Genetics Cooperation News Letter*, **33**: 95. 1959.
13. East, E. M., "Heterosis." *Genetics*, **21**: 375–397. 1936.
14. ———, and H. K. Hayes, "Inheritance in maize." Conn. Ag. Exp. Sta. *Bul. 167*. 1911.
15. ———, and H. K. Hayes, "Heterozygosis in evolution and in plant breeding." USDA Bur. Plant Indus. *Bul. 243*. 1912.
16. Eckhardt, R. C., and A. A. Bryan, "Effect of method of combining the four inbred lines of a double cross of maize upon the yield and variability of the resulting hybrid." *J. Am. Soc. Agron.*, **32**: 347–353. 1940.
17. ———, and A. A. Bryan, "Effect of the method of combining two early and two late inbred lines of corn upon the yield and variability of the resulting double crosses." *J. Am. Soc. Agron.*, **32**: 645. 1940.
18. Edwardson, J. R., "The restoration of fertility to cytoplasmic male-sterile corn." *Agron. J.*, **47**: 457–461. 1955.
19. Emerson, R. A., "The genetic relations of plant colors in maize." Cornell U. Ag. Exp. Sta. *Memoir 39*. 1921.
20. ———, G. W. Beadle, and A. C. Fraser, "A summary of linkage studies in maize." Cornell U. Ag. Exp. Sta. *Memoir 180*. 1935.
21. ———, and H. H. Smith, "Inheritance of number of kernel rows in maize." Cornell U. Ag. Exp. Sta. *Memoir 296*. 1950.
22. Frey, K. J., "The inheritance of protein and certain of its components in maize." *Agron. J.*, **41**(3): 113–117. 1949.

23. Gardner, C. O., "An evaluation of effects of mass selection and seed irradiation with thermal neutrons on yield of corn." *Crop. Sci.*, **1**: 241–245. 1961.

24. Garrison, H. S., and F. D. Richey, "Effects of continuous selection for ear type in corn." USDA *Bul. 1341*. 1925.

25. Genter, C. F., J. F. Eheart, and W. N. Linkous, "Oil and protein relationships between inbred lines and their single cross progeny." *Agron. J.*, **49**: 283–285. 1957.

26. Goodsell, S. F., "Male sterility in corn by androgenesis." *Crop. Sci.*, **1**: 227–228. 1961.

27. Hayes, H. K., F. R. Immer, and D. C. Smith, *Methods of Plant Breeding*, 2nd ed. New York: McGraw-Hill. pp 1–551. 1955.

28. Hull, F. H., "Recurrent selection for specific combining ability in corn." *J. Am. Soc. Agron.*, **37**: 134–145. 1945.

29. Jenkins, M. T., "Methods of estimating the performance of double crosses in corn." *J. Am. Soc. Agron.*, **26**: 199–204. 1934.

30. ———, "Corn improvement," in USDA Yrbk. of Ag. pp 455–495. 1936.

31. ———, "The segregation of genes affecting yield of grain in maize." *J. Am. Soc. Agron.*, **32**: 55–63. 1940.

32. ———, and A. M. Brunson, "Methods of testing inbred lines of maize in crossbred combinations." *J. Am. Soc. Agron.*, **24**: 523–530. 1932.

33. ———, and A. L. Robert, "Evaluating the breeding potential of inbred lines of corn resistant to the leaf blight caused by *Helminthosporium turcicum.*" *Agron. J.*, **51**: 93–96. 1959.

34. ———, and A. L. Robert, "Further genetic studies of resistance to *Helmintho-sporium turcicum* Pass. in maize by means of chromosomal translocations." *Crop. Sci.*, **1**: 450–455. 1961.

35. Jennings, H. S., "The numerical results of diverse systems of breeding." *Genetics*, **1**: 53–89. 1916.

36. Jones, D. F., "Dominance of linked factors as a means of accounting for heterosis." *Genetics*, **2**: 466–479. 1917.

37. ———, "Continued inbreeding in maize." *Genetics*, **24**(4): 462–473. 1939.

38. ———, and P. C. Mangelsdorf, "The production of hybrid corn seed without detasseling." Conn. Ag. Exp. Sta. *Bul. 550*. 1951.

39. Jones, L. M., *The Ten Chromosomes of Maize*. DeKalb, Ill.: DeKalb Ag. Assn., Inc. 1958.

40. Jugenheimer, R. W., "Hybrid maize breeding and seed production." FAO Ag. Dev. Paper No. 62. Rome, Italy. pp 1–369. 1958.

41. Kiesselbach, T. A., "The structure and reproduction of corn." Nebr. Ag. Exp. Sta. *Res. Bul. 161*. 1949.

42. Lindstrom, E. W., "Chlorophyll inheritance in maize." Cornell U. Ag. Exp. Sta. *Memoir 13*. 1918.

43. Longley, A. E., "Supernumerary chromosomes in *Zea mays.*" *J. Ag. Res.*, **35**(9): 769–784. 1927.

44. Lonnquist, J. H., "Recurrent selection as a means of modifying combining ability in corn." *Agron. J.*, **43**: 311–315. 1951.

45. ———, "The development and performance of synthetic varieties of corn." *Agron. J.*, **41**: 153–156. 1949.

46. ———, "Heterosis and yield of grain in maize." *Agron. J.*, **45**(11): 539–542. 1953.

47. ———, "Progress from recurrent selection procedures for the improvement of corn populations." Nebr. Ag. Exp. Sta. *Res. Bul. 197.* 1961.

48. Mains, E. B., "Inheritance of resistance to rust, *Puccinia sorghi,* in maize." *J. Ag. Res.,* **43**: 419–430. 1931.

49. Mangelsdorf, P. C., "The genetics and morphology of some endosperm characters in maize." Conn. Ag. Exp. Sta. *Bul. 279.* 1926.

50. ———, and R. G. Reeves. *The origin of Indian corn and its relatives* (monograph). Tex. Ag. Exp. Sta. *Bul. 574.* 1939.

51. Pate, J. B., and P. H. Harvey, "Studies on the inheritance of resistance in corn to *Helminthosporium maydis* leaf spot." *Agron. J.,* **46**: 442–445. 1954.

52. Penny, L. H., and F. F. Dicke, "Inheritance of resistance in corn to leaf feeding of the European corn borer." *Agron. J.,* **48**: 200–203. 1956.

53. ———, and F. F. Dicke, "A single gene-pair controlling segregation for European corn borer resistance." *Agron. J.,* **49**: 193–196. 1957.

54. Perry, H. S., and G. F. Sprague, "A second-chromosome gene, Y^3, producing yellow endosperm color in maize." *J. Am. Soc. Agron.,* **28**(12): 990–996. 1936.

55. Randolph, L. F., "Chromosome numbers in *Zea mays* L." Cornell U. Ag. Exp. Sta. *Memoir 117.* 1928.

56. ———, "Some effects of high temperatures on polyploidy and other variations in maize." Nat. Acad. Sci. *Proc.,* **18**: 222–229. 1932.

57. ———, "Genetic characteristics of the B chromosomes in maize." *Genetics,* **26**(6): 608–631. 1941.

58. ———, and D. B. Hand, "Relation between carotenoid content and number of genes per cell in diploid and tetraploid corn." *J. Ag. Res.,* **60**(1): 51–64. 1940.

59. Reeves, R. G., "The use of teosinte in the improvement of corn inbreds." *Agron. J.,* **42**(5): 248–251. 1950.

60. Rhoades, M. M., "The cytoplasmic inheritance of male sterility in *Zea mays.*" *J. Gen.,* **27**: 71–93. 1933.

61. ———, "The cytogenetics of maize," in *Corn and Corn Improvement.* New York: Academic Press. pp 123–219. 1955.

62. ———, and B. McClintock, "The cytogenetics of maize." *Bot. Rev.,* **1**: 292–325. 1935.

63. Richey, F. D., "The experimental basis for the present status of corn breeding." *J. Am. Soc. Agron.,* **14**: 1–17. 1922.

64. ———, "The convergent improvement of selfed lines of corn." *Amer. Nat.,* **61**: 430–449. 1927.

65. ———, "Corn breeding." USDA *Bul. 1489.* 1927.

66. ———, "Corn breeding," in *Advances in Genetics,* Vol. 3. New York: Academic Press. pp 159–192. 1950.

67. ———, and G. F. Sprague, "Experiments on hybrid vigor and convergent improvement in corn." USDA *Tech. Bul. 267.* 1931.

68. ———, and R. F. Dawson, "A survey of the possibilities and methods of breeding high-niacin corn (maize)." *Pl. Physiol.,* **23**: 238–254. 1948.

69. ———, and R. F. Dawson, "Experiments on the inheritance of niacin in corn (maize)." *Pl. Physiol.,* **26**(3): 474–493. 1951.

70. Rogers, J. S., and J. R. Edwardson, "The utilization of cytoplasmic male-sterile inbreds in the production of corn hybrids." *Agron. J.,* **44**(1): 8–13. 1952.

71. Russell, W. A., and A. L. Hooker, "Inheritance of resistance in corn to rust, *Puccinia sorghi*, Schw., and genetic relationships among different sources of resistance." *Agron. J.*, **51**(1): 21–24. 1959.

72. Saboe, L. C., and H. K. Hayes, "Genetic studies of reaction to smut and firing in maize by means of chromosomal interchanges." *J. Am. Soc. Agron.*, **33**: 463–470. 1941.

73. Smith, L. H., and A. M. Brunson, "An experiment in selecting corn for yield by the method of the ear-to-row breeding plot." Ill. Ag. Exp. Sta. *Bul. 271*. 1925.

74. Sprague, G. F., "Early testing of inbred lines of corn." *J. Am. Soc. Agron.*, **38**: 108–117. 1946.

75. ———, "The experimental basis for hybrid maize." *Biol. Rev.*, **21**: 101–120. 1946.

76. ———, "Corn breeding," in *Corn and Corn Improvement*. New York: Academic Press. pp 221–292. 1955.

77. ———, "The story of corn." USDA *ARS* **34-36**: 1–14. 1962.

78. ———, and L. A. Tatum, "General and specific combining ability in single crosses of corn." *J. Am. Soc. Agron.*, **34**: 923–932. 1942.

79. ———, and M. T. Jenkins, "A comparison of synthetic varieties, multiple crosses, and double crosses in corn." *J. Am. Soc. Agron.*, **35**: 137–147. 1943.

80. Stakman, E. C., J. J. Christensen, and H. E. Brewbaker, "Physiologic specialization in Puccinia." *Phytopath.*, **18**: 345–354. 1928.

81. Ullstrup, A. J., and A. M. Brunson, "Linkage relationships of a gene in corn determining susceptibility to a *Helminthosporium* leaf spot." *J. Am. Soc. Agron.*, **39**: 606–609. 1947.

82. Weijer, J., "A catalogue of genetic maize types together with a maize bibliography." *Bibliographica Genetica*, **14**: 189–425. 1952.

83. Wellhausen, E. J., "Genetics of resistance to bacterial wilt in maize." Ia. Ag. Exp. Sta. *Res. Bul. 224*. 1937.

84. Woodworth, C. M., E. R. Leng, and R. W. Jugenheimer, "Fifty generations of selection for protein and oil in corn." *Agron. J.*, **44**: 60–65. 1952.

85. Zuber, M. S., *et al.*, "Breeding high amylose corn." *Agron. J.*, **50**: 9–12. 1958.

PART III Wheat

Wheat

11. IMPORTANCE, HISTORY, AND ADAPTATION

ECONOMIC IMPORTANCE

Wheat (*Triticum* spp.) is the most widely cultivated of all cereals. A wheat crop is harvested somewhere in the world during every month of the year. In most areas of the world, it is the principal food of man. The properties of gluten in wheat are such that it produces breadstuffs generally superior to those from any of the other cereal grains [3].

Wheat is grown in all temperate countries and in most of the subtropical countries of the world, as well as at high elevations in some tropical countries. Most of the crop is produced in the temperate zone, and more than 90 per cent of the acreage lies in the northern hemisphere (Fig. 11-1). Wheat occupied about 17 per cent of the cultivated land of the world between 1920–34. About 75 per cent of the acreage is fall-sown [2]. The average annual area harvested from 1950–54 was 447.15 million acres with a production of 6.98 billion bushels, or 209.4 million short tons. The average yield per acre was 15.6 bushels. The nations that led in wheat production were the Soviet Union, United States, China, Canada, and West Germany [1].

The size of the wheat crop is on the increase. Wheat acreages in the non-Communist world have been growing larger every year since 1952. The average crop in 1952–57 was about 30 million tons larger than in 1934–38. Yields per acre were increased by more than 25 per cent over the same period. [21].

Wheat ranks next to corn in importance as a cereal in the United States. During the ten-year period 1952–61, the average annual harvested acreage was 54.2 million acres with a production of 1,150 million bushels. Winter wheat occupied about two-thirds of the total wheat acreage. The average yield of all wheat during the decade was 21.2 bushels per harvested

277

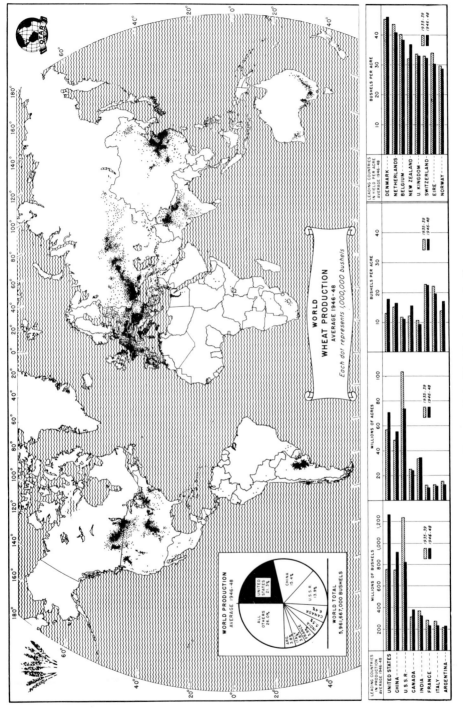

FIGURE 11-1. **World wheat production.**

(Courtesy US Department of Agriculture)

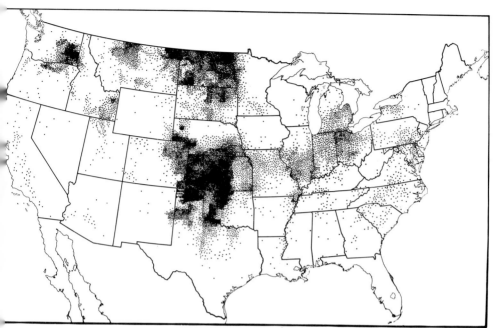

FIGURE 11-2. **Distribution of wheat seeded in the United States in 1959. Each dot represents 5,000 acres.**

(*Courtesy US Department of Agriculture*)

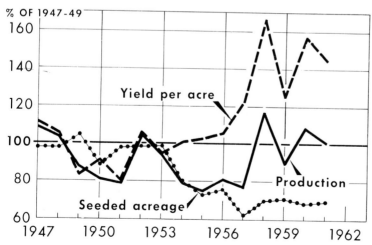

FIGURE 11-3. **Acreage, yield, and production of wheat in the United States, 1947-1961.**

(*Courtesy US Department of Agriculture*)

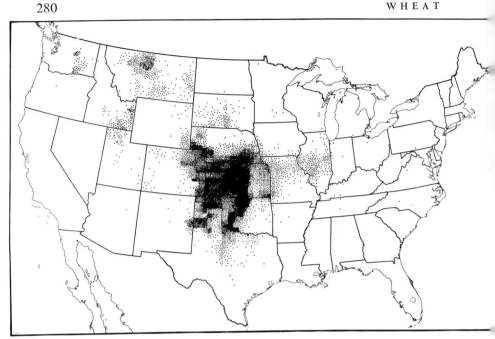

FIGURE 11-4. **Distribution of hard red winter wheat in the United States in 1959. Each dot represents 5,000 acres.**

(Courtesy US Department of Agriculture)

FIGURE 11-5. **Distribution of hard red spring wheat in the United States in 1959. Each dot represents 5,000 acres.**

(Courtesy US Department of Agriculture)

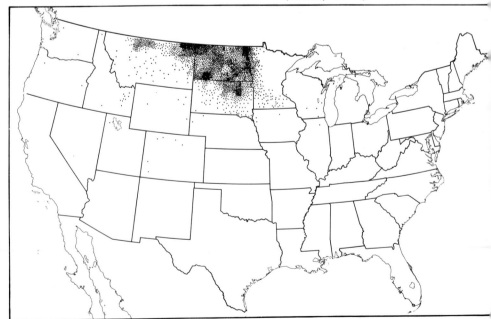

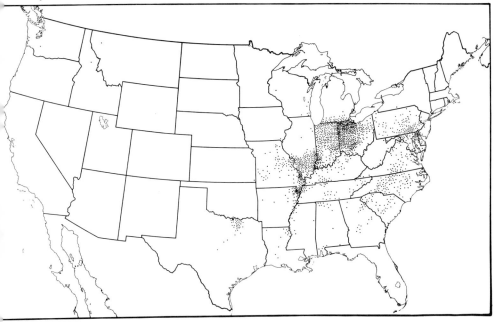

FIGURE 11-6. **Distribution of soft red winter wheat in the United States in 1959. Each dot represents 5,000 acres.**

(*Courtesy US Department of Agriculture*)

FIGURE 11-7. **Distribution of white wheat in the United States in 1959. Each dot represents 5,000 acres. Much of the white wheat in the Pacific Northwest is club wheat.**

(*Courtesy US Department of Agriculture*)

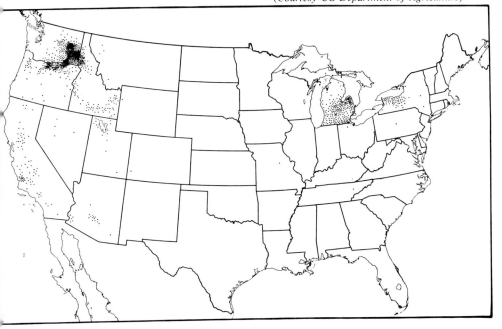

acre. The states that led in wheat production were Kansas, North Dakota, Montana, Nebraska, and Oklahoma (Fig. 11-2).

The acreage seeded to wheat increased from 1910–49, but with wide fluctuations. It declined more than 30 per cent from 1949–61 (Fig. 11-3), but increases in acre yields maintained and even increased total production. The expansion between World Wars I and II was largely on grasslands in the Great Plains. Domestic utilization of wheat has remained remarkably stable during the last half-century at around 600 million bushels—except during World War II and for several years thereafter, when excessive amounts were used for livestock feed and in industry. The increase in population has been offset by a decrease in the per capita consumption of wheat, which has declined steadily from 5.0 bushels in 1910 to 2.8 bushels in 1955 [14].

Commercial classes of wheat grown in the United States are hard red winter (Fig. 11-4), hard red spring (Fig. 11-5), soft red winter (Fig. 11-6), white (Fig. 11-7), and durum (Fig. 11-8).

FIGURE 11-8. **Distribution of durum wheat in the United States in 1959. Each dot represents 5,000 acres.**

(*Courtesy US Department of Agriculture*)

FACTORS IN WHEAT DEMAND

Because of its excellent baking quality, wheat has become the most important source of carbohydrates in the majority of countries in the temperate zones. In most Western countries, wheat has replaced the coarse grains and rye as a bread grain. Varieties of wheat differ in their baking qualities [21]. Durum wheat, for instance, is less satisfactory for bread, but it is superior to other wheats for the preparation of alimentary pastes like macaroni, spaghetti, and vermicelli.

The prevalence of wheat in human diets is a relatively modern development. In past centuries, common people in northern Europe had to rely to a much greater extent on the coarser grains, which were supplemented by potatoes after the 18th century. Modern European countries now use most of their crops of corn, barley, oats, and grain sorghum as feed for domestic animals. In underdeveloped countries, however, the coarse grains are still consumed chiefly by humans [21].

The demand for bread in most countries is sensitive to changes in incomes. Very poor people tend to use additional income largely for the purchase of more food. But as wealth continues to increase, the additional income is spent for more expensive protein foods and the demand for wheat tends to decline. Within the same country, wealthy classes tend to eat less bread grains than do the poorer classes. In North America, where the per capita income exceeds $1700, about 120 pounds of wheat per capita is consumed annually [21].

HISTORY OF WHEAT CULTURE

Wheat has been used as a food by man since prehistoric times. There is evidence that wheat was first used as a parched cereal. As time went on, the parched grains were probably ground and the coarse meal soaked in water to make a gruel [11, 6]. Wheat probably was grown in the Middle East as early as 10,000–15,000 BC [12]. Carbonized grains of wheat have been discovered by archaeologists in Turkey, Egypt, Iraq, and in many other countries. Some of these grains date back 6000 years or more [3]. Carbonized wheat kernels which date back to 6750 BC or earlier were recently found at the Jarmo site in the upland of eastern Iraq, the oldest village yet discovered. The wheats that were first cultivated were primitive hulled types firmly enclosed in the glumes. Those from the Jarmo site appear to be wild or cultivated einkorn and emmer [11, 6]. These primitive wheats are believed to have spread over most of Western Europe during the Stone Age. Archaeological evidence also indicates that some naked wheats—durum and possibly some poulard wheats [9]—were grown in ancient times.

Wheat was described by Theophrastus, a Greek philosopher, about 300 BC and by Columella, a Roman writer, in AD 55 [3]. Both hulled and naked species of wheat played a major role in the Mediterranean region in classical antiquity (500 BC–AD 500). Emmer and some einkorn predominated in the region at the beginning of the classical period, but they were largely replaced later with the naked wheats, durum and poulard. Toward the end of the classical period, durum lost ground to the common and club bread wheats [9].

During the Middle Ages, rye was much more important in Europe than all of the wheats. Common and club wheats were most important north of the Alps.

Wheat cultivation in the United States began along the Atlantic coast early in the seventeenth century. The crop was grown on Elizabeth Island (Massachusetts) in Buzzards Bay by Captain Gosnold in 1602. Wheat was sown in the Jamestown Colony as early as 1611, and in Plymouth Colony by 1621. Introductions from England were sown in New England as early as 1628, and in Maryland in 1634. Wheats from the Netherlands as well as from Sweden came with colonists to New York, New Jersey, and Delaware from 1622–38 [3]. Wheat moved westward with the settlement of the country, and was carried across the Alleghenies about 1700.

By 1840, wheat had spread to the prairies west of the Mississippi river; by 1855 it had reached the Great Plains. Wheat was established as a crop in Kansas between 1855 and 1870 [10]. Spanish missionaries grew wheat in California as early as 1770. The remains of club wheat have been found in adobe bricks of Spanish missions in California, built during the period 1770–1800. Wheat production began in the Pacific Northwest about 1846 [22].

ADAPTATION

The great wheat regions of the world are found in the temperate zones between 30–60° N. and 25–40° S. But wheat has also been grown north of the Arctic Circle and close to the Equator. It is grown near Archangel (Soviet Union) at a latitude of 60° N.; in the Tanana valley (Alaska) at 64° N.; and in the Peace River valley (Canada) at about 58° N. In regions with hot climates, wheat usually is grown only at high altitudes or in the cool season [8]. In dry subtropical climates, such as are found in the Mediterranean countries, wheat is produced successfully from fall seeding. It is grown at 15° N. on the Deccan Plateau in India, and, at high elevations, practically on the equator in Kenya and Ecuador. Wheat is of little importance in warm humid regions because of its susceptibility to diseases under such conditions [22], but it is grown below sea level near the Dead Sea and in the Imperial Valley of California, and at altitudes of 14,000–15,000 feet in Tibet [17].

Temperature

Wheat is a cool-season crop. It has a somewhat longer growing period as well as a somewhat higher minimum heat requirement than do the other small grains. Wheat is seldom grown in regions with a frost-free season of less than 100 days, or in areas with a subpolar climate where there are less than three months with average temperature above 50°F [22]. Only spring wheat is grown under such cold short-season conditions. The minimum growth temperature for wheat is 3–4°C (37.4–39.2°F), the optimum temperature about 25° C. (77°F), and the maximum from about 30–32°C (86–89.6°F). Winter wheat is more resistant to cold than winter barley or oats, but much less hardy than winter rye [8].

Optimum average preharvest temperatures for wheat appear to be approximately 58–60°F, whereas the annual average temperature should be about 12–16°F lower [2]. Annual as well as preharvest average daily temperatures significantly above 65°F appear to be associated with wheat yield levels below 14 bushels per acre. Warm temperatures during the early growth of wheat may retard heading. Daily maximum temperatures above 90°F during the three or four weeks after flowering may ripen the grain prematurely. High temperatures combined with high humidity may encourage the spread of rusts and cause a reduction in yield. In the cool climate of western Canada, above-average temperatures are beneficial at the time of sowing, detrimental during midsummer, and again beneficial prior to ripening [7].

Marquis spring wheat has ripened at Fairbanks, Alaska (64° N.), with a total summation of 2054 degree-days (computed above 32°F) from emergence to ripening. The same variety utilized 2816 degree-days at Lincoln, Nebraska (41° N.). It required 3711 degree-days at Tlalnepantla, Mexico (19° N.) where the day length is much shorter [15].

Moisture

The world wheat crop is grown where the average annual rainfall ranges between 10–70 inches, but about 75 per cent of the acreage is in areas that have 15–35 inches of annual precipitation. The effectiveness of precipitation varies with its seasonal distribution as well as with the temperature. Optimum annual precipitation ranges from 25–35 inches with 4–6 inches during the two months before harvest (Fig. 11-9). An annual precipitation of less than 20 inches together with a preharvest rainfall of less than 2–3 inches generally is relatively unfavorable for wheat yields [2].

Wheat is grown in winter rainfall regions of Australia and the Big Bend area of Washington with 10 inches or less of annual precipitation by the use of alternate summer fallow. In the Great Plains of the United States, summer rainfall prevails. In the northern portion, wheat is grown where the annual rainfall is as low as 14 inches, but in the southern Great Plains— where the evaporation is higher—the minimum is about 17 inches. Little wheat is grown in high rainfall areas, except in India where the annual rainfall—although 60 inches or more—occurs mostly during the summer when the land is in other crops [19].

Records of the consumptive use of water by winter wheat at Colby and Garden City in Kansas showed that an average of 7.37 inches of water was required before any grain was produced, whereas each additional 0.51 inch of water produced one bushel of wheat per acre [13].

Winter wheat is seeded in late September or early October in western Kansas. Rainfall that occurred there over the three months prior to seeding was helpful, but during a 27-year period, yield was influenced most by the amount of precipitation that occurred from seeding up to December 1, at which time the wheat plants entered the winter dormant stage. Although less effective than fall precipitation, there was a beneficial effect from above-average rainfall in the spring from about April 15 to June 1 during the stage of rapid plant growth—*i.e.*, stem elongation to heading. The benefits of additional rainfall decreased as wheat approached maturity [16].

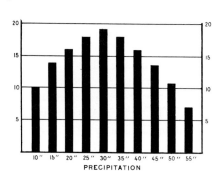

FIGURE 11-9. **Yields of wheat (bushels) on all farms in the United States in 1909, grouped on basis of precipitation received during the crop year.**

(*Courtesy US Department of Agriculture*)

In high rainfall areas, abundant precipitation in the spring may have an adverse effect on winter wheat yields. In general, wheat yields above normal were associated with subnormal rainfall for the months of March and May in Maryland [20], because certain diseases were less prevalent in the drier years.

Summer or early autumn rainfall, which largely determines the moisture content of the soil at seeding time, has been used as a guide for the prediction of the yields of winter wheat that might reasonably be expected in the western Great Plains. Yields are generally satisfactory when the soil is wet to a depth of three feet or more at seeding time [19]. In western Kansas, correlations as high as + 0.85 have been found between the moisture in the upper three feet of soil at the time of seeding and the yield of winter wheat [5]. Poor yields or crop failures usually result when the soil at seeding time is dry, or wet only to a depth of a few inches. In such cases, it often is advisable to leave the land fallow and seed the winter wheat the next year. In eastern Washington, winter wheat generally is sown when adequate soil moisture prevails in the fall. If the fall is unusually dry, seeding is delayed until spring when spring varieties are sown [18].

The yields of spring wheat at 19 field stations (387 crop years) in the Great Plains showed a correlation between precipitation and average yields of $r = 0.61$ to 0.90, with an average of 0.76 [4]. In North Dakota, good rainfall in May and June generally brought high yields of wheat, especially in the drier western portion of the state [23]. In western Canada, above-average rainfall usually results in higher yields. On fertile soil, however, heavy rainfall during the month before harvest caused reduced yields, probably due to lodging. In western Canada, where spring wheat is harvested in August and September, high precipitation was most beneficial when it occurred during the month of June [7].

Soil Conditions

Wheat is best adapted to fertile medium-to-heavy textured soils that are well drained. The silt and clay loams generally produce the highest wheat yields. In general, very sandy or poorly drained soils produce unsatisfactory yields. Acid or strongly leached soils, such as the gray forest (podsol) soils of northeastern Europe and the northern portions of the Great Lakes area of the United States, are poorly suited to wheat. The crop tends to lodge on rich bottom lands. The soil must be free of weeds. In the hard red spring wheat regions of Canada and the United States, increased weediness has caused a considerable shift from continuous wheat to alternation with fallow or intertilled crops [8]. The principal regions of wheat production in North America are located on Chernozem, Chestnut, and Red Chestnut soils.

REFERENCES

1. *Agricultural Statistics*, 1960. USDA. pp 1–633. 1961.
2. Bennett, M. K., and R. C. Farnsworth, "World wheat acreages, yields, and climates." Stanford U. Food Res. Inst.: *Wheat Studies*, 13(6): 265–308. 1937.
3. Clark, J. A., "Improvement of wheat," in USDA Yrbk. of Ag. pp 207–302. 1936.
4. Cole, J. S., "Correlations between annual precipitation and yield of spring wheat in the Great Plains." USDA *Tech. Bul. 636*. 1938.
5. Hallsted, A. L., and E. H. Cole, "A preliminary report of the relation between yield of winter wheat and moisture in the soil at seeding time." *J. Ag. Res.*, **41:** 467–477. 1930.
6. Helbaek, H., "Domestication of food plants in the Old World." *Science*, 130(3372): 365–372. 1959.

7. Hopkins, J. W., "Weather and wheat yields in western Canada. I: Influence of rainfall and temperature during the growing season on plot yields." *Can. J. Res.*, **12**: 306–334. 1935.

8. Jasny, N., *Competition Among Grains*. Stanford U. Food Res. Inst.: pp 1–606. 1940.

9. ———, "The wheats of classical antiquity." Johns Hopkins U. *Studies in Historical and Political Science*, **62**(3). 1944.

10. Malin, J. C., *Winter Wheat in the Golden Belt of Kansas*. Lawrence: U. of Kansas Press. pp. 1–290. 1944.

11. Mangelsdorf, P. C., "Wheat." *Sci. Am.*, **189**(1): 50–59. 1953.

12. Mann, H. H., "Wheat in the Middle East." *Emp. J. Exp. Ag.*, **14**(53): 31–42. 1946.

13. Mathews, O. R., and L. A. Brown, "Winter wheat and sorghum production in the Southern Great Plains under limited rainfall." USDA *Cir. 477.* 1938.

14. Nauheim, C. W., W. R. Bailey, and D. E. Merrick, "Wheat production." USDA *Info. Bul. 179.* 1958.

15. Nuttonson, M. Y., *Wheat-Climate Relationships and the Use of Phenology in Ascertaining the Thermal and Photothermal Requirements of Wheat*. Washington: Am. Inst. Crop Ecol. pp 1–388. 1955.

16. Pallesen, J. E., and H. H. Laude, "Seasonal distribution of rainfall in relation to yield of winter wheat." USDA *Tech. Bul. 761.* 1941.

17. Percival, J., *The Wheat Plant*. London: Duckworth. pp 1–463. 1921.

18. Pubols, B. H., and C. P. Heisig, "Historical and geographic aspects of wheat yields in Washington." Wash. Ag. Exp. Sta. *Bul. 355.* 1937.

19. Salmon, S. C., "Climate and small grains." in *Climate and Man*. USDA Yrbk. of Ag. pp 321–342. 1941.

20. Sando, W. J., "Climate and wheat yields at College Park, Maryland." *J. Am. Soc. Agron.*, **15**: 400–408. 1923.

21. Schlomer, F. C., "The social and economic importance of wheat," in *Progressive Wheat Production*. Geneva, Switzerland: Centre d'etude de l'azote. pp 1–27. 1960.

22. Van Royen, W., *The Agricultural Resources of the World*. Englewood Cliffs, N.J.: Prentice-Hall. pp 27–47. 1954.

23. Walster, H. L., and P. A. Nystuen, "North Dakota wheat yields." North Dakota Ag. Exp. Sta. *Bul. 350.* 1948.

$\mathcal{W}$heat
12. BOTANY

GENUS TRITICUM

The wheat species of the genus *Triticum* are characterized by spike-lets placed flatwise at each rachis joint. The plant is a midtall annual or winter annual grass with flat blades and a terminal spike. The spikelets are solitary with 1–5 flowers, sessile, and arranged alternately on the nodes of a zig-zag, channeled, or articulate rachis. The glumes are keeled, with three or more nerves, and obtuse, acute, or acuminate. The lemmas are keeled or rounded on the back, many-nerved, and terminated in a single tooth or awn [5].

MORPHOLOGY OF THE VEGETATIVE ORGANS

Wheat species and varieties differ greatly in growth habit, form, and structure.

Stem or Culm

The culm of the mature wheat plant is a hollow, jointed cylinder that comprises 3–6 nodes and internodes. The length of the internodes increases from the lowest one. The upper internode of the culm, the peduncle, bears the spike. The stems of most varieties are solid at the nodes, but the inter-nodes are hollow. Internodes are solid or nearly so in emmer, spelt, in some varieties of durum and poulard, and in a very few varieties of common wheat [5].

Stems are white to yellow or, in some varieties, mostly purple in color. The purple color in such varieties may not be apparent under all environ-ments. It usually is most distinct on the peduncle, but often runs down to the sheaths of the lower leaves [5].

Total plant height, with spike included, may vary from 2–5 feet, but

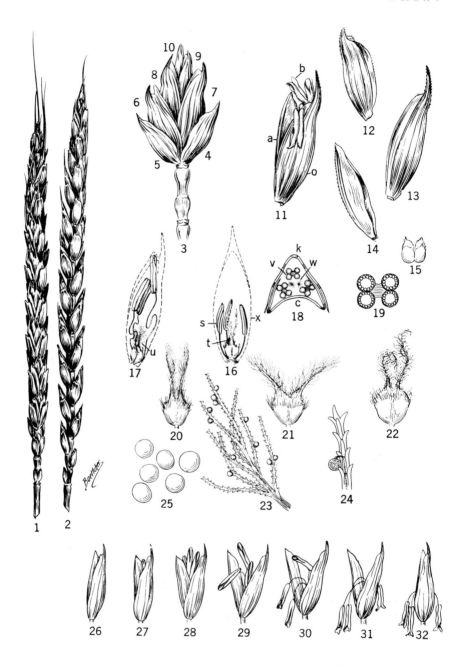

it may be even shorter in dryland areas. Wheats have been classified as short, midtall, and tall. For example, under good growing conditions, wheats from 1–3 feet in height would be classed as short; wheats from 2–4 feet, midtall; wheats from 3–5 feet, tall. The differences between classes would be less in many regions of the country [5].

Tillers or lateral branches develop from buds in the axils of the lower leaves attached to the basal or crown nodes below the soil surface. In field-sown wheat, the second and third buds usually develop into tillers (which make three culms per plant), but the fourth, fifth, and sometimes later buds may also develop tillers [24]. Secondary tillers may develop from basal buds on tillers, so that a single plant with ample space may bear from 30–100 or more culms. Although varieties differ in tendency, thin seeding, abundant moisture, and fertile soil favor increased tillering.

Wheat varieties with weak or slender stems may lodge or fall over under conditions of excessive moisture, high winds, or high nitrate content of soil.

Leaves

The wheat foilage leaf consists of the sheath, blade, ligule, and auricle. The leaf-sheaths normally enclose the lower two-thirds of the culm. The sheaths may be white or purple in color. The blade is narrowly linear to linear-lanceolate in shape. The leaf blades of wheat varieties vary considerably in dimension, shade of green color, and angle of projection from the culm. As the plant matures, the blades dry and frequently break off. The blade may be pubescent or glabrous. Blade color varies with the condition of the plant as affected by temperature, soil moisture, and soil solution. In general, the hard red winter wheats have dark green blades, whereas all durum wheat varieties have light green blades. The ligule, which arises at the junction of the blade and sheath, encircles the stem. It is a thin, colorless, membranous structure with an irregular edge fringed with minute hairs.

FIGURE 12-1. **The wheat inflorescence: 1. Spike, dorso-ventral view. 2. Spike, lateral view. 3. Spikelet, lateral view and subtending rachis. 4. Upper glume. 5. Lower glume. Nos. 6, 7, 8, 9 and 10, florets; No. 7 is largest and No. 6 second largest, while Nos. 8, 9 and 10 are progressively smaller. 11. Floret, lateral view, opening in anthesis. 12. Glume, lateral view. 13. Lemma, lateral view. 14. Palea, lateral view. 15. Lodicules, which swell to open the glumes. 16. Floret before anthesis, showing position of stamens (s) and pistil (t), enclosed in (x) lemma and palea. 17. Floret at anthesis showing position of pistil (u) and elongating filaments of the stamens. 18. Cross section of floret: (c) palea, (k), lemma, (v) stamen, and (w) stigma. 19. Cross section of anther. 20. Pistil before anthesis. 21. Pistil at anthesis. 22. Pistil after fertilization. 23. Portion of stigma (greatly enlarged) showing adhering pollen grains. 24. Tip of stigma hair (greatly enlarged) penetrated by germinating pollen grain. 25. Pollen grains (enormously enlarged). Nos. 26 to 32: Florets during successive stages of blooming and anthesis. Time required for stages 26 to 31 is about 2 to 5 minutes, for stages 26 to 32 about 15 to 40 minutes.**

(Courtesy US Department of Agriculture)

Auricles always are present on wheat leaves, usually being sharply curved. They are often purple in color in the early stage, but sometimes change to white as the plant matures [24, 5].

Roots

A maximum of 5–7 seminal roots may function throughout the life of the wheat plant. Normal coronal roots develop from the nodes of the main axis or its branches near the soil surface. Tillers develop a similar series of coronal roots [24].

The mature root system ordinarily reaches a maximum depth of 5–7 feet [87]. Winter wheat usually has a more extensive root system than does spring wheat. The extent of the root system also is markedly affected by texture, fertility, and moisture content of the soil. In Nebraska, roots of winter wheat were observed at a depth of 13 feet under favorable soil moisture conditions [40], but they grow only a short distance into a dry soil [87].

MORPHOLOGY OF THE INFLORESCENCE

The wheat inflorescence is a terminal spike (Fig. 12-1) which is usually 3–4 inches in length, but it may vary from 2–5 inches. Spikes may be flattened parallel, or at right angles to the plane of the face of the spikelets. They may be fusiform, oblong, clavate, or elliptical in shape. Spikes also may be lax, mid-dense, or dense [23, 5]. The spike bears 10–30 spikelets (Fig. 12-2) which are borne singly at nodes on alternate sides of a zig-zag rachis. Each short internode of the rachis is narrow at the base and broader at the apex. One side of the internode is convex; the side that faces the spikelet is flattened or concave. Spikes may be awnless, awnleted, or awned. An awn terminates the lemma on all spikelets of awned varieties.

The spikelet consists of 1–5 flowers or florets attached alternately to opposite sides of a central axis or rachilla (Fig. 12-3). One or more of the upper florets usually are sterile, with the result that only two or three kernels mature, except in some club wheats. The spikelet is subtended by two empty bracts or glumes, which are keeled, rigid, and obtuse, acute, or acuminate. The glume tip may be extended into a beak that resembles a short awn. The glumes may be glabrous or pubescent, and be white, yellow, brown, or black, according to the variety [5].

The wheat floret consists of a lemma and palea which enclose the sexual organs—three stamens and a single ovary. The lemmas, keeled or rounded on the back, often are awned. The palea, which occurs opposite

FIGURE 12-2. Spikes, glumes, and kernels of Thatcher common wheat, an
awnletted variety.

(*Courtesy US Department of Agriculture*)

FIGURE 12-3. Portion of spike of common wheat showing spikelets, florets,
and rachis. One opened floret shows
the anthers and stigma.

(*Courtesy US Department of Agriculture*)

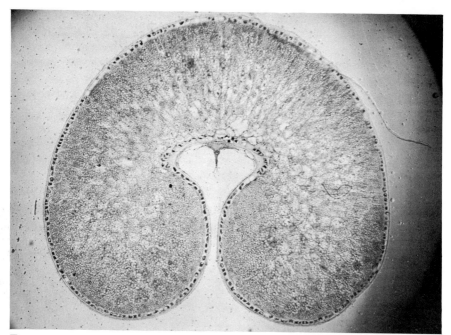

FIGURE 12-4. **Cross section of wheat kernel showing the crease and the endosperm cells. The dark cells near the outer periphery constitute the aleurone layer of the endosperm.**

to the lemma, is membranous, awnless, two-keeled, and with infolded margins. Near the base of the ovary are two small, ovate, membranous scales known as lodicules. In the mature floret, the caryopsis is enclosed between the lemma and palea [5].

KERNEL OR CARYOPSIS

The wheat kernel is a dry, one-seeded, indehiscent fruit or caryopsis. Kernels differ in shape, size, color, texture, and numerous other characteristics.

The kernel, which is roughly egg-shaped (ovate), ranges from 4–10 mm in length, depending on variety, location in the spike, and position in the spikelet during development. A well-filled kernel of most common varieties is smoothly curved on its dorsal surface, except at the base where the fruit coat (pericarp) is wrinkled over the underlying germ or embryo. On its ventral surface, the kernel has a furrow or crease between two cheeks, which extends inward nearly to the center in commonly grown varieties (Fig. 12-4). At the apex or tip of the kernel is a brush composed of many hairs. The color of the kernel usually is classified as white or red. Those of the white class may be white or may vary from cream to yellow, while those of the red class vary from light brown to the darker shades of red. The dark color of red wheats arises primarily from materials present in the seedcoat (testa), but it also is influenced by the texture of the endosperm as well as by the nature of the pericarp. Wheat kernels vary in texture—*i.e.,* soft, semihard, and hard. A normally developed soft kernel has a soft, mealy, or starchy endosperm. One that is hard has a corneous, horny, or vitreous endosperm. Semihard kernels are intermediate in texture [67, 5, 7].

The structure of the wheat kernel involves the pericarp, seedcoat, or testa, nucellar layer, endosperm, and embryo. The tissues of the pericarp form a thin protective layer over the entire kernel. The pericarp is composed of several layers developed from the ovary wall that include epidermis, hypodermis, remnants of thin-walled cells, intermediate cells, cross cells and tube cells (Fig. 12-5). The seedcoat or testa forms a nearly complete cover over the embryo and endosperm and is firmly united with the innermost cells of the pericarp. The testa of red-kerneled varieties contains

FIGURE 12-5. **A wheat kernel. Brush (b). Pericarp—consists of cuticle (c), outer epidermis (oe), parenchyma (p), cross-layer (cl), and inner epidermis (ie). Testa consists of outer integument of seed (oi), and inner integument (ii). Nucellar layer—epidermis of nucellus (en). Endosperm—consists of the aleurone (a and a′), starch, and gluten parenchyma (se and se′), and crushed empty cells of endosperm (d). Germ—consists of scutellum (sc), epithelium of scutellum (es), vascular bundle of scutellum (v), coleoptile (co), first foliage leaf (l₁), second foliage leaf (l₂), growing point (g), second node (n₂), first node (n₁), epiblast (e), primary root (r), root sheath or coleorhiza (rs), and root cap (rc). Hilum (h). The bran layer is comprised of the pericarp, testa, nucellar layer, and aleurone. (Drawn by M. N. Pope).**

(Courtesy US Department of Agriculture)

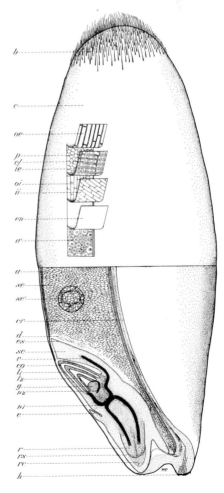

a brownish pigment, but that of white or amber varieties is practically un-pigmented. The nucellar layer is composed of a single row of compressed cells between the endosperm and the testa. The endosperm fills the interior of the grain, except for the embryo. The aleurone is the single row of large rectangular cells that comprise the outer periphery of the endosperm. It is the innermost layer of the bran. The aleurone layer contains no gluten or starch, but has reserve foods in the form of oil and aleurone (protein) granules. The starchy endosperm, the major portion, is composed of cells that contain many starch granules embedded in a matrix of proteinaceous material. The germ or embryo is partly embedded in the endosperm at the base of the kernel. It is composed of an embryonic axis partly enfolded by the shield-shaped scutellum. The embryonic axis consists of the shoot or plumule enclosed by the coleoptile, and the primary root or radicle covered by the coleorhiza. Attached to the embryonic axis, nearest to the endo-sperm, is the cotyledon or scutellum of the embryo. Opposite the scutellum, on the other side of the embryonic axis, is a small scalelike growth known as the epiblast [67, 24, 5, 7, 8, 9, 10].

A plump well-developed kernel consists of about 2.5 per cent germ, 9–10 per cent pericarp, 85–86 per cent starchy endosperm, and 3–4 per cent aleurone. Shrunken wheat of about one-half normal kernel weight may contain not more than 65 per cent of starchy endosperm.

WHEAT SPECIES

The wheats comprise several species of *Triticum*. These fall into three distinct groups; diploids, tetraploids, and hexaploids, with 7, 14, and 21 pairs, respectively, of chromosomes in their cells. The 12 cultivated species of *Triticum* are as follows:

Group	Number of Chromosomes	Species	Common Name
Diploid	7	*T. monococcum*	Einkorn
Tetraploid	14	*T. dicoccum*	Emmer
		T. durum	Durum
		T. persicum	Persian
		T. turgidum	Poulard or Rivet
		T. polonicum	Polish
Hexaploid	21	*T. vulgare*	Common
		T. compactum	Club
		T. spelta	Spelt
		T. sphaerococcum	Shot
		T. macha	Macha
		T. vavilovi	Vavilovii

BOTANICAL CLASSIFICATION OF THE SPECIES

All wheat species known at the present time were classified by C. A. Flaksberger and coworkers in 1939 [13]. An adaptation of their key to species follows:

Key to Species of Triticum

1a. Rachis tenacious; grain threshes free from glumes, lemma, and palea; spikes flattened on face of spikelets.

    2a. Glumes firm, shorter or no longer than lemma.

        3a. Keel of glume indistinct, except at tip, and often lacking near base; beaks short to long.

            4a. Spikes awned or awnless; dense, medium, or lax, with nearly square or rounded cross-section.....Common wheat (*T. vulgare* Host.) (*T. aestivum* L.).

            4b. Spikes mostly awnless, short, dense, width often less than thickness. Grains laterally compressed..................Club Wheat (*T. compactum* Host).

            4c. Spikes awnless or short-awned; short; glumes and lemmas rounded; grains short and rounded.................Shot wheat (*T. sphaerococcum* Perc.).

        3b. Keel narrow but extending to the base of glume; beaks long; spikes nearly square in cross section, awned.

            5a. Rachis joints of normal width (2–3 mm)...........................
            Abyssinian hard wheat (*T. abyssinicum* Vav.).

            5b. Rachis joints narrow (1.5 mm or less); spike flexible.................
            Persian wheat (*T. persicum* Vav.).

        3c. Keel broad and distinct from tip to base; awns long and usually erect (awnless forms rare); beaks short or medium length.

            6. Rachis joints slightly pubescent, glumes about as long as lemmas; spike width less than thickness; grain corneous..........................
            Durum wheat (*T. durum* Desf.).

            6b. Rachis joints pubescent; glumes shorter than lemmas; awns fragile; glumes, lemmas and grains distinctly convex (humped); unbranched spikes nearly as wide as thick but some varieties have branched spikes...
            Poulard wheat (*T. turgidum* L.).

    2b. Glumes papery, as long as or longer than the lemmas, lanceolate, distinctly nerved but indistinctly keeled. Spikes large, short-awned; grains very long and corneous.................................Polish wheat (*T. polonicum* L.).

1b. Rachis tenacious; grain threshes free from glumes, lemma, and palea; spikes composite. Glumes firm, shorter than lemma, and covered with bristlelike spines.......
    Vavilovii wheat (*T. vavilovi* Tum.) Jakub.

1c. Rachis semifragile or fragile; threshed grain mostly entire spikelets enclosed in glumes; spikes laterally compressed with sides flattened; nearly all awned.

        7a. Spikes of medium compactness; rachilla usually attached to base of spikelet.

            8a. Two-keeled palea not split at maturity; spikelets two-grained.

                9a. Glumes keeled, with sloping shoulder; rachis joints slightly pubescent; rachis semifragile.....Emmer (*T. dicoccum* Schubl.).

9b. Glumes indistinctly keeled, with notched shoulder and broad triangular beak.
    10a. Rachis joints pubescent on edges; rachis semifragile.......
        Timopheevi wheat (*T. timopheevi* Zhuk.).
    10b. Rachis joints densely pubescent; rachis fragile...........
        Wild emmer (*T. dicoccoides* Korn.).
8b. Two-keeled palea split at maturity; spikelets mostly one-grained but often two-grained; glume shoulder notched; broad triangular beak.
    11a. Rachis joints slightly pubescent; rachis semifragile.......
        Einkorn (*T. monococcum*).
    11b. Rachis joints densely pubescent with long hairs; rachis fragile.............Wild einkorn (*T. spontaneum* Flaksb.).
7b. Spikes lax or dense; threshed spikelets mostly attached to base of rachilla that lies along the face of the spikelet; glume shoulders broad and nearly flat.
    12a. Spikes lax; beaks obtuse..........Spelt (*T. spelta* L.).
    12b. Spikes lax or dense; beaks acute...................
        Macha wheat (*T. macha* Dek. et Mon.).

Descriptions of Principal Species

Of the 15 species of wheat that have been classified, eight are fairly well known. The species generally grown in the United States are common, club, and durum. Small acreages of spelt, emmer, poulard, and Polish are grown for livestock feed, and einkorn is sometimes planted for research purposes. These species have been described by Bayles and Clark [5].

Common wheat (*Triticum vulgare*) is distinguished from club wheat by a spike that is long in proportion to its thickness. The spike is usually dorsally compressed. The spikelets are 2–5 flowered, far apart, slightly overlapped, pressed close to the rachis, and nearly erect. The glumes are keeled only in the upper half, shorter than the lemmas, firm, and either glabrous or pubescent. The lemmas are awnless or bear awns less than 10 cm long. The palea, as long as the lemma, remains entire at maturity. The culm of the plant is usually hollow, but occasionally pithy within, and it varies in strength and height. The blades of the leaves are usually narrower than those of the durum and poulard wheats. The kernels may be either soft or hard, white or red. A total of 204 varieties cultivated in the United States have been described.

Club wheat (*T. compactum*) plants may be of either winter or spring habit and either tall or short. The stems usually are stiff and strong. The spikes—usually awnless but sometimes awned—are elliptical, oblong, or sometimes clavate or club-shaped, short (usually less than 2.5 inches in length), very compact, and laterally compressed (Fig. 12-6). The spike-

FIGURE 12-6. Spikes of 4 varieties of common wheat and one variety of club wheat: (1) fully awnless, (2) and (3) awnless (tip-awned), (4) fully awned, and (5) club wheat with tip awns.

FIGURE 12-7. Spikes of spelt (1), durum wheat (2), Timopheevi wheat (3), and winter emmer (4).

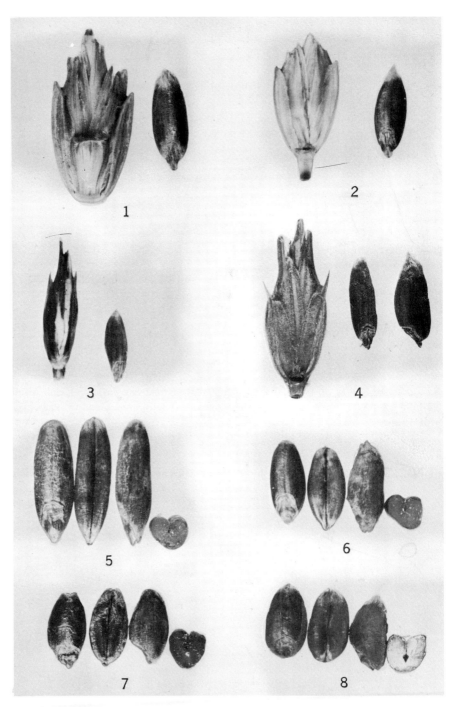

FIGURE 12-8. Spikelet and kernel of: spelt (1); spring emmer (2); einkorn (3); and Timopheevi wheat (4). Wheat kernels: Polish (5); durum (6); poulard (7); and club (8).

(*Courtesy US Department of Agriculture*)

lets usually contain five fertile florets and spread at nearly a right angle to the rachis. The kernels of club wheat are small and laterally compressed because of crowding in the compact spikes. Most of the club wheat kernels have a small, short brush and a narrow, very shallow crease. The grain may be either white or red. The club wheats are distinguished from common wheats by the shorter and denser laterally compressed spikes. Club wheat varieties, grown commercially in the United States, have been described [5].

Durum wheat (*T. durum*) plants are of spring habit. The peduncle is pithy, at least in the upper part. The spikes are laterally compressed; the glumes are sharply keeled; and the lemmas are awned (except in a few awnless forms which are not grown commercially). The awns are long and coarse, and white, yellow, brown, or black. The kernels are white or red and usually rather long and pointed; they are very hard and translucent, which makes the white-kerneled forms appear amber-colored. The kernels always have a short brush and angular cheeks. The durums, hardest of all known wheats, are sometimes very similar to certain poulard varieties. However, the spikes usually are much thinner, the glumes longer, and the kernels longer, more slender, and usually much harder. Varieties grown commercially in the United States have been described [5].

Spelt (*T. spelta*) may be of either winter or spring habit and awnless or awned. It has a long, narrow, lax spike with a brittle rachis (Fig. 12-7). The pedicel, or internode of the rachis, is long and wide; after threshing, the pedicel remains attached to the face of the spikelet below the spikelet that it bears. The spikelets are two-kerneled, arched on the inner side, and closely appressed to the rachis. The kernels, which remain enclosed in the glumes after threshing, are pale red, long, and laterally compressed. They have an acute tip as well as a narrow, shallow crease. Spelt is grown commercially only to a slight extent in the United States.

Emmer (*T. diococcum*) may be of either winter or spring habit. It is usually awned. The culms often are pithy within, while the leaves usually are pubescent. The rachis is brittle, while the spikes are very dense, laterally compressed, and narrow. The pedicel is short, narrow, and pointed; it remains attached to the base of the spikelet which it bears (Fig. 12-8). The spikelets, which are flattened on the inner side, usually contain two flowers. The kernels, which remain enclosed in the glumes after threshing, are red or white, long, and slender, with both ends acute. Emmer is distinguished from spelt by the shorter, denser laterally compressed spikes.

Poulard wheat (*T. turgidum*) may be of either winter or spring habit. The plants usually are tall with broad leaves. The culms are thick, usually solid, and sometimes pithy. The spikes are long and occasionally compound or branched (Fig. 12-9). The spikelets are compactly arranged on the spike. The glumes are short and compactly keeled. The kernels are thick, humped, and mostly hard, but usually very starchy. The poulards are most closely

FIGURE 12-9. **Composite or branched head of the Alaska variety of poulard wheat.**
(*Courtesy US Department of Agriculture*)

FIGURE 12-10. **Spikes and glumes of White Polish wheat and einkorn.**
(*Courtesy US Department of Agriculture*)

related to the durums. The glumes and kernels usually are shorter, while the kernels are thicker in dorsoventral diameter and somewhat shorter.

Polish wheat (*T. polonicum*) has a spring habit, tall stems, and a pithy peduncle. The spike is awned, large, and lax. The glumes are papery, very long, and narrow. The length of the glumes equals or exceeds the length of the lemmas (Fig. 12-10). The kernel is long and narrow; sometimes it is nearly a half-inch long. It is hard and somewhat similar in shape to a rye kernel.

Einkorn (*T. monococcum*) is a one-grained wheat. The spikes are awned, narrow, slender, and laterally compressed. The spikelets usually contain only one fertile floret. The terminal spikelets are aborted. The palea splits into two parts at maturity. The kernels remain enclosed in the spikelets after threshing; they are pale red, slender, and very much compressed. The kernel crease is very slight.

Shot wheat (*T. sphaerococcum* Perc.) differs from other hexaploid wheats in its short or dwarf stature (60–70 cm). It has small heads, small rounded grains, and hemispherical inflated glumes. It has a characteristic tufted appearance when growing, usually being profusely tillered. This species has erect stiff straw which is thick in proportion to its height. It may be awned or awnless. Awned forms never have long awns, but irregularly spreading ones, 1.5–2.0 cm long at the apex of the head and much shorter at the base. It occurs with red or white and glabrous or pubescent chaff, and may have red or white grains. This species is grown to a minor extent in northern India and West Pakistan for local consumption [67, 16].

Persian wheat (*T. persicum,* or *T. carthlicum*) is a fungus-resistant early-maturing spring wheat. It has a strong yellow or light red straw, with mostly solid nodes. The spikes are very flexible and lean over. They are similar to those of *T. vulgare* in that the face side is wider, or the same width, as the lateral side. The rachis is very narrow; the spikelets usually are three-kerneled. This species differs from others in that the glumes have long awnlike projections instead of beaks. Since awns also occur on the lemmas, the spike has a bushy appearance. The kernels are oval, almost always red, and hard in texture. This wheat is grown in Georgia in Soviet Russia.

Macha wheat (*T. macha*) is a late-maturing winter type. The plants have a prostrate growth habit. The speltlike spikes are lax or dense, fragile, and with rachises that break readily. The kernels are red and semihard. This species is cultivated in Georgia in Soviet Russia.

Vavilovii wheat (*T. vavilovi*) has considerable resemblance to spelt, except that it has a compound spike with glumes covered with bristlelike spines, a nonfragile rachis, black awns, and white grains. It too is grown in Soviet Russia.

ORIGIN OF CULTIVATED WHEAT

Most of the cultivated wheats appear to have had their origin in the Middle East [85]. The locus of domestication of a wild wheat undoubtedly is its area of natural distribution. Cultivated wheat seldom is able to survive in nature in competition with other plants.

Diploid (7-chromosome) Group

Cultivated einkorn—probably the ancestor of all the other cultivated wheats [49]—undoubtedly was domesticated from wild einkorn (*Triticum aegilopoides*) by selection of plants with slightly larger kernels, a slightly tougher stem, and heads that shatter less readily.

Einkorn may have originated somewhere in the Near East, since wild einkorn as well as a large number of *Aegilops* species were found there. Cultivated einkorn possibly originated in the mountains of northeastern Turkey or the southwestern Caucasus [85], or slightly farther south in the uplands of eastern Iraq [49], and then spread to Asia Minor [21], and Europe.

Tetraploid (14-chromosome) Group

The tetraploid (14-chromosome) wheats probably arose through hybridization of a 7-chromosome wheat with a 7-chromosome related grass. The wheat parent involved undoubtedly was einkorn or its wild relative, while the wild grass species may have been *Aegilops speltoides* [77]. Emmer possibly was derived directly from wild emmer, although it too may have been a product of hybridization [49].

The tetraploid wheats appear to have been of early importance largely in the Near East and Abyssinia. Wild emmer (*T. dicoccoides*) is indigenous to southern Armenia, northeastern Turkey, western Iran, Syria, and northern Israel, and was found in the Jarmo site in eastern Iraq. Cultivated emmer appears to have had its origin somewhere in Asia Minor, but there is a possibility that it was domesticated in the uplands of Iraq. By 4000 BC emmer, the earliest of the 14-chromosome wheats, was widely cultivated from the lower plain of Iraq to Asia Minor to the Rhine river in Europe. It may have been the chief cereal of the Near East from earliest times to the Greco-Roman period. The other species in this group are naked wheats, which are considered to be of more recent origin. Those which are believed to have originated in the Near East include durum, poulard, Persian, and Timopheevi (a wild type). Durum and poulard wheats also are found in the Abyssinian center of origin [85, 49, 21].

Hexaploid (21-chromosome) Group

Hexaploid wheats appear to have evolved most recently. No wild forms are known. These wheats seem to have originated by the hybridization of a 14-chromosome wheat with a wild 7-chromosome relative of wheat, probably from the genus *Aegilops* [49].

Spelt may have originated as a natural cross between emmer and *Aegilops squarrosa* in northern Syria where both species are found growing wild [36], but a recent Kyoto University expedition established the Caucasus mountains as the probable place of origin. Spelt has been produced synthetically from a cross between wild emmer and *Ae. squarrosa*. This synthetic hybrid closely resembles cultivated spelt, with which it hybridizes readily [55, 56, 36, 37]. Spelt may be the ancestral hexaploid wheat that arose in southeastern Europe or southwestern Asia, and was carried to central Europe [56]. One writer contends that it was once the principal wheat of central Europe, and may have originated there [85]. However, spelt seems to be of more recent origin than the other 21-chromosome wheats. No archaeological remains of spelt have been found anywhere in Asia.

Common wheat may have originated in northeastern Turkey, or adjacent areas of the Soviet Union, possibly about 2500 BC [49]. A 21-chromosome wheat that resembles common wheat was produced synthetically from a cross between Persian wheat and *Ae. squarrosa* [37]. Club wheat probably originated in Asia Minor, but it apparently was grown in Iraq as early as 3000 BC [21]. Kernels of shot wheat were found in the Mohenjo Daro site in India (now in Pakistan), which dates from about 2500 BC [49].

TYPES, CLASSES, AND VARIETIES

Wheat varieties change continually in many countries because of the development of new varieties or strains by plant breeders. New varieties currently grown in the United States usually are superior to the older ones in such characteristics as yield, disease resistance, insect resistance, strength of straw, and milling and baking quality. Most improved varieties now grown produce higher yields than those cultivated prior to 1900, chiefly because of greater resistance to unfavorable weather as well as to diseases and insects [91]. New varieties in most other countries display similar improvements.

Varieties Grown in the United States

A total of 212 distinct wheat varieties were grown in the United States in 1959, of which each of 16 varieties were sown on one million acres or more [73].

Hard red winter wheat varieties are grown chiefly in the southern half of the Great Plains in Nebraska, Kansas, Colorado, Oklahoma, Texas, and New Mexico. All varieties grown commercially are classified as common wheat (*T. vulgare*). Turkey was the most widely grown variety in this region before 1944, but it now has been replaced by new improved varieties. The principal varieties in 1959, in order of earliness and acreage sown, were Triumph, Wichita, and Pawnee. Others seeded on large acreages in the region were Cheyenne, Comanche, Ponca, Kiowa, Nebred, Bison, and Concho [73].

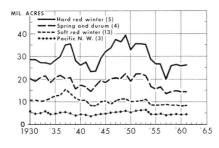

FIGURE 12-11. **Relative acreages and trends of 4 groups of wheat in the United States.**

(*Courtesy US Department of Agriculture*)

     Hard red spring wheat varieties are grown in the northern half of the Great Plains, particularly in Minnesota, the Dakotas, and Montana. Selkirk was seeded on more than half the entire spring wheat acreage in 1959. Lee was widely sown in the western part of the region, while Rescue was important where sawfly attacks spring wheat. All are varieties of common wheat.

    Soft red winter varieties of common wheat are grown primarily in the eastern half of the United States under subhumid to humid conditions. Varieties once important in this region were Fultz, Mediterranean, and Harvest Queen. The Knox variety was sown on 24 per cent of the soft red winter wheat acreage in 1959, being widely grown in the Ohio Valley. Other important varieties in the region are Seneca and Thorne. Anderson was the most widely grown variety in the Southeastern states [73].

    White wheat varieties are grown in the Western states and in Michigan and New York. Both common (*T. vulgare*) and club (*T. compactum*) white varieties are produced. Genesee, a soft white common variety, was the most widely sown variety in Michigan and New York in 1959. Burt, a hard white winter variety, was seeded on a considerable acreage in Washington and Oregon. Lemhi (or Lemhi 53) spring wheat was sown in Idaho and Utah, mostly on irrigated land. Ramona (or Ramona 44) was seeded principally in California and Arizona. Practically all of the white club wheats are grown in the Pacific Northwest, where they are fall seeded. Omar was sown on 83.6 per cent of the club wheat acreage in 1959 [73].

    Durum wheat (*T. durum*) varieties are grown almost exclusively in the North Central states in Minnesota and the Dakotas. Kubanka and Mindum were popular varieties in this region for many years. The varieties Langdon and Ramsey accounted for 86 per cent of the 1959 acreage sown to durum wheat [73].

The relative importance as well as the trends in acreage of the groups of wheat in four regions of the United States are shown in Fig. 12-11. The acreage in all regions has declined since 1953.

Varieties Grown in Some Other Countries

By far the most widely grown type in Canada is common wheat (*T. vulgare*) of the hard red spring class, with the main concentration in the Prairie Provinces (Manitoba, Saskatchewan, and Alberta). About 50 per cent of the acreage in 1960 was seeded to Thatcher, and 30 per cent to Selkirk. Durum wheat (*T. durum*) was grown on about 5 per cent of the wheat acreage in the southern parts of these provinces, where the Stewart variety is most widely grown. Small acreages of soft white winter, soft red winter, hard red spring, and white spring common wheats are grown in eastern Canada, particularly in Ontario [69].

In Argentina, approximately 97 per cent of the wheat land is sown with common wheat (*T. vulgare*), and only 3 per cent to durum (*T. durum*). Practically all the wheat is fall-sown. Hard red winter varieties occupy more than 50 per cent of the total wheat acreage, while semihard red types are grown on 40 per cent of the acreage. Soft white wheat is grown only in one state [70].

Practically all of the wheat grown in Australia is common white spring wheat, which is predominantly soft in texture. In Queensland and New South Wales, however, there is a considerable production of semihard to hard white wheat with a protein content that ranges from 12–14 per cent. The principal varieties of soft white wheat are Insignia, Bencubbin, Pinnacle, Olympic, Sherpa, Bungulla, and Dirk. The important varieties of semihard to hard white wheat are Spica and Lawrence. The Gabo variety is an important soft wheat on infertile soils, but it is used as a semihard wheat on fertile soils.

Most of the wheat grown in northwestern Europe is common (*T. vulgare*) soft wheat, which is of poor quality for making bread. The wheats of Great Britain are classified as common and poulard or rivet (*T. turgidum*). Common wheats are winter or spring types with red or white soft grains. Winter wheats are grown on about 70 per cent of the acreage. Poulard wheats are of minor importance, but a few varieties are able to withstand the winters in southern England. They are grown to be made into biscuit flour, or to mix with the flour of bread wheats [68].

Both winter and spring common wheats also are grown in Sweden. Suitable winter varieties are characterized by high quality and winter hardiness. In recent years, spring wheat has tended to replace winter wheat because of better milling and baking quality [1].

Common wheat is the chief species grown in the Soviet Union. Almost all regions produce high protein wheat. The principal types are hard red spring and hard red winter. Emmer and considerable durum wheat also are grown. Some soft red winter, soft white spring, and soft white winter types of common wheat are grown, but their commercial importance is limited [65].

Practically all important commercial wheat varieties in China are classified as common wheat, with a few varieties of club, poulard, and durum. Among the common wheats, soft to semihard red as well as white spring types are grown north of the Great Wall, while red winter wheat is produced in the Yellow River Valley. Soft wheats are sown in the Yangtze Valley and in the South.

The bulk of the wheat acreage in India is seeded to common wheat. The principal types grown are soft red, hard red, soft white, and hard white wheats. There are many varieties of each type adapted to different conditions. Durum wheat is of limited local commercial importance. Despite its importance in earlier times, shot wheat (*T. sphaerococcum*) is now grown only occasionally. Common wheat also is the most important species in West Pakistan, where hard white varieties are widely cultivated. Some soft white and hard red wheats also are grown.

Practically all of the wheat grown in Japan is soft red common wheat. Conspicuous features of most Japanese varieties are early maturity, profuse, tillering, and short stiff straw.

PROGRESSIVE NORMAL PLANT DEVELOPMENT

The embryo of the wheat grain consists of: (a) an axis with a terminal plumule completely enclosed in a tubular cone-shaped sheath, the coleoptile, which is entirely closed except for a vent or slitlike pore in its front face slightly below the tip; (b) a terminal primary root enclosed within a cone-shaped root sheath, the coleorhiza; (c) an oval, fleshy structure, the scutellum, attached to one side of the axis and which makes up most of the bulk of the embryo; and (d) opposite to the scutellum, a small scalelike structure, the epiblast. In all well-developed embryos there is a pair of opposite lateral lobes on the axis in the general region that bears the epiblast. These are the outward evidence of the lateral seminal roots [51].

Vegetative Stage

The growing wheat plant passes through a vegetative phase, followed by a reproductive or fruiting period. Stages of vegetative development include germination, root growth, tillering, jointing, culm elongation, and heading.

When the wheat grain is exposed to moisture, water is absorbed and the grain swells. At appropriate temperatures the embryo begins to push out both the coleorhiza and the coleoptile. The seed coat is ruptured, the coleoptile turns upward, and the primary root pierces the coleorhiza and turns downward. Shortly after the primary root has pierced the coleorhiza, the lower pair of lateral roots emerges through the axis cortex, followed soon after by a second pair just above the first, and sometimes by a third pair. This seminal root system remains functional throughout the life of the plant unless destroyed by disease or in some other way. As the coleoptile continues to elongate, the first foliage leaf of the plumule pushes through the vent. As growth continues, the second foliage leaf pushes out. Coronal roots arise from the node of the first foliage leaf, which becomes the first node of the crown. The crown region, much compressed, consists of several nodes and internodes. Two or more coronal roots are formed at each crown node. These crown roots, together with their branches, are the principal supply roots of the plant. A bud primordium lies in the leaf axil at each crown node. These bud primordia develop into tillers [51].

Young wheat plants in the fall consist mainly of crown, roots, and basal leaves. The culm internodes remain short during the early stages of development. The closely grouped leaves from the crown internodes of the primary axis and of the tillers produce a tuft or rosette characteristic of the so-called tillering stage [51].

Under Nebraska conditions, tiller production in winter wheat often starts about 15 days after the seed is sown in September, with a new tiller added every 4–5 days until December when cold weather stops plant growth. The seminal roots reached depths of 36–48 inches by December 15, whereas the coronal roots were 22 inches deep. Root growth ceased simultaneously with that of the above-ground parts [88]. In cold climates wheat plants never joint in the fall unless planted while hot weather prevails. Culm elongation starts on the resumption of growth in the spring. The growing tips immediately become prominent.

Reproductive Stage

When active growth of the wheat plant starts in the spring, the growing point begins to elongate in preparation for spike differentiation. Leaf initials also are produced at the base of the growing point. The initiation of the reproductive stage is soon apparent from the differentiation of the spikelets together with the increase in size of spikelet parts. Node and leaf initiation ceases. Spikelet differentiation begins in the middle of the spike and proceeds toward the base and tip. Within the spikelet, differentiation begins at the base of the spikelet and proceeds upward. Spikelet parts differentiate in order as follows: glumes and flowers 1, 2, 3, and so forth. Within the flower, the sequence of differentiation of its members proceeds from the outside inward: lemma, anthers, palea, and pistil. The wheat spike is a determinate inflorescence. It terminates in an apical spikelet. When the spikelets differentiate, the number is fixed, but the number of fertile flowers in a spikelet may adjust to growth conditions [6].

In Nebraska, the growing tips of winter wheat enlarged and began differentiation into spikes about April 1. The spikelets that existed at maturity in normal plants were readily counted on May 1, or 30 days before the heads appeared, and 60 days before the crop was ripe. The spike was about 1/10 inch long at that time. The florets were observed in the spikelets early in May, but apparently only the lower 1–3 out of 8–9 florets developed to maturity. The others remained rudimentary, dried up, and disappeared. It was concluded that spikelet counts were an unreliable basis for the early prediction of grain yields. The percentage of fertile spikelets, as well as the average kernel weight, still depended upon the environmental conditions that followed [35].

Tiller culms usually are shorter and produce shorter spikes than do the main culms. They also produce fewer fertile spikelets, total spikelets, grains per spike, grains per fertile spikelet, and lighter kernels. There are more sterile spikelets on the tiller spikes than on the spikes of the main culm. Favorable growth conditions result in a large number of tillers per unit area [81].

POLLINATION

Wheat is normally a self-pollinated plant. The time required for the wheat flower to open fully has averaged 3 minutes and 36 seconds. Approximately 86 per cent of the flowers may bloom in daylight [45]. In Japan most of the blooming in common and durum wheats occurs in the afternoon [26]. Flowers bloom over a temperature range of 56–78°F. Blooming usually is checked in certain flowers below 55°F, although pollen may be discharged from the anthers of previously opened flowers down to 52°F [45].

Natural cross-pollination sometimes occurs in wheat in 1–4 per cent of the flowers [17]. Wheat that is partly self-sterile from chromosomal irregularities, or from adverse environment, sometimes cross-pollinates extensively. In Virginia, a maximum of 34 per cent was observed in a strain of Fulcaster wheat in 1917. In one season, approximately six times as much natural crossing occurred in the secondary heads of five common wheat varieties as in the primary heads [46].

Blooming begins in the spikelets slightly above the middle of the spike and proceeds both upward and downward. Within a spikelet, the upper flowers bloom last. Under ordinary conditions, a wheat spike completes blooming within 2–3 days after the first anthers appear [45].

EFFECTS OF ENVIRONMENTAL FACTORS ON GROWTH

Growth and reproduction of the wheat plant is influenced by soil moisture, temperature, light, and mineral nutrition.

Soil Moisture

Wheat plants grown in Canada at four soil moisture levels showed a decrease in internode length and plant height as the soil moisture decreased [27]. The decreased length of internodes was attributed to a reduction in cell elongation [92].

Field observations on winter wheat in Wyoming under limited moisture conditions revealed that the Yogo variety produced a significantly better fall emergence than did the Cheyenne variety. Similar responses were obtained in the laboratory when wheat varieties were germinated under controlled conditions of moisture stress. There is apparently a difference in the ability of the seeds of different varieties to imbibe water from a soil with limited moisture [25].

Temperature

The optimum temperature for the germination of wheat is between 20–22°C. (68–71.6°F), whereas the minimum temperature is 4°C (39.2°F). At temperatures considerably above the optimum, the grains germinate irregularly and the embryo frequently dies. At temperatures as high as 35°C (95°F), the endosperm may undergo decomposition due to the activities of bacteria or fungi [67].

Cold-hardened winter wheat has survived temperatures as low as − 40°F when protected by snow, but they would probably survive as low as − 25°F without snow protection. Unhardened winter wheat plants may be severely injured by extended exposure to temperatures of 15–25°F.

Temperatures of 60–70°F generally are favorable for active spring growth of the wheat plant. Greenhouse studies with controlled soil temperatures indicate that plant height, root length, and tiller number decreased as temperatures rose from 22–42°C (71.6–107.6°F). Leaves were largest at 22°C (71.6°F), and became lighter in color as the temperature rose above 32°C (89.6°F). Heading was accelerated as much as 11 days as the temperature was increased from 22 to 34°C (71.6–93.2°F), but it was retarded or prevented at temperatures above 34°C (93.2°F). The greatest total dry weight of plants (tops plus roots) at harvest time was obtained when the plants were grown at 22°C (71.6°F) [93].

Light Effects

Development of the wheat plant from the vegetative to the reproductive stage depends on the intensity as well as the duration of daily illumination. The effects of light also are modified by temperature differences.

Reduction of light intensity to 64 or 34 per cent of normal light during a seven-week preripening period caused significant increases in plant height of the Pawnee variety of winter wheat. Further reductions of light intensity resulted in a marked decrease in plant height, grain yield, and kernel weight [32].

Longer days hasten the formation of inflorescences. Wheat normally flowers in the long days of spring or early summer. Short days increase the vegetative growth of the wheat plant. Spring wheats usually will flower at any day length, from less than eight hours up to continuous light, given sufficient time and favorable temperatures, but the process is accelerated with an increase in day length—more so in spring wheats than in winter varieties [14, 28, 59]. Spring wheats complete their life cycle quickly when given a long day with temperatures of 70°F or above. Winter wheats generally complete their life cycle most rapidly when given low temperatures during the early stages of growth, but a long day and high temperatures during the later stages of growth. Photoperiods that shorten the vegetative period of spring or winter wheat reduce the number of internodes and leaves on each tiller [59, 32].

Spring wheats grown under controlled conditions became progressively earlier as the photoperiod was increased from 8 to 24 hours [19] through acceleration of the development of the floral primordia. Division of the normal 24-hour day into several cycles, in which the same light-to-darkness ratio was maintained, also accelerated development as a result of shortened periods of darkness [75]. Vernalized (see p. 313) winter wheat plants grown under a daily eight-hour photoperiod failed to head until the photoperiod was lengthened [64].

Cool temperature may partly offset the effect of a long photoperiod in inducing flowering, even in a spring variety such as Federation which has a cold requirement. Increased day-length decreased the time of flowering to a much greater degree when the plants were grown at 69.8°F, than when they were grown at 53.6°F, a temperature too cool for rapid growth [28]. The Chinese variety, which is less sensitive to photoperiod than were three other spring wheat varieties, flowered earlier when grown under short days (8–10 hours) at cool temperatures (50–70°F), but was the latest when the temperature was increased to 80°F, or the photoperiod increased to 16 or more hours [19]. Chinese likewise was later than White Federation 38 under a long day (16–20 hours) and a warm temperature (80°F) [74].

Wheat plants under a short photoperiod of 8–9 hours may develop elongated and twisted internodes of the rachis [58]. Plants transferred from a controlled long day (18 hours) to a shorter day (12 hours or less), may develop such abnormalities as branched heads, elongated rachis, and compound lower spikelets [12].

Vernalization

Temperatures affect the flowering time of wheat. Winter wheat sown in the spring fails to produce heads unless the sprouting seeds or growing plants are subjected to cold or cool conditions. This reaction is called vernalization. Most winter varieties head when sown very early in the spring, or where low spring and summer temperatures prevail. Winter wheat sown in moist soil in late fall, during weather so cold that it fails to emerge until spring, also will head. This cooling can be accomplished also by placing slightly germinated seeds in dark rooms at a temperature of 37–42°F for 50–65 days before sowing [57].

Vernalized immature embryos of Comanche winter wheat produced plants that headed when subjected to a long photoperiod. The spikes had been detached from 8–12 days after anthesis and chilled at 32–40°F for 40–50 days with the stems in water in the refrigerator. These vernalized immature embryos retained much of the response after 30 weeks of storage at room temperatures [89]. A gibberellin spray on germinating seedlings of Vermillion soft red winter wheat reduced the necessary period of cold-treatment vernalization by as much as 28 days [90].

The effectiveness of vernalization of spring wheat may be diminished or destroyed, unless the variety has an appreciable cold requirement. When 36 spring wheats were vernalized, 27 responded with slightly accelerated flowering while 9 were retarded. The wheats that gave the greatest response, 2–4 days, had been produced in areas with relatively high temperatures during flowering and ripening of the parent plant [94]. The difference in rate of development between early (White Federation 38 and Progress) and late (Chinese and Warden) maturing varieties of spring wheat was overcome by a 60-day vernalization treatment. However, the response of plants grown from seed harvested in different years varies unpredictably [76].

FUNCTION OF AWNS IN KERNEL DEVELOPMENT

The presence of awns on the florets of wheat has tended toward the production of heavier kernels. High temperature or limited rainfall generally favor awned varieties, although certain awnless varieties also may yield well under such conditions. Kernels from awned florets are heavier than are those from florets on the same spike from which the awns have been clipped [78]. Deawning immediately after the plants headed has decreased kernel weight and weight of grain per head [61]. Higher test weights of grain from awned varieties than for comparable awnless varieties also have been reported [4, 82, 3].

In semiarid regions, awned types of wheat have rather consistently outyielded awnless or awnletted types, but usually there has been little or no yield superiority of awned types over awnless types under humid or cool irrigated conditions. In California, awnless Baart and awned Onas, derived by reciprocal backcrosses from an Onas × Baart cross, were compared with the original awned Baart and awnless Onas. The differences in favor of the awned lines were highly significant. The three-year average acre yields were 43.5 bushels of awned Baart and 39.4 bushels of awnless Baart. Awned and awnless Onas yielded 49.6 and 47.8 bushels per acre, respectively [82]. In a Texas experiment, the four-year average yields of ten pairs of isogenic awned and awnless lines were 26.0 and 24.9 bushels per acre, respectively. The differences in favor of the awned lines were greater during drought years [3]. Under humid conditions in Ohio, awned segregates from bulk-hybrid populations in F_3 or later generations, showed a negligible increase in yield over their awnless counterparts [43].

Awned heads transpire more than do deawned heads, but the water loss through the awns accounts for no more than 1–5 per cent of the total transpiration of the plant [18]. The awns also function as a depository for surplus minerals, chiefly silicates [43].

Awns carry on photosynthesis, with the result that an appreciable amount of photosynthate is translocated from the awns to the kernels. The contribution of the awns to kernel weight, when compared with that of the flag-leaf blade, becomes increasingly important at low soil moisture levels, when the lower leaves have dried. This may explain why awned varieties outyield awnless ones in semiarid regions, but also why there is little or no advantage of awned over awnless varieties in the humid regions. Under drought conditions, the awns may continue photosynthesis even after the upper (flag) leaf dries up. Under some circumstances, the contribution of the awns to total kernel dry matter may comprise as much as 12 per cent of that of the entire plant [54].

The tips of the spikes of awnless wheats often dry prematurely under hot dry conditions. Awned spike tips dry less rapidly, because of the shading or other effects of the awns.

WINTER HARDINESS

Low temperatures cause losses nearly as great as those from all wheat diseases combined. An average of 15 per cent of the winter wheat seeded is abandoned, much of it due to winter killing [72]. Winter killing may be due to the direct effect of low temperature on plant tissue, physiological drought, or heaving and smothering [79, 34]. Wheat varieties differ widely in their resistance to cold. The hardiest varieties grown are Yogo, Minter, Marmin, and Minturki [71].

Process of Freezing Injury

In frozen wheat plants, ice crystals are formed in the intercellular spaces from water withdrawn from the plant cells [47]. This brings about a concentration of the cell sap, with attendant increases in salts and hydrogen-ion concentration. When the ice melts, much of the water evaporates instead of returning to the plant cells. Ice expansion in the intercellular spaces may split the cells apart, while the concentrated cell sap may precipitate the cell proteins or disorganize the protoplasm beyond recovery.

More winter wheat plants survive low temperatures in moist soils than in dry soils. Plants in high-moisture soils suffer more quickly, but die more slowly [38]. An erect growth habit often indicates lack of hardiness, but a decumbent habit does not always indicate hardiness [39]. Injury in wheat plants progresses from the older to the younger leaves; the most hardy parts are the crown and meristematic tissues [50]. Wheat plants may survive almost completely even after all of the leaves have been frozen back to the soil surface. But when the crown tissue is killed, the vascular connections between the tops and roots is broken [66], and the plant dies. Late fall-sown wheat with shallow roots tends to heave more readily than does that sown early in the fall [29, 30, 31].

A cold-resistant wheat plant must have the ability to harden, an inherited characteristic that manifests itself only after exposure to cool temperatures with ample light. Hardening begins at temperatures below about 41°F—*i.e.,* the threshold value above which growth commences. The hardening range is between 32–41°F [22]. There is a concentration of sugars in the tissues of hardy wheat varieties which lowers the freezing point to some extent and decreases protein precipitation. A progressive increase in dry matter and sugar content of winter wheat plants follows low-temperature hardening [41]. However, water-soluble protein in the leaves and crowns of winter wheat seems to be more closely related to cold hardiness than is total sugar [47, 95]. The hardier the variety, the lower the moisture content of the leaves. In hardened leaves this water is bound under great force by hydrophylic colloids [62, 50, 63]. The more hardy wheat plants lose less water after thawing. After hardening, plants become more susceptible to cold injury with advanced age and season.

Loss or Lack of Cold Hardiness

Loss of cold resistance during the period of transition from dormancy to active growth is essentially a reversal of the hardening process. Dry matter and sugar decrease as dehardening progresses [41]. The supply of organic foods usually is depleted by respiration [15].

Varieties of winter wheat differ in the rate at which hardiness is lost in the winter-spring transition. In a Kansas experiment, Harvest Queen wheat lost its resistance to cold more slowly than did the hardier varieties Minturki, Kanred, Quivera, Turkey, and Blackhull. Thus, Harvest Queen retained a relatively high degree of cold resistance into the spring-growth stage. Such retention protects a variety against injury from early spring freezes [44]. Damage to winter wheat heads from late spring freezes is most serious when the head has just emerged from the boot. Early varieties thus are most likely to be exposed to injury by spring freezes. Floral sterility may occur with a four-hour exposure at 28.4°F, with a progressive increase with lower temperatures and longer exposure. The percentage of floret sterility is increased by wetting the heads just before freezing. High soil fertility greatly increased the susceptibility of the florets to low temperatures, although the susceptibility differed slightly among varieties [48].

Young spring wheat plants, especially of early varieties, also may be injured by freezing. In order of resistance to frost injury, several ranked as follows: Reliance, Red Fife, Marquis, Marquillo, and Hope [86]. In cold climates, wheat may freeze before maturity. All varieties are almost equally susceptible to freezing injury in the milk and soft dough stages of kernel development.

NUTRITION OF THE WHEAT PLANT

Nutrients absorbed by the wheat plant include nitrogen, phosphorus, potassium, calcium, chlorine, silicon, sulfur, and small amounts of numerous other elements. The amounts depend on the availability of the nutrient, the stage of growth of the plant, and various other factors. Most of the mineral matter, except nitrogen, is absorbed before or by the time the wheat plant blooms, but transference to the head may proceed until about a week before harvest.

The wheat plant absorbs much of its nitrogen, usually in the nitrate form, by the time it blooms, but absorption continues until the crop is nearly ripe. The plant attains a maximum quantity of nitrogen three weeks before harvest, but the elaboration of protein continues a week longer [42]. Only 8–22 per cent of the total amount of nitrogen in winter wheat plants in Kansas was absorbed from October to March. About 80 per cent of the nitrogen was absorbed during 7–12 weeks after March 15, after the resumption of spring growth. The amount of nitrogen in the stems and leaves reached its peak at about the time of heading, after which it decreased until harvest. Nitrogen began to increase in the heads about the time it started to decrease in the stems and leaves. The amount in the grain increases from the beginning of its formation until maturity [60]. There are no differences in total nitrogen content of the vegetative parts of high and low protein wheat varieties prior to heading, but thereafter nitrogen increases more rapidly in the heads of high protein varieties [80]. The absorption of nitrogen by wheat plants on low-nitrogen soils in North Dakota fell off rapidly after they had reached the heading stage, but continued on high-nitrogen soils [11]. In water cultures, kernels from plants whose nitrogen supply was continued until time of heading contained 2.90 per cent nitrogen. Kernels from plants whose supply was unlimited until maturity had 3.74 per cent nitrogen (21.3 per cent protein). The quality of gluten produced was not affected by the supply of inorganic nitrogen, even though the total protein content of the grain was markedly influenced [52].

The principal protein in the wheat kernel is gluten, composed of gliadin and glutenin. Nongluten proteins are albumin and globulin. The gluten is formed in the developing kernel from translocated amino acids and amides [2]. These more simple nitrogen compounds predominate at the very earliest formation of the kernel, but are rapidly changed into the proteins characteristic of the wheat grain [83]. When the protein is deposited in the kernel at a rapid rate relative to starch early in the postfloral period, but at a slower relative rate later in this period, then a short postfloral period favors a high protein percentage [2].

Phosphorus is important in the nutrition of the wheat plant, even though the total amount in the aerial parts never reaches 1 per cent on a dry basis. Winter wheat plants in Kansas absorb 12–25 per cent of their total phosphorus by March 1. Thereafter, absorption is very rapid [60]. The maximum quantity of phosphorus in the plant is attained two weeks before harvest [42]. In a phosphorus-deficient nutrient solution, wheat plants develop fewer and smaller kernels, and plant respiration is limited [33].

Potassium is essential to the nutrition of the wheat plant, particularly during the active formation of carbohydrates. In winter wheat in Kansas, the potassium absorbed by March 15 did not exceed 12 per cent of the maximal amount. The absorption of potassium markedly increases as soon as rapid growth begins in the spring [60], and the plant attains its maximum quantity seven weeks before harvest. A marked loss in potassium has been observed during the final six weeks before ripening of the grain [42], as this element is leached from dried leaves. A limited supply of potassium in water cultures is accompanied by a relatively increased absorption of calcium and magnesium [53]. The quality of grain is adversely affected by a restriction of potassium.

Sulfur metabolism in wheat has been studied in plants in nutrient solutions adequately supplied with radioactive sodium sulfate, and in plants fumigated with active sulfur dioxide. A high initial absorption of sulfur, as sodium sulfate, results in a maximum concentration in the leaves in 8–10 days, followed by a lowered concentration as this sulfur is distributed. Some 60–80 per cent of the sulfur is translocated to the grain during ripening. Most of the sulfur dioxide and sulfate is rapidly converted to organic forms. Apparently, organic sulfur in the leaves changes to sulfate for translocation, then changes back to organic forms in the roots and grain [84]. There is a marked concentration of sulfur in the embryo as well as in the periphery of the endosperm, particularly in the aleurone layer. The distribution of sulfur apparently is similar to the distribution of protein [20].

CARBOHYDRATES

With few exceptions, the total dry weight of the wheat plant increases to the time of harvest. The maximum rate of increase occurs between the jointing and blooming stages. The heads of wheat at maturity constitute from 25–40 per cent of the total dry weight of the plants. After blooming, the dry matter generally decreases in the stems and leaves, but increases in the heads [60].

The maximum percentage of sugars in the wheat plant occurs during the early stages of growth. In the heads, the maximum percentage occurs at the first stage of formation and then declines with some fluctuations until harvest. The maximum amount of sugar in the plants is reached at approximately the milk stage [60].

The greatest gain in the amount of carbohydrates in the stems and leaves occurs during the early stages of the formation of the heads. Most of the losses of carbohydrates take place during the three weeks before harvest. The greatest losses in the stems and leaves are observed when the greatest increases occur in the heads. The percentage of starch in the stems, leaves, and chaff rarely exceeds 2 per cent. The starch in the immature grain may vary from 27–37 per cent, most of it being deposited during the four weeks before harvest [60].

REFERENCES

1. Aberg, E., "Recent changes in Swedish crop production," in *Advances in Agronomy*, Vol. VII. New York: Academic Press. pp 39–74. 1955.

2. Alsberg, C. L., "Environment, heredity, and wheat quality." Stanford U. Food Res. Inst., *Wheat Studies.* **10**: 229–249. 1933–34.

3. Atkins, I. M., and M. J. Norris, "The influence of awns on yield and certain morphological characters of wheat." *Agron. J.*, **47**(5): 218–220. 1955.

4. Bayles, B. B., and C. A. Suneson, "Effect of awns on kernel weight, test weight, and yield of wheat." *J. Am. Soc. Agron.*, **32**: 382–386. 1940.

5. ———, and J. A. Clark, "Classification of wheat varieties grown in the United States in 1949." USDA *Tech. Bul. 1083.* 1954.

6. Bonnett, O. T., "The development of the wheat spike." *J. Ag. Res.*, **53**(6): 445–451. 1936.

7. Bradbury, D., I. M. Cull, and M. M. MacMasters, "Structure of the mature kernel of wheat. I: Gross anatomy and relationships of parts." *Cer. Chem.*, **33**(6): 329–342. 1956.

8. ———, M. M. MacMasters, and I. M. Cull, "Structure of the wheat kernel. II: Microscopic structure of pericarp, seed coat, and other coverings of the endosperm and germ of hard red winter wheat." *Cer. Chem.*, **33**(6): 342–360. 1956.

9. ———, M. M. MacMasters, and I. M. Cull, "Structure of the mature wheat kernel. III: Microscopic structure of the endosperm of hard red winter wheat." *Cer. Chem.*, **33**(6): 361–373. 1956.

10. ———, M. M. MacMasters, and I. M. Cull, "Structure of the mature wheat kernel. IV: Microscopic structure of the germ of hard red winter wheat." *Cer. Chem.*, **33**(6): 373–391. 1956.

11. Carpenter, R. W., H. J. Haas, and E. F. Miles, "Nitrogen uptake by wheat in relation to nitrogen content of soil." *Agron. J.*, **44**(8): 420–423. 1952.

12. Chinoy J. J., and K. K. Nanda, "Physiological studies in growth and development of crop plants. I: Photoperiodic induction of developmental abnormalities in Indian wheat." *Ind. J. Ag. Sci.*, **16**, Pt. 4: 390–399. 1946.

13. Clark, J. A., and B. B. Bayles, "Classification of wheat varieties grown in the United States." USDA *Tech. Bul. 795.* 1942.

14. Cooper, H. P., "The inheritance of the spring and winter growth habit in crosses between typical spring and typical winter wheats and the response of wheat plants to artificial light." *J. Am. Soc. Agron.*, **15**: 15–25. 1923.

15. Dexter, S. T., "Decreasing hardiness of winter wheat in relation to photosynthesis defoliation, and winter injury." *Pl. Phys.*, **8**: 297–304. 1933.

16. Ellerton, S., "The origin and geographical distribution of *Triticum sphaerococcum* Perc. and its cytogenetical behavior in crosses with *T. vulgare* Vill." *J. Gen.*, **38**: 307–324. 1939.

17. Garber, R. J., and K. S. Quisenberry, "Natural crossing in winter wheat." *J. Am. Soc. Agron.*, **15**: 508–512. 1923.

18. Gauch, H. G., and E. C. Miller, "The influence of awns upon the rate of transpiration from the heads of wheat." *J. Ag. Res.*, **61**: 445–458. 1940.

19. Gries, G. A., F. W. Stearns, and R. M. Caldwell, "Responses of spring wheat varieties to day-length at different temperatures." *Agron. J.*, **48**: 29–32. 1956.

20. Harrison, B. F., M. D. Thomas, and G. R. Hill, "Radioautographs showing distribution of sulfur in wheat." *Pl. Phys.*, **19**: 245–257. 1944.

21. Helbaek, H., "Domestication of food plants in the Old World." *Science*, **130** (3372): 365–372. 1959.

22. Harvey, R. B., "Physiology of the adaptation of plants to low temperatures." World Grain Exhib. and Conf. Proc., **2**: 145–151. 1933.

23. Hayward, H. E., *The Structure of Economic Plants*. New York: Macmillan. pp 141–178. 1938.
24. Hector, J. M. *Introduction to the Botany of Field Crops*, Vol. I, *Cereals*. Johannesburg, So. Afr.: Central News Agency. pp 92–213. 1936.
25. Helmerick, R. H., and R. P. Pfeifer, "Differential varietal responses of winter wheat germination and early growth to controlled limited moisture conditions." *Agron. J.*, **46**(12): 560–562. 1954.
26. Hirayoshi, I., "Some observations on the blooming of *Triticum* and its allied genera in relation to systematics." *Jap. J. Gen.*, **17**(6): 265–294. 1941.
27. Hopkins, J. W., "Comparative development of two wheat varieties under varying moisture supply." *Can. J. Res.*, **17**(C): 87–96. 1939.
28. Hurd-Karrer, A. M., "Comparative responses of a spring and a winter wheat to day length and temperature." *J. Ag. Res.*, **46**: 867–888. 1933.
29. Janssen, G., "Physical measurements of the winter wheat plant at various stages of development." *Pl. Phys.*, **4**: 477–491. 1929.
30. ———, "Effect of date of seeding winter wheat upon some physiological changes of the plant during the winter season." *J. Am. Soc. Agron.*, **21**: 168–200. 1929.
31. ———, "Effect of date of seeding of winter plant on plant development and its relationship to winter hardiness." *J. Am. Soc. Agron.*, **21**: 444–466. 1929.
32. Johnson, V. A., "Environmental factors affecting plant height in winter wheat." *Agron. J.*, **45**(10): 505–508. 1953.
33. Jones, W. W., "Respiration and metabolism in etiolated wheat seedlings as influenced by phosphorus nutrition." *Pl. Phys.*, **11**: 565–582. 1936.
34. Kiesselbach, T. A., "Winter wheat investigations." Nebr. Ag. Exp. Sta. *Res. Bul. 31*. 1925.
35. ———, and H. B. Sprague, "Relation of development of the wheat spike to environmental conditions." *J. Am. Soc. Agron.*, **18**: 40–60. 1926.
36. Kihara, H., "Discovery of the DD-analyser, one of the ancestors of the vulgare wheats." *Ag. and Hort.*, **19**: 889–890 Tokyo. 1944. (Eng. trans.)
37. ———, "Genome-analysis in *Triticum* and *Aegilops*. X: Concluding review" (by F. A. Lilienfeld). *Cytologia*, **16**(2): 101–123. 1951.
38. Klages, K. H. W., "Relation of soil moisture content to resistance of wheat seedlings to low temperatures." *J. Am. Soc. Agron.*, **18**: 184–193. 1926.
39. ———, "Metrical attributes and the physiology of hardy varieties of winter wheat." *J. Am. Soc. Agron.*, **18**: 529–566. 1926.
40. Kmock, H. G., *et al.*, "Root development of winter wheat as influenced by soil moisture and nitrogen fertilization." *Agron. J.*, **49**: 20–25. 1957.
41. Kneen, E., and M. J. Blish, "Carbohydrate metabolism and winter hardiness of wheat." *J. Ag. Res.*, **62**: 1–26. 1941.
42. Knowles, F., and J. E. Watkins, "The assimilation and translocation of plant nutrients in wheat during growth." *J. Ag. Sci.*, **21**: 612–637. 1931.
43. Lamb, C. A., "The relation of awns to the productivity of Ohio wheats." *J. Am. Soc. Agron.*, **29**: 339–348. 1937.
44. Laude, H. H., "Comparison of the cold resistance of several varieties of winter wheat in transition from dormancy to growth." *J. Ag. Res.*, **54**: 919–926. 1937.
45. Leighty, C. E., and W. J. Sando, "The blooming of wheat flowers." *J. Ag. Res.*, **27**: 231–244. 1924.
46. ———, and J. W. Taylor, "Studies in natural hybridization of wheat. *J. Ag. Res,*. **35**: 865–887. 1927.

47. Levitt, J., *The Hardiness of Plants.* Agronomy Monographs, Vol. 6. New York: Academic Press. p 278. 1956.

48. Livingston, J. E., and J. C. Swinbank, "Some factors influencing the injury to winter wheat heads by low temperatures." *Agron. J.,* **42**(3): 153–157. 1950.

49. Mangelsdorf, P. C., "Wheat." *Sci. Am.,* **189**(1): 50–59. 1953.

50. Martin, J. H., "Comparative studies of winter hardiness in wheat." *J. Ag. Res.,* **35:** 493–535. 1927.

51. McCall, M. A., "Developmental anatomy and homologues in wheat." *J. Ag. Res.,* **48**(4): 283–321. 1934.

52. McCalla, A. G., "The effect of nitrogen nutrition on the protein and non-protein nitrogen of wheat." *Can. J. Res.* **9**(C): 542–570. 1933.

53. ———, and E. K. Woodford, "Effects of a limiting element on the absorption of individual elements and on the anion-cation balance in wheat." *Pl. Phys.,* **13:** 695–712. 1938.

54. McDonough, W. T., and H. G. Gauch, "The contribution of awns to the development of the kernels of bearded wheat." Md. Ag. Exp. Sta. *Bul. A-103.* 1959.

55. McFadden, E. S., and E. R. Sears, "The artificial synthesis of *Triticum spelta.*" Gen. Soc. Am. *Records,* **13:** 26–27. 1944.

56. ———, and E. R. Sears, "The origin of *Triticum spelta* and its free-threshing hexaploid relatives." *J. Hered.,* **38**(3): 81–89, **38**(4): 107–116. 1946.

57. McKinney, H. H., and W. J. Sando, "Earliness and seasonal growth habit in wheat." *J. Hered.,* **24**(5): 169–179. 1933.

58. ———, and W. J. Sando, "Twisted wheat and twisted trees." *J. Hered.,* **25**(7): 261–263. 1934.

59. ———, and W. J. Sando, "Earliness and sexual reproduction in wheat as influenced by temperature and light in relation to growth phases." *J. Ag. Res.,* **51**(7): 621–641. 1935.

60. Miller, E. C., "A physiological study of the winter wheat plant at different stages of its development." Kans. Ag. Exp. Sta. *Tech. Bul. 47.* 1939.

61. ———, H. G. Gauch, and G. A. Gries, "A study of the morphological nature and physiological functions of the awns of winter wheat." Kans. Ag. Exp. Sta. *Tech. Bul. 57.* 1944.

62. Newton, R. A., "Comparative study of winter wheat varieties with especial reference to winter-killing." *J. Ag. Sci.,* **12:** 1–19. 1922.

63. ———, and W. R. Brown, "Frost precipitation of proteins of plant juice." *Can. J. Res.,* **5:** 87–110. 1931.

64. Noggle, G. R., "Some chemical changes associated with the transition from vegetative to reproductive growth of winter wheat." *Pl. Phys.,* **21:** 492–505. 1946.

65. Nuttonson, M. Y., "Wheat-climate relationships and the use of phenology in ascertaining thermal and photothermal requirements of wheat." Washington, D.C.: American Institute of Crop Ecology. pp 1–388. 1955.

66. Pauli, A. W., "Relation of crown tissue to winter survival in hard winter wheat." *Agron. J.,* **52:** 265–266. 1960.

67. Percival, J., *The Wheat Plant.* London: Duckworth. pp 3–6. 1921.

68. ———, *Wheat in Great Britain.* London: Duckworth. pp 1–126. 1934.

69. Peterson, R. F., "Twenty-five years progress in breeding new varieties of wheat for Canada." *Emp. J. Exp. Ag.,* **26**(102): 104–122. 1958.

70. *Progressive Wheat Production.* Geneva, Switzerland: Centre d'etude de l'azote. p 338. 1960.

71. Quisenberry, K. S., "Survival of wheat varieties in the Great Plains winter-hardiness nursery." *J. Am. Soc. Agron.*, **30**: 399–405. 1938.

72. ———, and J. A. Clark, "Hardiness and yield of winter wheat varieties." USDA *Cir. 141*. 1930.

73. Reitz, L. P., and L. W. Briggle, "Distribution of the varieties and classes of wheat in the United States in 1959." USDA *Bul. 272*. 1960.

74. Riddell, J. A., G. A. Gries, and F. W. Stearns, "Development of spring wheat. I. The effect of photoperiod." *Agron. J.*, **50**: 735–738. 1958.

75. ———, and G. A. Gries, "Development of spring wheat. II: The effect of temperature on response to photoperiod." *Agron. J.*, **50**: 739–742. 1958.

76. ———, and G. A. Gries, "Development of spring wheat. III: Temperature of maturation and age of seed as factors influencing their response to vernalization." *Agron. J.*, **50**: 743–746. 1958.

77. Riley, R., J. Unrau, and V. Chapman, "Evidence on the origin of the B genome of wheat." *J. Hered.*, **49**(3): 91–98. 1958.

78. Rosenquist, C. E., "The influence of awns upon the development of the kernel of wheat." *J. Am. Soc. Agron.*, **28**: 284–288. 1936.

79. Salmon, S. C., "Why cereals winterkill." *J. Am. Soc. Agron.*, **9**: 353–380. 1917.

80. Seth, J., T. T. Hebert, and G. K. Middleton, "Nitrogen utilization in high and low protein wheat varieties." *Agron. J.*, **52**: 207–209. 1960.

81. Sprague, H. B., "Correlations and yield in bread wheats." *J. Am. Soc. Agron.*, **18**: 971–997. 1926.

82. Suneson, C. A., B. B. Bayles, and C. C. Fifield, "Effects of awns on yield and market qualities of wheat." USDA *Cir. 783*. 1948.

83. Teller, G. L., "Changes in nitrogen compounds in the wheat grain at different stages of development." *Pl. Phys.*, **10**: 499–509. 1935.

84. Thomas, M. D., *et al.*, "A study of sulfur metabolism of wheat, barley, and corn using radioactive sulfur." *Pl. Phys.*, **19**: 227–244. 1944.

85. Vavilov, N. I., *The Origin, Variation, Immunity, and Breeding of Cultivated Plants.* *Chron. Bot.*, **13**(1–6). (trans. by K. Starr Chester). 1949–50.

86. Waldon, L. R., "Frost injury to spring wheat with consideration of drought resistance." *J. Am. Soc. Agron.*, **23**: 625–638. 1931.

87. Weaver, J. E., *Root Development of Field Crops.* New York: McGraw-Hill. pp 133–161. 1926.

88. ———, J. Kramer, and M. Reed, "Development of root and shoot of winter wheat under field environment." *Ecol.*, **5**: 26–50. 1924.

89. Weibel, D. E., "Vernalization of immature winter wheat embryos." *Agron. J.*, **50**: 267–270. 1958.

90. Weibel, R. O., "Effect of gibberellin on the vernalization period of winter wheat." *Agron. J.*, **52**: 122–123. 1960.

91. "Wheat production." USDA ARS *Ag. Info. Bul. 179*. 1958.

92. Whiteside, A. G. O., "Effect of soil drought on wheat plants." *Sci. Ag.*, **21**: 320–334. 1941.

93. Wort, D. J., "Soil temperature and growth of Marquis wheat." *Pl. Phys.*, **15**: 335–342. 1940.

94. ———, "Responses of various spring wheats to vernalization." *Pl. Phys.*, **15**: 137–141. 1940.

95. Zech, A. C., and A. W. Pauli, "Cold resistance in three varieties of winter wheat as related to nitrogen fractions and total sugar." *Agron. J.*, **52**: 334–337. 1960.

Wheat

13. CULTURAL PRACTICES

CROP ROTATIONS OR SEQUENCES

Wheat regularly is grown in rotation with other crops in humid, sub-humid, and irrigated areas, but in semiarid regions it often is grown continuously or in alternation with summer fallow.

Continuous Wheat

The oldest experiments on the growing of continuous wheat are those on Broadbalk Field at the Rothamsted Experimental Station in England, where the rainfall averages about 29 inches per year. The Broadbalk experiments were laid out in a permanent form in 1852. The unmanured continuous wheat showed a steady deterioration in yield caused by weed accumulation, reduction in soil fertility, and increased insect pests and fungus diseases. The yield per acre fell from about 20 bushels to 10 bushels within about 20 years, but then remained fairly stable except when excessive numbers of weeds were present. The mean yield of continuous wheat from 1852 to 1918 was 12.3 bushels per acre. The plants on the continuous manured plots were no more healthy than those on the unmanured plots, but they had more heads and more grain per head. The yields of unmanured continuous wheat started on a light sandy soil at Woburn in 1876 deteriorated faster than those on the heavier Rothamsted soils [53].

Continuous wheat has not shown declining yields during 30 or more years at various experiment stations in the Great Plains States of the United States where the annual precipitation ranges from 18–25 inches, provided the weeds were kept under control. The average yield of unfertilized wheat grown continuously for 65 years on a phosphorus-deficient soil in Oklahoma has not declined appreciably. About 50 per cent of the organic matter and nitrogen on the unfertilized land disappeared as a result of the continued production of wheat. The average grain yield of unfertilized wheat was about 12.6 bushels per acre, while wheat fertilized with barnyard manure at varying intervals for 59 years yielded 20.5 bushels [15].

Crop Rotations under Humid Conditions

Under humid conditions, wheat is grown in rotations with a legume or grass sod crop, as well as with one or more intertilled crops which aid in weed control.

At the Rothamsted Station in England, wheat and fallow have alternated on two strips of unmanured land on Hoos field since 1856. At first, the wheat yields were more than 50 per cent greater on the Broadbalk continuously manured plot, but after 50 years the difference in yield was very small. For the 1932–39 period, the average yield of wheat was 10.2 bushels per acre after fallow, and 7.2 bushels per acre after continuous culture. The principal benefit of fallow was in weed control [53].

On the Agdell field at Rothamsted, the old Norfolk four-course rotation of roots, barley, clover (or beans), and wheat was started in 1848. The nitrogenous fertilizers applied to the root crop had no effect on the wheat. The yields of wheat after clover in 1939 were as follows: with complete fertilizers applied to the roots, 16.7 bushels; minerals only (phosphates and potash), 17.0 bushels; no fertilizers, 12.5 bushels [53]. The rotation was discontinued in 1951 because of severe acidity (pH 5.0–5.5) on the plots fertilized with phosphorus and potash [66].

In the eastern United States, rotations with wheat are likely to contain a small-seeded legume, or a legume-grass mixture, and one or more cultivated crops. Wheat often follows corn, being seeded between the rows or on land disked after the corn is harvested. Sometimes wheat follows oats [56].

In the American Corn Belt, a widely practiced rotation is wheat, clover and timothy (1–2 years), corn, and oats. Sometimes soybeans are substituted for the oats, while alfalfa and brome grass often replace the timothy and clover. Wheat can be grown successfully directly after legume or sod crops only on soils of moderate or low productivity, but corn is well suited to following these meadow crops. Wheat may be seeded after soybeans or corn when these crops are harvested early enough [35]. A six-year rotation satisfactory for eastern Nebraska is corn, oats with sweetclover, sweetclover harvested for forage, corn, barley, and winter wheat. Wheat in this rotation produced an average yield of 40.3 bushels per acre, while that in a comparable rotation without the legume yielded 36.6 bushels [22]. A popular rotation in northeastern Kansas is red clover (or sweetclover), corn, oats, and wheat seeded to clover [54]. In eastern Kansas, wheat is more likely to fail after a sod legume, such as alfalfa or sweetclover, than after a small grain because legumes deplete subsoil moisture. A satisfactory rotation is

FIGURE 13-1. **Wheat growing in strips alternating with fallow is a popular practice in northcentral Montana and other semiarid areas in the Great Plains where soil blowing is prevalent. The strips usually range from 100 to 350 feet in width.**

(*Courtesy US Department of Agriculture*)

alfalfa (2–3 years), sorghum, corn, oats, and wheat [25]. In Missouri, lespedeza may be seeded in the spring on fall-sown wheat, and is left to produce a crop of hay or seed after the wheat is harvested. A common rotation is corn; wheat; lespedeza for pasture, hay, or seed; and wheat.

In the Cotton Belt, it is impossible to sow winter wheat immediately after cotton because of the late maturity of the cotton crop. A satisfactory rotation for the region is as follows: wheat, followed by cowpeas or soybeans for hay or seed; cotton well-fertilized, with vetch or Austrian winter peas planted between the rows for green manure; and corn, with the stalks cut and removed from the field.

Crop Rotations under Semi-Arid Conditions

In the northern Great Plains, a common practice is to grow spring wheat after corn or some other cultivated crop. Wheat yields after corn are intermediate between those after fallow and those after wheat. Spring wheat also follows sorghum satisfactorily in the region. Cultivated crops aid in the control of weeds which become a serious problem with a continuous small-grain rotation [56]. Long-term experiments in Montana, where the mean annual precipitation ranged from 11.6 to 15.0 inches, indicate that green manure crops of sweetclover, field peas, and winter rye grown during part of the fallow period had no beneficial effects on dryland wheat yields, test weight, or protein content. Spring wheat yields after green manure crops were actually lower than those obtained after fallow (Fig. 13-1). There was no evidence that continued use of green manures materially affected soil nitrogen content [1].

Alternate wheat and fallow often has been a practical sequence under dryland conditions in western Kansas [25], as indicated in Table 13-1.

TABLE 13-1. **Average Yields of Wheat for 3 Kansas Stations.**

		Wheat Yields in Bushels per Acre	
Location*	Period	Continuous Wheat	Wheat after Fallow
Colby	1915–50	8.9	17.6
Garden City	1929–44	8.3	16.6
Hays	1908–45	16.4	22.5

* Colby and Garden City are in areas of lower rainfall than is Hays.

In western Kansas, the yields of winter wheat sown immediately after row crops (corn or sorghum) often are lower than those after small grains because the soil is kept cultivated for nearly three months between wheat harvest and fall seeding, which conserves moisture and releases nitrates. A typical rotation is grain sorghum, fallow, and winter wheat [25].

In eastern Colorado, where the annual precipitation generally is less than 18 inches, winter wheat produced an average of 16.3 bushels per acre on fallowed land, as compared with 7.1 bushels per acre on small-grain stubble land, during a 30-year period, 1909–38. A suggested rotation for eastern Colorado hard lands is (a) fallow; (b) winter wheat; (c) grain sorghum and field beans in alternate strips; and (d) sorghum or proso on the sorghum land, with oats or barley on the bean land [6].

On very sandy land in the southern Great Plains, alternate wheat and fallow failed to prevent crop failure at Woodward, Oklahoma, where the rainfall averaged nearly 24 inches annually. Fallowing increased yields in years of fair to high rainfall. The average yield of wheat was 22.2 bushels per acre on fallow, and 17.3 after wheat. But the coarse soil was not able to store enough additional moisture to justify fallowing in a region of that much rainfall. The yield of wheat after sorghum was as much as eight bushels per acre lower than after wheat, for sorghum grows until late in the fall and leaves the seedbed deficient in moisture for wheat [28]. A winter wheat-sorghum-fallow rotation has aided in the stabilization of crop production in the Texas Panhandle where the soil is heavier and the rainfall lower than at Woodward, Oklahoma. Wheat after fallow yielded an average of 17.9 bushels per acre; continuous wheat, 12.2 bushels. A reduction in yield occurred when winter wheat alternated with sorghum [45]. On the basis of long-term weather records, alternate wheat-fallow and wheat-sorghum-fallow sequences on the southern high plains can be expected to produce more than ten bushels of wheat per acre approximately 80 per cent of the time. Continuous cropping to wheat can be expected to produce more than ten bushels of grain only 50 per cent of the time [2].

Rotation experiments were conducted in Utah in the Great Basin, a winter rainfall area. In total production of winter wheat on the land over a 41-year period, alternate wheat and fallow was the highest, followed by two wheat crops in three years, then by continuous wheat, and last by one wheat crop in three years. The standard alternate wheat-fallow practice produced significantly higher yields than when wheat followed intertilled peas or potatoes [13]. In the Pacific Northwest, some of the land in the 18–20 inch annual precipitation belt is now planted to alternate wheat and peas. Alternate wheat and fallow is a widely used sequence, however, and is practiced almost exclusively in areas with 9–15 inches of annual precipitation. In the Palouse area, crop rotations that include legume-grass sod crops are more effective for erosion control, soil organic matter maintenance, and high wheat yields than are the unfertilized pea-wheat and fallow-wheat systems. Summer fallow causes the largest erosion losses as well as the most rapid depletion of organic matter [18]. Organic matter cannot be maintained unless all the wheat residues are returned to the soil. Despite some adverse effects, fallowing has assured high yields of wheat for more than 75 years in that area.

In Australia, most of the wheat is grown in regions with an annual precipitation of 10–15 inches. Fallowing for 6–8 months previous to seeding wheat usually assures a crop, whereas wheat sown on stubble land has been a complete failure [67]. Alternate wheat and fallow also is practiced in the drier parts of the Prairie Provinces of Canada [17].

FERTILIZERS

Only about 8.4 per cent of all commercial fertilizers consumed in the United States in 1947 were used directly on the wheat crop. More than 90 per cent of the fertilizer applied to the crop was used in the more humid states east of the Great Plains where only about 20 per cent of the wheat acreage was located [56].

Fertilizers under Humid Conditions

Wheat generally responds to the direct application of commercial fertilizers as well as to lime where the annual precipitation exceeds 35 inches. The wheat crop also benefits from the residual effects of fertilizers applied to other crops in the rotation.

In Pennsylvania, 50–60 field experiments on fertilizers applied to wheat were conducted over a nine-year period [34]. Under nearly all conditions, a starter fertilizer in the grain drill, when applied at a rate of not over ten pounds of nitrogen per acre, was desirable. Treatments such as 300 pounds of 3-12-6, 200 pounds of 5-10-10, or even 200 pounds of 7-7-7 would start the crop. A supplemental application composed chiefly or solely of nitrogen generally was needed in the spring sometime before May 20. Late applications after the tillering period were generally ineffective. A spring topdressing with nitrogen also was ineffective when wheat followed immediately after clover or alfalfa sod, or where the soil has received abnormally high applications of manure.

In Virginia experiments, nitrogen fertilizers were applied to wheat on April 11, April 24, and May 14. The highest grain yields were obtained from the first date of application, with declining yields as the time of application approached the heading stage. The later the application, the greater the increase in protein content of the grain [9], but a higher protein is undesirable in the soft red winter wheats grown in that area.

The supply of nutrients available to the wheat plant probably is the most important soil factor regulating the amount of protein [4]. On soils low in nitrogen, the yield of wheat can be progressively increased—within certain limits—with each increment of nitrogen. Results of numerous experiments in Tennessee show that an average of 3.5–4.0 pounds of nitrogen is required to produce each additional bushel of wheat. An application of nitrogen as a topdressing in the spring was more effective than fall application at the time of seeding. Split applications, with half of the nitrogen applied in the fall and the other half topdressed in the spring, produced the highest yield [29]. Other experiments in Tennessee indicated that yield as well as quality of wheat and flour is influenced by nitrogen fertilization. Nitrogen topdressings were applied as shown in Table 13-2.

TABLE 13-2. **Results With Nitrogen Topdressings Applied to Wheat in Tennessee.**

Date of Nitrogen Topdressing	Amount Nitrogen Applied per Acre, Lb	Acre Yields Wheat, Bu	Protein Content Wheat, Per Cent
November 20	25	24.5	10.8
	50	30.2	11.0
March 8	25	28.7	10.6
	50	26.9	11.5
May 4	25	18.3	13.9
	50	18.9	15.3
L.S.D. (0.05)	—	7.0	—

Yields were significantly lower when the nitrogen application was delayed until May 4, but the protein content of the wheat was higher [30], which again was of no advantage.

Indiana investigations indicate that fall applications of nitrogen fertilizers had little effect on kernel hardness. Applications of phosphates or mixed fertilizers that contained phosphates increased the yields but decreased the vitreousness and protein content of the grain as well as the loaf volume of the bread. The unfertilized plots produced wheat of low yield, shrunken grains, and relatively high protein content. Application of lime alone increased the yield considerably, but the grains still were small and high in protein. When fertilizers were used in addition to lime, the yields were higher but the grains were lower in protein content, higher in kernel weight, higher in test weight, and lower in vitreousness [62].

Illinois experiments indicate that wheat is especially sensitive to a shortage of phosphates during the early stages of plant growth. Topdressed nitrogen fertilizer applications gave variable results. They were ineffective on fertile lands, where they often caused the crop to lodge. Early spring applications of 100–125 pounds per acre of ammonium sulfate are recommended on nitrogen-deficient soils. Drill applications of phosphate or phosphate and potash fertilizers are effective where soils are low in these nutrients. Standard grades of 0-20-0 or 0-20-10 fertilizers may be applied at the rate of 100–125 pounds per acre at seeding time, but the rate should be increased to 200–250 pounds when broadcast before seeding. Mixed fertilizers topdressed in the spring are less effective than when drilled at seeding time [35].

Tests on heavy soils at 101 locations in Michigan indicate that 40 per cent of the wheat fields yielded more when adequate amounts of nitrogen were available. Wheat grown in cash-crop rotations responded markedly to topdressed nitrogen applications. The results indicate that 20 pounds of nitrogen per acre was the most effective rate of application. Wheat was topdressed effectively early in the spring while the soil was still frozen, and prior to heading. [51].

The most commonly used fertilizer formulas for fall applications in the eastern United States include 2-12-6 and 3-8-3, or others of similar composition. The wheat usually receives a topdressing of nitrogen in the spring. Where potassium in the soil is adequate, superphosphate often is applied at rates of 100–400 pounds per acre, and nitrate of soda or ammonium sulfate at the rate of 100–150 pounds per acre. In such cases, the nitrogen fertilizer often is applied wholly or in part as a topdressing in the spring.

In the eastern half of Kansas, where the need for nitrogen is more general than that for phosphorus, wheat responds to commercial fertilizers. Wheat grown after alfalfa, sweetclover, and red clover seldom needs nitrogen [25]. Significant increases in yields were obtained when urea was used as a foliar spray on wheat before flowering. One spraying of urea at flowering increased the protein content of the grain by 4.4 per cent [12].

In Nebraska experiments, spring applications of nitrogen—at the rate of 40 pounds of nitrogen per acre—to winter wheat at the 3–6 inch growth stage produced yield increases of about eight bushels per acre in the eastern two thirds of the state. Spring applications generally were slightly superior to fall applications from the standpoint of yield as well as protein content of the grain. The nitrate form of nitrogen generally was more effective than the ammonium form for spring broadcast treatments. Under most conditions, 20–30 pounds of available P_2O_5 per acre were adequate [40].

Fertilizers under Semiarid Conditions

The use of commercial fertilizers for wheat in the Great Plains is rather recent. In the eastern part, increased yields often are obtained with nitrogen, or phosphorus, or both fertilizers. Farther west, increases have been obtained almost entirely from nitrogen fertilizers in years when soil moisture was above normal. Fertilizers often have increased wheat yields on lands under irrigation.

The response of wheat to fertilizers in western Kansas is variable because moisture has a greater effect on wheat production than does fertilizer. Wheat rarely needs nitrogen when grown on fallow land, but irrigated lands require it for high yields. When needed, 30–50 pounds of nitrogen per acre may be applied at planting time or in a split application. Phosphorus needs usually are met with 20–40 pounds of P_2O_5 per acre [25].

In eastern Colorado, there is evidence of nitrogen deficiency on the lighter-textured or sandy dryland wheat lands. In 1953, wheat yielded 13.0 bushels per acre with no fertilizer, 17.8 bushels with 25 pounds of nitrogen, and 20.1 bushels with 50 pounds of nitrogen. Summer fallowed noneroded loams and clay loams—i.e., "hard land" soils—failed to produce increased yields from nitrogen fertilizer applications [14]. The recommended rate of application for sandy soils is 30 pounds of nitrogen per acre [16].

Fertilizer experiments with winter wheat at Woodward, Oklahoma, in the southern Great Plains showed average yields of 26.6 bushels per acre in a manured rotation, and 18.5 bushels in an unmanured rotation. The yield response to stable manure generally was greatest in years of high production and least in years of low production. On a field of relatively low fertility due to sheet erosion, the average yield of wheat that received commercial fertilizers was 17.2 bushels per acre, whereas the unfertilized wheat yielded 12.7 bushels. The fertilizer application was eight pounds of nitrogen per acre applied both in the fall and spring and 67.5 pounds of phosphorus applied in the fall. On more fertile soil, the average yield of wheat on continuously cropped land was 27.6 bushels per acre on the plots fertilized with nitrogen (ten pounds per acre in the fall and 20 pounds in the spring) and phosphorus (67.5 pounds per acre applied in the fall). The yield for nitrogen alone was 21.5 bushels [28].

Commercial nitrogen fertilizers applied to dryland winter wheat in Utah showed increases in yield, protein content, or both. The most economical rate was 40 pounds of nitrogen per acre. The nitrate form of nitrogen generally was slightly more effective than the ammonium form when applied in the spring, but the two forms were about equally effective when applied in the fall. There was no benefit from phosphate fertilizers [43].

Nitrogen fertilizers applied to wheat generally have given yield responses in the Far West, particularly where the annual precipitation exceeds about 14 inches. Where wheat is grown on fallow in areas of 14–18 inches of annual precipitation in the Pacific Northwest, the use of nitrogen fertilizers permits the retention of the straw on the surface for erosion control without a depression in yield of the subsequent wheat crop. Increased wheat yields from phosphate applications occur only on a few soils [56].

In the Palouse area of eastern Washington, nitrogen fertilizers increased the yields as well as the nitrogen content of the grain of continuous wheat where soil nitrogen was limited [10]. Each 5.7 pounds of nitrogen applied produced an additional bushel of wheat. However, nitrogen fertilizers failed to produce increased yields on alternate wheat and fallow land [59]. Yields of wheat, as affected by straw residues and nitrogen fertilizers at Pullman (Washington) for the period from 1922–45, are given in Table 13-3.

TABLE 13-3. **Average Wheat Yields as Affected by Fertilizer Treatments in Washington.**

	Yield of Wheat per Acre	
	*Annual Wheat Cropping**	*Alternate Wheat and Fallow***
Treatment		
	(Bu)	(Bu)
None	20.0	44.1
Straw	19.5	42.0
Straw plus sodium nitrate	30.3	45.3
Sodium nitrate	29.4	44.7
Straw plus ammonium sulfate	31.1	45.1
Manure	28.4	43.6

* All materials applied before fall plowing; binder stubble returned to all plots.
** All materials applied before plowing for summer fallow.

Irrigated spring wheat in Montana produced increased yields from nitrogen fertilizer applied at rates of 50 and 100 pounds (as nitrogen) per acre when all treatments also received a uniform application of phosphorus. The yield response was due largely to increases in number of heads per acre, but increases in number of kernels per head or in kernel weight were also noted. The heading date was hastened from 1–4 days by the nitrogen application. A high rate of nitrogen availability late in the growth period is necessary for maximum protein content [33].

Method of Fertilizer Application

Heavy applications of highly soluble potassium fertilizer placed in direct contact with wheat seed at the time of sowing may reduce the stands and subsequent growth, but moderate nitrogen applications in contact with the seed is only slightly detrimental. Band application of mixed fertilizer below or 1.5 inch to the side and below the seed proved to be the most desirable from the standpoint of emergence and growth of the plant and uptake of fertilizer phosphorus [26].

In some Kansas experiments with nitrogen fertilizer on heavy soils under ideal soil moisture conditions, there was no damage to wheat germination when as much as 300 pounds per acre of ammonium nitrate—in combination with some phosphate and potash—was applied in the drill row directly in contact with the seed. Under droughty conditions, damage was negligible when 40 pounds of nitrogen per acre (as a component of a mixed fertilizer) was placed in direct contact with the seed. Some delay in germination was caused by the extra nitrogen, but the ultimate stand of wheat plants was about the same as for the nonfertilized plants. Phosphates also can be applied in direct contact with the seed wheat at the time it is drilled. Under droughty conditions, no damage occurred when 200 or more pounds of a 0-45-0 fertilizer were used in this manner. However, potash caused injury to germination, even in rather moderate amounts, particularly when combined with the same amount of nitrogen [58].

SEEDBED PREPARATION

Humid Eastern States

Seedbed preparation in the humid eastern United States is determined largely by the position of wheat in rotations with other crops. When winter wheat is grown after corn, the wheat may be drilled in the standing corn or it may be seeded on disked land after the corn crop is removed or shocked. When wheat follows oats or barley, the land usually is plowed just far enough in advance of seeding to provide a well-settled seedbed [56]. The plowed land usually is disked and harrowed immediately before the wheat is sown.

Similar practices in seedbed preparation for wheat are followed in eastern Nebraska, Kansas, and Oklahoma where the most commonly used implements are the plow, the spiketooth harrow, and the disc harrow. When winter wheat follows winter wheat, the most important feature in seedbed preparation is early plowing. In eastern Nebraska, early seedbed preparation, accompanied by sufficient tillage to control weeds, conserved soil nitrates and also firmed the seedbed. Plowing 7 inches deep on September

15, followed by disking on September 25, gave an average yield of 20 bushels per acre, whereas plowing 7 inches deep on July 15 followed by disking August 15 and September 25 gave a yield of 33.9 bushels. Land plowed July 15 at depths of 4, 5.5, 7, and 10 inches, followed by disking August 15 and September 25 gave nearly equal yields of 33.6, 34.7, 33.9, and 34.0 bushels per acre, respectively [21, 22]. Experiments in eastern Kansas indicate that one bushel of wheat per acre is lost for each week that plowing is delayed after July 15. Plowing deeper than 7 inches generally failed to increase wheat yields, whereas plowing as shallow as 3 inches generally was detrimental to best wheat yields. Acre yields for the July 15 date of plowing at depths of 3, 7, and 12 inches averaged 23.5, 25.0, and 23.8 bushels per acre, respectively, for a 40-year period. Although plowing of dry soils may be difficult, the advantages of early tillage are sufficient to make it worthwhile. However, too-wet soils should not be plowed or cultivated because such soils tend to puddle. Cultivation after plowing is considered desirable only for weed control or to prepare a firm seedbed [25].

Semi-Arid Western States

In the Great Plains, where lack of moisture is the most important limiting factor in wheat production, methods of seedbed preparation are tied closely to moisture conservation. The most common dryland tillage implements are one-way discs, blade sweeps, and field cultivators, with rod weeders often used to control weeds and volunteer growth after initial tillage.

Summer fallow is the primary method used for moisture storage in dryland areas. Tillage during the fallow period should keep the soil receptive to moisture penetration as well as free of weeds. The efficiency of moisture storage in the soil during fallow is rather low. Under average Kansas conditions, only 15–16 per cent of the precipitation falling during the fallow period is stored, but even this much extra moisture is very beneficial to the next wheat crop. For fallowing in western Kansas, the initial tillage should start early in the spring after wheat harvest. Late fall plowing has no advantage over May plowing, but May plowing gave wheat yields 2–4 bushels per acre higher than June plowing. However, fall-listed land gave yields from 1–5 bushels per acre more than May-plowed land. Other tillage implements for fallow preparation show little superiority of one implement over another from the standpoint of wheat yields [25]. The one-way disc plow is widely used for seedbed preparation and is especially useful on heavy stubble. However, when used repeatedly on land with only a small amount of crop residue, it is likely to promote serious wind erosion through excessive soil pulverization [56].

In some of the western drier areas, such as north central Montana, it is a common practice to sow wheat in strips in alternation with fallow (Fig.

13-1). Fallowing conserves moisture for the next wheat crop, while the strips of wheat keep the soil from blowing on the bare fallow [3]. The wheat stubble also holds drifting snow.

Stubble-mulch tillage has been widely practiced under semi-arid conditions in the Western states since 1930. This type of tillage includes any type of cultivation that leaves enough plant residue on the surface to protect it from erosion, regardless of type of implement used. It appears to be well adapted to continuous winter wheat or to the alternate wheat and fallow sequence. When the stubble contains only a few weeds in the fall, the initial tillage may be delayed until spring when weeds start to grow. The first operation may be with a one-way disc plow operated at a shallow depth to leave the straw on the surface. Later, when the weeds start growing again, sweeps may be used to undercut the soil to about the depth of ordinary plowing. The next crop of weeds may be controlled with a rod weeder. Just prior to seeding (Fig. 13-2), the rod weeder may be used again to kill small weeds as well as to pack the soil below the seeding depth. Several modifications of stubble-mulch tillage (subtillage) are possible [11]. In general, sweeps two feet or more in width have been well adapted for the management of surface residues. In the drier regions, the residues left on

FIGURE 13-2. **Drilling wheat on stubble land prepared by subtillage to leave crop residues on the surface.**

(Courtesy Deere and Company)

FIGURE 13-3. **Early spring growth of winter wheat in Kansas. Above: Sown October 20; Below: Sown October 6, near the optimum date.**

(Courtesy US Department of Agriculture)

the soil surface have either increased wheat yields or failed to lower them significantly [70].

SEEDING PRACTICES

Time of Seeding

Medium-season seeding of winter wheat is generally most favorable. Late-sown winter wheat usually suffers more winter injury (Fig. 13-3), tillers less, and may fail to emerge until spring. In very cold climates, wheat seedlings that reach the three-leaf stage survive the winter as well as or

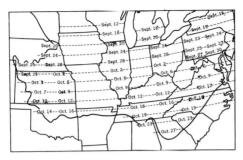

FIGURE 13-4. **Fly-free date for sowing winter wheat.**

(*Courtesy US Department of Agriculture*)

better than those that are larger as a result of earlier seeding. A difference of two months in fall seeding date may make a difference in date of ripening of only one week or less. Winter wheat sown too early in the fall may exhaust the soil moisture, joint in the fall, suffer winter injury, become infected by root rots, or be attacked by the Hessian fly where that insect is prevalent.

In the Eastern states, the optimum period for seeding winter wheat is about the Hessian-fly-free date for the region, or a few days earlier (Fig. 13-4). This date varies from September 16 in Michigan, September 21 to October 1 in eastern Nebraska [22], to as late as October 27 in Georgia. To

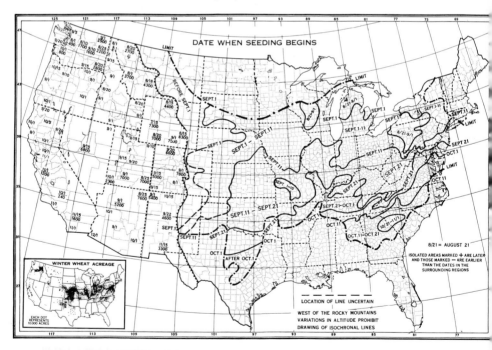

FIGURE 13-5. **Dates when winter wheat seeding begins in the United States.**

(*Courtesy US Department of Agriculture*)

avoid winter injury by heaving, winter wheat should be sown in humid regions early enough for the plants to become well-rooted before growth ceases in the fall. Wheat interseeded in wide corn-row spaces (72 inches) in Ohio at Hessian-fly-free dates yielded two bushels per acre more than when seeded after corn harvest two weeks later. It yielded 13 bushels more where poor soil drainage led to winter killing in the late sowing [61].

In the Western states, the optimum date of seeding winter wheat occurs when the mean daily temperature lies between 50–60°F. The higher temperatures prevail in the South, whereas the lower ones apply in the North [32]. In the semiarid Great Plains, the optimum date of seeding ranges from September 1 in Montana to about October 15 in the Texas Panhandle. However, the increased use of wheat for grazing from Nebraska to Texas has tended to advance the seeding date; much of the crop is now seeded between August 20 and September 15 [45], (Fig. 13-5). Seeding before September 15 in eastern Colorado may subject winter wheat to damage by the dryland foot-rot disease [50]. In the southern Great Plains, many growers intentionally seed earlier than the optimum date in order to provide plant cover for the protection of erodable soils from wind erosion. Hessian-fly-resistant varieties are sometimes sown early in order to obtain fall pasture for livestock. When the soil is very dry, a common practice is to delay seeding

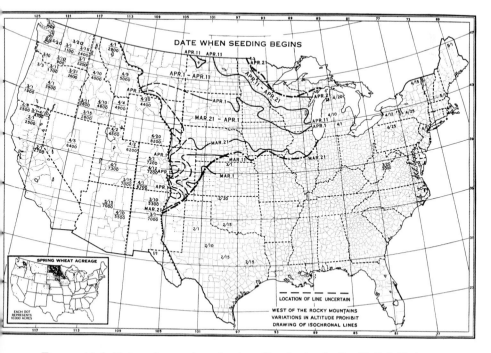

FIGURE 13-6. **Dates when spring wheat seeding begins in the United States.**

(*Courtesy US Department of Agriculture*)

as long as possible [56]. Winter wheat is seeded about September 15 in the Pacific Northwest, but November or early December seeding is most favorable in California as well as in southern Arizona.

Early seeding of spring wheat generally results in the highest grain yields. The usual practice is to sow spring wheat as soon as the soil can be worked into a satisfactory seedbed (Fig. 13-6). Tests have shown a marked reduction in yields when spring wheat is sown late. Early-sown wheat is most likely to escape injury from drought, heat, and diseases which become more prevalent as the season advances [32]. In the extreme northern United States, spring wheat may be sown as late as May 1 without serious reduction in yield. The optimum dates are earlier to the south.

Rate of Seeding

In the eastern United States, winter wheat is sown at a rate of 5–8 pecks (75–120 pounds) per acre (Appendix Table A-9). Generally, 6 pecks (90 pounds) or more per acre will produce larger grain yields than a lesser quantity. In extensive Ohio tests, seeding at the rate of 8 pecks (120 pounds) per acre produced the highest yields, but seeding 6 and 7 pecks (90 and 105 pounds) was only slightly inferior. Heavier seeding than usual is advised where seeding is delayed beyond the normal date, because the plants have less opportunity to tiller. The rate of seeding is generally higher for spring than for winter wheat. The Illinois Station recommends approximately 8 pecks (120 pounds) of seed per acre [5].

The optimum rate of seeding wheat in the western half of the United States is practically independent of soil type, moisture, locality, date of seeding, cultural treatment, and variety. In general, 4–6 pecks (60–90 pounds) per acre have produced the highest net grain yields (yield minus seed) of both winter and spring wheat [32], but lower rates have been successful for early seeding in the western Great Plains.

A range in seeding rates for winter wheat may have only a minor effect on yield. In Nebraska, winter wheat sown at the rates of 3, 4, 5, and 6 pecks per acre produced yields of 24.9, 26.2, 26.5, and 27.1 bushels per acre, respectively. A reduction in the amount of seed tended to be offset by more tillers per plant, larger heads, and larger kernels. A rate of 5–6 pecks of seed per acre is recommended for eastern Nebraska, with a gradual reduction westward to 2–3 pecks in the Nebraska Panhandle [21]. Similar results have been obtained in Kansas [25].

In the semiarid Great Plains, winter wheat may be seeded at a rate as low as two pecks per acre on clean, moist, firm seedbeds, often without any reduction in yields. Results obtained in eastern Colorado indicate that two pecks per acre are sufficient for seeding on summer fallow or cornland on optimum dates, that is, between September 1 and 15, as shown in Table 13-4.

TABLE 13-4. **Yield Data for Winter Wheat Sown at Various Rates on Different Dates at Akron, Colorado.**

Seeding Rate per Acre (pecks)	*Yield per Acre in Bushels for Wheat Sown on —*					
	Aug. 15	*Sept. 1*	*Sept. 15*	*Oct. 1*	*Oct. 15*	*Average*
1	10.2	14.5	15.3	10.6	9.9	12.1
2	12.0	16.2	15.5	11.5	11.1	13.3
3	13.0	16.1	15.4	12.2	11.3	13.6
4	13.8	16.1	14.9	12.4	11.8	13.8
5	14.5	16.4	14.5	12.4	12.3	14.0
Average	12.7	15.9	15.1	11.8	11.3	13.4

The data indicate that slight yield increases were obtained when more than two pecks were seeded at earlier or later dates [50]. A two-peck rate was also found to be the optimum seeding rate in the Panhandle of Texas, but 35–45 pounds are advised on sandy lands or for late sowing in November on the heavier soils [45]. Nevertheless, an extra 1–2 pecks is cheap insurance against thin stands, since the thicker seeding does not reduce yields when good stands prevail.

Spring wheat in the Western states is usually sown at a heavier rate. Thin stands, which increase competition with weeds, are likely to result when spring wheat is sown at rates lower than four pecks per acre [56]. On irrigated soil in the Western states, spring wheat sown at 50–60 pounds per acre yields as well as at higher rates, except when sown late. Higher rates of 80 or more pounds for late seeding aid in the control of weeds and diseases, but may increase lodging where the tendency is present [68]. However, yields of irrigated spring wheat in eastern Washington increased with an increase in plant populations up to about 27 plants per square foot. Because kernel sizes differ, such a population would require 103, 108, and 136 pounds of seed per acre for the Lemhi 53, Marfed, and Pilcraw varieties, respectively [38].

Methods of Seeding

In early American history, wheat was sown broadcast for lack of satisfactory seeding implements, but now it is almost all sown with a drill. In tests in Nebraska, broadcast winter wheat yielded an average of 23.7 bushels per acre, whereas drilled wheat yielded 27.2 bushels [22]. Drilled wheat usually is characterized by higher germination, more uniform stands, less winter injury, and generally higher yields.

Wheat generally is seeded either with a common surface drill or with a furrow drill. The common single-disc drill is most widely used in humid

FIGURE 13-7. **A semifurrow drill with packer wheels in each furrow.**
(Courtesy Deere and Company)

regions. The common drill spaces the seed in rows 6, 7, or 8 inches apart. Furrow drills, with a row spacing of 12 or 14 inches, are widely used for seeding winter wheat in the drier portions of the Great Plains. Semifurrow drills, that place seed in shallow furrows 10 or 12 inches apart, have become extensively used in western Kansas and Nebraska in recent years (Fig. 13-7). Some drills space the rows 16–18 inches apart.

In the drier regions, the furrow drill sometimes makes it possible to place the seed in moist soil, which assures better germination than with the surface drill. However, only rarely is this an important advantage, because when autumn rainfall is insufficient to germinate the surface-drilled seed, the crop prospects for furrow-drilled wheat are very poor. During the winter, the plants also are protected somewhat by snow that lodges in the furrows. There is also some protection from wind erosion, but in some cases the plants may be partly covered by soil drifts [25].

Increases in yields from the use of the furrow drill may be expected where partial winter killing often occurs, as in Montana where furrow drilling was first practiced on a farm scale. In Nebraska experiments, surface drilling in 7-inch rows has produced an average yield of 25.8 bushels per acre, furrow drilling in 14-inch rows produced 23.3 bushels, while the yield from 10-inch rows was 23.8 bushels. The wheat crop evidently is unable to occupy the land fully at the wider spacings. Surface drilling is considered as advantageous for eastern Nebraska conditions [22]. In eastern Colorado, the average yield of winter wheat from furrow-drill seeding was 13.2 bushels per acre, whereas that from common-drill seeding was 12.4 bushels [6].

The furrow drill generally has failed to show any superiority over the common drill for seeding spring wheat.

Wheat generally is sown from 1.0–1.5 inches deep in humid regions. It is desirable to place the seed in moist soil in semiarid regions to assure germination, so sometimes the seed is sown 2–3 inches deep.

WEED CONTROL

Weeds often are a serious problem in wheat fields in the eastern United States. The most serious perennial weeds are field bindweed, Canada thistle, and wild onion. Troublesome winter annual weeds include cheat (Fig. 13-8), corncockle, dogfennel, chickweed, and skeletonweed [5]. In Kansas and adjacent states, winter wheat competes well with weeds except in thin stands or when it emerges late. Wheat begins its growth in the late fall when temperatures are too low for most weeds to start growth; it makes such rapid growth in the early spring that seedling weeds are shaded out. In seasons of deficient fall moisture, wheat may germinate unevenly to produce poor stands which may result in weedy fields. Annual weeds—particularly cheat, Russian thistle, kochia, lambsquarter, pigweed, and wild buckwheat—are the most common in fall-seeded wheat in Kansas. The most serious perennial weed is field bindweed. Weeds in wheat fields may be controlled by cultural practices or by the use of chemicals [25].

Cultural Practices

The first approach to weed control in wheat fields is suitable cultural practices. The use of clean seed, together with summer tillage or rotations that include cultivated crops, effectively controls many weeds. In eastern Kansas, field bindweed may be controlled by a rotation of close-drilled sorghum, fallow, and wheat. In western Kansas, bindweed has been eradicated in a wheat-fallow sequence where the fallow is cultivated every 2–3 weeks until the winter wheat is seeded (about October 1). Immediately after the wheat is harvested, the land should be plowed and clean cultivation repeated until wheat is planted again. Bindweed generally is eliminated after a third wheat crop [25]. Such clean cultivation will also control annual weeds.

Chemical Control

Since 1950, the use of various formulations of 2,4-dichlorophenoxy-acetic acid (2,4-D) to control weeds in wheat fields has become wide-

FIGURE 13-8. Two weeds of wheat fields, cheat (left) and goat grass (right) that resemble wheat plants in the early growth stages. Formerly, superstitious farmers believed that cold or other injuries changed wheat into these weedy grass plants.

(Courtesy US Department of Agriculture)

spread. The chemical is applied as a spray for killing broadleafed weed species without serious damage to the grain crop. Excessive or untimely applications of 2,4-D often injure the wheat. A two-pound rate caused morphological injury, or a decrease in yield, or both, but had no effect on the nitrogen content of the grain [42]. In other experiments, yield reductions up to 10 per cent in winter wheat from 2,4-D treatments with 0.5 pound of the ester or 1.0 pound of the amine per acre and higher rates caused more severe injury [23, 24]. A common recommendation is that 2,4-D be applied as a spray at the rate of 0.25–0.50 pound of the acid equivalent in the ester form or as much as 0.75 pound in the amine form per acre [25].

Wheat yields are markedly reduced by 2,4-D sprays applied at two critical periods: when the plants are from 1–5 inches tall; and from the early boot stage until flowering is completed. Between these periods little or no damage results when the plants are sprayed with the ester formulation at the 0.50 and 0.75 pound rates. Applications at the early boot or flowering stages result in more injury than those at the jointing or late-boot stage [24]. External damage consists of onionlike leaves, branched spikes, supernumary spikelets, and elongated internodes [41]. The greatest injury to wheat may occur when wheat is sprayed in the fall when the plants are small. The 2,4-D spray generally is applied to wheat in the spring when the plants are between the tillering and jointing stages [69].

Spraying a few days before harvest to kill and dry the tops of green weeds does not affect wheat yields but may facilitate combine harvesting.

IRRIGATION

Considerable wheat is grown under irrigation in the western United States, as well as in certain Mediterranean, Near East, and Middle East countries. High wheat yields can be obtained with a comparatively small

TABLE 13-5. **Average Acre Yields of Spring Wheat in Colorado from 6 Inches of Irrigation Water.**

Growth Stage when Irrigated	Grain Yield, Lb	Straw Yield, Lb
Germination	685	1,457
Tillering	794	1,785
Jointing	900	1,908
Heading	833	1,664
Blossoming	762	1,486
Filling	657	1,357
Distributed*	1,135	2,249

* A one-inch irrigation at each of the above six stages.

amount of irrigation water. In Colorado, one irrigation on heavy soil, or two on sandy land, generally are sufficient to mature a spring wheat crop. At least one more irrigation per season usually is required when it is necessary to irrigate to effect germination. Excessive irrigation may result in a decreased yield, particularly when it causes lodging.

The critical period of irrigation of spring wheat is at the jointing stage, as illustrated in Table 13-5, which gives results from an experiment in Colorado.

The highest yield was obtained from six one-inch irrigations, but such small applications are impractical under field conditions. Irrigations made during one year may have a carryover effect on the next wheat crop [19, 48].

WHEAT AS PASTURE

Wheat is a highly nutritive pasture crop because the young plants contain nearly as much protein as does alfalfa hay. Winter wheat in early November in Kansas contained 27–28 per cent protein as well as 12–15 per cent ash on a dry basis. Sometimes winter wheat is sown in humid or subhumid regions exclusively for pasture. In most areas, the crop is grown primarily for grain with pasturage a secondary consideration. Wheat is pastured extensively in the fall, winter, and spring in the southern half of the Great Plains, except in dry years. Approximately 65 per cent of the winter wheat acreage in Kansas is pastured to a greater or lesser extent between November and April when satisfactory fall growth occurs [63].

Effect of Grazing on Grain Field

Wheat yields after winter grazing depend upon the amount of stored moisture in the seedbed, the severity of grazing, and the duration of the grazing period.

In general, the yield of winter wheat is reduced little or none when the plants are grazed in a state of vigorous early growth, particularly when the crop was sown on a well-prepared seedbed adequately supplied with stored moisture. Such conditions generally prevail in Kansas when wheat is sown on fallow. The crop should be grazed moderately, and neither too early nor too late in the season. The yield of wheat is reduced when the crop has made a limited fall growth because of a lack of moisture or inadequate seedbed preparation. When winter wheat is severely grazed over an extended period, or the grazing is continued too late in the spring, the reduction in yield may range from 5–50 per cent [63], as indicated in Table 13-6.

TABLE 13-6. **Wheat Pasturing Experiments at Hays, Kansas.**

Method Grazed	Time Grazed	5-Year Average Grain Yield per Acre	
		Fallow Land	Wheat Stubble Land
		(Bu)	(Bu)
Fall Grazing	October 15–December 15	29.6	25.3
Moderate seasonal grazing	October 15–December 15 March 1–April 15	28.9	25.0
Check (ungrazed)	————————	26.6	26.2
Spring grazing	March 1–April 15	25.6	23.5
Severe seasonal grazing	October 15–December 15 March 1–April 15	23.5	21.3
Late spring grazing	April 15–May 1	20.4	——

Yields were slightly improved by grazing wheat sown on fallowed land with fall or moderate seasonal grazing, whereas they were somewhat reduced by severe seasonal or spring grazing. Yields on continuous wheat land were reduced in all cases [63]. Moderate fall and winter grazing caused little reduction in grain yields in the Texas Panhandle [45].

In eastern Nebraska, grazing winter wheat reduced grain yields in all cases (Table 13-7).

TABLE 13-7. **Effects of Grazing Winter Wheat in Eastern Nebraska.**

Time Pastured	5-year Average Grain Yield per Acre (Bu)
Unpastured	21.3
Fall: November 20–29	18.2
Fall and Spring: November 21–30; April 13–26	15.4
Fall and Spring (late): November 21–30; April 11–May 7	10.9
Spring: April 9–27	16.2
Spring (late): April 12–May 8	12.0

Grazing reduced vegetative growth, delayed maturity, and caused a loss of main heads after the plants started to joint. Jointing usually began between April 20 and May 1 [22].

In Indiana, winter wheat grain yields were significantly increased by clipping treatments to simulate the effects of grazing between April 1–20. The wheat was sown on a fertile Brookston silty clay loam soil and temperature and rainfall conditions in March and April were favorable, but clipping after April 20 greatly reduced yields. In the case of wheat sown on a relatively infertile Crosby silt loam soil, all clipping treatments reduced the grain yield. Favorable weather conditions prevailed in March but not in April [8]. In New Jersey, grain production was increased by fall grazing, but decreased by grazing in the spring [60].

Pasturing of winter wheat tends to reduce the number of culms per plant and the extent of lodging [63]. It delays internode elongation in the spring and thus retards maturity [60].

Pasture Management Practices

Wheat to be pastured often is seeded earlier and sometimes thicker than when sown for grain alone [63]. Wheat sown on fallow is more likely to produce sufficient growth for grazing.

In Kansas, grazing of winter wheat is started in the fall after the plants are firmly rooted, or about November 1, but it usually is stopped in December when the wheat plants enter winter dormancy. Grazing may be resumed when growth starts again in the spring, the animals being removed about April 1, or when the plants grow erect just previous to jointing [63]. In the Texas Panhandle, livestock should be removed by March 15 from mid-season wheat varieties such as Comanche and Westar, and by March 1 from early varieties like Wichita and Triumph [45]. Wheat plants may be injured at any time after their growing points are above the ground line. Permanent injury results when the culm tips are grazed because severed culms never produce heads [20].

In the fall, 5–7 acres of green wheat usually are required in Kansas to carry an adult animal, whereas 2–4 acres may be sufficient in the spring [63].

Some cattle losses occur from grazing wheat, due primarily to bloat of animals grazed on lush frosted wheat, or plants wet from rain or dew. Grass tetany or "wheat poisoning" sometimes occurs when cattle are grazed on wheat in late fall or early spring. The danger appears to be greater under droughty conditions, or when frost at night is followed by days warm enough for the resumption of plant growth. Symptoms in livestock appear suddenly as tremors, stiffness, staggers, finally convulsions, and often death. Treatment consists of injection of a solution of calcium gluconate into the jugular vein [63].

HARVEST

About 94 per cent of the American wheat crop was harvested in 1950 with a combine [56], but the percentage was higher ten years later. The binder is still used in some localities, while the cradle is used occasionally to harvest small fields in the southeastern states. The header is rarely used now, except when combines are unavailable. Binders are used in many fields in Europe, while the hand sickle is used by numerous growers on small farms of the eastern hemisphere.

Methods of Harvest

For direct combine harvest, the moisture content of the wheat should be dried to 14 per cent or less. Thus, the crop must stand for 7–10 days or more after the wheat is physiologically mature and ready for binder harvest. Damp grain will spoil in the bin unless it is dried artificially. Green weeds in wheat fields increase the moisture content of the threshed grain when the crop is combined directly, because the excess moisture in green weed fragments is transferred to the grain in 24 hours or less. Such fields may be sprayed with a chemical herbicide or dessicant a few days before harvest, or may be windrowed and then combined after the weeds have dried out by using a pickup attachment on the combine [49]. The loss of grain was 2.6 per cent in combine harvest, 3.3 per cent with a header, and 6.1 per cent with a binder, in numerous fields in the Great Plains [47].

Wheat is ready for binder harvest when the straw is well-colored, either purple or yellow, and the grain has reached the hard-dough stage. At that stage the grain may contain 25–35 per cent of moisture. The bundles are shocked immediately, 10 or 12 bundles in a shock, and sometimes capped with two or more bundles. The wheat may be threshed directly from the shock 1–2 weeks later after the grain has dried to a moisture content of 14 per cent or less, or the wheat bundles are stored in the barn, or stacked in the field or yard, to be threshed later. Where the Angoumois grain moth is prevalent, it is especially desirable to thresh as soon as the grain is dry enough for storage [5].

Wheat may be harvested with a header when the grain contains 18 per cent moisture or less. The heads are piled in long low stacks in the field and left to dry for 2–4 weeks before threshing.

Effects of Different Stages of Harvest

In Nebraska, wheat harvested in the early dough, late dough, and mature stages yielded 21.7, 27.6, and 30.7 bushels per acre, respectively, with grain protein contents of 12.4, 12.8, and 13.1 per cent [22].

The translocation of material from the straw to the grain ceases when the moisture content of the grain drops below 40 per cent. Since ripening and drying are not uniform, some increase in dry matter in the grain continues until the average moisture content drops to 30–35 per cent. Wheat that stood in the field for two weeks after it was fully mature in Nebraska

TABLE 13-8. **Usual Range of Dates of Seeding and Harvesting Winter and Spring Wheat in Various Countries.**

Region or Country	Fall-Sown Wheat		Spring-Sown Wheat*	
	Seeding	Harvest	Seeding	Harvest
United States	August–December	May–September	March–June	July–September
Canada	August–October	July–September	April–June	July–October
Mexico	November–January	April–May	June–July	October–December
Brazil	May–July	November–December	—	—
Argentina	April–August	November–January	—	—
Chile	April–July	October–January	—	—
Northern Europe	August–October	July–September	February–April	August–October
Soviet Union	August–December	July–September	March–June	July–October
Poland	September–October	July–September	March–April	July–September
Southern Europe	September–December	May–July	January–March	June–August
North Africa	October–January	April–July	—	—
Egypt	October–December	March–May	—	—
Kenya	May–July	December–February	—	—
South Africa	April–June	October–December	—	—
Syria	September–January	June–July	—	—
India	September–December	January–June	—	—
China	September–December	May–June	April–May	August–September
Japan	September–December	May–July	—	—
Australia	April–June	October–December	—	—

* Countries for which no dates are shown grow little or no spring wheat. The data are compiled from various sources.

suffered an eight-year average loss of 3–5 per cent from shattering. The alternate wetting and drying that resulted from exposure to rain and dew caused the kernels to swell, and this lowered the test weight of the grain two pounds per bushel. The baking properties were unaffected [22].

High moisture content of the grain frequently causes delayed harvest in the soft red winter wheat area of the eastern United States. Varieties differ in rate of drying to the 14 per cent moisture level in the field after rains or dews. Rates of moisture gains and losses increase during the delayed harvest period, being related to internal changes in kernel structure [44].

Dates of Harvest

Winter wheat harvest in the United States begins in May in the southern latitudes, in June or July in the central latitudes, and in July or August in the Northern states or in the high-altitude sections of the Intermountain states (Fig. 13-9). Spring wheat harvest begins in July or August in the United States (Fig. 13-10).

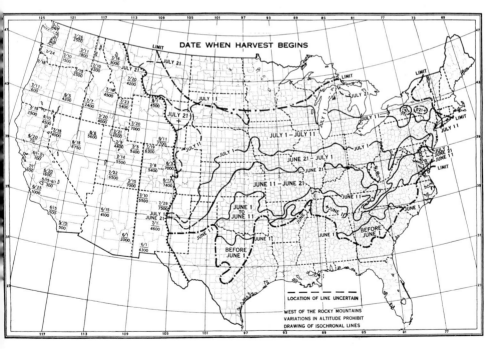

FIGURE 13-9. **Dates when winter wheat harvest begins in the United States.**

(Courtesy US Department of Agriculture)

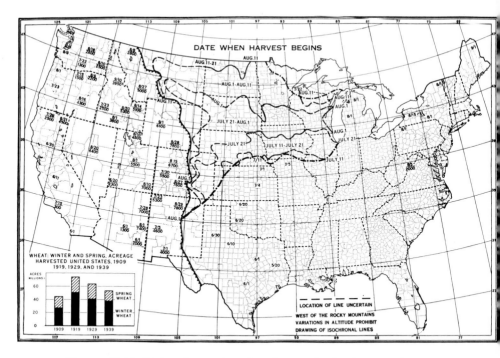

FIGURE 13-10. **Dates when spring wheat harvest begins in the United States.**
(*Courtesy US Department of Agriculture*)

The usual range of dates for the seeding and harvesting of wheat in various countries is shown in Table 13-8. Both the seeding and harvesting of wheat are going on somewhere in the world throughout the year.

CULTURAL PRACTICES IN OTHER COUNTRIES

Methods of wheat production around the world vary from primitive Iron Age hand culture to the most modern mechanized procedures.

Canada

Wheat is the most important farm crop in Canada. About 96 per cent of the total wheat acreage is in the three prairie provinces of Manitoba, Saskatchewan, and Alberta, where the precipitation ranges from 12–21 inches per year. Over 90 per cent of the Canadian crop is hard red spring wheat [17].

The most common crop rotation in the drier prairie provinces is summer fallow followed by one or more years of grain. In the black-soil zone where precipitation is favorable, hay crops are grown in rotation with small grain. Mixed alfalfa and timothy for hay in the rotation greatly increased the yields of grain crops that followed later [17].

Little manure is used in the drier regions of the prairie provinces. Green manures have failed to increase wheat yields. Application of small quantities of commercial fertilizer, such as 25–50 pounds per acre of a 11-48-0 fertilizer, has given considerable increase in wheat yields in some regions. The fertilizer usually is applied in the drill row with a combination grain-fertilizer drill. There is little or no response to fertilizers in the drier regions, but profitable returns have been obtained in areas with more favorable moisture conditions.

Subsurface tillage, rather than plowing, has been practiced in the prairie provinces for many years. Spring tillage is most effective, because stubble retains winter snows. The one-way disc and the blade cultivator are the standard tillage implements for summer fallowing. Wind erosion may be serious when two or more dry years occur successively, because then little crop residue is available to check erosion. Such land sometimes is deep-plowed or listed to create large lumps of soil. Strip cropping, with wheat and summer fallow in alternate strips about 16 rods wide, is practiced extensively in southern Alberta as a safeguard against wind erosion [17].

Almost all of the wheat in Canada is harvested with combines.

Australia

Wheat is grown in West Australia, South Australia, Victoria, and north through New South Wales to southern Queensland.

The wheat is sown in late autumn or early winter (April–June), and is harvested in late spring or early summer (November–December). Although fall-sown, all varieties grown in Australia have a spring growth habit. Light frosts occur regularly during the winter months, but snow is practically unknown in the wheat belt. Nearly all the wheat is grown under semiarid conditions [67]. The Australian wheat belt generally is within areas that receive between 9–15 inches of rain in the period from May to October [7].

Red-brown soils are the most important wheat soils in Australia. They are characteristic of the best wheat lands in New South Wales, South Australia, and Victoria. The Malle soils are located on the margins of the red-brown soils, while Podsol soils are found near the coast in areas that receive the highest rainfall. Black soils occur in northern New South Wales and southern Queensland, but gray-brown heavy soils are found in the Wimmera of Victoria [7].

At first, wheat was grown continuously without fertilizers, but the application of superphosphate and the practice of cultivated fallow soon doubled the average yield [67]. In recent years, the general rotation in the red-brown soil zone has been modified to fallow, wheat, and pasture [7].

Nitrogen fertilizers are used in small quantities in conjunction with superphosphate on stubble land in the higher rainfall regions. Superphosphate is generally applied at rates of from 50–200 pounds per acre, except in Queensland or in parts of northern New South Wales. Sown in the drill rows with the wheat [67], superphosphate has been found to increase the yield of wheat grown on fallow, but it has given little or no increase in yield on stubble unless applied with ammonium sulfate [7].

Fallowing controls weeds, conserves soil moisture, and accumulates soil nitrates. The cultivator or scarifier frequently is used as a substitute for the plow. Four pecks are sufficient to sow an acre [67].

A rough survey indicates that half the wheat land in Australia is affected detrimentally to a greater or less extent by wind or water erosion. Effective controls have been contouring, stubble mulching, and the withdrawal of steep slopes from cultivation [67].

Soviet Union

Normally, wheat is the principal crop of the Soviet Union, since it is grown on about 30 per cent of the total crop acreage. Spring wheat accounted for approximately two-thirds of the total wheat acreage in the country before World War II [65].

Wheat is primarily a crop of the black-soil or Chernozem area. The crop is of little importance north of the black-soil zone, but in southeastern European Russia, wheat extends into the brown soils of the arid steppes. The wheat area in Siberia coincides with the black-soil zone or with the brown-soil area to the south. Wheat is grown on the brown soils of the arid regions so far as the moisture supply permits [64].

A continental climate exists over a large part of the Soviet Union. It is characterized by cold prolonged winters, hot short summers, and moderate or light precipitation. Annual precipitation in the black-soil zone averages from 16–20 inches, but many other wheat-growing areas receive less than 16 inches [65].

Most of the spring wheats in the Soviet Union are grown in regions of severe winters, whereas the winter wheats are produced where the climate is milder. The spring wheat belt is largely in the Middle and Lower Volga Basin, the Urals, Western Siberia, and Kazakhstan. Thus, spring wheat is a typical crop of the semiarid zone, where it suffers from frequent droughts. Climatic conditions are more favorable in the winter wheat belt which comprises the Ukraine, Crimea, much of North Caucasus, and the irrigated regions of Central Asia and Transcaucasia [65].

In regions where summer fallow is practiced, the land generally is sown to winter wheat. However, in many winter wheat regions, the shortage of fallow land necessitates sowing winter wheat after wheat or after other crops. Spring wheat is seeded on plowed fallow land only in the eastern regions, but in other areas it follows other crops or is grown continuously for a number of years [65].

Seeding of spring wheat in the Soviet Union begins first in the southern regions and extends north. About 10 per cent of the acreage is seeded in March, mostly in the Central Asiatic Republics, which constitute a considerable proportion of the wheat area. The usual seeding period is from April 1–May 15, particularly in the European regions. However, wheat seeding in Asiatic regions normally continues through May and often it extends into June. Late seedings are more vulnerable to drought, weeds, and plant diseases which often cause lower yields. In most winter wheat regions, the optimum period of seeding is from September 1 to October 15. Seeding begins first in the north, but is influenced in different regions by the Hessian-fly-free dates [65].

Sowing rate for wheat in the Soviet Union varies from 1.5–2.4 bushels per acre. Spring wheat is sown at a somewhat heavier rate than winter wheat because it tillers less and is less resistant to droughty conditions. The amount of seed used diminishes from the more humid western regions to the drier eastern regions. The quantity of winter-wheat seed sown increases from north to south because of decreased tiller production [65].

Winter-wheat harvest begins early in July in the southern regions, but extends through July in the northern areas. The harvest of spring wheat begins in the south in late July and extends through August, but in Siberia it extends through September. Most of the wheat on collective farms is now harvested with tractor-drawn combines. Delayed harvest often results in losses because of shattered grain [65]. In remote areas, some wheat probably still is harvested by primitive implements such as hand sickles and scythes [64].

China

Wheat is primarily a winter crop in China. Only about 2 per cent of the crop is spring wheat, which is produced in the northwest provinces where the altitude is higher and the climate colder than in other parts of the country. Wheat is grown in every province in China, but it is important as a crop only from the Yangtze Valley north. Wheat is the principal crop in North China, where it occupies about 50 per cent of the cultivated land. In the Yangtze Valley, 20–40 per cent of the crop land is planted to winter

354   WHEAT

wheat. In South China, less than 10 per cent of the cultivated land is used for winter wheat production [52].

Competitive summer crops limit the winter wheat acreage in North China. Some of these crops occupy the land beyond the optimum time for seeding wheat, whereas others must be planted in the spring before the wheat is harvested. In some areas, peanuts are planted between the wheat rows several weeks before the wheat crop is harvested. In some parts of the Yangtze Valley, cottonseed is broadcast in wheat fields about a month before harvest, with the result that the cotton plants are already 1–3 inches high by the time the wheat is cut. In other parts of the Yangtze Valley, as well as to a considerable extent in South China, the land is left fallow over winter because the farmer desires to conserve his fertilizer resources for more profitable summer crops [52].

Wheat production in China is by intensive culture with hand labor. In Shantung Province, a typical wheat production area, 238 man-hours were required to produce an acre of wheat in 1939 [52].

Winter wheat generally is planted in China in September and October, while it usually is harvested between May 20 and June 10. In South China, however, the crop is planted later in the fall and harvested earlier in the spring [52].

In the preparation of the land for wheat in China, the farmer used a donkey, cow, or horse to plow and harrow the field. In North China, where most of the wheat is planted in rows, farmers usually have a small drill pulled by a work animal. Most of the wheat in the Yangtze Valley is broadcast by hand [52].

Most Chinese farmers apply fertilizer in the form of manure or vegetable-oil cakes to wheat fields, especially in North China where wheat is the most profitable crop. Man labor often is required for the irrigation of wheat in North China, wherever irrigation facilities are available. Wheat generally is harvested by hand sickles or the plants pulled. The grain is threshed by a flail or small bundles are beaten over slats which allow the grain to fall to the ground. The farmer generally makes use of wind to separate the grain from the chaff, although in some areas fanning mills are used [52].

The quality of Chinese wheat depends on the area where it is grown as well as on the weather conditions. Yangtze Valley wheat generally is considered poor because of the small kernels, low gluten content, and a high percentage of moisture. Rainy weather conditions usually prevail at ripening time, which makes harvest difficult. The quality of the wheat in North China also depends to a considerable extent on the weather. In years of sufficient rainfall, the grain compares favorably in quality with wheat produced in the Western countries. The grains are small, but the gluten strength is near that of Canadian wheat [52].

Argentina

In Argentina, the principal wheat area is a central productive zone, the pampas. This includes practically all of the provinces of Entre Rios, Santa Fe, Cordoba, Buenos Aires, and a small part of the Territory of La Pampa. Almost the entire region is arable [39].

The climate of the Argentine wheat zone is comparatively mild. The average annual precipitation varies from 18 inches on the western edge to more than 40 inches in Entres Rios on the eastern side.

The soils in the central region are fertile, black, and silty; those to the north contain somewhat more clay but are very fertile; and those to the west and southwest are lighter in texture and color, somewhat sandy, and less productive.

Wheat cultivation on the whole is large-scale and mechanized. However, horse traction predominates because feed is cheap, whereas tractor fuel is expensive. The crop is seeded from April to August. Late plantings frequently suffer from high January temperatures. Frost injury often occurs in October and November in the province of Buenos Aires and in the Territory of La Pampa. Wheat is harvested with headers, binders, or combines from November to January [39, 37].

India

Wheat is most widely grown in the northern part of India, where Uttar Pradesh Province has the largest acreage. It generally is grown on very small tracts primarily for local needs. Most of the crop is produced with hand tools or with ox-drawn implements of the simplest type.

In the preparation of the seedbed, the recommended practice is to plow the land initially with a soil-inversion plow such as the Victory or Punjab. This usually is followed by eight or more plowings and cross-plowings with a "Desi" (noninversion) plow, after which the soil is harrowed or floated into a fine seedbed.

Wheat yields are increased considerably by fertilization. Organic manures should be applied 4–6 weeks before seeding. Nitrogen fertilizers generally are applied for nonirrigated wheat just before seeding; for the irrigated crop, half is applied before seeding and the other half topdressed with the first irrigation. From 10–50 pounds of nitrogen per acre are applied for wheat in different provinces [57].

Wheat is primarily a winter crop in India, and is planted after the summer rains are over. By that time the soils contain sufficient moisture to support growth of the wheat plant until the light rains of the winter monsoons occur. The optimum seeding time is from October 15–November 15 on the plains, but seeding in the hills begins about September 15. Late seeding reduces wheat yields through rust damage as well as from premature drying of the crop [57]. Early varieties that flower between January 1–15 largely escape rust in Uttar Pradesh [36].

Wheat generally is seeded in rows 9–11 inches apart. The traditional country planter consists of a tube or set of tubes through which seed is dropped by hand. This planter is being replaced in some areas by small grain drills (Rambo, 1953). Wheat is seeded 2.5–3 inches deep under rainfed conditions, but only from 1.5–2 inches deep under irrigated conditions [57]. The sowing rate varies from 75–100 pounds per acre in Uttar Pradesh.

The highest wheat yields in India are produced under irrigation. Irrigation water is commonly applied at the tillering and blossom stages for most efficient results. From 3–4 irrigations are needed in years when the winter rains fail [57].

Normally, wheat is harvested in India in early spring before the onset of the hot dry weather that precedes the summer monsoon. Harvest generally is over by late May or early June. The crop is harvested with hand sickles. The traditional method of threshing is to lay the bundled grain on the ground in a circle about 30 feet in diameter. Bullocks are driven round and round the threshing ring for about 12 days to thresh the grain which is later separated from the straw by winnowing. Threshers are considered impractical because they leave the straw unbroken [46].

Japan

In recent years, wheat has become one of the major crops in Japan. The crop is grown in almost all parts of Japan, but the principal areas of production are in Kyushu and Central Honshu, especially on the Kanto Plain. The fields range from 0.25–2.5 acres in size. Except in the northern island of Hokkaido, the varieties generally grown are soft red winter or spring wheats seeded in the fall. Spring wheats seeded in the fall are limited to Kyushu and southern Honshu. About half the wheat in Hokkaido is seeded in the spring [55].

Most of the wheat in Japan is grown alternately with another crop in the same year. When wheat follows rice on paddy land, the field is generally ridged or bedded so that the crop can be planted on top of the ridges or beds. On upland fields, it is a common practice to plant sweet potatoes, soybeans, or upland rice between the rows of standing wheat before the grain is harvested [27].

Wheat is fall-seeded from September 10–December 10, or as soon as the land can be prepared after removal of the previous crop. The general practice is to drop the seed by hand in rows 20–24 or more inches apart. On ridges it may be seeded in single or double rows. In Kyushu the seed often is broadcast in rows or bands 6–8 inches wide, either lengthwise or crosswise of the beds which are 3–5 feet wide. The seed is covered with a rake or similar implement. Neither ridges nor beds are used on upland fields where drainage is adequate, but the wheat is always seeded in rows [27].

Most of the wheat crop in Japan is harvested in June with hand sickles. The grain is either laid in the swath for several days or tied in bundles and hung on wooden or bamboo frames. The dried grain is threshed with small foot-powered or motor-driven threshers. The grain is usually winnowed to separate it from the chaff. The cleaned grain is dried on straw mats to a moisture content of about 13 per cent before it is stored [27].

Middle East

Cereals occupy about 90 per cent of the cropped area in the Middle East countries of Egypt, Israel, Jordan, Syria, Lebanon, Iraq, Turkey, and Iran. Wheat comprises from 29 per cent to as high as 65 per cent of the cereal acreage in these countries [31]. Durum (*T. durum*) is the most widely grown wheat.

In the Middle East, nearly all the rain falls during the winter months, November to March, and the summers are very hot. The rainfall is so low in Egypt, Arabia, and on the Syro-Arabian desert that wheat production is possible only under irrigation [31].

In the Middle East, wheat is sown in the fall, except at high elevations or in some regions, such as Ethiopia, which have summer rainfall. The wheats have a spring growth habit. The seeding date is determined by the autumn rains that come from late September to November [31].

REFERENCES

1. Army, T. J., and J. C. Hide, "Effects of green manure crops on dryland wheat production in the Great Plains area of Montana". *Agron. J.*, **51**: 196–198. 1959.
2. ———, J. J. Bond, and C. E. Van Doren, "Precipitation-yield relationships in dryland wheat production on medium to fine textured soils of the southern high plains." *Agron. J.*, **51**: 721–724. 1959.
3. Ausemus, E. R., and R. M. Heerman, "Hard red spring and durum wheats: Culture and varieties." USDA *Farmers Bul. 2139*. 1959.
4. Bayfield, E. G., "The influence of climate, soil and fertilizers upon quality of soft winter wheat." Ohio Ag. Exp. Sta. *Bul. 563*. 1936.
5. Bayles, E. B., and J. W. Taylor, "Wheat production in the eastern United States." USDA *Farmers Bul. 2006*. 1951.
6. Brandon, J. F., and O. R. Mathews, "Dry land rotation and tillage experiments at the Akron (Colorado) Field Station." USDA *Cir. 700*. 1944.

7. Callaghan, A. R., and A. J. Millington, *The Wheat Industry in Australia.* Sydney: Angus and Robertson. pp 1–486. 1956.

8. Cutler, G. H., S. D. Pavez, and R. R. Mulvey, "The effect of clipping to simulate pasturing winter wheat on the growth, yield, and quality of the crop." *Agron. J.*, **41**: 169–173. 1949.

9. Davidson, J., "The effect of nitrates applied at different stages of growth on the yield, composition, and quality of wheat." *J. Am. Soc. Agron.*, **14**(4): 118–122. 1922.

10. Doneen, L. D., "Nitrogen in relation to composition, growth, and yield of wheat." Wash. Ag. Exp. Sta. *Bul. 296.* 1934.

11. Duley, F. L., "Stubble-mulch wheat farming methods for fallow areas." Nebr. Ag. Exten. Serv. *Cir. 54–100.* 1954.

12. Finney, K. F., *et al.*, "Effect of foliar spraying of Pawnee wheat with urea solutions on yield, protein content, and protein quality." *Agron. J.*, **49**: 341–347. 1957.

13. Greaves, J. E., and A. F. Bracken, "Effect of cropping on the nitrogen, phosphorus, and organic carbon content of a dry-farm soil and on the yield of wheat." *Soil Sci.*, **62**: 355–364. 1946.

14. Greb, B. W., R. S. Whitney, and R. H. Tucker, "Commercial fertilizer experiments with non-irrigated wheat in eastern Colorado in 1953." Colo. Ag. Exp. Sta. *General Series Paper No. 564.* 1954.

15. Harper, H. J., "Sixty-five years of continuous wheat on reddish prairie soil in central Oklahoma." Okla. Ag. Exp. Sta. *Bul. B-531: 1–38.* 1959.

16. Haus, T. E., *et al.*, "Winter wheat production in Colorado." Colo. Ag. Exp. Sta. *Bul. 507-S.* 1960.

17. Hopkins, E. S., "Wheat production in Canada." *Emp. J. Exp. Ag.*, **16**(66): 91–104. 1949.

18. Horner, G. M., "Effect of cropping systems on runoff, erosion, and wheat yields." *Agron. J.*, **52**: 342–344. 1960.

19. Kezer, A., and D. W. Robertson, "The critical period of applying irrigation water to wheat." *J. Am. Soc. Agron.*, **19**: 80–116. 1927.

20. Kiesselbach, T. A., "Winter wheat investigations." Nebr. Ag. Exp. Sta. *Res. Bul. 31.* 1925.

21. ———, A. Anderson, and W. E. Lyness, "Cultural practices in winter wheat production." Nebr. Ag. Exp. Sta. *Bul. 286.* 1934.

22. ———, and W. E. Lyness, "Growing the winter wheat crop." Nebr. Ag. Exp. Sta. *Bul. 389.* 1954.

23. Klingman, D. L., "Effects of spraying cereals with 2,4-dichlorophenozyacetic acid." *J. Am. Soc. Agron.*, **39**: 445–447. 1947.

24. ———, "Effects of varying rates of 2,4-D and 2,4,5-T at different stages of growth on winter wheat." *Agron. J.*, **45**: 606–610. 1953.

25. Laude, H. H., *et al.*, "Growing wheat in Kansas." Kans. Ag. Exp. Sta. *Bul. 370.* 1955.

26. Lawton, K., and J. E. Davis, "Influence of fertilizer analysis and placement on the emergence, growth, and nutrient absorption of wheat seedlings in the greenhouse." *Agron. J.*, **52**: 326–328. 1960.

27. Leonard, W. H., "Principal field crops of Japan." USDA *Foreign Ag.*, **12**(8): 174–180. 1948.

28. Locke, L. F., and O. R. Mathews, "Relation of cultural practices to winter wheat production, Southern Great Plains Field Station, Woodward, Okla." USDA *Cir. 917.* 1953.

29. Long, O. H., and J. A. Ewing, "Fertilizer studies on small grains with special emphasis on time and rate of nitrogen application." Tenn. Ag. Exp. Sta. *Bul. 209.* 1949.

30. ——, and C. D. Sherbakoff, "Effect of nitrogen on yield and quality of wheat." *Agron. J.,* **43**(7): 320–321. 1951.

31. Mann, H. H., "Wheat in the Middle East." *Emp. J. Exp. Ag.,* **14**: 31–42. 1946.

32. Martin, J. H., "Factors influencing results from rate and date of seeding experiments with winter wheat in the western United States." *J. Am. Soc. Agron.,* **18**: 193–225. 1926.

33. McNeil, F. H., and D. J. Davis, "Effect of nitrogen fertilization on yield, culm number, and protein content of certain spring wheat varieties." *Agron. J.,* **46**(8): 375–378. 1954.

34. Merkle, F. G., "Experiments on fertilizing wheat." Natl. Joint Committee on Fertilizer Application *Proc.,* **26**: 202–204. 1950.

35. Miller, L. B., and F. C. Bauer, "Soil treatments for winter wheat: a summary of field experiments." Ill. Ag. Exp. Sta. *Bul. 503.* 1944.

36. Mitra, A. K., and V. S. Mathur, "Early varieties and early sowings as a method of combating the wheat rust menace in U. P." *Agriculture and Animal Husbandry,* Vol. 6, Nos. 4 and 5, Wheat Special Number. 1955.

37. Moore, O. K., "Argentine farming and trade." USDA For. Ag. Serv. *Report No.* 25. pp 1–85. 1948.

38. Nelson, C. E., "Effects of plant populations and nitrogen fertilizer rates on three varieties of irrigated spring wheat." Wash. Ag. Exp. Sta. *Bul. 611.* 1960.

39. Nyhus, P. O., "Argentine wheat." USDA *For. Ag.,* **2**(7): 323–348. 1938.

40. Olsen, R. A., and H. F. Rhoades, "Commercial fertilizers for winter wheat in relation to the properties of Nebraska soils." Nebr. Ag. Exp. Sta. *Res. Bul. 172.* 1953.

41. Olsen, P. J., *et al.,* "Sensitivity of wheat and barley at different stages of growth to treatment with 2-4,D." *Agron. J.,* **43**: 77–83. 1951.

42. Overland, A., and L. W. Rasmussen, "Some effects of 2,4-D formulations in herbicidal concentrations on wheat and barley." *Agron. J.,* **43**: 321–324. 1951.

43. Patterson, H. B., "Effect of nitrogen fertilizer on yield and protein content of winter wheat in Utah." Utah Ag. Exp. Sta. *Bul. 353.* 1952.

44. Pool, M., and F. L. Patterson, "Moisture relations in soft red winter wheats. I: Varietal differences and delayed harvest effects. *Agron. J.,* **50**: 153–157. 1958.

45. Porter, K. B., I. M. Atkins, and C. J. Whitfield, "Wheat production in the Panhandle of Texas. Tex. Ag. Exp. Sta. *Bul. 750.* 1952.

46. Rambo, E. K., "Farm machinery in India." USDA *For. Ag.,* **17**: 9–12. 1953.

47. Reynoldson, L. A., *et al.,* "The combined harvester-thresher in the Great Plains." USDA *Tech. Bul. 70.* 1928.

48. Robertson, D. W., *et al.,* "Studies on the critical period for applying irrigation water to wheat." Colo. Ag. Exp. Sta. *Tech. Bul. 11.* 1934.

49. ——, *et al.,* "Winter wheat production in Colorado." Colo. Ag. Exp. Sta. *Bul. 470.* 1942.

50. ——, *et al.,* "Rate and date of seeding Kanred winter wheat and the relation of seeding date to dry-land foot rot at Akron, Colo." *J. Ag. Res.,* **64**: 339–356. 1942.

51. Robertson, L. S., P. J. Rood, and J. A. Porter, "Nitrogen top dressings for wheat on heavy soils." Mich. Ag. Exp. Sta. *Quart. Bul.*, **34**(3): 226–231. 1952.

52. Rossiter, F. J., "Agriculture in China." USDA *For. Ag.* **3**(10): 431–498. 1939.

53. Russell, E. J., and D. J. Watson, "The Rothamsted field experiments on the growth of wheat." Imp. Bur. Soil Sci. Tech. Comm. No. 40, Harpenden, England. 1940.

54. Salmon, S. C., and R. I. Throckmorton, "Wheat production in Kansas." Kans. Ag. Exp. Sta. *Bul. 248.* 1929.

55. ———, "Crop improvement in Japan." *J. Am. Soc. Agron.*, **40**(11): 1017–1035. 1948.

56. ———, O. R. Mathews, and R. W. Leukel, "A half century of wheat improvement in the United States," in *Advances in Agronomy*, Vol. 5. New York: Academic Press, pp 1–151. 1953.

57. Sen, S., "Wheat and barley." *Indian Farming*, **2**(5): 8–11, 22. 1952.

58. Smith, F. W., "Placing fertilizer for efficient production of small grains." Natl. Joint Comm. on Fertilizer Application, *Proc.*, **29**: 59–62. 1953.

59. Smith, H. W., S. C. Vandecaveye, and L. T. Kardos, "Wheat production and properties of Palouse silt loam as affected by organic residues and fertilizers." Wash. Ag. Exp. Sta. *Bul. 476.* 1946.

60. Sprague, M. A., "The effect of grazing management on forage and grain production from rye, wheat, and oats." *Agron. J.*, **46**: 29–33. 1954.

61. Stringfield, G. H., and J. L. Haynes, "Wide corn-row spaces and wheat interseedings." *Agron. J.*, **51**: 390–391. 1959.

62. Sullivan, J. T., *et al.*, "Effects of fertilizer applications and other cultural practices on some kernel characteristics of winter wheat." Ind. Ag. Exp. Sta. *Bul. 432.* 1938.

63. Swanson, A. F., and K. Anderson, "Winter wheat for pasture in Kansas." Kans. Ag. Exp. Sta. *Bul. 345.* 1951.

64. Timoshenko, V. P., *Agricultural Russia and the Wheat Problem.* Stanford, Cal.: Stanford U. Food Res. Inst., pp 1–571. 1932.

65. Volin, L., *A Survey of Soviet Russian Agriculture.* USDA Agriculture Monograph 5. pp 1–194. 1951.

66. Warren, R. G., "The residual effects of the manurial and cropping treatments in the Agdell rotation experiment." Rothamsted Exp. Sta. *Annual Report*, pp 252–260, Harpenden, England. 1957.

67. Watt, R. D., "The problems and possibilities of growing wheat in Australia." Emp. *J. Exp. Ag.*, **16**(64): 187–194. 1948.

68. Woodward, R. W., "The effect of rate and date of seeding small grains on yield." *Agron. J.*, **18**: 160–162. 1956.

69. Woofter, H. D., and C. A. Lamb, "The retention and effect of 2,4-Dichlorophenozyacetic acid. (2,4-D) sprays on winter wheat." *Agron. J.*, **46**: 299–320. 1954.

70. Zingg, A. W., and C. J. Whitfield, "A summary of research experience with stubble-mulch farming in the western states." USDA *Tech. Bul. 1166*, pp 1–56. 1957.

$\mathcal{W}$heat

14. COMPOSITION, PROCESSED PRODUCTS, AND UTILIZATION

COMMERCIAL CLASSIFICATION OF WHEAT

Commercial wheats grown in the United States are: common (*Triticum vulgare*), durum (*T. durum*), and Club (*T. compactum*). Common wheat comprises about 95 per cent of the total production. Under the official grain standards of the United States, the term *wheat* excludes emmer, spelt, einkorn, Polish wheat, and poulard wheat. These, except einkorn, are grown occasionally in the United States but are used for feed.

Classes and Subclasses

Under the official grain standards, wheat is divided into seven classes—primarily on the basis of color, kernel texture, and variety characters. These classes are: Hard Red Spring, Durum, Red Durum, Hard Red Winter, Soft Red Winter, White, and Mixed wheats (Fig. 14-1). The standards specify that wheat of any class, except Mixed, may contain not over 10 per cent of wheat of a different class or classes either singly or combined [27].

Hard Red Spring and Hard Red Winter wheats are especially suitable for the manufacture of bread flour because they contain a strong elastic gluten, and have a high protein content when grown where they are best adapted. These classes are equal in intrinsic baking value when they have the same protein content [18], but Hard Red Spring wheats usually have a higher protein content. Soft Red Winter and White wheats, both usually low in protein, produce flours suitable for pastries, crackers, biscuits, and cakes. Durum wheat is used for the manufacture of semolina that is used

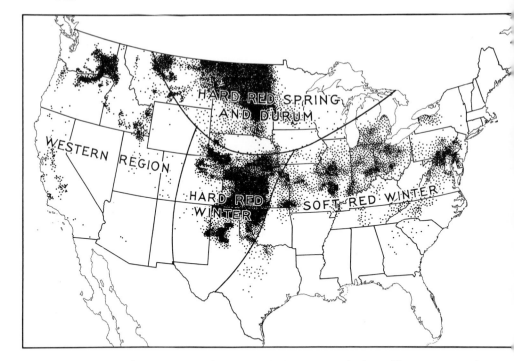

FIGURE 14-1. **General production areas of the classes of wheat. The western region produces mostly white, but some hard red winter, hard red spring, and soft red winter also.**

(Courtesy US Department of Agriculture)

to make macaroni, spaghetti, vermicelli, and other alimentary pastes. Red Durum, the Pentad variety, formerly was used only for livestock or poultry feed [8], but none was reported in the United States in 1959 [30]. Wheat varieties within a commercial class may have important inherent differences in quality.

The wheat classes, except Red Durum, are divided further into subclasses on the basis of kernel texture, except for the two Western subclasses based on other characters and geographical origin. Texture is specified in the wheat standards in terms of "dark, hard, and vitreous kernels" in the case of Hard Red Spring and Hard Red Winter wheats, in terms of "hard (not soft and chalky) kernels" in the case of White wheat, and in terms of "hard and vitreous kernels of amber color" in the case of Durum wheat [8].

Wheat subclasses are as follows:

Class	*Subclasses*
Hard Red Spring	(a) Dark Northern Spring
	(b) Northern Spring
	(c) Red Spring

Class	Subclasses
Hard Red Winter	(a) Dark Hard Winter
	(b) Hard Winter
	(c) Yellow Hard Winter
Durum	(a) Hard Amber Durum
	(b) Amber Durum
	(c) Durum
Red Durum	————
Soft Red Winter	(a) Red Winter
	(b) Western Red
White	(a) Hard White
	(b) Soft White
	(c) White Club
	(d) Western White

Wheat Grades

Each lot of wheat in each subclass is assigned a numbered or sample grade on the basis of quality and condition, after examination of a sample by a licensed inspector.

In general, quality in wheat refers to plumpness, soundness, and the amount of foreign material present. These properties are measured by determinations of test weight per bushel, and the percentages of damaged kernels, dockage, and other foreign material. Plumpness of grain is an important index of flour yield; damaged kernels result in flour that produces bread of poor quality. Objectionable forms of damage include kernels or pieces of kernels that are heat damaged, sprouted, frosted, badly ground damaged, badly weathered, moldy, diseased, or otherwise materially damaged.

Dockage is foreign material that is removable with appropriate cleaning devices. Some dockage, such as wild oats and other grains, is valuable for feed, but chaff, weed seeds, and dust is nearly worthless. Unseparated foreign material that remains in the wheat lowers the grade. Test weight is widely used to measure milling quality because there is a positive correlation between test weight and flour yield. This function is linear between 51 and 65 pounds per bushel, but nonlinear below this range. The relationship between test weight and flour yield loses its significance when decreased test weight is due to alternate wetting and drying [23]. Delayed harvest over a period of 45 days has been shown to lower test weight, increase kernel softness, and increase the amount of fine flour produced in Soft Red Winter wheat [28].

Condition factors include moisture content; odor, presence of smut, garlic, and insects; and the extent of weather damage. Wheat that contains

TABLE 14-1. **U. S. Market Grades for Hard Red Spring Wheat.**

Grade Requirements for (a) Dark Northern Spring, (b) Northern Spring, (c) Red Spring.

Grade No.	Minimum Test Weight per Bushel, Lb	Damaged Kernels Total	Damaged Kernels Heat-Damaged	Foreign Material	Wheats of Other Classes Total	Wheats of Other Classes Durum and/or Red Durum
1 Heavy*	60	2.0	0.1	0.5	5.0	1.0
1*	58	2.0	0.1	0.5	5.0	1.0
2*	57	4.0	0.2	1.0	5.0	2.0
3*	55	7.0	0.5	2.0	10.0	3.0
4	53	10.0	1.0	3.0	10.0	10.0
5	50	15.0	3.0	5.0	10.0	10.0

Maximum Limits, Per cent

Sample Grade: Sample grade shall include wheat which does not come within the requirements of any of the grades from No. 1 Heavy to No. 5, inclusive; or which contains more than 16.0 per cent of moisture; or which contains stones; or which is musty, or sour, or heating; or which has any commercially objectionable foreign odor except of smut or garlic; or which contains a quantity of smut so great that any one or more of the grade requirements cannot be applied accurately; or which is otherwise of distinctly low quality.

* The wheat in grades No. 1 Heavy, No. 1, and No. 2 of this class may contain not more than 5.0 per cent, and in grade No. 3 not more than 8.0 per cent of shrunken and broken kernels.

more than approximately 14 per cent of moisture often will spoil during storage or transportation. In warm climates or under improper storage conditions, it may spoil even with a lower moisture content. Wheat standards specify maximum moisture limits for all regular grades. When the moisture exceeds this limit, the word "tough" is added to the grade designation. For Hard Red Spring, Durum, and Mixed wheats, "tough" is added when the moisture content falls between 14.5–16.0 per cent, but for other classes the moisture limits are 14.0–15.5 per cent. Wheat that is musty or sour, or has a commercially objectionable odor, is graded "Sample grade." Such odors usually are carried into the flour.

Special grades are provided for wheat that is tough, smutty, garlicky, weevily, ergoty, or treated.

Commercial Wheat Standards

Standards for Hard Red Spring and Hard Red Winter classes are given below. Those for the Durum, Red Durum, Soft Red Winter, White, and Mixed classes are available in the Official Grain Standards of the United States [27].

Hard Red Spring wheat may include not more than 10 per cent of wheats of other classes. This class is divided into three subclasses on the basis of the percentages of dark, hard, and vitreous kernels: (a) Dark Northern Spring, 75 per cent or more; (b) Northern Spring, 25–75 per cent; and (c) Red Spring, less than 25 per cent. The grades are given in Table 14-1.

Hard Red Winter wheat may include not more than 10 per cent of wheats of other classes. This class also is divided into three subclasses on the basis of percentages of dark, hard, and vitreous kernels: (a) Dark Hard Winter, 75 per cent or more; (b) Hard Winter, 40–75 per cent; and (c) Yellow Hard Winter, 40 per cent or less. The grades are presented in Table 14-2.

TABLE 14-2. **U. S. Market Grades for Hard Red Winter Wheat.**

Grade Requirements for (a) Dark Hard Winter, (b) Hard Winter, (c) Yellow Hard Winter.

		Maximum Limits, Per cent				
					Wheats of Other Classes	
	Minimum Test Weight per Bushel, Lb	Damaged Kernels		Foreign Material		Durum and/or Red Durum
Grade No.		Total	Heat- Damaged		Total	
1*	60	2.0	0.1	0.5	5.0	0.5
2*	58	4.0	0.2	1.0	5.0	1.0
3*	56	7.0	0.5	2.0	10.0	2.0
4	54	10.0	1.0	3.0	10.0	10.0
5	51	15.0	3.0	5.0	10.0	10.0

Sample Grade: Sample grade shall be wheat which does not meet the requirements for any of the grades from No. 1 to 5, inclusive; or which contains more than 15.5 per cent of moisture; or which contains stones; or which is musty, or sour, or heating; or which has any commercially objectionable foreign odor except of smut or garlic; or which contains a quantity of smut so great that any one or more of the grade requirements cannot be applied accurately; or which is otherwise of distinctly low quality.

* The wheat in grades No. 1 and No. 2 of this class may contain not more than 5.0 per cent and in grade No. 3 not more than 8.0 per cent of shrunken and broken kernels.

CHEMICAL COMPOSITION

Chemical composition of wheat varies with the climate, soil, variety, and stage of maturity.

Composition of Wheat Plant

The approximate composition of the wheat plant, straw, and grain is given in Table 14-3 [9].

TABLE 14-3. **Percentage Composition of the Wheat Plant.**

Material	Mois-ture	Ash	Crude Protein	Ether Extract	Crude Fiber	N.F.E.[1]	Cal-cium	Phos-phorus
Green Weight:								
Immature plants	82.3	2.1	3.8	0.9	3.0	7.9	0.07	0.10
Mature plants	68.7	2.6	2.4	0.7	8.6	17.0	0.06	0.08
Dried Weight:								
Wheat Hay	9.6	4.2	3.4	1.3	38.1	43.4	0.14	0.15
Straw	6.8	5.4	4.3	3.4	36.8	43.3	—	—
Grain	10.6	1.8	12.0	2.0	—	71.6	0.05	0.38

[1] N.F.E. = nitrogen free extract.

Kernel Composition

The range in percentage composition of the wheat kernel is as follows: Starch, 63–71; proteins, 8–15; water, 8–17; cellulose, 2.0–2.5; fat, 1.5–2.0; sugars, 2–3; and mineral matter, 1.5–2.0 [16]. In a well-filled wheat kernel, the germ comprises about 2–3 per cent of the kernel, the bran 13–17 per cent, and the endosperm the remainder. The bran layers are high in protein, cellulose, hemicelluloses, and minerals. The germ is rich in protein, lipids, sugar, and ash constituents. The endosperm consists largely of starch grains embedded in a matrix of protein [11].

The average composition of wheats on a moisture-free basis, of the different commercial classes grown in the United States, is given in Table 14-4 [31].

The proteins in the inner endosperm of the wheat kernel consist chiefly of gliadin and glutenin in approximately equal amounts. Embryo proteins consist of nucleoproteins, an albumen (leucosin), a globulin, and proteoses. In wheat bran, gliadin predominates with lesser quantities of albumens and globulins. The endosperm proteins, gliadin and glutenin, form

TABLE 14-4. **Percentage Composition of Wheat Grain of Commercial Classes.**

Class	Protein	Starch	Sugar	Ash	Oil
Hard Red Spring	16.5	61.2	3.19	2.04	2.00
Durum	16.0	63.0	3.58	2.19	2.19
Red Durum	16.8	61.3	3.33	2.14	1.98
Hard Red Winter	15.3	63.5	2.84	1.92	1.67
Soft Red Winter	12.4	66.5	2.90	2.07	1.66
White	11.2	66.6	4.02	1.86	1.80

a colloidal complex with water called "gluten." Gluten makes wheat superior to other cereals for the production of leavened bread because it makes possible the formation of a dough which retains carbon dioxide produced by yeast or chemical leavening agents. From the nutritive standpoint, wheat endosperm proteins are low in the amino acids, lysine, and tryptophane [11].

Starch is the principal polysaccharide found in the wheat kernel. Small quantities of dextrins usually are present. Pentosans are found primarily in the bran tissue. Sucrose is the principal sugar present, the greatest amounts being in the germ tissues [11].

Two important enzymes in the wheat kernel are alpha-amylase and beta-amylase involved in the breakdown of starch. Alpha-amylase will act on raw as well as gelatinized starch to convert it to dextrins. Beta-amylase is primarily responsible for maltose formation from gelatinized starch and dextrins [11].

Wheat grains contain vitamins of the B-group, that is, thiamine, riboflavin, nicotinic acid (niacin), pyridoxine, and pantothenic acid. The kernel lacks Vitamins C and D. The oils of the embryo of the kernel are high in Vitamin E. Thiamine is located mainly in the scutellum and its epithelium, in the aleurone layer, in the endosperm cells adjacent to the embryo, and in those cells at the base of the crease. Thiamine appears to be in or adjacent to the cell walls. Riboflavin is much more uniformly distributed in these kernel structures than is thiamine [33].

Mineral composition of the wheat kernel as a percentage of the weight has been reported as follows: potassium, 0.48; calcium, 0.05; magnesium, 0.17; phosphorus, 0.40; and sulfur, 0.18 [4]. Other elements found in the wheat kernel include iron, sodium, and chlorine. Most of the mineral material is in the germ and bran.

Composition of Wheat Flour

The chemical composition of white flour of 72 per cent extraction in percentages is approximately as follows: moisture, 13–15.5; starch, 65–70;

protein, 8–13; cellulose (fiber), trace–0.2; fat, 0.8–1.5; sugar, 1.5–2.0; and mineral matter, 0.3–0.6 [16].

The compositions of graham, straight, and patent flours are approximately as shown in Table 14-5 [7]:

TABLE 14-5. **Percentage Composition of Different Wheat Flours.**

Flour	Water	Protein	Fat	Ash	Carbo-hydrates	Feed Value per Pound, Calories
Graham (all types)	11	13.0	2.0	1.6	72.4	1630
Straight (all types)	12	11.2	1.1	0.5	75.2	1615
Patent						
All-purpose	12	10.8	0.9	0.4	75.9	1610
Bread	12	11.8	1.1	0.5	74.6	1615
Cake or pastry	12	8.3	0.8	0.4	78.5	1610

Composition of Flour Byproducts

Byproducts of flour manufacture are widely used as livestock feedstuffs. Approximate composition of wheat flour byproducts is given in Table 14-6 [9]:

TABLE 14-6. **Percentage Composition of Wheat-Flour By-Products.**

Wheat or Mill By-product	Mois-ture	Ash	Crude Protein	Ether Extract	Crude Fiber	N.F.E.[1]	Cal-cium	Phos-phorus
Wheat Kernel	10.6	1.8	12.0	2.0	2.0	71.6	0.05	0.38
Wheat Product								
Bran	9.4	6.4	16.4	4.4	9.9	53.5	0.10	1.14
Brown shorts	10.8	4.0	17.8	4.8	5.8	56.8	—	—
Flour middlings	10.4	3.3	18.8	4.0	4.2	59.3	0.09	0.80
Gray shorts	11.0	4.1	17.5	4.4	5.4	57.6	0.08	0.86
Mixed feed	9.9	4.4	18.2	4.4	6.9	56.1	0.11	0.96
Red Dog	11.1	2.2	18.3	3.4	2.3	62.7	0.12	0.83
Standard middlings	10.4	3.9	17.0	4.3	5.4	59.0	0.09	0.90
White shorts	10.9	2.2	15.6	3.7	2.4	65.2	—	—
Waste, shredded	8.0	1.6	12.4	1.6	2.6	73.8	—	—

[1] N.F.E., nitrogen-free extract.

FACTORS THAT AFFECT PROTEIN CONTENT

Climate, soil, and variety determine the protein content of the ripened kernel [2, 3, 11].

Climate

Cold winters, followed by hot dry summers that induce rapid ripening characterize the Great Plains of North America and the steppes of Soviet Russia where hard wheats of high protein content are produced. Moist cool summers following mild winters result in large, plump, soft wheat kernels that are low in protein. Such climates are typical of northwestern Europe and eastern North America. The mild climates of the Mediterranean countries and the Pacific Coast of the United States also result in low protein wheats. Ample irrigation in a dry region increases yields but lowers the protein content. Also, high rainfall or heavy irrigation leach nitrates from the soil. Drought curtails kernel development, but often produces a high protein content [2, 21, 32, 11].

In North Dakota, high day temperatures from ten days before heading until about July 15 were conducive to high protein content in hard red spring wheat [37]. The protein content was above 13 per cent when the average July temperature was above 70°F, while it was above 12 per cent when the July temperature averaged slightly above 65°F (preceded by a low June temperature). Also, high rainfall in May, June, and July reduced the protein content of the wheat [21]. Similar results have been obtained in Canada for July and August, the ripening months for spring wheat [32]. Loaf volume and dough mixing time have been found to decrease, in general, with an increase in accumulated degrees Fahrenheit above 90 during the last fifteen days of the fruiting period of several hard red wheat varieties [10].

The shorter the period between the formation and ripening of the kernel, the higher the percentage of gluten [32]. The fruiting period (heading to ripening) tends to be prolonged when the weather is cool and soil moisture adequate. Under such conditions, a relatively large amount of starch tends to be deposited to produce a plump starchy kernel. Hot dry weather, which retards starch deposition more severely than it does gluten formation, results in nonplump kernels high in gluten [1].

Soil Conditions

Most of the mineral nutrients derived from the soil are absorbed by the wheat plant before it blooms, and some of these are translocated to the kernel later. Nitrates are absorbed by the plant until the grain is nearly ripe, but the more rapid photosynthesis of carbohydrates after the shooting stage causes a decrease in the nitrogen content of the plant. Nitrification, active in the soil early in the season, is favored by warm weather, but the nitrates are depleted by the growing crop.

Wheat of high protein content is produced on soils, such as the Chernozem and Chestnut soils, that are relatively high in nitrogen—particularly nitrates. However, rainfall determines the soil type to a large degree, and also affects the nitrogen supply. The available moisture in soils that produce wheats of high protein content usually is largely exhausted by the time the wheat is mature [2]. Nitrification requires available moisture in the surface soil and thus declines when the growing crop has exhausted the moisture from the surface 6–12 inches. In Alberta, the superior quality of spring wheat grown on the black soils, as compared with that grown on gray soils, was accounted for by the higher protein content made possible by the higher soil nitrogen supply. The black soils, but not the gray soils, contained ample nitrogen for growth of the wheat plant [40].

Nitrogenous fertilizers, particularly in inorganic forms, usually increase the protein content of the grain when applied late in the growing period up to the heading stage or later [21, 13, 20]. The addition of phosphate fertilizers in liberal amounts often increases the grain yield with a consequent reduction in protein content. Potash fertilizers generally have not materially affected the protein composition of the grain [2]. Cultural practices—such as fallowing or early seedbed preparation for winter wheat—that build up or retain soil nitrates, increase the protein content of the grain. These practices also result in larger grain yields [17, 5]. The grain produced on wheat plants attacked heavily by stem rust is shrunken and low in starch and protein. Shrunken wheat resulting from drought during the ripening period usually is high in protein when the soil is high in nitrates.

Variety Factor

Formerly, differences in protein content among varieties grown under comparable conditions seldom were greater than 1 per cent when the grain yields were approximately the same, regardless of whether they were soft or hard varieties. The protein content of varieties in a test often is inversely proportional to the yield. However, five soft red winter wheat varieties, with Frondoso and Fronteira in their parentage, averaged 12.05 per cent protein and 28 bushels per acre when grown in the southern United States. Eight older varieties averaged 10.91 per cent protein and only 24.0 bushels per acre in the same tests. The protein content of the Hardired variety was 10.1 per cent when the new Atlas 66 variety averaged 13.3 per cent. Thus, in Atlas 66 and similar varieties, high protein content does not necessarily connote low yields [22]. The sowing of seed wheat of high protein content does not assure a crop with high protein, unless the variety grown has genetic factors for high protein such as are found in Atlas 66.

Soft and hard wheats of the same protein content are not equally good for bread or pastry flours. The hard wheats produce a more granular flour which is desirable for bread making but unsuitable for making cakes, cookies, and crackers. Furthermore, the protein quality varies widely between varieties even when the protein content is the same.

ROLLER MILLING

Wheat is milled in order to separate the endosperm of the grain as completely as possible from the bran and germ; then the endosperm is pulverized into flour. The various kernel structures are separated mechanically on the basis of differences in physical properties [35, 11, 29]. Bread flours are milled primarily from hard wheats, pastry flours from soft wheats, and semolina from durum wheats. There are wide variations in quality between varieties and also between different lots of the same variety grown under different soil, weather, cultural, or disease conditions. Wheats of different lots are blended by the miller to produce a flour of constant uniform quality.

Cleaning

After the wheat has been properly blended, it is cleaned to remove the impurities, such as chaff, sticks, straw, weed seeds, other cereal grains, smut balls, soil, and the like. The machines for removing these impurities are equipped with screens (Fig. 14-2), air suction or blasts (Fig. 14-3), and disk (Fig. 14-4) or indented-cylinder separators (Fig. 14-5). Next, the wheat is dry-scoured to rub off the brush hairs and dirt from the kernels. In the scourer, the wheat grains are thrown against a perforated iron casing by beaters fixed to a rapidly revolving drum. When wheat is appreciably smutty or dirty, it also is put through wheat washers in which the grain is scrubbed under a stream of water. The washed wheat is passed through a centrifuge to remove the excess water. Smutty wheat sometimes is limed before it is scoured. An impact machine, known as an entoleter, frequently is used to kill live insects in wheat on its way to the first break rolls (see p. 373) to remove them before the wheat is milled.

Tempering

The wheat next is conditioned or tempered by the addition of water to toughen the bran. The amount of water added is sufficient to raise the moisture content from the usual 12–13 per cent to normally 15–16 per cent. Some of the water required is added—to wheat that is washed—in the washers. After the water is added, the wheat is stored a sufficient length of time to allow the moisture to penetrate the kernels to the proper depth to toughen the bran and mellow the endosperm. Tempering time varies from 2–24 hours, but usually 4–6 hours, for different wheat lots. Excessive moisture causes the endosperm to flake, whereas insufficient moisture leads to pulverization of the bran along with the endosperm when milled. Wheats frequently are heated to accelerate the tempering process, particularly in Europe.

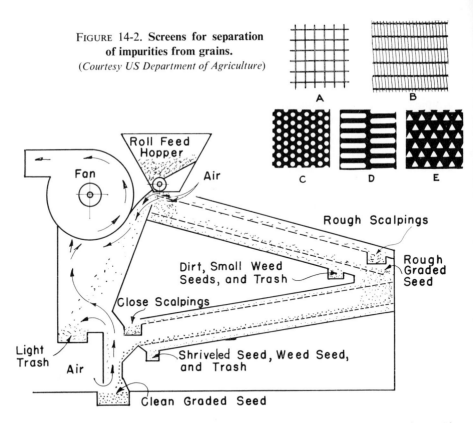

FIGURE 14-2. Screens for separation
of impurities from grains.
(*Courtesy US Department of Agriculture*)

FIGURE 14-3. Cross section of an elevator type grain cleaner using air and sieves. Air suction removes the chaff and dust as the grain is fed into the cleaner. Shaking sieves separate coarse and fine impurities from the grain.

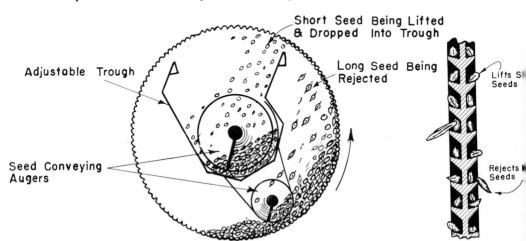

FIGURE 14-5. An indented-cylinder
wheat separator.

FIGURE 14-4. Diagram showing the
principle of a disk wheat separator,
which picks up wheat kernels but
discards oats.

Heat generated in grinding and the aeration of the milled products during sifting, purifying, and movement through the mill, generally reduces the moisture content in the milled products to about 13–13.5 per cent. When wheat has a moisture content higher than 13.5 per cent before it is tempered, there is an invisible loss in weight in milling due to evaporated water, but that with less than 13 per cent moisture usually shows a gain in weight of milled products.

Breaking

After the wheat is tempered, it is ready for the grinding process. The first part of the process is carried out on corrugated rolls, known as break rolls, which revolve in opposite directions (Fig. 14-6). The grain and its fragments are cracked and crushed gradually through a series of 4–6 break rolls. The break rolls, which consist of two per stand, usually are 24–30 inches in length and 9 inches in diameter. The surface of the break rolls is roughened by sharp, lengthwise, and slightly spiral corrugations. The break rolls run at a differential speed of about 2.5:1, which produces a shearing action on the grain. The grist from each break is sifted to remove the flour,

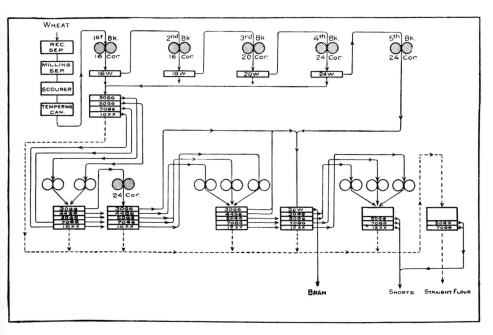

FIGURE 14-6. **Flow sheet for a simple flour mill: Sep = separator; Bk = break rolls; Cor = corrugations with indicated number per inch on the roll. The unshaded circles are smooth reducing rolls. The numbered bars indicate sieve size opening.**

(Courtesy US Department of Agriculture)

and then aspirated to remove bran particles. The coarsest particles are conducted to successive break rolls where the process is repeated.

Each successive pair of break rolls has finer corrugations, as well as closer distances between rolls, in order to grind the grain into progressively smaller particles. The first break rolls usually have 10–12 corrugations per inch, whereas the fifth or sixth break rolls may have as many as 26–28 corrugations per inch (Fig. 14-7).

Bolting

After each passage through break rolls, the crushed material or chop moves to a sifter or bolter equipped with a series of inclined sieves. The break sifters have a relatively coarse sieve at the top and progressively finer sieves towards the bottom, and operate with a gyratory motion. The coarse fragments retained on the top sieves are conveyed to the next break rolls. The medium-sized granular particles, chiefly endosperm, retained on the other sieves, are called "middlings." The fine particles, which pass through the fine-silk bottom sieves, are known, as "break flour"—*i.e.,* first break flour, second break flour, and so forth. The stock at each successive break contains less and less endosperm until finally only bran remains after sifting the fifth or sixth break.

Purification

The middlings are composed of endosperm fragments mixed with bran particles and germ. In the sifter, the middlings are graded on the basis of size, after which the various streams are combined in order to bulk particles of the same size and degree of refinement. The middlings next pass to machines known as purifiers where small bran particles are removed so far as possible by further bolting and by aspiration.

Reduction

After purification, the middlings are passed through a series of reduction rolls that revolve at a differential speed of about 1.5:1. These rolls, which are smooth, are spaced so that each successive reduction produces finer particles. Flour is sifted out after each reduction. By the last reduction, most of the endosperm has been converted to flour while most of the bran has been separated by the reduction sifters. The final mixture, which consists of bran, some very fine middlings, and some germ, is known as gray shorts and is used for feed.

FIGURE 14-7. **Two rows of milling roll units in a flour mill.**

(*Courtesy US Department of Agriculture*)

FLOUR TREATMENTS

Flour can be fractionated by air classification to obtain portions that are very high (20–25 per cent) or very low (3 per cent) in protein content. Thus, some high-protein flour could be made from low-protein wheat. Micrograinding, to reduce the size of all flour particles less than 70 microns in diameter, facilitates this separation [39]. Freshly milled flour is improved in color as well as in baking quality by storage or "aging" for several months, but the same result can be obtained in a few minutes by the use of chemicals. In addition, flours may be enriched to restore certain nutrients removed from the wheat kernel in the milling process.

Flour Bleaching

Freshly milled flour obtained by the roller mill process contains small quantities of yellow pigments which impart to it a creamy color. The principal pigment is xanthophyll. These carotinoid pigments are changed to colorless compounds upon oxidation, with bleaching agents, or during storage, with the result that the flour becomes nearly pure white.

Some bleaching agents, such as chlorine, nitrosyl chloride (NOCl), and chlorine dioxide (ClO_2), age the flour, yielding a product that is comparable to naturally aged flour in all respects. Nitrogen peroxide (N_2O_4) and benzoyl peroxide ($(C_6H_5CO)O_2$) are bleaching agents with little or no aging effect. Freshly milled flour is treated with a bleaching agent in a special mixing unit called an agitator.

Flour Enrichment

Flour often is enriched to restore or supplement certain vitamins and minerals that are found in the unmilled wheat kernel but which are largely lost to the byproduct feeds after milling. The average amounts of nutrients in unenriched flours, and the minimum and maximum levels in federal standards for enriched flours, are as follows:

Ingredient	Unenriched White Flour	Enriched White Flour
	(mg/lb)	(mg/lb)
Thiamine	0.30	2.0– 2.5
Niacin	3.50	16.0–20.0
Riboflavin	0.15	1.2– 1.5
Iron	3.00	13.0–16.5

Two other ingredients, Vitamin D and calcium, are optional for enriched flours. Since soluble iron salts catalyze the development of rancidity, an insoluble form of iron, such as sodium iron pyrophosphate, is used as a source of iron for flour enrichment [11]. The ingredients are mixed thoroughly with the flour to assure uniform distribution.

Increased Amylase Activity

Patent flours often are low in amylase activity, a condition that may be corrected by the addition of small quantities of malted wheat flour or malted barley flour [11]. Wheat malt as grain may be mixed with the mill grist of wheat—in amounts up to 0.2 per cent—before milling [38].

WHEAT FLOUR GRADES

The different breaks and reductions in flour manufacture afford as many as 30 flour streams in large mills. Flour is produced by each break as well as by each reduction. The flour streams come in part from different portions of the endosperm; they vary in protein content and in degree of refinement, as indicated by the ash content and the presence of bran particles. Flour from the first middling separation is the most highly refined, while that from each successive reduction contains increased proportions of bran and germ particles. Flour obtained from the last reduction, called red dog, is dark in color due to a high content of branny material. It is largely unsuitable for baking [29].

Standard Flour Grades

Flour grades depend upon which flour streams are combined in the final product. Straight flour is obtained when all streams, except red dog, are combined. In the usual milling practice, the streams of the finer and whiter particles that comprise 70–80 per cent of the total flour are combined into patent flour. Common types of commercial bread-wheat flours, together with the approximate percentages of the total flour, are as follows: family patent, 70–75; short patent, 75–80; medium patent, 80–85; and long or standard patent, 90–95 [11]. The residual clear flours are called fancy clear, first clear, and second clear. They decrease in refinement in the order named. The lower grades of clear flour are too dark in color, as well as too low in quality, to make satisfactory bread flours. Some of the better grades of clear flour are mixed with rye flour.

Relationships between the various grades of white flour are shown in the diagram below. [38].

72% of Wheat = 100% Straight Flour		28% of Wheat = feed	
		14% Bran	14% Shorts
40% Extra Short or Fancy Patent	55%		
60%	Fancy Clear		
Short or First Patent Flour	70% 25%		
Short Patent Flour	80%	Poor Second Clear	
Medium Patent Flour	90%		
Long Patent	95%		
Straight Patent	100%	16% Bran	12% Shorts

Since the grades gradually merge into one another, a 95 per cent straight flour might be identical with a 95 per cent long patent flour.

Milled Flour Yields

The fact that only about 72 per cent of the weight of cleaned wheat is recovered as white flour, whereas wheat averages about 85 per cent endosperm, indicates the difficulty of making a complete separation of the kernel parts in the milling process. Particles of the endosperm, particularly the aleurone, cling to the bran, and are carried to the feed or by-product streams. Thus, about 28 per cent of the cleaned wheat is used for feed which is approximately 14 per cent bran and 14 per cent shorts, including red dog.

Shrunken wheat kernels have a low percentage of endosperm which is difficult to separate from the bran. Yields of total flour range from less than 62 per cent for 49 pound wheat to more than 79 per cent for wheat with a test weight of 64 pounds.

High extraction wheat flour, which consisted of 82–100 per cent of the grain, was used in some European countries during both world wars as means of extending food supplies. Heavy consumption of such flour increased the incidence of digestive disorders and rickets. Bran contains a phosphorus compound called phytin, part of which is converted into phytic acid during digestion. The phytic acid combines with calcium to form calcium phytate which is not absorbed by the human system. This results in a calcium deficiency, and additions of calcium to the diet serve only to produce more calcium phytate.

Graham flour is the entire wheat grain ground into flour. It was named for Dr. Sylvester Graham, who published a book in 1837 in which he extolled the virtues of flour made from the entire wheat kernel. Formerly, whole wheat and entire wheat flour consisted of graham flour with part of the bran removed, or an extraction of about 80–90 per cent of the wheat kernel. Under federal definitions formulated in 1941, they are the same as graham flour. Often graham flour is ground in a burr mill or even between old-fashioned stone burrs. When the germ is retained in the flour, as in graham and certain special flours, the fat in the germ tends to become rancid, making the flour unpalatable. Graham flour becomes infested with insects more quickly than does white flour. Because of these storage risks and because of the small quantity marketed, graham flour usually sells at a higher price. The calorific content of whole wheat products is fully as high as that of patent flour products because whole wheat includes the germ which is high in fat content. However, the net energy value of whole wheat might be slightly lower because of lower digestibility.

Flour Preferences

Apparently, the people of the Stone Age ground their flour into graham flour. However, the ancient Egyptians learned to bolt flour through papyrus sifters, while the ancient Romans succeeded in making a fairly white flour. The tendency through the centuries has been to make the whitest flour possible.

White flour now constitutes about 97 per cent of wheat flour manufactured in the United States. It is often mixed with dark flours, or rye flour, in making some kinds of bread. About 93 per cent of the bread baked is made from white flour only, 1 per cent from graham flour, and the remainder from mixed white and dark flours. These proportions represent the tastes of the American public.

CHARACTERISTICS OF WHEAT FLOUR

Nature of Flour Particles

Starch granules in flour are oval or spherical in shape, and range in size from 0.00024–0.0015 inch. The outer walls of these granules consist of a cellulose material that protects and encloses the starch proper. The cellulose cover must be ruptured before the starch can be converted to sugar, and only a few of the starch particles gelatinize in making bread [36]. The physical structure of flour protein particles has never been seen, but they are believed to consist of fibrils or interlaced meshworks—*i.e.,* a nucleus or center from which their filaments extend in all directions [36].

Dough is formed when water is combined with the flour. Part of the water is taken up by the starch, and part by the protein particles, which behave like a sponge. It is calculated that the protein particles in dough absorb as much water as do the starch particles even though the amount of starch is 6–7 times as great. The protein particles join together and form filaments, while the dough acts as though it is permeated by a mass of elastic strings, filaments, strands, or fibers. The starch is loosely enmeshed in the strands of protein. Dough for leavened products must have a capacity to produce and retain gas—*i.e.,* when yeast starts fermentation, the dough must be able to retain the carbon dioxide produced and have enough firmness to hold its shape until coagulated or set by oven heat. Bubbles produced under yeast action are spherical forms of dough material. The protein particles constantly rearrange themselves in dough as it rises, and they stretch sufficiently to retain the gas [36].

Role of Protein in Flour Quality

The important proteins in wheat are gliadin and glutenin which, together with water and salts, form wet gluten. The gliadin content is approximately 4 per cent, while the glutenin content is still higher. However, the quality of gluten in flour is more important than the quantity [36].

Hard wheat flours as a rule are high in bread-making quality—*i.e.,* they produce a large, light, well-piled loaf of bread of good uniform texture and color. Strong wheats—*i.e.,* those with ample gluten (protein) of good quality—are high in water absorption. Because of its greater ability to retain moisture, a barrel of flour made from such wheats usually produces more one-pound loaves of bread than does a barrel of the weaker flours made from soft wheats. A light loaf can be made from a weak flour but the pores of such bread are large and the loaf tends to dry out quickly.

Flour strength is difficult to define because flour quality is determined by a variety of physical characteristics of the dough, none of which is independent of other variables. Baking strength depends on protein content and gluten quality. And inherent gluten structure is determined by the variety of the wheat as well as by the conditions of growth, ripening, and storage.

Ash Content in Flour

The ash content of flour is an important factor to flour merchandisers. The chief constituents of wheat ash are phosphorus, potash, magnesium, sulfur, and calcium. Highly refined patent flour usually has an ash content of 0.4 per cent or less. The more bran particles the flour contains, the higher the ash content. Therefore, clear and straight flours have a higher ash content than does patent flour. Flour buyers often purchase flour on a guaranteed maximum allowable ash basis. High ash content is not necessarily an indication of high extraction, poor milling, or dirty wheat because ash content is determined by the variety of wheat—hard wheat flours, for instance, usually have a higher ash content than do soft wheat flours—and by weather conditions.

UTILIZATION OF WHEAT AND ITS PRODUCTS

Of the total domestic American wheat crop, about 9–10 per cent is used for seed, 13–14 per cent is fed to livestock on farms where it is produced, 1–3 per cent is ground at home mills or exchanged for flour, and the balance is sold for commercial purposes.

Wheat Products in Human Consumption

Wheat as human food is used principally in the form of flour for baked products such as bread, biscuits, pastries, crackers, and pretzels. A small amount of wheat is converted into prepared breakfast foods such as wheat flakes, puffed wheat, and shredded wheat. Purified middlings of hard winter wheat, called "farina," and those of hard spring wheat, called "cream of wheat," are also used as breakfast foods.

In the Middle East, wheat is used to make bulgur, an important staple food. Essentially, it is parboiled, dried, and cracked wheat with some of the bran removed. It has culinary uses similar to those of rice [12].

Wheat flour consumption in the United States declined from 224 pounds per capita in 1900 to about 120 pounds in 1957. This marked decrease in flour consumption has been brought about by the increased use of other foods in improved diets, made possible by higher incomes, as well as by the reduced human energy requirements that have resulted from the increased use of machinery [11].

Wheat as Livestock Feed

Although considerable quantities of common wheat are fed on farms on the Pacific coast and in the Eastern states, the use of wheat grain as livestock feed is limited because its price is higher than that of the feed grains; the nutritive value of wheat is about equal to that of corn. Wheat for feed generally is ground, except for poultry.

Flour milling by-products are used almost entirely for livestock feed. They are usually marketed as bran, shorts, and sometimes white middlings. The wheat germ is usually added to the shorts, but because of its high vitamin content, some of it is sold as a human food supplement. Some bran also is used for human food.

Industrial Uses

Industrial uses of wheat include the manufacture of starch, gluten, distilled spirits, malt, paste, and core-binder flour. A small quantity of wheat flour is used in the manufacture of starch and gluten. Wheat starch is utilized chiefly in the laundry and textile industries, although processes also have been developed for its conversion into sirup, sugar, or industrial alcohol [19]. Gluten is used in gluten breads for diabetics and for the production of monosodium glutamate (known in the Orient as *adjunomoto*), a product that intensifies the flavor of foods. Some low-grade flours are used in the manufacture of pastes for wall papering and plywood adhesives, and in iron foundries as a core binder [38].

REFERENCES

1. Alsberg, C. D., and E. P. Griffing, "Environment, heredity, and wheat quality." Stanford U. Food Res. Inst. *Wheat Studies*, **10**: 229–249. 1934.
2. Bailey, C. H., *The Chemistry of Wheat Flour*. New York: Chem. Cat. Co., pp 1–324. 1925.
3. ———, "Protein surveys of American hard spring and soft winter wheats." Minn. Ag. Exp. Sta. *Tech. Bul. 147.* 1941.
4. Beeson, K. C., "The mineral composition of crops with particular reference to the soil in which they were grown." USDA *Miscel. Pub. No. 369.* 1941.
5. Burke, E., and R. M. Pinkney, "The influence of fallow on yield and protein content of wheat." Mont. Ag. Exp. Sta. *Bul. 222.* 1929.
6. Carter, E. P., and G. Y. Young, "Role of fungi in the heating of moist wheat." USDA *Cir. 838.* 1950.
7. Chatfield, C., and G. Adams, "Proximate composition of American food materials." USDA *Cir. 549.* 1940.
8. Combs, W. B., and F. G. Smith, "Grain grading primer." USDA *Handbook No. 59*, pp 1–67. 1953.
9. Ellis, N. R., W. R. Kauffman, and C. O. Miller, "Composition of the principal feedstuffs for livestock," in *Food and Life*. USDA Yrbk. of Ag., pp 1065–1074. 1939.
10. Finney, K. F., and H. C. Fryer, "Effect on loaf volume of high temperatures during the fruiting period of wheat." *Agron. J.*, **50**: 28–34. 1958.
11. Geddes, W. F., "Cereal grains," in *Food and Food Products*, Vol. II, 2d. ed. New York: Interscience.; pp 1022–1133. 1951.
12. ———, "Recent developments in foods from cereals." *Ag. and Food Chem.* **7**: 605–610. 1959.
13. Gericke, W. F., "On the quality of bread from wheats supplied with nitrogen at different stages of growth." *Cereal Chem.*, **4**: 73–86. 1927.
14. Glass, R. L., *et al.*, "Grain storage studies. XXVIII: The influence of temperature and moisture level on the behavior of wheat stored in air or nitrogen." *Cereal Chem.*, **36**: 341–356. 1959.
15. Hummel, B. C. W., *et al.*, "Grain storage studies. XIII: Comparative changes in respiration, viability, and chemical composition of mold-free and mold-contaminated wheat upon storage." *Cereal Chem.*, **31**: 143–150. 1954.
16. Kent-Jones, D. W., and A. J. Amos, *Modern Cereal Chemistry*, 4th ed. Liverpool: Northern Publ. Co. 1947.
17. Kiesselbach, T. A., "Winter wheat investigations." Nebr. Ag. Exp. Sta. *Res. Bul. 31.* 1925.
18. Lamour, N. K., "A comparison of hard red winter and hard red spring wheats." Kans. Ag. Exp. Sta. *Bul. 289.* 1940.
19. Langford, C. T., and C. E. Rist, "Starch from wheat," in *Science in Farming*. USDA Yrbk. of Ag., 1943–47. pp 744–749. 1947.
20. Long, O. H., and C. D. Sherbakoff, "Effect of nitrogen on yield and quality of wheat." *Agron. J.*, **43**: 320–321. 1951.
21. Mangels, C. E., "Pre-harvest factors that affect wheat quality." *Cereal Chem.*, **4**: 376–388. 1927.

22. Middleton, G. K., C. E. Bode, and B. B. Bayles, "A comparison of the quantity and quality in certain varieties of soft wheat." *Agron. J.*, **46**: 500–502. 1954.

23. Miller, B. S., and J. A. Johnson, "A review of methods for determining the quality of wheat and flour for breadmaking." Kans. Ag. Exp. Sta. *Tech. Bul. 76.* 1954.

24. Milner, M., C. M. Christensen, and W. F. Geddes, "Grain storage studies: V. Chemical and microbiological studies on 'sick' wheat." *Cereal Chem.*, **24**: 23–38. 1947.

25. ———, C. M. Christensen, and W. F. Geddes, "Grain storage studies. VI: Wheat respiration in relation to moisture content, mold growth, chemical deterioration and heating." *Cereal Chem.*, **24**: 182–199. 1947.

26. ———, C. M. Christensen, and W. F. Geddes, "Grain storage studies. VII: Influence of certain mold inhibitors on respiration of moist wheat." *Cereal Chem.*, **24**: 507–517. 1947.

27. "Official Grain Standards of the United States." USDA *SRA–AMS–177*, pp. 1–93. 1960.

28. Pool, M., F. L. Patterson, and C. E. Bode, "Effect of delayed harvest on quality of soft red winter wheat." *Agron. J.*, **50**: 271–275. 1958.

29. Pyler, E. J., *Baking Science and Technology*, Vol. I. Chicago: Siebel Publ. Co., pp 191–236. 1952.

30. Reitz, L. P., and L. W. Briggle, "Distribution of the varieties and classes of wheat in the United States in 1959." USDA *Stat. Bul. 272.* 1960.

31. Shollenberger, J. H., *et al.*, "The chemical composition of various wheats and factors influencing their composition." USDA *Tech. Bul. 995.* 1949.

32. Shutt, P. T., and S. N. Hamilton, "Quality of wheat as influenced by environment." *Emp. J. Exp. Ag.*, **2**: 119–138. 1934.

33. Somers, G. F., M. N. Coolidge, and K. C. Hammer, "The distribution of thiamine and riboflavin in wheat grains." *Cereal Chem.*, **22**: 333–340. 1945.

34. Sorger-Domenigg, H., *et al.*, "Grain storage studies. XVII: Effect of mold growth during temporary exposure of wheat to high moisture contents upon the development of germ damage and other indices of deterioration during subsequent storage." *Cereal Chem.*, **32**: 270–285. 1955.

35. Swanson, C. O., *Wheat and Flour Quality*. Minneapolis: Burgess Publ. Co. p 227. 1938.

36. ———, "The meaning of quality in wheat." Assn. Op. Millers *Bul.*, pp 257–262. 1928.

37. Waldren, L. R., *et al.*, "Protein and quality in hard red spring wheat with respect to temperature and rainfall." N. Dak. Ag. Exp. Sta. *Bul. 311.* 1942.

38. "Wheat, its products and uses." USDA Northern Reg. Res. Lab. *Paper ACE–189.* 1942.

39. Wichser, F. W., "Baking properties of air-classified flour fractions." *Cereal Sci. Today*, **5**(5): 123–126. 1958.

40. Woodward, E. K., and A. G. McCalla, "The absorption of nutrients by two varieties of wheat grown on the black and gray soils of Alberta." *Can. J. Res.*, **14**(C): 245–266. 1936.

$\mathcal{W}heat$

15. DISEASES AND INSECT PESTS

Wheat Pest Problem

Wheat is subject to attack by numerous diseases, the symptoms of which are stunted plants, leaf or stem spots, galls, shriveled or discolored grain, and various root or crown rots. Most of the wheat diseases are caused by fungus parasites, but a few are caused by bacteria or viruses. Wheat diseases may cause an imperceptible reduction in yields or a total loss. Numerous insect pests also attack wheat at various stages of plant development.

A. DISEASES

RUSTS

Rusts are among the most serious diseases of wheat. The rusts that attack wheat are stem rust (*Puccinia graminis tritici*), leaf rust (*Puccinia recondita*), and stripe rust (*Puccinia glumarum*).

Stem Rust

Stem rust, caused by the fungus, *Puccinia graminis tritici,* probably is the most serious of wheat diseases and may cause heavy yield losses. It is found wherever wheat is grown, but particularly in the humid and sub-humid regions. In the United States, Canada, Mexico, Australia, India, and many other countries, it may cause local or widespread epidemics in years when conditions are favorable to its spread. In the United States, it is most severe in the hard red spring wheat region. The disease is epidemic in the Mississippi Valley in occasional years when rust spores that develop in Texas and Mexico are carried northward by wind and encounter weather conditions favorable for their multiplication.

Yield losses range up to 85–90 per cent, at which point the crop is not worth harvesting. Yield reductions of from 6.7–7.2 per cent for each recorded 10 per cent increase of stem rust intensity have been reported in Canada [33], but less damage occurs from similar rust infection in the central and southern latitudes of the United States. In California, the rust-susceptible Baart variety yielded from 25–47 per cent less than the comparable resistant Baart 46. Baart 38, with only moderate resistance, yielded from 6–20 per cent less than Baart 46 [89].

Stem rust of wheat is characterized by elongated reddish-brown pustules (uredial stage) that occur on the stems, leaves, sheaths, floral bracts, and sometimes on the awns of the wheat plant. These pustules, which often break through the epidermis, contain brick-red uredospores. As the season advances, the pustules as well as the spores are replaced by black ones (telial stage) (Fig. 15-1). It is the red-spore stage which is responsible for

FIGURE 15-1. **Rusted wheat culms (left), and resistant rust-free culms (right).**

(*Courtesy US Department of Agriculture*)

the damage. The rust fungus utilizes the water and nutrient materials needed for the development of the wheat kernel, and the rusted plants also transpire water at a greatly accelerated rate. The kernels may be so shriveled that many of them are blown out with the chaff when the grain is threshed. The remaining grains may not exceed one-half to two-thirds their normal size. The rusted straw turns brown, becomes dry and brittle, and soon breaks over [58]. Heavily rusted fields also ripen unevenly [68].

In the Southern states and northern Mexico, the red or uredospore stage of the stem rust fungus lives throughout the year on susceptible wheat and other grasses. In the spring, the uredospores spread to other wheat plants. A new generation of spores may be produced every 1–3 weeks, with a single rust pustule producing as many as 350 thousand spores. The disease spreads rapidly under warm moisture weather conditions. The spores, which are carried north by winds or air currents, may follow the development of the wheat crop from the Southern states to Canada. For example, a heavy epidemic of stem rust in Texas in April may be expected to produce a similar epidemic in southern Canada in July, when seasonal conditions favor rust development throughout the intermediate wheat-growing region. In late summer or early fall, the uredospores are blown southward where they may attack volunteer or early-sown wheat and certain grasses. These plants provide rust inoculum for fall-sown wheat in the South where rust may live over the winter [58].

In India, there is an annual recurrence of stem rust from uredospores carried down by air currents from the Himalayan Mountains where wheat is grown at an altitude of 9000 feet. In the mountains, the rust lives over from one wheat crop to the next in the uredial stage on stubble or volunteer wheat. Rust infections start in the mountains from where the spores are blown to wheat in the foothills and later to wheat on the plains, where the summer heat destroys local sources of infection [70, 80].

In Australia, stem rust is carried over in the uredospore stage on volunteer wheat, other small grains, and on some grasses [101]. Rust epidemics are relatively infrequent in Australia because the long dry summers often destroy the spores on volunteer wheat plants or susceptible grasses. But in some years, early-sown wheat crops in Queensland serve as a source of infection for crops farther south [14].

In the northern half of the United States, the stem rust fungus may pass through additional stages in its life cycle. The brick-red uredospores on the plants are replaced by black teliospores in the same pustules as the wheat approaches maturity. These teliospores overwinter on the straw or stubble, germinate in the spring, and produce sporidia which infect the leaves of the common barberry (*Berberis vulgaris*) (Fig. 15-2). The sporidia also may infect certain wild native species such as *B. canadensis* in the eastern Allegheny region, and *B. fendleri* in the Rocky Mountains [57]. The pycniospores, which develop on the barberry, constitute the sexual reproductive cells of the fungus. The union of these cells produces tissues which give rise to cluster cups (aecia) in which aeciospores are borne. The aeciospores then are blown from the barberry bush to wheat or grass plants where uredospores are produced to complete the life cycle. Since the teliospores seldom survive the summer south of Nebraska, barberry bushes rarely are infected in the South. Moreover, the uredospores seldom survive the winter north of Texas. Barberry bushes in the Northern states may be expected to spread stem rust to nearby wheat fields, from where it spreads to other fields. The amount of inoculum spread by barberry bushes is small when compared with that from vast wheat fields or grass pastures. Wheat

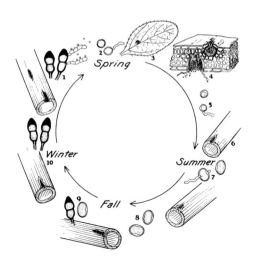

FIGURE 15-2. **Life cycles of stem rust in the northern half of the United States: Germinated teliospores produce basidiospores (1) which germinate (2) and penetrate the upper surface of the barberry leaf (3), where a pycnidium (4, above) is formed. There arise the pycniospores (sexual cells) which unite and give rise to an aecium (4, below) from which aeciospores (5) are released. The germ tubes from these enter the stomata of the wheat leaf where pustules (6) produce red uredospores (7) which spread to other wheat plants (8) where more uredospores and later teliospores (9) are produced. The black teliospores overwinter on wheat stems (10).**

(Courtesy US Department of Agriculture)

near barberry bushes becomes infected 2–3 weeks earlier than that infected by spores from the South [57].

Stem rust is composed of many parasitic strains or physiologic races. There are about 275 known races and biotypes of stem rust in the world, but only a few are of economic importance in any one year. For ten or more years prior to 1950, most of the losses from stem rust in the United States were caused by Races 17, 38, and 56 [76]. There was a sharp change in the physiologic race flora of the entire Mississippi Valley in 1950 when a new race—15B—suddenly appeared in epidemic proportions. First found near a barberry bush in Iowa in 1939, race 15B is the most virulent stem rust ever found in North America [34]. In 1954 it caused heavy losses in all commercial wheat varieties grown in the United States, particularly durum wheat, and occurred in 65 per cent of the uredial collections [86]. It also is prevalent in western Canada [48]. The most important races of stem rust in Uttar Pradesh in India are 15, 40, 42, 75, 24, and 21 [80]. Races 126 and 126B are widespread in Australia [102].

Stem rust races are comparatively stable in their behavior. New races arise by hybridization on barberry bushes [21, 85]. Some ten times as many races of rust may occur on or near barberry bushes as on grains or grasses in barberry-free areas [76]. New pathogenic races or biotypes also may arise by mutation [103].

In the United States, a federal-state barberry eradication program was started in 1918 and now operates in 18 states. From 1918–53, more than 462 million barberry bushes were destroyed, but eradication is far from complete. In areas where barberry bushes are the principal source of infection, their eradication was accompanied by a marked reduction in wheat losses. In the Mississippi Valley, however, where rust spores are blown in from the South, the eradication of barberry bushes can reduce total rust damage on susceptible varieties only to a minor degree.

Stem rust can be controlled by the application of sulfur dust or other fungicides to wheat fields. The method generally is uneconomical because several applications are required to protect the wheat during the period of exposure to the infection, and the applications must be made before infection begins when it is not yet known whether or not serious damage is likely to occur. In India, four applications of sulfur dust at 30 pounds per acre at 10-day intervals is a recommended control measure [80].

Early-sown wheat or early-maturing varieties tend to escape severe rust damage. Wheat fertilized heavily with nitrogen sometimes suffers more severe damage. Apparently, the rust fungus is favored by the increased density of the stand and delayed maturity [84]. In India, it has been recommended that only 50 pounds of nitrogen per acre be added for wheat grown in Uttar Pradesh [80].

Breeding wheat varieties resistant to stem rust has been one of the notable achievements of American agriculture. Rust-resistant wheats were introduced into the United States by M. A. Carleton of the United States Department of Agriculture about 1900. Some of these varieties furnished rust-resistant parents for wheat crosses from which suitable commercial varieties later were selected. These resistant varieties greatly reduced rust damage until the appearance of Race 15B in 1950 [76].

The Hope and H-44 wheats, developed by E. S. McFadden of the United States Department of Agriculture, furnished the most important basic material for breeding rust-resistant wheats throughout the world. These wheats were selected from a cross between Marquis wheat and Yaroslav emmer released in 1926. Thatcher wheat, developed cooperatively at the Minnesota Agricultural Experiment Station, was the result of another interspecies cross in which rust resistance was obtained from durum wheat. Thatcher is a selection from a double cross: (Marquis × Yumillo durum) × (Marquis × Kanred) [35]. In the late 1930's, the old rust-susceptible varieties generally were replaced by resistant varieties in the northern spring wheat region of the United States and Canada, where stem rust had been common. Among the Hope and H-44 derivatives are Lee, Pilot, Rival, Newthatch, Mida, and Cadet (developed in the United States) and Redman,

Renown, Apex, and Regent (produced in Canada). Rust-resistant varieties grown in California include Baart 38, Baart 46, and Federation 38 which were produced from backcrosses that involved the Hope variety. Several stem rust-resistant winter wheats—which include Tenmarq, Pawnee, Comanche, Kawvale, Austin, and Seabreeze—are grown in the South Central states. These varieties are resistant to certain stem rust races but none, except Austin and Seabreeze, possesses the high degree of resistance found in spring wheat varieties [75]. All these varieties, however, are susceptible to Race 15B.

Several wheats from Kenya, Egypt, South Africa, and South America are resistant to stem rust Race 15B, but none is commercially acceptable in the United States or Canada. Consequently, breeders have had to transfer resistance to Race 15B into adapted varieties. Two bread wheats resistant to Race 15B as well as to many other races of stem rust are Selkirk (developed in Canada) and Willet (developed in the United States) [76]. Selkirk, however, is susceptible to certain biotypes of Race 15B [48].

In India, new wheats that proved resistant to stem rust in the 1946–47 epidemic were: NP 710, NP 775, NP 720, and NP 733 [80]. A new hybrid, NP 809, appears to have resistance to the prevalent races of stem rust as well as to other rusts in the hill country of India. Ridley, a variety introduced from Australia, also appears to be resistant to all of the rusts in India [70]. Stem rust-resistant wheat varieties grown in Australia include Gabo, Sabre, Saga, Hofed, Warigo, Glenwari, Lawrence, Panther, Fedweb 1 and 2, Celebration, and Spica [14].

Leaf Rust

The leaf rust disease, caused by a fungus (*Puccinia recondita*), is found all over the world, particularly in humid and subhumid regions [17]. It is more destructive in the eastern half of the United States, where weather conditions usually are favorable for its development, than in the irrigated areas of the Western states where—although usually present—it seldom does extensive damage.

Leaf rust of wheat occurs more frequently and usually affects larger acreages than does stem rust. It may cause much damage to some wheat varieties in certain regions when infections are heavy. In some years, leaf rust causes considerable damage in the hard red spring and hard red winter wheat regions. In 1938, a leaf rust epidemic in several states from Texas to Canada caused losses up to 30 per cent [78]. A Kansas study showed that Malakof (susceptible) was reduced in yield by 55.7 per cent, while Fulhard (resistant) suffered a loss of 22.3 per cent. The leaves of rusted plants died early, the weight of straw was decreased, and fewer and lighter kernels were produced [43]. When wheat plants are rusted in an

FIGURE 15-3. **Leaf rust of wheat. The leaf at the left shows light-colored flecks that indicate resistance.**
(*Courtesy US Department of Agriculture*)

early growth stage, the yield of a susceptible variety may be reduced as much as 94 per cent. Kernels are seldom shriveled, even when the wheat plant is severely damaged [46]. Protein percentage in the grains of susceptible varieties of both hard and soft winter wheats has been significantly reduced by severe infection [12].

The leaf rust fungus enters the wheat plant through the stomata. It manifests itself on the green plant as orange to orange-brown pustules which represent the red (uredial) or summer stage. These pustules are smaller than those of stem rust, more nearly round, and less likely to unite (Fig. 15-3). Leaf rust usually attacks the leaf blades and sheaths, but it sometimes occurs on the stem, glumes, and awns. The pustules are more numerous on the upper surface of the leaf than on the lower. Since the pustules are relatively small, they seldom rupture the epidermis. The pustules of the black or winter stage (telia) of leaf rust appear as the wheat plants approach maturity. The telial pustules are about the same size of those of the red stage, and appear to be a lead gray color because the black spores are almost always covered by the surface leaf tissues.

The red or summer stage continues as long as the wheat plants continue to grow. The orange-red pustules contain thousands of uredospores which are carried by the wind to other wheat plants, where they cause new infections. The red stage may recur every week in moist warm weather, and is able to overwinter in most areas in the United States where wheat is grown [68]. It can be found at all times of the year in the Southern states, but also in some years in the Northern states. When weather conditions in late summer or early fall are favorable, the red rust stage attacks volunteer wheat where it may remain over the winter. In the spring, the red rust spores increase rapidly when the weather is warm and moist and are blown to wheat plants [58]. Spores also may be carried northward from southern Texas and Mexico by winds during the early spring months. The process is reversed in the fall: red spores are blown southward where they cause infections on volunteer or fall-sown wheat. The aecial stage of leaf rust of wheat occurs on some species of meadow rue (*Thallictrum*), but this stage is of no practical importance in the United States [45], for native species are not infected under normal conditions.

Leaf rust can be controlled by applications of fine dusting sulfur, but usually 3, 4, or more treatments are necessary during the season. Because the rate of application is high (the sulfur dust must be replaced when washed off by frequent rains) and treatments must begin before the rust damage appears, the method is too expensive for practical use on a field scale in the United States.

The most practical method of controlling leaf rust is the breeding of resistant wheat varieties. Breeding for resistance is complicated by the existence of 183 known physiologic races of the fungus [44], at least 85 of which have been identified in the United States [58]. The five most common races found in this country from 1925–50 among identified isolates were: Race 9 (10.7 per cent), Race 128 (10.4 per cent), Race 126 (8.8 per cent), Race 5 (8.7 per cent), and Race 15 (6.8 per cent). The racial composition varied from year to year. Race 9 was predominant from 1925–40, Race 128 from 1941–45, and Race 126 from 1946–50 [53]. Many races are localized geographically; others are widely distributed.

In Australia, Races 26 and 95 were present in 63 per cent of leaf rust isolates. They were the only races in that country until 1946, but since then Races 135 AB, 135 BB, 138 AB, and 138 BB have appeared [101].

Wheat varieties resistant to some leaf rust races often are extremely susceptible to others. There is considerable leaf rust resistance in some North American varieties of soft red winter and hard red spring wheats [42]. Leaf rust resistance also has been found among some foreign wheat varieties, particularly some from Australia and South America [68]. Some selections from Kawvale × Marquillo and Hope × Hussar crosses have been highly resistant to leaf rust from the seedling stage to maturity. The most resistant wheat species are einkorn, Timopheevi, and most durums. Emmers vary from resistant to susceptible [78]. Timstein, a spring wheat, is resistant to leaf rust races that commonly occur in Kansas, *i.e.,* Races 5, 9, 15, 44, and 126. It was selected from what was first reported to be a *T. vulgare* variety Steinwedel × *T. timopheevi* cross [37].

Several leaf rust resistant wheat varieties, developed by plant breeders, have been released for commercial production in the eastern United States. Some of the more important ones are Vigo in Indiana, Saline in Illinois, Chancellor in Georgia, Atlas 50 and 66 in North Carolina, Anderson in North and South Carolina, and Coastal in South Carolina. Several hard red spring wheat varieties resistant to both leaf rust and stem rust are: Rival, Pilot, Regent, Newthatch, Mida, Rushmore, and Lee [58]. Lee, a selection from a Hope × Timstein cross, is resistant—both in the seedling and mature-plant stages—to 22 races of leaf rust [108]. Two hard red winter wheats, Ponca and Concho, have high resistance to leaf rust in the field. Some susceptible varieties, like Triumph and Wichita, often escape damage through early maturity [68].

Stripe Rust

Stripe rust of wheat (*Puccinia glumarum*), sometimes called yellow rust, was not recognized in the United States until 1915, but it had been collected as early as 1892. Stripe rust occurs sporadically over the western half of the United States, is prevalent in the cooler plains of Argentina, and is widespread in the cooler regions of Europe and in China, Japan, and India. In Europe, it causes more damage than does stem rust, but it has caused only negligible losses in the United States. It also attacks barley, rye, and more than 60 species of grasses.

Stripe rust may damage wheat when infection occurs during the milk stage or earlier. Infection in early growth stages reduces root and top growth as well as grain yield. There is a decrease in both size and number of heads. The results are similar to those of leaf rust, except that stripe rust also shrivels the kernels [6]. Badly rusted kernels may germinate poorly, but infection is not transmitted to plants grown from such seed [58].

Stripe rust develops most abundantly on the glumes, leaf blades, and leaf sheaths, but it also may attack the stems and kernels of wheat. Linear, narrow, yellow pustules (uredia) later coalesce in rows of various lengths to give the appearance of fairly narrow yellow stripes. Some of these pustules break through the epidermis. The fungus develops mycelia and uredospores abundantly on wheat or other susceptible grasses in late autumn. The mycelia, and occasionally the uredospores, remain viable over winter. In the spring, the rust develops until the wheat crop is mature unless checked by hot weather. Since an alternate host has never been found, the aecial stage is unknown. The black stage of stripe rust is formed after the yellow or summer stage, but may develop on the host plant at any time during the growing season. The black pustules (telia) also are produced more or less in rows that appear as long, narrow, dark-brown, or black stripes [58].

Dry hot summers or dry cold winters probably limit the spread of stripe rust. Considerable sunshine is necessary for spore production, but temperatures above 20°C (68°F) seem to result in poor infection.

The growing of resistant varieties is the most practical control for stripe rust. Many common American wheat varieties are resistant, and most club wheats are susceptible, but the durum wheats tend to be resistant [7]. Several stripe rust-resistant varieties have been developed in India. The variety NP 809, grown in the hill country of northern India, is resistant to stripe rust as well as to stem and leaf rusts. Another variety, NP 770, developed from a cross between a Japanese wheat (Kononso) and the NP 4 Indian variety, has a high resistance to stripe rust. It is grown at the higher elevations in the Indian hills [70]. Three races of the stripe rust fungus have been identified in North America. A total of eleven races have been reported in India [80].

WHEAT SMUTS

The principal smuts that attack wheat are bunt or stinking smut (*Tilletia caries,* formerly *T. tritici,* and *T. foetida,* formerly *T. levis*), loose smut (*Ustilago tritici*), and flag smut (*Urocystis tritici*). Bunt is the most widely distributed as well as the most destructive.

Bunt or Stinking Smut

Bunt or stinking smut (*Tilletia caries* and *T. foetida*) is found on wheat all over the world, but generally is more prevalent in the drier regions. In India, bunt is restricted to the cooler regions of 5000 feet or more in elevation [80]. Bunt is particularly destructive in regions where the spores overwinter in the soil, as in the Pacific Northwest of the United States, in Australia, and in some parts of India. A distinct type or race of *T. caries,* known as dwarf bunt, occurs in North America in the Pacific Northwest, but it also is found in Wyoming, Colorado, and New York [40]. A third species of bunt, *T. indica,* occurs in India [66]. The published information on bunt has been summarized by various authorities [106, 38, 25].

Bunt apparently has been a plague of wheat since the crop was first cultivated. It is still an economic threat in wheat production, especially for winter wheat. Bunt causes a reduction in yield as well as an inferior quality of grain. The loss in yield due to bunt averages 1.3 per cent in the United States [40], but it ranges from 1–10 per cent in India [80]. In highly susceptible varieties the reduction in yield is nearly equal to the percentage of smutty heads [30, 51]. In eastern Washington, each 1 per cent of smut reduced yields by an average of 0.77 per cent [81]. Growers also suffer losses when the market price of the wheat is discounted because of smut balls, darkened kernels, and offensive, fishy, smutty odor. Smut-contaminated wheat must be washed before it can be milled. Clouds of bunt spores are a fire or explosion hazard during threshing.

Common bunt shortens the plants to as much as half the height of normal plants. Plants infected with dwarf bunt are one-half to one-fourth the height of healthy plants. Dwarf bunt stimulates excessive tillering of infected wheat plants [39]. Smutted wheat heads usually are bluish-green or grayish-green in color before they mature. Diseased heads tend to be more lax and to ripen sooner than healthy ones. The wheat awns on infected plants either may fail to develop or may drop off.

In most regions, the bunt fungus is carried over from one wheat crop to the next as black spores on the seed or as smut balls (Fig. 15-4) mixed with the seed. In regions with little summer rainfall, as in the Pacific and Intermountain states, airborne bunt spores carried to summer-fallowed fields at harvest time remain viable on the soil. After the fall rains, the bunt spores germinate along with fall-sown wheat and infect the young seedlings. Spores of common bunt in the soil perish in less than one year, whereas those of dwarf bunt may remain viable for seven years [40]. The greatest infection occurs at soil temperatures between 43–59°F [51]. The fungus grows within the infected wheat seedlings, keeping pace with the development of the wheat plant. At maturity, smut balls with a gray or grayish-brown coat and completely filled with black spores are formed in place of the wheat kernel.

Bunt can be controlled by treating seeds with fungicides such as hexachlorbenzene, copper carbonate, Ceresan M, and Arasan where the soil is not infested. Copper carbonate dust usually is applied to the seed in a treating machine at the rate of 2–3 ounces per bushel, whereas Ceresan M is applied at the rate of 0.5 ounce per bushel (Fig. 15-5). Slurry treatments, in a special machine which eliminates the hazards of dust treatments, are applied in a concentrated water suspension or slurry in such small amounts that the seed is not appreciably wetted. The Panogen fungicide is applied as a concentrated liquid at the rate of 0.75 fluid ounce per bushel of seed. Most fungicides are only partly effective in the control of common bunt where the soil is contaminated with spores, but two ounces per bushel of 40 per cent hexachlorbenzene controls both seed and soil infestation [74]. Dwarf bunt cannot be controlled by seed treatment because of heavy soil infestation where it occurs, but applications of hexachlorbenzene in the drill row during seeding are partly effective.

Losses from bunt are considerably decreased by growing resistant wheat varieties, although such varieties may be susceptible to certain phys-

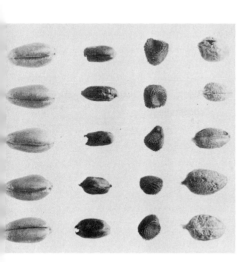

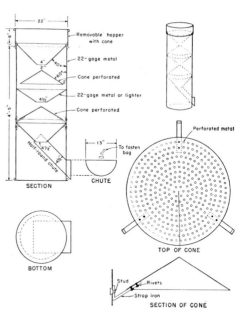

FIGURE 15-4. **Left to right: Sound wheat, nematode galls, cockle seeds, bunt balls.**

(*Courtesy US Department of Agriculture*)

FIGURE 15-5. **Construction of gravity seed treater for applying dust seed disinfectants.**

(*Courtesy US Department of Agriculture*)

iologic races of the fungus. About 25 races are recognized in the United States [40]. Several varieties of white common or club wheat—including Omar, Brevor, Burt, and Gaines—are resistant to groups of physiological races of bunt. Hard red winter wheats with resistance to some race or races of bunt include Comanche, Pawnee, Nebred, Oro, Ridit, Rio, Minturki, Marmin, Yogo, Minter, Relief, Cache, and Wasatch [47]. Bunt-resistant spring wheats include Pilot, Renown, Regent, and Rival. Wheat varieties grown commercially in the Pacific Northwest that are resistant to some races of dwarf bunt include Omar and Gaines, as well as Relief, Wasatch, Cache, Hymar, and Rex [39].

In Kansas, losses from bunt are reduced by seeding winter wheat as soon as possible after the Hessian-fly-free date while soil temperatures are generally high [68].

Loose Smut

Loose smut, caused by the fungus *Ustilago tritici,* may occur wherever wheat is grown, but it is most abundant under humid, subhumid, and irrigated conditions. The disease is generally distributed in eastern North America.

FIGURE 15-6. **Healthy wheat head (left), with 3 stages of loose smut spore shedding.**

(*Courtesy US Department of Agriculture*)

Loose smut is of economic importance only where the summer humidity is high enough to insure floral infection of wheat. The losses it causes are less severe than those caused by bunt. Average infection seldom exceeds 1 per cent. In India, infection may be 20 per cent or more in some years [80]. In the United States, loose smut caused annual losses that ranged from 3–18 million bushels from 1917–39 [40].

The loose smut disease is first evident when the wheat plants head. Infected heads appear earlier than normal ones, and the florets are almost completely replaced by black smut masses. The spores are soon scattered by wind, rain, insects, and other agencies, and nothing remains of the wheat head except the naked rachis (Fig. 15-6).

Spores shed from smutted heads about the time normal heads are in bloom cause floral infection. Spores germinate in the flowers and form infection threads (mycelia) which grow down the pistil into the young kernel. Initial infection rarely occurs after the fertilized ovary has attained one-third of its mature size. Infected kernels cannot be distinguished from smut-free kernels. When infected wheat seed is sown, the loose smut fungus inside the seed starts to grow as the kernel germinates, and continues to develop within the wheat plant. When the heads emerge from the sheath, they are composed of smut masses which have replaced the kernels [90, 52].

Loose smut is best controlled by sowing smut-free seed. Surface seed disinfectants are ineffective in the control of loose smut because the fungus is within the kernel. The disease can be controlled by hot water seed treatment: the seed is soaked for 4–12 hours in cold water, then dipped in water at 120°F for one minute, then placed in a hot water tank at 129°F for 10 minutes, and finally dipped in cold water for one minute. The temperature in the hot water tank should never be allowed to rise above 131°F nor drop below 125°F. Treated seed is spread in a thin layer to dry. It can be sown as soon as it is dry enough to feed through a drill. Since the hot water method often is injurious to seed, it is advocated as a practical means for the elimination of loose smut from a few bushels of seed for use as a foundation seed supply. It is seldom used on the average farm or for large quantities of seed. Fair control also is obtained by steeping the seed for 6 hours in water followed by 72 hours storage in a full oil drum or other air-tight container [5]. In India, the grain is merely steeped for 24–30 hours at 20–24°C (68–75.2°F), and dried before sowing.

The growing of resistant wheat varieties restricts losses from smut. In the United States, 11 distinct races of the fungus have been reported [8], while two races have been identified in India [80]. Club wheats are relatively susceptible to loose smut, while durum wheats are generally resistant. Some resistant common wheat varieties grown in the United States are Forward, Fulhio, Kawvale, Leap, Valprize, Pilot, Ridit, and Pawnee. Dundee, Ford, and Gular are resistant to at least one race of loose smut in Australia [14]. Wheat varieties resistant to the two races of loose smut found in India are NP 114, NP 120, NP 165, and NP 710 [80].

Flag Smut

Flag smut, caused by *Urocystis tritici,* occurs chiefly on winter wheat, in most of the major countries where wheat is grown. It has caused heavy losses only in Australia, where it was recognized before 1868. Flag smut is a very important disease in China, especially in the northern wheat-growing regions [107], and also occurs in Japan, India, South Africa, Italy, and Spain [42]. Its presence in the United States was first established in Illinois in 1919, and shortly afterwards it was found in localized areas in Missouri and Kansas. It was reported in central Washington in 1941 [40]. Two physiologic races have been reported in the United States.

Flag smut attacks only wheat, and it may cause yield losses of 10–20 per cent or more on susceptible varieties. Wheat plants infected with flag smut usually are dwarfed, with twisted leaf blades and sheaths marked by grayish-black stripes (Fig. 15-7). Infected plants rarely produce heads, but some smutted heads appear. At maturity, the dried-up diseased tissues become shredded, and the stripes rupture to expose the black spore masses. Symptoms may appear on infected plants any time from the fourth-leaf stage up to the heading stage. One or all culms of a plant may be infected [40].

FIGURE 15-7. **Wheat leaves infested with flag smut spores.**
(*Courtesy US Department of Agriculture*)

The flag smut spores are carried to the next wheat crop both on the seed and in the soil of infested fields. Wheat seedlings become infected during germination, usually before the seedlings emerge from the soil [32]. Systemic development of the fungus within the plant follows. The cycle is completed with the production of spore masses in diseased tissues. The spores are disseminated by wind, man, animals, or harvest machinery [52, 40].

The flag smut spores germinate at temperatures of 40–80°F, and soil temperatures of 57–70°F are favorable for infection [40]. In Australia, flag smut infection often is serious on light sandy soils which contain little organic matter [10].

Flag smut can be controlled by the same seed treatments used for bunt when the seed is planted in noninfested soil, but seed treatments with fungicides are ineffective against soil-borne spores. The growing of resistant wheat varieties offers the most practical means of control. Soft red winter wheats highly resistant to flag smut include Trumbull, Fulhio, Kawvale, and Fulcaster. Resistant hard red winter wheat varieties include Cheyenne, Kanred, Turkey, and Tenmarq. Harvest Queen, Gypsy, Red Wave, Jones Fife, and Fultz are among the susceptible soft wheat varieties [32, 52]. In Australia, crop rotations in which wheat is sown on the same field only every third year, have provided adequate control for flag smut [10].

POWDERY MILDEW

Powdery mildew (*Erysiphe graminis tritici*) is found in many wheat-growing countries and may cause considerable damage under moist cool conditions. At present, it is a major disease of winter wheat in the southeastern United States. It may cause considerable damage in Kansas in wet seasons, particularly on low fields.

Heavy attacks of powdery mildew reduce the size of wheat kernels and the yield of grain, particularly when infection occurs between the tillering and jointing stages of the wheat plant.

Powdery mildew is most conspicuous on the leaf blades, but it also may develop on the sheaths and on the floral bracts. Diseased parts become covered with a white or gray powdery mass of fungus tissue which often covers the entire blade. As the disease progresses, affected leaves turn yellow and gradually become dry. Late in the spring the small fruiting bodies (perithecia) of the fungus may be found imbedded in the gray fungus mats.

Powdery mildew is carried over from year to year by the perithecia of the fungus. These contain the ascospores which cause the initial infection of the next generation of wheat seedlings. Conidia soon develop which are disseminated by wind, rain, and insects to cause new infections.

Nine physiologic races of powdery mildew on wheat have been identified in the southeastern United States [54]. Several races also occur in Canada, Argentina, and Germany.

Increased damage from powdery mildew in the southeastern United States followed the emergence of new races of the pathogen, while more general application of nitrogen fertilizers probably also contributed to the increased incidence of the disease. The growing of resistant wheat varieties is the most practical control for the disease. Spring wheats resistant to Races 1, 2, and 3, are Chul, Converse, Indian, Sturgeon, and *Triticum timopheevi*. Michigan Amber Selection is a winter variety resistant to the same races [91]. Sulfur dusts or other fungicides used for the control of wheat rusts also will control powdery mildew, but their use generally is uneconomical.

MOSAICS

Soil-borne mosaic and streak mosaic are important virus diseases of wheat in the United States, and also infect some other grasses.

Soil-borne Mosaic

Soil-borne wheat mosaic occurs in Illinois, Indiana, Iowa, Kansas, Maryland, Missouri, Nebraska, North Carolina, Oklahoma, South Carolina, and Virginia [63]. It has been found in nearly half of the counties of Illinois [49]. The disease was first identified on Harvest Queen wheat in Illinois in 1919. It was called "wheat rosette" until it was found to be caused by a soil-borne virus [61, 104]. A similar soil-borne wheat mosaic has been reported from Japan [93].

Soil-borne wheat mosaic sometimes causes extensive damage to susceptible wheat varieties [60]. In eastern Kansas, yield reductions of 5–13 per cent occurred in some fields in 1952, but losses averaged 15–25 per cent in some diseased spots in 1954 [68].

FIGURE 15-8. **Wheat plants: Healthy (left), stunted by soil-borne mosaic (center), rosette phase of soil-borne mosaic (right).**

(*Courtesy US Department of Agriculture*)

The disease in wheat fields is most noticeable in the spring, when it appears as yellowish to light-green areas caused by irregular streaks and blotches on the leaves. In some varieties, the mosaic produces a rosette condition in which the leaves and tillers remain short (Fig. 15-8). In other varieties of wheat, the plants are severely stunted with few stems and heads, short heads, delayed maturity, and lightweight kernels. Soil-borne mosaic is dangerous only for wheat, barley, and rye. Spring-sown wheats seldom are damaged [49].

Yellow and green types of the soil-borne wheat mosaic virus have been described. Yellow mosaic is characterized by yellowish-green mottled and striped leaves; dwarfed plants; and excessive tillering in some varieties. Green mosaic is identified by the mild light-green mosaic condition, but the plants also are rosetted [62, 63]. When the two viruses occur together in Japan, affected wheat plants have composite symptoms [93].

Cool weather with soil temperatures near 60°F, together with comparatively high soil moisture, favor infection [63]. The virus persists in the soil for a year or even up to 12 years. Insect carriers or other vectors are unknown. The disease is not carried on seed, but it can be carried to other fields by wind-borne dust [49].

The most satisfactory control for soil-borne mosaic is the growing of resistant wheat varieties. Resistant soft red winter wheat varieties for Illinois include Royal, Vigo, Saline, Seneca, and Newcaster. The Pawnee and Westar hard red winter wheats have moderate resistance. In Kansas, both Comanche and Concho hard red winter wheats are resistant to this mosaic disease [68]. Crop rotation is not considered an adequate control measure [49].

Streak Mosaic

Wheat streak mosaic is a destructive virus disease in western Kansas, has damaged wheat in Nebraska, South Dakota, and Colorado, and has been found in Wyoming, Oklahoma, Iowa, Arizona, California, and Canada.

Streak mosaic has been present in Kansas at least since 1929, but the first severe outbreak occurred in 1949 when it caused a loss of 7 per cent of the Kansas wheat crop and much damage in Nebraska. Outbreaks also occurred in Kansas in 1951 and 1954 when yield reductions in infested fields ranged from 20–70 per cent or more [68].

Wheat streak mosaic is spread by the Eriophyid or wheat curl mite (*Aceria tulipae*). The virus is neither soil-borne nor seed-borne.

Streak mosaic is most evident in the spring, when winter wheat starts to grow. The first symptoms is a faint green mottling of the leaves, followed by the appearance of light-colored streaks along the veins and stunting of the plants. Chlorosis becomes more pronounced as the disease progresses. Infected plants have yellowish-green to markedly yellow mottled and striped leaves. Infected plants produce either poorly filled heads with shriveled kernels or no heads at all [87].

Streak mosaics overwinters in live diseased wheat plants or in some perennial grasses. Wheat plants that volunteer before or immediately after harvest maintain the disease and favor the multiplication of mites during the summer months. Then the virus is carried to early fall-sown wheat. Apparently, the virus is unable to live in stubble or in dead plant remains [87].

The most effective control for streak mosaic is to sow winter wheat at the latest recommended date for the area. This aids the young wheat plants to escape the early-fall infection by the mites. Destruction of volunteer wheat and weedy grasses helps to eliminate host plants. No known wheat variety is resistant to severe outbreaks of the disease.

Barley Stripe Mosaic

Barley stripe mosaic is a virus disease that also attacks wheat. Since the disease is seed-borne in wheat, it can be transmitted simply by sowing seed that was harvested from diseased plants.

Barley stripe mosaic on wheat in Montana caused moderate to severe reduction in plant height, total culms, dry-matter production, and test weight. It also caused an average grain yield reduction of 32.8 per cent. The protein content of wheat from diseased areas was higher than that from healthy plots [65]. Because of their poorer growth, diseased plants absorbed less soil nitrogen than did healthy plants [3]. The application of nitrogen fertilizer to irrigated land actually increased development of the disease.

FUSARIAL HEAD BLIGHT OR SCAB

This disease is most prevalent on wheat in temperate humid to sub-humid areas. It is particularly destructive in the North Central states where it also attacks barley, rye, and some grasses.

This disease reduces the stand, yield, and quality of wheat (Fig. 15-9), especially when the relative humidity and temperature are high after the plants head. Serious epidemics of the disease occurred in the United States in 1919, 1928, and 1935, with heavy damage in some regions in other seasons [78]. Grain that contains 5 per cent or more of badly scabbed kernels, when fed to hogs, causes vomiting, loss of appetite, and arrested growth [23, 24].

FIGURE 15-9. **Healthy wheat plants and grain (left), scab-diseased plants and scabbed grain (right).**

(Courtesy US Department of Agriculture)

Head blight develops on wheat in warm humid weather at any stage from kernel formation to maturity. Infected spikelets first show a water-soaked appearance, then become yellow, and finally turn a bleached-straw color. Often the entire head becomes infected. A pink cast generally can be detected, especially at the base and in the crease of the kernel. Infected kernels are shriveled and scabby due to tufts of white to pink mycelium. The disease pathogens also cause a seedling blight, characterized by light-brown to reddish-brown lesions that appear before or after seedling emergence. Crown and culm rot may occur as the plants approach maturity.

The fungus most commonly associated with fusarial head blight on wheat is *Gibberella zeae*. The conidial stage is *Fusarium graminearum*. Another species often associated with the disease is *F. culmorum*. The disease is carried from season to season on the seed and on old crop refuse, such as cornstalks.

Partial control measures for fusarial head blight include crop rotation, suitable soil preparation, early seeding, and seed treatment. The disease is most severe when wheat follows corn in rotation. Complete coverage of stubble or other crop refuse when plowing aids considerably in the control of head blight. Seed treatment with organic mercury compounds generally will control seedling blight. Wheat varieties differ somewhat in susceptibility to head blight, but no known variety is highly resistant. Most durum wheats are more susceptible than common wheats [19].

CROWN, FOOT, AND ROOT ROTS

Some of the more important crown, foot, and root rot diseases that attack wheat include take-all, Pythium root rot, Helminthosporium crown and root rot, snow mold, Rhizoctonia blight, and foot or culm rot caused by *Cercosporella* and *Leptosphaeria*. Injury to the host plant usually is confined to the underground parts, although symptoms may be evident in other parts of the plant.

Take-all

Take-all, caused by *Ophiobolus graminis,* is a world-wide disease of wheat, but it is particularly serious in the United States, Canada, and Australia. All varieties of wheat are susceptible to take-all. It is a major disease of wheat in Australia, where it reduces the wheat yields 50 per cent in some fields [11]. In the United States, take-all generally occurs in the drier winter wheat region of the Southwestern and Northwestern states. It is a serious disease in Kansas, where losses as high as 95 per cent have been reported in some fields [68]. The greatest losses seem to occur on porous, light-textured, alkaline soils where winter wheat culture is continuous or associated with grass culture [31].

Wheat is the most susceptible of the cereals to the take-all disease. When wheat is 100 per cent infected in Australia, barley may show 60 per cent, rye 25 per cent, and oats 4 per cent of infected plants [79].

Wheat plants attacked by take-all at first become yellow, then wilt, turn ash-gray in color, and die. This may occur at any time between the seedling and mature stages. Diseased plants are stunted in different degrees and occur in patches in the field. The heads, when present, turn white (hence the name "white-heads"). Kernels of diseased plants are slightly to badly shriveled. The bases of the culms of severely infected plants are blackened. Plants killed by take-all have decayed roots [68].

The take-all fungus lives over in the soil in association with residues and roots of cereals and grasses. The active mycelia can penetrate the roots, crowns, and culms of living wheat plants. Agencies that move soil particles or plant debris may carry infestation of take-all. Infected roots of live host plants appear to be most effective in the dissemination of the disease to a new location [28]. The fungus may remain viable for over two years in either moist or dry soil [27].

The optimum soil temperature for the development of take-all is approximately 24°C (75.2°F). The prevalence of the disease varies with the summer rainfall in Saskatchewan, Canada, and with spring rainfall in South Australia, but little damage is caused unless the rainfall exceeds 10–12 inches in three months [31].

Take-all can be reduced materially by crop rotations which include nonsusceptible crops such as alfalfa, sweetclover, flax, and corn. The land should be kept out of susceptible crops such as wheat, barley, rye, and some grasses for at least three years before it is returned to wheat [68]. Experiments in Australia have shown that a long period of fallow or rotation with oats tended to minimize take-all damage [1]. Fertilization to maintain ample available phosphorus and nitrogen also has reduced losses [88].

Pythium Root Rot

Pythium root rot, caused by *Pythium arrhenomanes* and other *Pythium* species, occurs in the United States, Canada, Brazil, India, Italy, and probably exists in other countries where wheat or other cereals are grown. The fungus is widespread in the northern Great Plains, is present in the Pacific coast states of the United States, and prevalent in the prairie provinces of Canada [83].

Pythium root rot causes considerable damage to wheat under moist soil conditions, especially when the crop is grown under continuous culture or following a grass crop. The causal fungus is soil-borne.

Wheat plants infected by pythium root rot generally show a lack of vigor, as well as discoloration of the leaves, short straw, lack of tillering, delayed maturity, and poor spike exsertion. Diseased plants seldom are killed outright. Infected roots develop reddish-brown lesions, and the fine rootlets are destroyed. The disease, which rarely attacks the crown or basal stem tissues, is characterized in Canada by a browning of the lower wheat leaves in early June [9].

Control measures for pythium root rot of wheat are inadequate. All known varieties are susceptible under conditions favorable for the disease. In Canada, the disease can be reduced by applications of phosphate fertilizers. The disease appears to be worse in crops after fallow than in those sown on stubble land, because fallow increases the amount of available nitrogen in the soil [31].

Helminthosporium Crown and Root Rot

Helminthosporium crown and root rot, caused by *Helminthosporium sativum* and other species, is widely distributed in countries where wheat is grown. It also attacks other cereals and many grasses. *H. sativum* has been reported as the most important root fungus that attacks wheat in North Dakota. It may reduce stands and lower the yields of wheat.

Symptoms of the disease on wheat include a seedling blight with dark-brown lesions on the coleoptile, as well as a crown and root rot that develops below the soil surface in older plants. A leaf blotch also may occur. Diseased plants have weakened root systems. The black-point disease of the wheat kernel is partly due to the same fungus.

Injury from this fungus varies with environmental conditions, but it is most severe under continuous wheat culture.

The principal control measures are seed treatment, crop rotation, and field sanitation.

Snow Mold

Snow mold is a fungus disease common on winter wheat and on other winter cereals in northern Europe, Asia, and in the Pacific Northwest of the United States. The disease has been destructive in Idaho and central Washington in recent years, and may cause considerable damage to winter wheat.

Two types of snow mold in the Pacific Northwest are caused by soil-borne fungi. Pink snow mold is caused by *Fusarium nivale* (Perithecial stage, *Calonectria graminicola*), while spotted snow mold is caused by *Typhula itoana* and *T. idahoensis*. The occurrence of the two diseases together in the same region is unusual. The disease usually follows a heavy unfrozen snow cover [59].

Pink snow mold is characterized by salmon-pink colored mold growth that appears on the leaf and crown tissues of winter wheat as the snow melts in the spring. The leaves of affected wheat plants are not flattened on the soil surface. The mold disappears rapidly after growth starts in the spring. The affected leaves dry to a dead rusty color [59].

Spotted snow mold is characterized by light to dark-brown sclerotia dispersed on bleached or dead leaves and stems flattened on the ground. The winter wheat plants apparently are infected under the snow where portions of the leaves appear scalded and discolored in spots. As the snow disappears, layers of the white fungus growth appear on the infected plants. Soon the infected leaves lose their color, dry out, and become matted on the ground. Plants are killed by the dead leaf tissue as well as by the rotted culms, crowns, and roots [59].

Snow mold causes much less damage to winter wheat when the ground freezes before it is covered with snow. Optimum temperatures for most snow mold organisms are 48–51°F, and the fungi cease activity as soon as the temperature reaches 52°F [59]. The disease seems to be favored by heavy alkaline soils with a high moisture content [31].

The control methods for snow mold include the growing of adapted hardy winter varieties, good soil drainage, and the rotation of wheat with alfalfa or sweetclover with a maximum of three wheat crops before the land is returned to legumes. In western Idaho, winter wheat should be drilled between August 15 and September 1. Early-seeded plants with a good fall growth are apparently better able to recover from snow mold damage. A spring application of nitrogen fertilizer at the rate of 20 pounds of actual nitrogen per acre also was recommended to aid plant recovery from snow mold [83, 59].

Other Root-rot Diseases

Cercosporella root rot is prevalent in the United States only in the Columbia Basin of the Pacific Northwest. This root rot, caused by the fungus, *Cercosporella herpetrichoides* (sometimes called foot rot or stem break) attacks wheat, barley, and rye. It may be the same as *Leptosphaeria herpotrichoides,* the cause of the destructive stem break of winter wheat in northern Europe [18]. Infected plants tend to fall over as the heads fill. This results in patches of lodged and tangled plants. The disease causes eyespot lesions at the base of the culms and rot around the roots in the upper crown nodes. Cercosporella root rots usually are most severe under moist soil conditions, high precipitation, and high humidity. Destructive attacks follow when heavy rains occur in early or midspring of the crop season [82]. The disease may be controlled by delayed fall seeding of wheat in crop rotations that include legumes and spring grains.

Rhizoctonia blight, caused by *Rhizoctonia solani,* is world-wide in distribution, but it is a minor disease on wheat. The disease occurs in patches in which affected plants are stunted. The plants may be killed or so weakened that maturity is delayed. Tan-colored lesions occur on the roots and the basal leaf sheaths. Control measures consist of crop rotation and maintenance of a balanced soil fertility [25].

Other root rots of wheat are caused by *Fusarium* species, particularly *F. culmorum* and *F. graminearum.* Fusarium root rot usually is most destructive in the spring wheat region. The percentage of seed infected with

Fusarium species is closely associated with the percentage of germination, stand, amount of seedling blight, and number of stunted and deformed plants [18].

OTHER WHEAT DISEASES

Septoria blight or blotch, caused by *Septoria* species, occurs on wheat throughout the world. The disease was widespread in Australia in New South Wales in the wet year of 1950. It attacks wheat over much of the eastern United States when weather conditions favor the fungus. Septoria blight causes spots or blotches on infected plant parts. *Septoria tritici* usually attacks the leaves, while *S. modorum* attacks the leaves, culms, and heads. Damage to the wheat crop largely results from shriveled kernels and lodged plants. The only control measures for the disease are crop rotation, plowing under old straw, and the growing of resistant varieties [24, 25]. The Xonduct variety is resistant to *S. tritici* in Australian fields [14].

Ergot (*Claviceps purpurea*) is found on wheat, other small grains, and on grasses in the humid to subhumid wheat regions of the world. It is most prevalent in the United States in the spring wheat region. The fungus is destructive on durum wheat and on some varieties of hard red spring wheat, but it seldom attacks other wheats. Since ergot spreads from grasses to the cereal crops, neither crop rotation nor ergot-free seed will completely control the disease. Other control measures include the destruction of grasses in grain fields, especially quack grass, brome grass, and the wheat grasses; and mowing grasses near grain fields before they head [24].

Black chaff is a bacterial disease caused by *Xanthomonas translucens* f. sp. *undulosa*. It is widely distributed on wheat, but usually causes only slight damage. It occurs in the United States in the Midwest where it may cause losses of the wheat crop in seasons of excessive moisture. The most characteristic feature of black chaff is the brown to purple-black blotches on the glumes and on the stems just below the heads. Severe cases of the disease shrivel the grain. The bacteria are carried on the seed as well as on diseased plant tissues where they may remain alive for as long as two years. Control measures include seed treatment with organic mercury fungicides and crop rotation [68].

Basal glume rot (*Pseudomonas atrofaciens*) is a bacterial disease that occurs in most of the wheat-growing regions of the world, especially where moisture is abundant at the time the crop is heading. The disease is characterized by a black tip of the kernel at the germ end. A light brown rot develops at the base of the glumes. Crop rotation will aid in control of the disease [68].

A yellow leaf spot of wheat (*Helminthosporium tritici-vulgaris*) was reported first in Pennsylvania and Virginia, but it has now spread westward into the hard red winter wheat areas of Kansas and Nebraska. Fusiform spots on the leaf blades are yellowish to dark brown in color, followed later by spreading indefinite areas of dead tissue. The disease is of minor importance because it is not severe on most wheat varieties [24].

Karnal bunt (*Neovossia indica* or *Tilletia indica*) is a smut fungus that damages wheat in parts of India. The disease symptoms are similar to those for covered smut, except that usually only a part of the mature kernel is affected. The loss in grain yields is seldom more than 1 to 5 per cent in India. The spores remain viable in the soil for two years. The disease can be controlled by seed treatment and crop rotation [80].

B. INSECT PESTS

Wheat may be attacked by numerous insect pests. Severe losses occur somewhere every year, and in nearly all wheat-growing areas in some years. The principal insects that attack the wheat plant are the Hessian fly, wheat jointworm, wheat-stem sawfly, wheat strawworm, greenbugs and other aphids, several species of grasshoppers, Mormon crickets, wireworms, chinch bugs, wheat-stem maggot, cutworms, stinkbugs, billbugs, and armyworms. Several other insects seriously damage wheat in storage.

GENERAL METHODS OF INSECT CONTROL

Much of the loss to the wheat crop from insect pests can be prevented by proper cropping practices. The destruction of volunteer wheat and associated weeds will aid in the control of some insects, particularly the Hessian fly and some migratory aphids, and is a desirable practice where it will not increase soil erosion. Crop rotation reduces damage to wheat by some insect pests, particularly the Hessian fly, wheat strawworm, and other insects that attack few other plants. Alternate wheat and summer fallow often accomplishes the same purpose in the arid wheat regions. Soil tillage destroys insects or exposes them to cold, birds, or other enemies. Delayed seeding is an important control measure for insects like the Hessian fly. Timeliness of application is important when chemicals are used for insect control. Generally young insects are more easily killed than full-grown ones [69].

HESSIAN FLY

The Hessian fly (*Phytophaga destructor*) is one of the most serious insect enemies of wheat in the United States, particularly east of the 100th meridian. It also occurs in California and in the Pacific Northwest. The insect is believed to have been brought to Long Island during the Revolutionary War by Hessian troops in their straw bedding. The Hessian fly also is found in Canada, North Africa, Europe, Asia, and New Zealand.

Hessian fly damage to wheat occurs in the fall and spring. Losses in yield are heavy when serious outbreaks occur. In the fall, the larvae may kill many tillers and young plants. Fall damage results in a thinner stand. In the spring, wheat culms weakened by infestation break over somewhat before harvest. Many infested culms remain erect, but the heads on such culms often yield 25–30 per cent less than heads on uninfested culms [69].

The fall generation of Hessian fly, which usually inflicts the greatest damage to the wheat crop, begins with the deposition of eggs by the adult fly on the young leaves of the wheat plant (Fig. 15-10). The adult female lives only a few hours. The maggots, which hatch from the eggs in a few days, crawl down between the leaf sheath and stem. There they feed on the plant juices for nine or more days. After the maggots have attained full growth, they transform into the inactive puparium or "flaxseed" stage. In

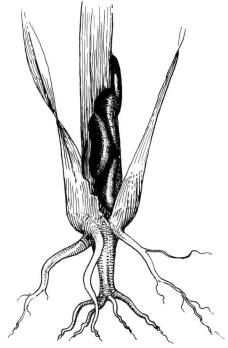

FIGURE 15-10. **Adult Hessian fly resting on wheat stem (left), and larvae or maggots (right).**

(*Courtesy US Department of Agriculture*)

the spring, or sooner when conditions are favorable, the flaxseed changes into a pupa and then into the adult fly. The female fly deposits eggs on young wheat plants to start another generation. Ordinarily, there are only two or three broods a year, but in Kansas as many as five broods have been recorded in a 12-month period. Wheat is the principal host plant of the Hessian fly, but it can mature on most varieties of barley, rye, and on a few wild grasses [41, 69].

Weather conditions that favor wheat also favor the Hessian fly. This insect requires fairly moist mild conditions. Abundant volunteer wheat also favors the increase of this insect. Hot dry weather lengthens the life cycle of the Hessian fly which often reduces infestations [69].

The most practical control measure is to seed winter wheat late enough so that the main brood of flies will have emerged and died before the young wheat plants emerge [99]. Tests generally have shown that the safe or "fly-free" date for seeding winter wheat to escape fly injury (Fig. 13-4) in years of normal rainfall usually coincides closely with the proper time of seeding the crop to obtain maximum grain yields. There is an increased hazard of yield reduction due to winter killing in extremely late seeding [96, 41]. Other effective cultural practices include crop rotation, plowing of wheat stubble soon after harvest to prevent infestation of the new crop, and destruction of all volunteer wheat as soon as it sprouts, in order to prevent an increase of flies during the summer.

Another important control measure for Hessian fly is to grow resistant adapted varieties of wheat. Resistant wheats infested with Hessian fly at the first-leaf stage undergo little stunting of subsequently developed leaves. Normal growth of resistant leaves appears to be detrimental to the larvae [15]. Dual, a soft red winter wheat variety highly resistant to Hessian fly in the eastern United States, is grown from Missouri to Maryland. It provides protection from both fall and spring broods of Hessian fly, gives increased grain yields from more timely planting, and permits safe early seeding for pasture [13]. In the hard red winter wheat region, Pawnee has considerable resistance to the Hessian fly, while Ponca is highly resistant in Kansas [69]. Some resistant California varieties are Big Club 43, Poso 44, and Poso 48 [78].

WHEAT JOINTWORM

As a wheat pest, the wheat jointworm (*Harmolita tritici*) ranks next to the Hessian fly in the majority of the states east of the Mississippi River. It also occurs in Utah, California, Oregon, Montana, Iowa, Kansas, Missouri, Oklahoma, North Dakota, and South Dakota.

In some years, the wheat jointworm causes losses of millions of bushels of wheat. The damage to wheat from lodging of infested straws varies from slight injury to total destruction. Hard woody galls, usually formed just above the second or third culm nodes, weaken the stem so that they later lodge or break. Moreover, the kernels are smaller than normal [72].

The wheat jointworm is the larva or grub of a wasp that resembles a small black ant with wings. One generation is produced per year. In April or May, the adult females insert their eggs in the stems of wheat plants above the nodes. The larvae, which hatch from the eggs in about 12 days, feed on the juices of the wheat plant. They mature just before the wheat ripens, but remain in the stubble after harvest. By November or December, the larvae transform to pupae. The adults emerge from the pupae in April or May. The mated females search for growing wheat in which to lay their eggs.

Large numbers of larvae and pupae are killed when the galls are exposed to unusually wet conditions in cold winter weather. Emergence of the adults is early in warm sunny springs, but late in cool cloudy springs in Oregon [16].

The wheat jointworm can be controlled by plowing wheat stubble under so deep that the adult jointworms are unable to emerge. This is impractical where grass, clover, or some other legume is seeded with wheat, except where heavy infestations occur. Rye may be substituted for wheat in the Northern states where the jointworm is abundant [72]. Insecticides have been ineffective against the jointworm. None of the commercial wheat varieties now grown is resistant to the pest.

WHEAT-STEM SAWFLY

The wheat-stem sawfly (*Cephus cinctus*) has become a pest of major importance in the prairie provinces of Canada, as well as in Montana and North Dakota. The insect originally lived in the native grasses of North America, but with the conversion of the grasslands to cereal production, the sawfly adopted wheat as one of its primary hosts [2, 26].

The sawfly frequently causes severe damage to the wheat crop, particularly in the prairie provinces of Canada where the annual loss has been estimated at 20 million bushels [78]. This insect caused an estimated loss of about 2 million bushels of wheat in Montana in 1952 [64]. The chief loss is from broken stems which are difficult to harvest.

The adult female of the wheat-stem sawfly splits the wheat stem with a pair of sawlike oviposter appendages and then deposits an egg inside the stem. The cannibalistic larvae feed downward inside the stem. The final survivor chews a groove or ring just above the soil surface, which causes the stem to fall over.

The most practical control method for the wheat-stem sawfly is the growing of resistant varieties. Stem solidness is the only visible characteristic known to be associated with lessened sawfly damage. Durum wheats, which have solid stems, generally show more resistance to the sawfly than any other spring wheats [26]. The solid-stem character has been incorporated in the Rescue hard red spring wheat variety released in Canada in 1946. It was introduced into the United States a year later, and is now grown extensively in sawfly areas to reduce losses.

Cultural methods that reduce losses from sawfly damage include rotation of wheat with crops that the sawfly does not attack, such as barley, oats, corn, flax, or mustard; early harvest before many of the stems have fallen; and plowing the stubble under deeply so that the sawflies cannot emerge from it during the next summer. The practice of strip cropping in Canada and Montana, in which narrow strips of wheat alternate with strips of fallow, provides ideal conditions for the migration of the sawfly to the wheat crop. Late spring seeding reduces sawfly injury in Montana, but, to be effective, seeding would need to be postponed until after June 1 [64], which is too late for best wheat yields. Phosphorus applied alone or mixed with nitrogen was closely associated with an increase in the amount of sawfly damage on both winter and spring wheats. Plants that showed the most growth response from fertilizers had the highest percentage of infested and cut stems [56].

Similar pests, the black grain stem sawfly (*Cephus tabidus*) and the European wheat stem sawfly (*C. pygmacus*), occur in the Eastern-Central states [92].

WHEAT STRAWWORM

The wheat strawworm (*Harmolita grandis*) occurs in the United States wherever wheat is grown regularly from year to year. It often is a serious pest in the wheat-growing areas east of the Mississippi River, but it is an important wheat pest in other regions. It causes losses that range from slight injury to total destruction of the crop [73].

This insect has two generations each year. The spring form is most injurious to winter wheat. The female adult of the spring or first generation deposits its eggs in or near the embryonic wheat head when the young plants are only a few inches tall. The adult is an antlike shiny black insect, usually without wings. The light straw-colored larva develops within and near the base of the plant where it destroys the tiller. The tiller usually becomes bulblike at the point of infestation where the larva occupies a cavity. Finally the larva pupates, after which the winged adult of the second generation emerges. The second-generation adult lays its eggs on winter wheat in the bloom stage. The injury caused by this summer form is less severe except in spring wheat. The insect overwinters in the pupal stage in wheat straw. Propagation of the insect is favored by infested stubble left on the ground after the use of subsurface tillage implements and the one-way plow [73].

Since the wheat strawworm lives only on wheat, an effective control measure is to avoid planting wheat within 65–75 yards of wheat straw or stubble of the previous season. In Virginia, wheat can safely follow wheat on the same land when all stubble is plowed under after harvest. The land is then sown to cowpeas which are disked into the soil in time to seed winter wheat again. In Kansas, infestation in winter wheat has been reduced by growing varieties that mature earlier than Turkey. Where spring wheat is grown, all volunteer wheat should be destroyed when the pest is abundant in order to prevent reinfestation [73].

GREENBUGS AND OTHER APHIDS

The greenbug or spring grain aphis (*Toxoptera graminum*) occurs in most wheat-growing states. In some years it causes severe losses, especially in Texas, Oklahoma, Kansas, and Missouri. First reported in the United States in 1882, it is also known in Europe, Asia, Africa, and in North, Central and South America [69].

In outbreak years, the greenbug often appears suddenly in the early spring when it kills areas of wheat. The dead wheat in the center of a typical greenbug spot looks as though it had been scorched. The infested spot is surrounded by a narrow circle of wheat plants covered by active greenbugs. Later the spots may spread until most or all of the field is destroyed. Winged aphids may scatter to many fields. In Kansas, greenbugs sometimes accumulate behind the upper leaf sheath in May and June. This results in stunted, spindle-shaped wheat heads, with grains developed only in the center of the head. Plants in infested fields appear ragged. In cool fall weather, greenbugs may kill small wheat plants, stunt others, and prevent normal tillering. The greenbug also attacks oats, barley, and some grasses [69].

This insect is a small, green, plant louse. Adults as well as young bugs feed on wheat plants throughout their lives. Greenbugs reproduce very rapidly in the summer by vivipary (live birth). They reproduce later by eggs, with or without fertilization. Many generations may be produced in a year under favorable conditions. Greenbugs have lived through mild winters as far north as Kansas.

Greenbugs are most likely to become abundant when a cool moist summer is followed by a mild winter and a late cool spring. They can bring forth live young at a temperature of 40°F, but a prolonged temperature of 0°F at the ground level will kill many greenbugs [69].

Several different species of ladybird beetles feed on greenbugs as well as nabids, lacewing flies, and syrphid flies [22]. One parasite, a small wasp-like insect (*Aphidius testaceipes*), effectively keeps the greenbug in check in many seasons. These greenbug enemies are active when the temperatures go above 65°F.

Some control of the greenbug may be obtained by the destruction of all volunteer wheat, oats, and barley in the community during summer and fall [97]. Parathion sprays or dusts afford good greenbug control when applied at the rate of four ounces of actual parathion per acre. The best results are obtained when the temperature is at least 50°F at the time of application. Another effective chemical is tetraethyl pyrophosphate (TEPP) used at the rate of 4–5 ounces per acre when the temperature is 75°F or above. Treated wheat should not be pastured or cut for hay or grain for at least three days after the application of TEPP, or fifteen days after the use of parathion [69]. In irrigated wheat, treatments made as soon as possible after water is applied insure the best kill [22]. The Wichita, Denton, Early Blackhull, and Blackhull varieties of wheat are somewhat resistant to light or medium greenbug attacks [4].

GRASSHOPPERS

Several species of grasshoppers attack wheat and many other crops, but the four most important species are: the lesser migratory grasshopper (*Melanoplus mexicanus*), differential grasshopper (*M. differentialis*), two-striped grasshopper (*M. bivatlatus*), and the red-legged grasshopper (*M. femur-rubrum*). Grasshoppers are most destructive in the western United States where wheat is an important crop and the annual rainfall is 25 inches or less. Dry seasons favor the buildup of large populations.

Grasshoppers damage wheat chiefly by eating the leaves, stems, and sometimes the heads. Lesser migratory grasshoppers feed on leaves of the wheat plant until harvest. They live on weeds in the stubble until volunteer wheat plants develop. In the fall, they move from the stubble fields to wheat fields where they consume the young plants. In the spring, as the wheat heads emerge, grasshoppers tend to climb the stalks and gnaw the ripening kernels which are then shattered. Sometimes the heads are severed [69].

Most grasshoppers deposit their eggs enclosed in sacs about 1–2 inches below the soil surface of cropped, idle, or waste land. Egg-laying may extend from early summer until fall. The eggs usually hatch in the spring, but many eggs of the lesser migratory grasshopper hatch in August and September in Kansas. When hatched, the nymphs attack wheat plants immediately. Nymphs mature in 5–9 weeks [71, 69].

Plowing may destroy many grasshopper eggs. Most nymphs are unable to emerge when the eggs are plowed under 5–6 inches deep. Moldboard or disc plows with attachments to turn under the furrow slice are effective for the purpose. Volunteer grain on summer fallowed land should be destroyed. Some insecticides are highly effective for control, particularly aldrin, chlordane, dieldrin, toxaphene, and heptachlor. They may be applied as sprays, dusts, or in poisoned baits by ground equipment or airplane. In general, sprays are preferable to baits. The amount of actual toxicant to be applied per acre for different chemicals is as follows [69]:

Toxicant	Quantity		Days between Poison Application and use by Animals
Aldrin	1.5 to 2	oz.	15
Chlordane	0.5 to 1	lb.	30
Dieldrin	0.75 to 1	oz.	30
Heptachlor	3 to 4	oz.	10 to 15
Toxaphene	1 to 1.5	lb.	40

When dusts are used, the dosages of actual toxicants per acre should be increased about 50 per cent.

The Ceres, Pilot, and Rival hard red spring wheat varieties suffer less damage from grasshopper attacks than do Reward and Thatcher. Resistant varieties have more mechanical tissue in the hypodermal region of the culm 1 cm below the peduncle than did susceptible ones [36].

MORMON CRICKET

The Mormon cricket (*Anabrus simplex*) has been a periodic scourge to agriculture since the early settlement of the northern Great Plains, and the Intermountain, and Pacific coast states. It devours range grasses, small grains, and other crops. Probably the greatest financial losses occur in small-grain crops, especially wheat. Headed grain crops may be completely stripped of kernels [95].

The Mormon crickets are large wingless grasshoppers. Outbreak centers or holdover places are located in areas remote from cultivated crops. Under favorable conditions, the crickets increase to large numbers, form in bands, and migrate long distances on foot [20].

Mormon cricket control is effected by the use of poison bait, such as steamed rolled wheat mixed with a solution of one pound of toxaphene in 0.5 gallon of oil to each 100 pounds of wheat. The material usually is spread by aircraft or ground equipment at the rate of 3–5 pounds per acre. The bait is spread in holdover areas, or in strips across the front of cricket bands on the move [95].

TRUE WIREWORMS

Wheat is attacked by several species of true wireworms. The Great Basin wireworm (*Otenicera pruinina* var. *noxia*) destroys considerable wheat in the Pacific Northwest, particularly in areas with less than 15 inches of annual precipitation [50]. Some other species are adapted to higher moisture conditions.

In wheat fields, true wireworm injury is evident from the presence of dead plants in the fall or early spring [29]. These wireworms may attack the seed as it germinates, but their greatest damage to wheat is caused by feeding on the roots or on the underground portion of the stems of small plants [69]. Thin stands often result.

True wireworms are small yellowish or reddish-brown larvae one inch or more in length. They pupate in cells in the soil. The adults are brownish to black click beetles. The adults live only a few weeks, but the larvae may survive in the soil for 1–9 years in different species [29].

Partial control of true wireworm damage can be attained by clean fallow and thick seeding. The young larvae are starved when fallowed land is kept free of weeds or volunteer wheat plants. Crop rotation also aids in the control of this insect. Application of insecticides to the soil generally is uneconomical. The larvae of one-year-cycle wireworms may be controlled by a soil application of heptachlor at the rate of two pounds per acre, worked into the soil 3–6 inches deep [29]. Seed treatment affords protection of small grains from wireworms when a dust that contains 20–40 per cent of the purified gamma benzene hexachloride (BHC) is applied to the seed. Sufficient dilute dust should be put on the seed to provide one ounce of actual benzene hexachloride per acre, or generally not more than one ounce per bushel of seed. Seed grain should be treated within 1–2 weeks of planting to avoid lowered germination. Sowing treated seed in dry soil should be avoided.

FALSE WIREWORMS

False wireworms (*Eleodes* spp.) in the United States are distributed chiefly in states west of the Mississippi River. They inhabit vast areas of arid and semiarid lands. There are numerous species of the false wireworm, but *Eleodes hispilabrus* is the most important one on dryland wheat in Idaho [94]. The three species that have done most of the damage to wheat in Kansas are *E. tricostata, E. opaca,* and *E. suturalis* [69].

False wireworms may cause heavy losses in wheat fields in epidemic years. In Idaho, the average seasonal loss was estimated as 10 per cent of the wheat crop [94]. The larvae cause the greatest injury to wheat in dry fall seasons that follow dry summers when their numbers increase rapidly.

Damage is greatest when seed wheat is sown in soil that is too dry to permit rapid germination. The larvae follow the drill rows and eat the germs of the kernels. Numerous larvae often cut off young seedlings below the soil surface [69].

The adult false wireworms are black or grayish-black, angular, awkward, robust beetles with fused wing covers. The larvae are yellow cylindrical worms that turn dark as they become older. The pupae are creamy white at first, but turn to a creamy yellow as they develop. The female adult deposits eggs in dry soil from 0.5–3 inches deep over an extended period from about July 15 to late November. In Kansas, the larvae burrow below the frost line in the fall and remain inactive until spring. The larvae return to the surface when the soil temperature rises in the spring, and pupate from late May through June. The beetles emerge in about 20 days [69]. In some regions, the beetles hibernate in waste places [94].

Some control of false wireworms can be attained by sowing fall wheat only when there is sufficient soil moisture to stimulate rapid germination. Clean culture associated with summer fallow tends to reduce the amount of injury. Crop rotation that includes sorghum, legumes, and other crops is an aid in control. The continuous cycle of wheat also can be broken by summer fallow. Chemical control is possible, but generally impractical. Seed treatment with insecticides appears to be more economical than soil treatment. Aldrin or heptachlor applied at the rate of 2–3 ounces of actual toxicant to 100 pounds of seed appears to be effective without causing seed injury [69].

OTHER WHEAT INSECT PESTS

The chinch bug (*Blissus leucopterus*) often damages wheat and other cereals from Illinois westward to the central Great Plains. It is more destructive to barley, corn, and sorghum than to wheat. When extremely abundant, chinch bugs may stunt wheat or cause it to die in small areas [67]. Infestations can be controlled by a 20 per cent toxaphene dust applied at the rate of 25 pounds per acre [29], but the treatment ordinarily is uneconomical on wheat or other small grains.

The fall armyworm (*Laphygma frugiperda*) attacks wheat in the central and southern states. Control in wheat fields consists in the use of poison bran baits in areas where the worms are feeding. Furrow barriers are effective in preventing infestation of wheat by migrant worms. Delayed seeding of winter wheat, as for Hessian fly control, also is recommended [55, 98].

The armyworm (*Cirphis unipuncta*) has been destructive in many areas of the eastern half of the United States [100]. It may cause severe damage to wheat in outbreak years. The armyworm may be controlled with poison bran bait and the use of a ditch or furrow to check the migration of the worms. The application of toxaphene at two pounds per acre as a spray has been an effective control [29].

Billbugs (*Calendra* spp.) attack wheat as well as other crops. The chief control measure is crop rotation.

The spring generation of the wheat-stem maggot (*Meromyza americana*) feeds on the wheat stem just above the top node. It severs the peduncle, which causes the head to turn white. Two or three other generations may occur on volunteer wheat or grasses before the insect passes the winter as a larva in the tiller of a volunteer or fall-sown wheat plant. Larvae that infect wheat in the fall or late summer kill the young plant or tiller infested. The spring infestation in Kansas has been reduced by the recent extensive introduction of early-maturing wheat varieties. Fall infestations may be reduced by seeding on Hessian-fly-free dates [69].

The pale western cutworm (*Agrotis orthogonia*) destroys considerable wheat in the dryland regions of Montana, North Dakota, Kansas, and other states. The light gray larvae hatch out in the spring. They feed on the underground portions of wheat and other grasses. The moths deposit eggs on loose cultivated soil in the fall. The most practical control method is clean summer fallow to destroy all weeds, grass, and volunteer grain to starve the larvae. This cutworm also can be controlled by a soil treatment with one-half pound of aldrin or dieldrin to the acre, applied before wheat is seeded, and cultivated into the surface six inches of soil [69].

The wheat midge (*Sitodiplosis mosellana*) is found in North America, particularly in British Columbia and in the Pacific Northwest. The damage to wheat is caused by the larvae that feed on the developing kernels. Fall-sown wheat generally is not injured by the midge, and spring wheat seeded by the first week in April usually escapes severe injury. Infested wheat stubble should be plowed under before the overwintered midges emerge in late June [77].

The brown wheat mite (*Petrobia latens*) is a serious pest of dryland wheat in western Kansas. Heavily infested plants appear to be dried out, even though sufficient moisture is within the reach of the plant roots. A fine mottling of the wheat leaves occurs. A crop rotation with wheat planted every third year may be used to lower mite populations. Damage to summer-fallow wheat is less severe than damage to continuously cropped wheat. The wheat curl mite (*Aceria tulipae*) is responsible for transmission of the wheat-streak mosaic disease [69].

Three general groups of white grubs injure growing wheat plants in Kansas: the one-year-cycle grub (*Cyclocephala immaculate*), wheat white grub (*Phyllophaga lanceolata*), and several three-year-cycle species of *Phyllophaga*. Control measures consist of clean culture, crop rotation, and late seeding of winter wheat. Soil applications of DDT, aldrin, chlordane, and heptachlor will control white grubs in wheat, but such chemical treatments generally are too expensive [69].[1]

NEMATODES

The wheat nematode, *Anguina tritici,* occasionally damages wheat in Southeastern United States. It also occurs in India and many other countries. Infested plants are deformed and curled (Figure 15-11), while later

[1] Insects that attack wheat in storage [105] are discussed in Chapter 4.

FIGURE 15-11. **Deformed stems and leaves of wheat plants infested by the wheat nematode.**

(*Courtesy US Department of Agriculture*)

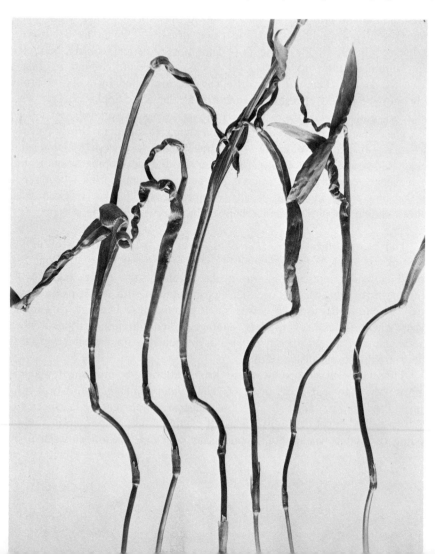

the grains are replaced by galls (Figure 15-4) filled with tiny, almost microscopic, nematodes or eelworms. Nematodes in the soil, or from galls planted with the seed, enter the young wheat plants and prevent the formation of grain. Control is obtained by sowing wheat seed that is free from nematodes in clean soil. Since the nematodes remain alive in the soil no longer than a year, rotation with crops other than rye for 2 years frees the soil from this pest.

REFERENCES

1. Adam, D. B., "The control of take-all in wheat after a long period of pasture." *Austral. J. Ag. Res.*, **2**: 273–282. 1951.
2. Ainslie, C. N., "The western grass-stem sawfly a pest of small grains." USDA *Tech. Bul. 157*. 1929.
3. Army, T. J., and F. H. McNeal, "Effect of nitrogen fertilization on symptoms development, nitrogen content, and nitrogen uptake of spring wheat infected with barley stripe mosaic." *Agron. J.*, **50**(2): 106–109. 1958.
4. Atkins, I. M., and R. G. Dahms, "Reaction of small-grain varieties to green bug attack." USDA *Tech. Bul. 901*. 1945.
5. ———, *et al.*, "Wheat production in Texas." Tex. Ag. Exp. Sta. *Bul. 948*. pp 1–21. 1960.
6. Bever, W. M., "Influence of stripe rust on growth, water economy, and yield of wheat and barley." *J. Ag. Res.*, **54**: 375–385. 1937.
7. ———, "Reaction of wheat, barley, and rye varieties to stripe rust in the Pacific Northwest." USDA *Cir. 501*. 1938.
8. ———, "Physiologic races of *Ustilago tritici* in the eastern soft wheat region of the United States." *Phytopath.*, **37**: 889–895. 1947.
9. Bruehl, G. W., "Pythium root rot of barley and wheat." USDA *Tech. Bul. 1084*. 1953.
10. Butler, F. C., "Flag smut of wheat." New South Wales Dep. Ag. *Plant Disease Leaflet No. 29*. 1952.
11. ———, "Take-all of wheat." New South Wales Dep. Ag. *Plant Disease Leaflet No. 33*. pp 1–3. 1952.
12. Caldwell, R. M., *et al.*, "Effect of leaf rust (*Puccinia triticina*) on yield, physical characters, and composition of winter wheats." *J. Ag. Res.*, **48**: 1049–1071. 1934.
13. ———, *et al.*, "Utilization of the W38 resistance of wheat to Hessian fly." *Agron. J.*, **49**: 520. 1957.
14. Callaghan, A. R., and A. J. Millington, *The Wheat Industry in Australia*. Sidney: Angus and Robertson. pp 1–486. 1956.
15. Cartwright, W. B., R. M. Caldwell, and L. E. Compton, "Responses of resistant and susceptible wheat to Hessian fly attack." *Agron. J.*, **51**(9): 529–531. 1959.
16. Chamberlin, T. R., "The wheat jointworm in Oregon, with special reference to its dispersion, injury, and parasitization." USDA *Tech. Bul. 784*. 1941.

17. Chester, K. S., "The nature and prevention of the cereal rusts as exemplified by the leaf rust of wheat." *Chronica Botanica*, pp 1–269. 1946.

18. Christensen, J. J., "Root rots of wheat, oats, rye, and barley," in *Plant Diseases*. USDA Yrbk. of Ag. pp 321–328. 1953.

19. ———, E. C. Stakman, and F. R. Immer, "Susceptibility of wheat varieties and hybrids to Fusarial head blight in Minnesota." Minn. Ag. Exp. Sta. *Tech. Bul. 59*. 1929.

20. Cowan, F. T., H. J. Shipman, and C. Wakeland, "Mormon crickets and their control." USDA *Farmers Bul. 1928*. 1943.

21. Craigie, J. H., "Discovery of the function of the pycnia of the rust fungi." *Nature*, **120**: 765–767. 1927.

22. Daniels, N. E., *et al.*, "Greenbugs and some other pests of small grains." Tex. Ag., Exp. Sta. *Bul. 845*. 1956.

23. Dickson, J. G., "Influence of soil temperature and moisture on the development of seedling blight of wheat and corn caused by *Gibberella saubinetii*." *J. Ag. Res.*, **23**: 837–870. 1923.

24. ———, "Leaf and head blights of cereals," in *Plant Diseases*. USDA Yrbk. of Ag. pp 344–349. 1953.

25. ———, "Diseases of field crops," 2d ed. New York: McGraw-Hill, pp 1–517. 1956.

26. Ekroth, E. G., and F. H. McNeal, "Association of plant characters in spring wheat with resistance to the wheat-stem sawfly." *Agron. J.*, **45**: 400–404. 1953.

27. Fellows, H., "Effect of certain environmental conditions on the prevalence of *Ophiobolus graminis*." *J. Ag. Res.*, **63**: 715–726. 1941.

28. ———, and C. H. Ficke, "Soil infestation by *Ophiobolus graminis* and its spread." *J. Ag. Res.*, **58**: 505–519. 1939.

29. Fenton, F. A., *Field Crop Insects*. New York: Macmillan, pp 1–405. 1952.

30. Flor, H. H., E. F. Gaines, and W. K. Smith, "The effect of bunt on yield of wheat." *J. Am. Soc. Agron.*, **24**: 778–784. 1932.

31. Garrett, S. D., *Root Disease Fungi*. Waltham, Mass.: *Chron. Bot.*, pp 1–177. 1944.

32. Griffiths, M. A., "Experiments with flag smut of wheat and the causal fungus, *Urocystis tritici*, Kcke." *J. Ag. Res.*, **27**: 425–450. 1924.

33. Greaney, F. J., J. C. Woodward, and A. G. O. Whiteside, "The effect of stem rust on yield, quality, and chemical composition, and milling and baking properties of Marquis wheat." *Sci. Ag.*, **22**: 40–60. 1941.

34. Hart, H., "Stem rust on new wheat varieties and hybrids." *Phytopath.*, **34**: 884–859. 1944.

35. Hayes, H. K., *et al.*, "Thatcher wheat." Minn. Ag. Exp. Sta. *Bul. 325*. 1936.

36. Hehn, E. R., and J. E. Grafius, "Resistance of spring wheat varieties to grasshopper attack." *Agron. J.*, **41**: 467–469. 1949.

37. Heyne, E. G., and C. O. Johnston, "Inheritance of leaf rust reaction and other characters in crosses among Timstein, Pawnee, and Red Chief wheats." *Agron. J.*, **46**: 81–85. 1954.

38. Holton, C. S., and F. D. Heald, *Bunt or Stinking Smut of Wheat*. Minneapolis, Minn.: Burgess Publ. Co., pp 1–211. 1941.

39. ———, R. H. Bamberg, and R. W. Woodward, "Progress in the study of dwarf bunt of winter wheat in the Pacific Northwest." *Phytopath.*, **39**: 986–1000. 1949.

40. ———, and V. F. Tapke, "The smuts of wheat, oats, barley," in *Plant Diseases*. USDA Yrbk. of Ag. pp 360–368. 1953.

41. Horton, J. R., and L. Haseman, "The Hessian fly in Missouri." Mo. Ag. Exp. Sta. *Res. Bul. 384*. 1944.

42. Johnston, C. O., "The occurrence of strains resistant to leaf rust in certain varieties of wheat." *J. Am. Soc. Agron.*, **21**: 568–573. 1929.

43. ———, "The effect of leaf rust infection on the yield of certain varieties of wheat." *J. Am. Soc. Agron.*, **23**: 1–13. 1931.

44. ———, "Sixth revision of the International register of physiological races of *Puccinia recondita* Rob. ex Desm. (formerly *P. rubigo-vera tritici*)." USDA *ARS*, **34-27**: 1–15. 1961.

45. ———, and E. B. Mains, "Studies on physiologic specialization in *Puccinia triticina*." USDA *Tech. Bul. 313*. 1932.

46. ———, and E. C. Miller, "Relation of leaf-rust infection to yield, growth, and water economy of two varieties of wheat." *J. Ag. Res.*, **49**: 955–981. 1934.

47. ———, K. S. Quisenberry, and L. P. Reitz, "Reaction of hard red winter wheats to bunt in uniform bunt nurseries (1943–1947)." *Agron. J.*, **43**: 61–66. 1951.

48. Knott, D. R., "Wheat stem rust in western Canada." U. Saskatchewan *Cir. 562*. 1954.

49. Koehler, B., W. M. Bever, and O. T. Bonnett, "Soil-borne wheat mosiac." Ill. Ag. Exp. Sta. *Bul. 556*. 1952.

50. Lane, M. C., "The Great Basin wireworm in the Pacific Northwest." USDA *Farmers Bul. 1657*. 1931.

51. Leukel, R. W., "Studies on bunt or stinking smut of wheat and its control." USDA *Tech. Bul. 582*. 1937.

52. ———, et al., "Wheat smuts and their control." USDA *Farmers Bul. 1711*. 1938.

53. Levine, M. N., E. R. Ausemus, and E. C. Stakman, "Wheat leaf rust studies at St. Paul, Minnesota." USDA *Plant Disease Reporter*, Suppl. 199. Mar. 30, 1951.

54. Lowther, C. V., "Pathogenicity of physiologic races of *Erysiphe graminis tritici* in the southeastern United States." *Phytopath.*, **40**: 872. 1950.

55. Luginbill, P., "The fall army worm." USDA *Tech. Bul. 34*. 1928.

56. ——— and F. H. McNeal "Effect of fertilizers on the resistance of certain winter and spring wheat varieties to the wheat stem sawfly." *Agron. J.*, **46**: 570–573. 1954.

57. Lungren, E. A., and L. W. Durrell, "Black stem rust control in Colorado." Colo. Ag. Exp. Sta. *Bul. 447*. 1938.

58. Martin, J. H., and S. C. Salmon, "The rusts of wheat, oats, barley, rye," in *Plant Diseases*. USDA Yrbk. of Ag., pp 329–343. 1953.

59. McKay, H. C., and J. M. Raeder, "Snow mold damage in Idaho winter wheat." Ida. Ag. Exp. Sta. *Bul. 200*. 1953.

60. McKinney, H. H., "Investigations of the rosette disease of wheat and its control." *J. Ag. Res.*, **23**: 771–800. 1923.

61. ———, "A mosaic disease of winter wheat and rye." USDA *Bul. 1361*. 1925.

62. ———, "Mosaic diseases of wheat and related cereals." USDA *Cir. 442*. 1937.

63. ———, "Virus diseases of cereal crops," in *Plant Diseases*. USDA Yrbk. of Ag. pp 350–360. 1953.

64. McNeal, F. H., M. A. Berg, and P. Luginbill, "Wheat stem sawfly damage in four spring wheat varieties as influenced by date of seeding." *Agron. J.*, **47**: 522–525. 1955.

65. ———, *et al.*, "The influence of barley stripe mosaic on yield and other plant characters of 8 spring wheat varieties grown at 4 nitrogen levels." *Agron. J.*, **50**(2): 103–105. 1958.

66. Mitra, M., "Studies on the stinking smut or bunt of wheat in India." Indian *J. Ag. Sci.*, **7**: 459–478. 1937.

67. Packard, C. M., and C. Benton, "How to fight the chinch bug." USDA *Farmers Bul. 1780*. 1937.

68. Pady, S. M., *et al.*, "Diseases of wheat in Kansas." Kans. Ag. Exp. Sta. *Bul. 368*. 1955.

69. Painter, R. H., E. R. Bryson, and D. A. Wilbur, "Insects and mites that attack wheat in Kansas." Kans. Ag. Exp. Sta. *Bul. 367*. 1954.

70. Pal, B. P., R. S. Vasudeva, and S. P. Kohli, "Breeding rust resistant hill wheats in India." Indian Council Ag. Res. Series No. 5. 1954.

71. Parker, J. R., "Grasshoppers and their control." USDA *Farmers Bul. 1828*. 1939.

72. Phillips, W. J., and F. W. Poos, "The wheat jointworm and its control." USDA *Farmers Bul. 1006*. 1940.

73. ———, and F. W. Poos, "The wheat strawworm and its control." USDA *Farmers Bul. 1323*. 1953.

74. Purdy, L. H., "Control of common bunt of wheat by seed treatment in the Pacific Northwest." USDA ARS **34-21**: 1–8. 1961.

75. Quisenberry, K. S., O. J. Webster, and T. A. Kiesselbach, "Varieties of winter wheat for Nebraska." Nebr. Ag. Exp. Sta. *Bul. 367*. 1944.

76. "Race 15B stem rust of wheat." USDA *ARS-22-10*. 1954.

77. Reeher, M. M., "The wheat midge in the Pacific Northwest." USDA *Cir. 732*. 1945.

78. Salmon, S. C., O. R. Mathews, and R. W. Leukel, "A half century of wheat improvement in the United States," in *Advances in Agronomy*, Vol. V. New York: Academic Press. pp 1–151. 1953.

79. Scott, R. C., "New wheat varieties and disease resistance." S. Austral. Dep. Ag. *Leaflet No. 11/48*. pp 1–5. 1948.

80. Singh, B., "Wheat diseases and their control." *Agr. and An. Husb.*, **6**(4-5): 57–70. 1955.

81. Slinkard, A. C., and F. C. Elliott, "The effect of bunt incidence on the yield of wheat in eastern Washington." *Agron. J.*, **46**: 439–441. 1954.

82. Sprague, R., "Influence of climatological factors in the development of Cercosporella root rot of winter wheat." USDA *Cir. 451*. 1937.

83. ———, *Diseases of Cereals and Grasses*. New York: Ronald Press. pp 1–538. 1950.

84. Stakman, E. C., and O. S. Aamodt, "The effect of fertilizers on the development of stem rust of wheat." *J. Ag. Res.*, **27**: 341–380. 1924.

85. ———, *et al.*, "Relation of barberry to the origin and persistance of physiologic forms of *Puccinia graminis*." *J. Ag. Res.*, **48**: 953–969. 1934.

86. ———, *et al.*, "Physiologic races of *Puccinia graminis* in the United States in 1954." USDA ARS-**81-3**. 1955.

87. Staples, R., and W. B. Allington, "Streak mosaic of wheat in Nebraska and its control." Nebr. Ag. Exp. Sta. *Res. Bul. 178*. 1956.

88. Stumbo, C. R., P. L. Gainey, and F. E. Clark, "Microbiological and nutritional factors in the take-all disease of wheat." *J. Ag. Res.*, **64**: 653–665. 1942.

89. Suneson, C. A., "Effect of stem rust on the yield of wheat." *Agron. J.*, **46**(3): 112–114. 1954.

90. Tapke, V. F., "Influence of humidity on floral infection of wheat and barley by loose smut." *J. Ag. Res.*, **43**: 503–516. 1931.

91. Taylor, J. W., H. A. Rodenhiser, and B. B. Bayles, "Physiologic races of *Erysiphe graminis tritici* in the southeastern United States." *Agron. J.*, **41**: 134–135. 1949.

92. Udine, E. J., "The black grain-stem sawfly and the European wheat-stem sawfly in the United States." USDA *Cir. 607*. 1941.

93. Wada, E., and H. Fukano, "On the difference and discrimination of wheat mosaics in Japan." *J. Imp. Ag. Exp. Sta.*, **3**: 93–128 (Eng. summary). Tokyo. 1937.

94. Wakeland, C., "False wireworm injurious to dry-farmed wheat and a method of combatting them." Ida. Ag. Exp. Sta. *Res. Bul. 6*. 1926.

95. Wakeland, C., and J. R. Parker, "The Mormon cricket," in *Insects*. USDA Yrbk. of Ag. pp 605–608. 1952.

96. Walkden, H. H., J. R. Horton, and F. M. Wadley, "Hessian fly control in Nebraska by late sowing of winter wheat." Nebr. Ag. Exp. Sta. *Bul. 360*. 1944.

97. Walton, W. R., "The green-bug or spring grain aphis." USDA *Farmers Bul. 1217*. 1921.

98. ———, and P. Luginbill, "The fall armyworm, or grassworm." USDA *Farmers Bul. 752*. 1936.

99. ———, and C. M. Packard, "The Hessian fly and how losses from it can be avoided." USDA *Farmers Bul. 1627*. 1936.

100. ———, and C. M. Packard, "The armyworm and its control." USDA *Farmers Bul. 1850*. 1940.

101. Waterhouse, W. L., "Australian rust studies. IX: Physiological race determinations and surveys of cereal rusts." Linn. Soc. N.S.W. *Proc.*, **77**(Parts 3–4): 209–258. 1952.

102. Watson, I. A., and W. L. Waterhouse, "Australian rust studies. VII: Some recent observations on wheat stem rust in Australia." Linn. Soc. N.S.W. *Proc.*, **74**: 113–131. 1949.

103. ———, and D. Singh, "The future for rust resistant wheat in Australia." *J. Austral. Inst. Ag. Sci.*, **18**: 190–197. 1952.

104. Webb, R. W., "Further studies on the soil relationships of the mosaic disease of winter wheat." *J. Ag. Res.*, **36**: 53–75. 1928.

105. Wilbur, D. A., and G. Halazon, "Pests of farm stored wheat and their control." Kans. Ag. Exp. Sta. *Bul. 371*. 1955.

106. Woolman, H. M., and H. D. Humphrey, "Summary of literature on bunt or stinking smut of wheat." USDA *Bul. 1210*. 1924.

107. Wu, Yu-saw, "Temperature and cultural studies on *Urocystis tritici* Koern." *Can. J. Res.*, **27**(C): 66–72. 1949.

108. Wu, C. S., and E. R. Ausemus, "Inheritance of leaf rust reaction and other characters in a spring wheat cross." *Agron. J.*, **45**(2): 43–48. 1953.

$\mathcal{W}$heat

16. BREEDING

NATURE OF WHEAT IMPROVEMENT

Wheat varieties have been improved in many ways, particularly by breeding for better adaptation to local or regional environmental conditions, and for resistance to or escape from the hazards of production. Desirable attributes have been incorporated into different types of wheat, which have resulted in greater yield of grain per acre, earlier maturity, greater winter-hardiness, resistance to disease, resistance to insects, stiffer straw, non-shattering heads, heavier test weight per bushel, and improved milling and baking quality. Such improvements add to the stability of production [65]. Average wheat yields in the United States were 16 bushels per acre in 1940 and 1941 and nearly 25 bushels 20 years later.

In many regions, satisfactory wheat varieties must have tolerance to unfavorable weather conditions, such as drought, heat, or cold. In semiarid regions, severe damage from heat and drought often is escaped by early-maturing varieties of wheat. In India, only early-maturing varieties can be raised because the crop must complete its growth within the short period from about November 1–March 31 on account of the limitations imposed by climate, particularly high temperatures [57], as well as the need for growing some other summer crop on the same land. Winter hardiness is an important requirement of winter wheat in regions with severe winter climates, such as found in the Great Plains of America and the Steppes of Russia.

Resistance to various rusts and smuts is sought in most wheat regions of the world. Resistance to both stem and leaf rusts is necessary for high yields in the northern Great Plains of the United States. Resistance to prevalent destructive insect pests also is essential.

High-yielding wheat varieties also must resist lodging and shattering, especially where the crop is harvested with a combine. Short-strawed varieties lodge less than do tall varieties of the same straw strength. Selections from a cross, Norin No. 10 × Brevor, which are approximately two-thirds as tall as the local Brevor variety in the Pacific Northwest, produced notably high grain yields and less straw. Norin No. 10 is a semidwarf Japanese variety [82]. The presence of awns favors higher yields in hot climates, and also promotes faster drying of ripe standing wheat. The latter feature promotes earlier combine harvest [60].

High milling quality includes kernel plumpness and high test weight, which usually is associated with high flour yield. High protein content of a quality that produces a strong dough is desired in the bread wheats, such as in the hard red spring or hard red winter wheats. Soft wheat varieties, such as the white wheats with a low protein content and easily pulverized endosperm, are most suitable for pastry flours [69, 2].

Basic studies of the cytology, genetics, and cytogenetics of wheat characters have aided in the breeding of new improved varieties.

CROSSABILITY WITHIN WHEAT GROUPS

The diploid, tetraploid, and hexaploid wheats have 7, 14, and 21 pairs of chromosomes, respectively (see Chap. 12). The three sets of 7 chromosomes in the wheats are designated as the A, B, and D (or C) genomes. The diploid species are AA, the tetraploids AABB, and the hexaploids AABBDD (or AABBCC).

All species of hexaploid wheat are readily intercrossed, with chromosome pairing often as good as that between varieties within the same group [43]. Three species, *Triticum spelta, T. compactum,* and *T. sphaerococcum,* each differ from *T. vulgare* in only one basic gene. The basic differences between *T. vulgare* and the other hexaploid species, *T. macha* and *T. vavilovi,* also appear to be rather simply inherited. Most of the tetraploid species are readily intercrossed [74].

INTERSPECIES HYBRIDS IN TRITICUM

Many plants of pentaploids (AABBD), from crosses between durum or emmer (AABB) and common wheats (AABBDD), are sterile in the F_2 generation, but some are fertile. Such fertile lines eventually stabilize their chromosome numbers as AABB or AABBDD in later generations [37]. Well-known examples are the Hope and Marquillo varieties produced by crossing tetraploid with hexaploid wheats. These fertile hexaploids are ancestors of many of the rust-resistant wheats grown over the world today.

Genome Homologies in Triticum

Many corresponding genes in the A-genome in AB tetraploid wheats are carried in the A-genome in diploid wheats [68, 67, 72]. A close relationship of the two emmer genomes (AB) with the A and B genomes of the hexaploids also has been reported. Some hybrids between emmer and common wheat have marked irregularities in chromosome pairing [40], but others regularly have 14 good chromosome pairs at meiosis. However, *T. timopheevi* has very little homology with the B-genome of the emmers, or with the A-genome of other tetraploid wheats.

Hybrids between groups have more or less regular pairing between chromosomes of the same genomes, but the ABD × AB hybrid is the only combination in which pairing is nearly normal and the progeny have appreciable fertility. The D-genome of the hexaploid wheats has been identified as homologous with the genome of *Aegilops squarrosa* (n = 7) [50, 36].

Amphiploids within Triticum

An amphiploid is a hybrid that carries all chromosomes of both parent species. Nine different amphiploids among *Triticum* species have been reported: *T. durum* × *T. monococcum, T. timopheevi,* and *T. vulgare; T. timopheevi* × *T. vulgare* and *T. monococcum; T. monococcum* × *T. persicum; T. turgidum* × *T. timopheevi;* and *T. polonicum* × *T. timopheevi.* Chromosome pairing usually is poor in amphiploid wheats, with comparatively low fertility where the amphiploid chromosome number is n = 28 or more [72]. The chromosome number of some of these amphiploids has been doubled artificially to avoid sterility.

Autoploids and Haploids in Triticum

The first autoploids were induced in *T. durum, T. polonicum,* and *T. vulgare* [15]. Later, an autotetraploid of *T. monococcum* was obtained, but it failed to produce mature spikes [16].

Haploids have been reported in all three groups of the genus *Triticum.* They occur with frequencies that approach 1 per cent in diploid wheat, but rarely in other *Triticum* groups. The frequency of haploids in *T. monococcum* has been increased by X-ray treatment of the pollen, or by delaying pollination until six or more days after emasculation [72].

INTERGENERIC HYBRIDS WITH WHEAT

Species of the genus *Triticum* have been hybridized with some species in the genera *Secale, Aegilops, Agropyron,* and *Haynaldia,* for scientific studies or to transfer resistance to cold, diseases, or insects to wheat. These

FIGURE 16-1. A natural wheat-rye F_1 hybrid found in 1914 (center, compared with spikes of the probable parental varieties of wheat (left) and rye (right).

(Courtesy US Department of Agriculture)

five genera of the subtribe Triticinea have 7 basic chromosomes [74]. Natural hybrids between *T. vulgare* and *Aegilops cylindrica* have been collected in Kansas.

Wheat-Rye Hybrids

Hybrids between wheat and rye were among the first intergeneric combinations obtained. This cross occasionally occurs naturally (Fig. 16-1). Wheat-rye hybrids have been made by many breeders, sometimes in an attempt to make use of such rye characters as cold tolerance and low-fertility requirement. Triticale, the wheat-rye amphidiploid $(2n = 56)$ from a cross between hexaploid wheat and diploid rye, is not fully fertile due to a reduction in chromosome pairing. As in inbred lines of rye, such low fertility probably is due to the homozygous condition of recessive genes that are unfavorable to chromosome pairing. Some univalent rye chromosomes also are a characteristic feature in wheat-rye crosses. Reduced fertility varies with the wheat and rye varieties or lines crossed [55, 74, 54].

There is considerable doubt that rye genes are transferred to wheat chromosomes because the much larger rye chromosomes rarely or never pair with those of wheat [56]. "Hairy neck," or pubescent peduncle, a common character in rye, frequently is present in wheatlike segregates of wheat-rye crosses that carry a pair of rye chromosomes in addition to 21 pairs of wheat chromosomes. The hairy-neck character in such hybrids is very unstable because the rye chromosomes often are lost during meiosis. However, hairy neck appeared to be inherited as a simple Mendelian character when certain wheat-rye lines were crossed with normal wheat [32].

Hybrids with Other Genera

Crosses of wheat with *Agropyron* species in attempts to transfer certain desirable characters to wheat, such as resistance to cold, drought, disease, and alkali, and perennial growth habit, sometimes are called *Agrotriticum* hybrids. Tall wheat grass (*A. elongatum*) with 35 chromosome pairs was crossed with common wheat (*T. vulgare*) in the Soviet Union and the United States many years ago. Selections from such advanced generation hybrids appear to be stable for certain disease reactions and morphological characters, but they carry genes for meiotic instability [46].

The F_1 plants of crosses between common wheat and *Agropyron trichophorum* are generally intermediate, but with many characters dominantly *Agropyron*. The pubescence and perennial habit of *Agropyron* were still present after two backcrosses to wheat, but the plants resembled the recurrent wheat parent in spike type, awn type, and kernel size and shape. Fertility increased with each backcross. Some plants were highly resistant to leaf rust [80]. Fertile hybrids between *A. trichophorum* and the Pentad variety of durum wheat (*T. durum*) also have been obtained. The hybrid had 56 chromosomes [17]. Other *Agropyron* species reported to have been crossed with wheat include *A. intermedium, A. cristatum, A. repens,* and *A. junceum* [48].

Several *Aegilops* species have been crossed with wheat. It appears feasible to transfer desirable characters from einkorn to the A-genome, from *Aegilops speltoides* to the B-genome, and from *Ae. squarrosa* to the D (or C) genome [51, 67].

The chromosomes of *Haynaldia villosa* ($n = 7$) have shown little or no pairing with wheat chromosomes when crossed with various *Triticum* species [74].

CYTOGENETICS OF WHEAT

Nullisomics and Monosomics

The wheat chromosomes have been numbered I–XXI. Those of the AB (emmer) genomes are numbered I–XIV, while those of the D (*Ae. squarrosa*) genome are designated XV–XXI [73].

The full set of nullisomic plants of common hexaploid wheat, each of which lacks one of the normal 21 pairs of chromosomes, have been produced. These 20-chromosome nullisomics are not vigorous or very fertile but may survive to maturity. Nearly all are dwarfed in size, with marrow leaves and slender culms. A corresponding set of monosomics, which have 20 pairs of chromosomes plus one univalent chromosome, likewise have been produced by crossing the Chinese variety of spring wheat with diploid species. Nullisomes and monosomes were used to determine the chromosome in which 29 specific genes are carried [73, 74]. The genes include several for disease resistance as well as some for morphological characters [74]. Monosomic analysis indicates that the gene for resistance to Race 9 of leaf rust in Pawnee winter wheat lies in chromosome X [28].

Speltoids and Other Mutations

The speltoid mutation occurs only in common wheat (*T. vulgare*). Speltoids resemble spelt (*T. spelta*) in having long, slender spikes and short, square-shouldered, strongly keeled, indurated glumes. Speltoids arise as a loss or a change of a gene in chromosome IX [30]. They can be produced by chromosome deficiency, or deficiency-duplication. They also occur spontaneously, probably by gene mutation, in pure line material with a frequency of 0.6–0.7 per cent. Speltoids occur by the inactivation of the Q factor, or by the loss of this factor in deficiencies or monoploids. The Q gene has a pleiotropic effect on spike density as well as on certain glume characters [43].

The square-head or compactoid gene also occurs in chromosome IX as a reduplication of the factor Q. The square-head type can be produced by chromosome substitution, chromosome addition, isochromosome formation, simple duplication, and deficiency duplication [43].

Lethal genetic combinations have been reported infrequently in crosses of common wheat varieties. In a cross between Atlas 66, a soft red winter wheat, and Quanah, a hard red winter wheat, the F_1 plants made a normal fall growth but all were dead by the end of March. The parent varieties grown under similar conditions were normal. It was concluded that lethal genetic factors were operative [26].

GENETIC FACTORS IN POLYPLOID WHEATS

Many characters or qualities of the tetraploid and hexaploid wheats have been studied genetically [2, 3, 49, 72]. Inheritance of wheat is complex because of the multiple genomes present. In the hexaploid group, there may be three pairs of factors that condition similar characters, one pair in each of the three genomes. Numerous instances of duplicate or triplicate factors in the wheats have been reported [3].

Seed or Grain Color

Red kernel color is dominant to white (Rr) in the F_1 generation. In crosses between different red and white varieties, ratios of 3:1, 15:1, and 63:1 generally have been obtained for red versus white pericarp color in the F_2 generation. Thus, the F_2 progeny of different crosses may segregate for one, two, or three factor pairs. The red color factors are cumulative in effect, that is, there is an increased intensity of red color with an increase in the number of dominant factors present. White kernels in the hexaploid wheats are obtained only when recessive genes for all three factors are present. H. Nilsson-Ehle worked out the multiple-factor genetic hypothesis from studies of the inheritance of kernel color in wheat in Sweden in 1911.

Head or Spike Characters

Spike density sometimes is conditioned by a single gene pair with density dominant [4], but digenic and multigenic ratios also have been obtained [3]. A two-factor hypothesis is necessary to explain the appearance of clavate head type in the F_2 generation of a cross that involves two nonclavate parents. The clavate head type appeared when a gene, Cl, occurred in the absence of an epistatic gene, I. The constitution of the Vernal emmer parent was IIClCl, while Mindum durum was iiclcl. Plants with clavate heads have the genotype iiClCl and iiClcl. Clavateness of head also has been reported as being controlled by three or four genes in tetraploid wheat hybrids. The I gene also appears to be one of the major factors in glume tenacity [77, 39].

Wheat spikes of different varieties range from fully awned to completely awnless. Fully awned wheats lack two dominant inhibiting factors. In crosses of tip-awned with awned varieties, the F_1 plants are long tip-awned, while the F_2 progeny segregate into a 1:2:1 ratio of tip-awned, long tip-awned, and awned. Crosses between completely awnless and fully awned wheats segregate in a two-factor ratio with 1/16 each of the population being fully awnless or fully awned, while the remainder have varying degrees of tip-awn development. Modifying factors and environment affect the expression of the two main factors [12].

Glume color (Cc) usually segregates into a 3:1 ratio of red or brown versus white (or yellow) in the F_2 generation [35], but a 15:1 ratio of brown to white glumes was reported in one cross [41]. Hairy glumes (Gg) usually are controlled by one or two gene pairs, but multiple alleles also have been reported.

Resistance to grain shattering is controlled by at least two major factor pairs in some crosses between wheat varieties, while multigenic differences are involved in others [61]. Varieties resistant to shattering have more sclerenchymatous tissue in the basal portions of the glumes than do susceptible varieties.

Stem or Leaf Characters

Dwarfness in wheat may result from one, two, or three factor-differences [2, 3, 53]. A dwarf factor, D, when present, produces dwarfs except in the presence of an inhibitor, I. Segregation for these two genes in the F_2 generation gives a ratio of 13:3 normals to dwarfs. When D is homozygous and I heterozygous, a ratio of 3:1 normal to dwarf is obtained [2]. Ratios of 15:1 and 63:1 of normals to dwarfs were reported in a Kota × Marquis wheat cross [83]. Three complementary factors, D_1, D_2, and D_3, and their duplicate factors, D_1', D_2', and D_3', and a factor I that inhibited the complementary effect of these dwarf genes also have been reported [58].

Hairy leaf (Lh) and straw color (Sc) are monogenic. Solidness of stem (S) is controlled by one, two, or more factors in different crosses. Growth habit (Hg) is controlled by one, two, three, or multiple factors.

Winter Hardiness

Relative resistance to winter injury or cold generally is regarded as being controlled by multiple genetic factors, which may be partly independent of growth habit [25], but also is greatly influenced by environmental conditions. Crosses between winter wheats with different degrees of hardiness show that inheritance is transgressive in many cases [63, 11].

Maturity

Inheritance of time of maturity or date of heading usually has been explained on the basis of multiple factors with earliness at least partly dominant [79], but some workers have reported a simple segregation of 3:1 for early to late plant maturity [10, 19]. In one cross, segregation was explained on the basis of three independent factors that have equal effects, with earliness recessive [59].

Protein Content of Kernel

Protein content of the soft red winter wheat kernel is heritable with partial dominance of low protein, but this character also is influenced by environmental conditions [14].

INHERITANCE OF DISEASE RESISTANCE

Inheritance of disease reaction in wheat involves genes in the host and in each physiologic race of the pathogen [1, 2, 3].

Stem Rust Resistance

Early observations showed that einkorn and some emmers and durums were more highly resistant to stem rust (*Puccinia graminis tritici*) than were common wheats. The seedling reaction of Khapli emmer to Race 15B appears to depend on two independent genes. The adult reaction is controlled by at least four independent genes from Khapli, two partially dominant and two recessive for resistance [27].

The stem rust resistance of emmer and durum varieties has been incorporated into common wheats. Some varieties of wheat are resistant to many physiologic races, with only a few genes necessary to control this resistance. For example, the Hope and H-44 varieties carry two independent dominant factors for mature plant resistance.

Stem rust resistance in common wheat is conferred by at least 12 genes, Sr1–Sr12. Genes Sr1–Sr4 confer adult-plant resistance, where Sr5 is the Kanred immunity gene which controls resistance to several physiologic races. Genes Sr6–Sr12 have been identified by seedling reactions to Races 15B and 56 [3]. Genes Sr6, Sr8, and Sr9 substituted into Marquis wheat conferred a uniform type of resistance to most of 107 cultures of North American and Australian stem rust, whereas genes Sr7 and Sr10 conferred only moderate resistance to a few cultures [22]. Resistance in different crosses may be inherited as a single factor, a single factor with inhibitor, two factors, three factors, or multiple factors. Physiologic resistance is effective both in the seedling and mature-plant stages [3]. Seedling resistance to stem rust Race 15B appears to be conditioned by three independent genes in two common wheat crosses [33].

Resistant wheat varieties later may prove to be susceptible to new stem rust races that arise by mutation or hybridization. For example, none of the wheat varieties grown in quantity in New South Wales (Australia) in 1952 was resistant to stem rust, probably as a result of the appearance of new races. This necessitated additional crossing to combine different resistant genes [84].

Leaf Rust Resistance

Mature plant resistance to the leaf rust fungus, *Puccinia rubigo-vera tritici,* is controlled by one, two, three, or multiple factors [45, 3, 47]. For example, a Lee × Mida cross was exposed to a collection of races in the field. Resistant Lee is differentiated from susceptible Mida by two pairs of independently inherited genes, with susceptibility partially dominant [85].

The inheritance of resistance vs. susceptibility to Races 1, 8, and 12 (Lr 1) is monogenic; resistance vs. susceptibility to Race 5 is monogenic; and resistance vs. susceptibility to Races 5 and 12 (Lr) is digenic in inheritance in certain crosses [3]. In a cross of Thatcher × (Premier × Bobin-Gaza-Bobin) II-39-2, seedling reaction to Races 1, 2, 5, 15, 28, and 128 was determined by six genetic factors, one for each race. Susceptibility was dominant. There also was evidence of linkage among the six genes. Probably 8–12 genetic factors control seedling reaction of Races 1, 2, 3, 5, 15, 28, 58, 126, and 128A [47]. Resistance of soft red winter wheat to Races 9, 15, and 76 are controlled by single dominant genes designated Lr4, Lr5, and Lr6, respectively. Resistance to Race 65 is controlled by duplicate recessive genes designated as Lr7 and Lr8 [18].

Bunt or Covered Smut

Inheritance of reaction to bunt, caused by *Tilletia foetida* and *T. caries,* has been studied by several workers. Two resistant varieties, Florence and Genoa, were developed in Australia many years ago [2]. In some crosses resistance is controlled by several factors [21].

Single genetic factor pairs are involved in resistance vs. susceptibility for the Martin (M or B1), Hussar (H or B2), Turkey (T or B3), and Rio (R or B4) types of resistance to one race of bunt [3]. Two other minor genes appear to be involved in bunt resistance. The Martin and either the

Turkey or Rio genes gave resistance to all 25 known races and also to dwarf bunt [6]. Two genes (M and M2) in the Martin variety control resistance to 18 known races in the two bunt species [71]. Research in California indicates that a total of seven genes condition resistance to Race 1 of *T. caries* [70].

Other studies of resistance vs. susceptibility (B) to bunt have been explained on the basis of one, two, or multiple factors [3].

Loose Smut

Resistance to loose smut, caused by *Ustilago tritici,* depends upon a single genetic factor, with resistance dominant in some crosses [62]. Two factors for resistance to Race 11 have been indicated in a Kawvale (resistant) × Clarkan (susceptible) cross, with resistance dominant [29]. The Hope variety carries three incompletely dominant factors for resistance and these have a cumulative effect [81].

Other Wheat Diseases

Resistance to powdery mildew, caused by *Erysiphe graminis tritici,* is differentiated by one or two genetic factors in different crosses [44, 64].

Flag smut (Fs) resistance has been reported as controlled by one, three, or multiple factors. Resistance to leaf blotch (Lb) and to soil-borne wheat mosaic are each conditioned by one genetic factor [3].

INHERITANCE OF INSECT RESISTANCE

Wheat varieties have been reported as resistant or tolerant to at least 15 insects besides the Hessian fly [31].

Five genes have been described that influence the reactions of common wheat to the Hessian fly (*Phytophaga destructor*). The resistance of Dawson, in crosses with the susceptible Poso and Big Club varieties, was found to depend upon two dominant genetic factors, H_1 and H_2 [9]. Two resistant varieties, Poso 42 and Big Club 43, were derived from the cross. Fly resistance of the common spring wheat variety, W38, was controlled by the incompletely dominant gene, H_3 [8]. A fourth recessive gene (h_4) controls resistance to the Hessian fly in the Java variety [78]. A fifth incompletely dominant gene also conditions Hessian fly resistance in Rubeiro and other wheat varieties [75].

Wheat stem sawfly resistance is associated with stem solidness [34]. Two varieties, Rescue and Chinook, are resistant to the sawfly (*Cephus cinctus*). Thatcher (hollow stem) has been found to differ from Rescue (solid stem) by one major factor pair and possibly 2–4 minor modifying factors for stem solidness [52].

Resistance to greenbug (*Toxoptera graminum*) appears to be conditioned by one gene pair (Gbgb) with susceptibility dominant [13].

LINKAGE RELATIONS

Several genes in tetraploid and hexaploid wheats have been found to be linked. They are summarized by Ausemus, *et al.* [3] as follows:

Characters Linked	Percentage Recombinations
Two nonallelic pairs of factors for awnedness (Aa)	35–38
Awnedness (A) and beak shape (Bs)	Unknown
Awnedness (A) and hairy node (No)	0–5
Awnedness (A) and keeled glume (Gs)	26–39
Awnedness (A) and head shape	35
Two nonallelic pairs of factors for bunt reaction (B)	34
Three nonallelic pairs of factors for bunt reaction (B)	2.4 and 28.1
Beak shape (Bs) and width of glume shoulder	Unknown
Black chaff and mature stem rust reaction (Sr)	Unknown
Coleoptile (Co) and straw color (Sc)	Unknown
Dwarfness (D) and spike density (Sd)	Unknown
Two pairs of factors for dwarfness (D)	Unknown
Gluten strength (G) and glume color (Gc)	30–39
Glume color (Gc) and hairy glumes (Gg)	Unknown
Stem rust reaction (Sr) and leaf rust reaction (Lr)	Unknown
Stem rust reaction (Sr) and emmer and durum type plants	Unknown
Stem rust reaction (Sr) and seedling reaction to race 41 of stripe rust	Unknown
Leaf rust reaction (Lr) and mildew reaction (Ms)	Unknown 20.8
Protein (P) and kernel color (R)	25–30
Phenol color reactions of kernel (Pk) and spike (Ps)	Unknown
Stem rust reaction (Sr) and seedling reaction	Unknown

Linkage has been established between the Hussar (H) and Martin (M) genes for resistance to bunt race T-1, with a recombination value of 37.2 ± 4.2 per cent. The Rio (R) and Turkey (T) genes also are linked in the same group with a recombination value of 15.2 ± 1.6 per cent. The order of genes is indicated to be as follows [70]:

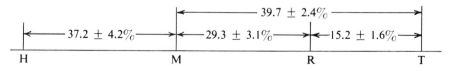

In a Mindum durum × Vernal emmer cross, the genes for awns and rachis bristles (long versus short) were linked with a recombination value of 32.3 per cent [39].

A total of 56 X-ray-induced mutants of diploid einkorn have been described in the United States and 36 in Japan. These are chiefly chlorophyll deficiencies or morphological abnormalities, but increased earliness also has been reported. Most of the mutants are inherited as single-factor differences, but one is controlled by two complementary factors. All seven linkage groups have been established in einkorn [76, 38].

METHODS OF WHEAT BREEDING

New varieties of wheat are obtained through introduction, selection, and hybridization. Most of the wheat breeding in the United States now is concerned primarily with crosses within species.

Introduction

The introduction of good varieties from other countries was the first step in wheat improvement in the United States. Important wheat varieties introduced into the United States include Marquis, Kubanka, Turkey, Mediterranean, Baart, and Federation [11]. Today, varieties from other countries are used chiefly for crossing with local varieties to incorporate certain desirable characters into improved new varieties.

Selection

Continuous mass selection of desirable wheat plants was practiced from prehistoric times until late in the nineteenth century. The acceptance of the pure-line theory advanced by W. L. Johannesen in 1901 turned wheat breeders from continuous selection to the selection of pure lines which were progeny-tested to determine their relative merits. Continuous selection within pure lines was being attempted in the Soviet Union as late as 1961. The selection of new types or improved strains of domestic wheats that contained heterogenic lines created such varieties as Fultz, Kanred, and Blackhull [11].

Hybridization

Hybridization was practiced rarely before the twentieth century, but it has been the accepted method for wheat improvement since 1915. It is the only means for combining the desirable characters of two or more varieties into one variety. The crosses may be made either in the field or in the greenhouse (Fig. 16-2). Large plant populations are desirable when several characters are to be combined, or when the inheritance of a character is complex.

FIGURE 16-2. **Cross-pollinating wheat (right) after emasculation by removing the 3 anthers from each flower as shown at left. The white bags protect emasculated flowers from fertilization by undesired foreign pollen.**

(Courtesy US Department of Agriculture)

When a hybrid population is maintained by the pedigree method, the seed from the first to fourth-generation hybrid plants are space-planted in progeny rows to facilitate individual plant selection. Sufficient F_1 plants are grown to provide for 300–10,000 plants in the F_2 generation. In the F_3 and later generations 100–200 progeny rows usually are grown from desirable plants selected in the previous generation. Selection within lines is continued until relatively homozygous lines are obtained, usually in the F_4–F_6 generations. Selected lines are bulked after they appear homozygous, after which the different lines are tested in comparative yield trials (Fig. 16-3). Concurrently each strain may be grown in "disease gardens" to determine its reaction to various diseases [24, 2].

Sometimes the early F_2–F_6 generations of crosses are grown in bulk. Individual plant or head selection follows, as in the pedigree method. Bulk plots may be subjected to disease epidemics or other special conditions to eliminate susceptible or weak plants by the aid of natural selection. A larger number of crosses can be maintained by the bulk method than by the pedigree method, but no information is afforded on the genetics of the material [2]. Selection for individual plant yield in F_5 bulk hybrids is of little value for predicting the yields of pure line selections [20], because single-plant yields of even pure strains are extremely variable.

FIGURE 16-3. **Harvesting nursery rows of wheat.**
(*Courtesy US Department of Agriculture*)

The backcross method has been used extensively in the improvement of wheat, particularly in California [5, 7]. In this method, one variety—the recurrent parent—is productive and well-adapted but has certain weaknesses. Another variety, the nonrecurrent parent, has some desirable character lacking in the otherwise superior variety. The goal is to produce a new variety exactly like the recurrent parent, except for the added character transferred from the nonrecurrent parent. The F_1 plants, or sometimes selected F_2 plants, are backcrossed to the recurrent parent, individual backcrossed plants are grown in progeny rows, and plants are selected that have the desirable character from the nonrecurrent parent but otherwise resemble the recurrent parent. These selected plants again are backcrossed to the recurrent parent. Backcrossing may continue for 2–6 generations. When the desired character in the nonrecurrent parent is recessive, it usually is preferable to grow selfed progenies from backcrossed plants in each backcross generation so that the desired gene or genes from the nonrecurrent parent are evident among the segregates. Selected plants, or self progenies homozygous for the desired genes, are then backcrossed to the recurrent parent. The backcrossing of selected segregates may be helpful even for dominant characters. Six backcross generations, with careful selection, usually will result in adequate recovery of the genotype of the recurrent parent. At this stage, one or two selfed generations are grown to ensure that the genes from the non-recurrent parent are in the homozygous condition. The recovered lines are very similar to the recurrent parent in performance, and in all characters except those that were added [2].

In the multiple-cross method, certain varieties are crossed in pairs, and then F_1 plants of different crosses are intercrossed to obtain double-crosses. The resultant F_1 plants are then intercrossed. This method produces compound crosses which must be grown in large populations to provide sufficient suitable segregates. Such populations may be carried by the pedigree or bulk method.

Special Techniques

Special techniques have been developed for artificial production of disease epiphytotics, and in milling and baking tests, for the evaluation of selections from crosses [2].

Artificial epidemics of stem rust may be induced in the field by inoculating border rows of susceptible varieties that were planted in the nursery about ten days earlier than the experimental lines. At the Minnesota Agricultural Experiment Station a mixture of 30–60 races is used to inoculate the border rows during the early stage of plant elongation. Inoculations are made either by hypodermic injection or by spraying an aqueous suspension of spores. Supplemental overhead irrigation helps to maintain a high humidity in dry seasons. Segregating populations also are tested in the greenhouse for stem rust resistance, either in the seedling or mature-plant stage.

In tests for bunt resistance, the seed of experimental lines is dusted with a mixture of spores from several collections. For spring wheat, the seed should be sown as early as possible because the optimum temperature for infection is about $12°C$ ($53.6°F$).

An epidemic of loose smut may be produced by dusting a collection of spores on the heads of the experimental material at the time of heading.

Resistance of Fusarium head blight (*Gibberella zeae*) can be determined by growing experimental wheat plants under epidemic conditions. High humidity is essential to the development of the blight. It usually is desirable to spray the plants at heading time with a spore suspension of the pathogen to insure adequate infection. Tents or shades are necessary in dry years [23].

Micromilling and baking techniques for 100-gram wheat samples have been developed [2].

General Accomplishments

From an exhaustive study reported in 1953 [69], it was concluded that increases in annual wheat production due to new improved varieties in the United States was over 232 million bushels at that time.

New varieties of hard red winter wheat have largely replaced varieties grown 25 years ago. Gains of from 10–30 per cent in grain yield have been attained by growing the new varieties. Weight per bushel has been increased as much as five pounds above the old Kharkov variety. The higher-yielding new varieties generally mature from 5–14 days earlier than Kharkov. Winter-hardiness has been increased only slightly in varieties in the northern region, while those in other regions are no more winter-hardy than Kharkov. Some hard red winter wheat varieties have been obtained which are resistant to leaf rust and stem rust, but none is resistant to all prevalent races [66].

REFERENCES

1. Ausemus, E. R., "Breeding for disease resistance in wheat, oats, barley, and flax." *Bot. Rev.*, **9**: 207–260. 1943.
2. ———, "Weizen (*Triticum* L.) II: Wheat in North America," in *Handbuch der Pflanzen-Zuchtung.* Berlin: Paul Parey. Lieferung 9, Band II, Bogen 11–15, pp 187–216. 1956.
3. ———, *et al.*, "A summary of genetic studies in hexaploid and tetraploid wheats." *J. Am. Soc. Agron.*, **38**: 1082–1099. 1946.
4. Boshnakian, S., "The genetics of squareheadedness and of density in wheat, and the relation of these to other characters." Cornell U. Ag. Exp. Sta. *Memoir 53.* 1922.
5. Briggs, F. N., "The use of the backcross in crop improvement." *Am. Nat.*, **72**: 285–292. 1938.
6. ———, and C. S. Holton, "Reaction of wheat varieties with known genes for resistance to races of bunt, *Tilletia caries* and *T. foetida.*" *Agron. J.*, **42**: 483–486. 1950.
7. ———, and R. W. Allard, "The current status of the backcross method of plant breeding." *Agron. J.*, **45**: 131–138. 1953.
8. Caldwell, R. M., W. B. Cartwright, and L. E. Compton, "Inheritance of Hessian fly resistance derived from W38 and durum P.I. 94,587." *J. Am. Soc. Agron.*, **38**: 398–409. 1946.
9. Cartwright, W. B., and G. A. Wiebe, "Inheritance of resistance to the Hessian fly in the wheat crosses Dawson × Poso and Dawson × Big Club." *J. Ag. Res.*, **52**: 691–695. 1936.
10. Clark, J. A., "Segregation and correlated inheritance in crosses between Kota and Hard Federation wheats for rust and drought resistance." *J. Ag. Res.*, **29**: 1–47. 1924.
11. ———, "Improvement of wheat," in USDA Yrbk. of Ag. pp 207–302. 1936.
12. ———, and J. R. Hooker, "Segregation and correlated inheritance in Marquis and Hard Federation crosses, with factors for yield and quality of spring wheat in Montana." USDA *Bul. 1403.* 1926.

13. Curtis, B. C., A. M. Schlehuber, and E. A. Wood Jr., "Genetics of greenbug (*Toxoptera graminum* Rond.) resistance in two strains of common wheat." *Agron. J.*, **52**: 599–602. 1960.

14. Davis, W. H., G. K. Middleton, and T. T. Hebert, "Inheritance of protein, texture, and yield in wheat." *Crop. Sci.*, **1**: 235–238. 1961.

15. Dorsey, E., "Induced polyploidy in wheat and rye." *J. Hered.*, **27**: 155–160. 1936.

16. ———, "Chromosome doubling in cereals." *J. Hered.*, **30**: 393–395. 1939.

17. Elliott, F. C., "A stiffhair wheatgrass — Pentad durum gene source for common wheat." *Agron. J.*, **43**: 131–136. 1951.

18. Fitzgerald, P. J., R. M. Caldwell, and O. E. Nelson, "Inheritance of resistance to certain races of leaf rust of wheat." *Agron. J.*, **49**: 539–543. 1957.

19. Florell, V. H., "Studies on the inheritance of earliness in wheat." *J. Ag. Res.*, **29**: 333–347. 1924.

20. Fowler, W. L., and E. G. Heyne, "Evaluation of bulk hybrid tests for predicting performance of pure line selections in hard red winter wheat." *Agron. J.*, **47**: 430–434. 1954.

21. Gaines, E. F., "Genetics of bunt resistance in wheat." *J. Ag. Res.*, **23**: 445–480. 1923.

22. Green, G. J., *et al.*, "Seedling reactions to stem rust of lines of Marquis wheat with substituted genes for rust resistance." *Can. J. Pl. Sci.*, **40**: 524–538. 1960.

23. Hanson, E. W., E. R. Ausemus, and E. C. Stakman, "Varietal resistance of spring wheats to Fusarial head blight." *Phytopath.*, **40**: 909–914. 1950.

24. Harrington, J. B., "Cereal breeding procedures." Rome: FAO Devel. *Paper No. 18.* pp 122. 1952.

25. Hayes, H. K., and O. S. Aamodt, "Inheritance of winter hardiness and growth habit in crosses of Marquis with Minhardi and Minturki wheats." *J. Ag. Res.*, **35**: 223–236. 1927.

26. Hebert, T. T., and G. K. Middleton, "Lethality in a wheat cross." *Agron. J.*, **47**: 196. 1955.

27. Heerman, R. M., "Inheritance of stem rust reaction in tetraploid wheat hybrids. II: Genes for resistance to race 15B in Khapli emmer." *Agron. J.*, **52**: 107–110. 1960.

28. Heyne, E. G., and R. W. Livers, "Monosomic analysis of leaf rust reaction, awnedness, winter injury, and seed color in Pawnee wheat." *Agron. J.*, **45**: 54–58. 1953.

29. ———, and E. D. Hansing, "Inheritance of resistance to loose smut of wheat in the crosses of Kawvale × Clarkan." *Phytopath.*, **45**: 8–10. 1955.

30. Huskins, C. L., "Fatuoid, speltoid, and related mutations of oats and wheat." *Bot. Rev.*, **12**: 457–514. 1946.

31. Jones, E. T., "Insect resistance in wheat." *J. Am. Soc. Agron.*, **35**: 695–703. 1943.

32. Jones, J. W., and N. F. Jensen, "Behavior of the hairy-neck character in wheat-rye hybrids." *Agron. J.*, **46**: 78–80. 1954.

33. Jones, G. L., and E. R. Ausemus, "Inheritance of the mode of reaction to stem rust, particularly race 15B, and leaf rust in two crosses of *vulgare* wheats." *Agron. J.*, **48**: 435–439. 1956.

34. Kemp, H. J., "Studies of solid stem wheat varieties in relation to wheat stem sawfly control." *Sci. Ag.*, **15**: 30–38. 1934.

35. Kezer, A., and B. Boyack, "Mendelian inheritance in wheat and barley crosses." Colo. Ag. Exp. Sta. *Bul. 249.* 1918.

36. Kihara, H., "Genome-analysis in *Triticum* and *Aegilops*. X: Concluding review" (by F. A. Lilienfeld). *Cytologia*, **16**: 101–123. 1951.

37. ———, "Wheat and its relatives," in *Int. Genetics Symposia*, 1956. Sci. Coun. Japan. pp 33–54. 1956.

38. ———, and K. Yamashita, "X-ray induced mutants and reciprocal translocation types and their linkage relations in Einkorn wheats." Wheat Info. Service *No. 1*, pp 13–15. 1954.

39. Lebsock, K. L., and G. S. Smith, "The inheritance of head characters in tetraploid wheat hybrids. II: Rachis, bristles, awns, glume tenacity, clavate head, and seed color." *Agron. J.*, **49**: 202–205. 1957.

40. Love, R. M., "Chromosome behavior in F_1 wheat hybrids. I: Pentaploids." *Can. J. Res.*, **19**: 351–369. 1941.

41. Love, H. H., and W. T. Craig, "Methods used and results obtained in cereal investigations at the Cornell Station." *J. Am. Soc. Agron.*, **10**: 145–157. 1918.

42. MacKey, J., "The taxonomy of hexaploid wheats." *Svensk Bot. Tidsk.*, **48**: 579–590. 1954.

43. ———, "Neutron and X-ray experiments in wheat and a revision of the speltoid problem." *Hereditas*, **40**: 65–180. 1954.

44. Mains, E. B., "Inheritance of resistance to powdery mildew, *Erysiphe graminis tritici*, in wheat." *Phytopath.*, **24**: 1257–1261. 1934.

45. ———, C. E. Leighty, and C. O. Johnston, "Inheritance of resistance to leaf rust, *Puccinia triticina* Erikss. in crosses of common wheat, *Triticum vulgare*, VIII." *J. Ag. Res.*, **32**: 931–972. 1926.

46. Marshall, H. G., and J. W. Schmidt, "A study of the meiotic stability of certain Agrotriticum hybrids." *Agron. J.*, **46**: 383–388. 1954.

47. Martinez, L. M., E. R. Ausemus, and C. R. Burnham, "Inheritance of reaction to leaf rust, *Puccinia rubigo-vera tritici* (Erikss.) Carleton, and of certain other characters in a wheat cross." Minn. Ag. Exp. Sta. *Tech. Bul. 205*. 1953.

48. Matsumura, S., "Genetics of some cereals." Annual Rpt. Natl. Inst. Genetics (Japan), **1**: 22–27. 1951.

49. Matsuura, H., "A bibliographical monograph of plant genetics," 2d. ed. Sapporo, Japan: Hokkaido Imp. U. pp 419–465. 1933.

50. McFadden, E. S., and E. R. Sears, "The origin of *Triticum Spelta* and its free-threshing hexaploid relatives." *J. Hered.*, **38**: 81–89, 107–116. 1946.

51. ———, and E. R. Sears, "The genome approach in radical wheat breeding." *J. Am. Soc. Agron.*, **39**: 1011–1026. 1947.

52. McNeal, F. H., "Inheritance of stem solidness and spikelet number in a Thatcher × Rescue wheat cross." USDA *Tech. Bul. 1125*. 1956.

53. Morrison, J. W., "Dwarfs, semi-lethals, and lethals in wheat." *Euphytica*, **6**: 213–223. 1957.

54. Muntzing, A., "Cytogenetics studies in ryewheat." Int. Genetics Symposia *Proc.*, 1956. Tokyo: Science Council Japan, pp 51–56. 1957.

55. ———, and S. Akdik, "Cytological disturbances in the first inbred generations of rye." *Hereditas*, **34**: 485–509. 1948.

56. O'Mara, J. G., "The cytogenetics of Triticale." *Bot. Rev.*, **19**: 587–605. 1953.

57. Pal, B. P., "The Pusa wheats: The wheat-breeding work of the Imperial Agricultural Research Institute." *Emp. J. Exp. Ag.*, **12**(46). 1944.

58. Pao, W. K., *et al.*, "Inheritance of dwarfness in common wheat." *J. Am. Soc. Agron.*, **36**: 417–428. 1944.

59. Poehlman, J. M., "Inheritance of earliness in crosses between Early Premium and Kawvale varieties of common wheat." Mo. Ag. Exp. Sta. *Res. Bul. 430.* 1949.

60. Pool, M., and F. L. Patterson, "Moisture relations in soft red winter wheat. II: Awned versus awnless and waxy versus nonwaxy glumes." *Agron. J.*, **50**: 158–160. 1958.

61. Porter, K. B., "The inheritance of shattering in wheat." *Agron. J.*, **51**: 173–177. 1959.

62. Pugsley, A. T., "The resistance of White Federation 45 and Dundee 48 wheat to *Ustilago tritici* (Loose smut of wheat)." *J. Austral. Inst. Ag. Sci.*, **19**: 238–240. 1953.

63. Quisenberry, K. S., and J. A. Clark, "Hardiness and yield of winter wheat varieties." USDA *Cir. 141.* 1930.

64. Ray, D. A., T. T. Hebert, and G. K. Middleton, "Inheritance of resistance to powdery mildew in wheat." *Agron. J.*, **46**: 379–383. 1954.

65. Reitz, L. P., "Wheat breeding and our food supply." *Econ. Bot.*, **8**: 251–268. 1954.

66. ———, and S. C. Salmon, "Hard red winter wheat improvement in the Plains." USDA *Tech. Bul. 1192.* 1959.

67. Riley, R., J. Unrau, and V. Chapman, "Evidence on the origin of the B genome of wheat." *J. Hered.*, **49**(3): 91–98. 1958.

68. Sakar, P., and G. L. Stebbins, "Morphological evidence concerning the origin of the B genome in wheat." *Am. J. Bot.*, **43**: 297–304. 1956.

69. Salmon, S. C., O. R. Mathews, and R. W. Leukel, "A half century of wheat improvement in the United States," in *Advances in Agronomy*, Vol. 5. New York: Academic Press. pp 1–151. 1953.

70. Schaller, C. W., and F. N. Briggs, "Linkage relationships of the Martin, Hussar, Turkey, and Rio genes for bunt resistance in wheat." *Agron. J.*, **47**: 181–186. 1955.

71. ———, C. S. Holton, and E. L. Kendrick, "Inheritance of the second factor for resistance to bunt, *Tilletia caries* and *T. foetida*, in the wheat variety Martin." *Agron. J.*, **52**: 280–282. 1960.

72. Sears, E. R., "The cytology and genetics of the wheats and their relatives," in *Advances in Genetics*, Vol. II. New York: Academic Press, pp 239–270. 1948.

73. ———, "The aneuploids of common wheat." Mo. Ag. Exp. Sta. *Res. Bul. 572.* 1954.

74. ———, "Weizen (*Triticum L.*). I: The systematics, cytology, and genetics of wheat." *Handbuch der Pflanzen-Zuchtung.* Berlin: Paul Parey, Lieferung 9, Baad II, Bogen 11–15, pp 164–187. 1956.

75. Shands, R. G., and W. B. Cartwright, "A fifth gene conditioning Hessian fly response in common wheat." *Agron. J.*, **45**: 302–307. 1953.

76. Smith, L., "Mutants and linkage studies in *Triticum monococcum* and *T. aegilopoides.*" Mo. Ag. Exp. Sta. *Res. Bul. 298.* 1939.

77. Smith, G. S., "Inheritance of head characters in tetraploid wheat hybrids. I: Glume tenacity and head type in Mindum durum × Vernal emmer." *Agron. J.*, **49**: 138–141. 1957.

78. Suneson, C. A., and W. B. Noble, "Further differentiation of genetic factors in wheat resistance to the Hessian fly." USDA *Tech. Bul. 1004.* 1950.

79. Thompson, W. P., "Earliness in wheat and its inheritance." *Sci. Ag.*, **1**: 193–197. 1921.

80. Thompson, D. L., and J. E. Grafius, "Cytological observations of the F_1 and two backcross generations of *Triticum vulgare* $\times$ *Agropyron trichophorum*." *Agron. J.*, **42**: 298–303. 1950.

81. Tingey, D. C., and B. Tolman, "Inheritance of resistance to loose smut in certain wheat crosses." *J. Ag. Res.*, **48**: 631–655. 1934.

82. Vogel, O. A., *et al.*, "Semi-dwarf growth habit in winter wheat improvement for the Pacific Northwest." *Agron. J.*, **48**: 76–78. 1956.

83. Waldron, L. R., "A study of dwarfness in wheat accompanied by unexpected ratios." *Genetics*, **9**: 212–246. 1924.

84. Watson, I. A., and D. Singh, "The future for rust resistant wheat in Australia." *J. Inst. Ag. Sci.*, **18**: 190–197. 1952.

85. Wu, C. S., and E. R. Ausemus, "Inheritance of leaf rust reaction and other characters in a spring wheat cross." *Agron. J.*, **45**: 43–48. 1953.

PART IV Rye, Barley, and Oats

17. RYE

ECONOMIC IMPORTANCE

Rye (*Secale cereale*) is an important bread grain, especially in parts of northern Europe where poor soils and severe winters make rye a surer as well as a cheaper bread grain [66], although wheat generally is grown and consumed in preference to rye where climate and soil are suitable.

The world average acreage for rye was about 90 million acres with a production of 1,460,000,000 bushels from 1950–54. The average acre yield was 16.1 bushels. The leading countries in rye grain production are the Soviet Union, Poland, West Germany, East Germany, Czechoslovakia, Hungary, and the United States. Approximately 50 per cent of the production is in the Soviet Union, while more than 95 per cent of the world rye crop is produced in Europe and Asiatic Russia (Fig. 17-1).

Rye is the principal crop on the sandy podzolized soils in the vast region that extends across northern Europe and Asia, mainly between the 50th and 60th parallels of latitude. Rye also is produced as far south as Spain, Italy, Greece, and Turkey [66]. Rye grows well in Argentina everywhere within the "wheat crescent" as well as outside of it, especially to the west and south. In southern Australia, rye is grown on the sandy soils of the Mallee to check wind erosion [74, 58, 20].

Rye for all purposes was seeded in the United States anunally on an average of about 4.1 million acres during the ten-year period from 1952 to 1961. Approximately 40 per cent of this area, or 1.645 million acres, was harvested for grain. The remainder of the acreage was devoted to pasture, hay, or green manure, or was abandoned. The average annual grain production for the decade was 25.45 million bushels, or an average of 15.5 bushels an acre. The production of rye from 1950–60 was slightly less than that produced from 1900–10. The principal rye states are North Dakota, South Dakota, Minnesota, Nebraska, and Indiana [2] (Fig. 17-2).

In the North Central and Western states, rye is grown primarily for

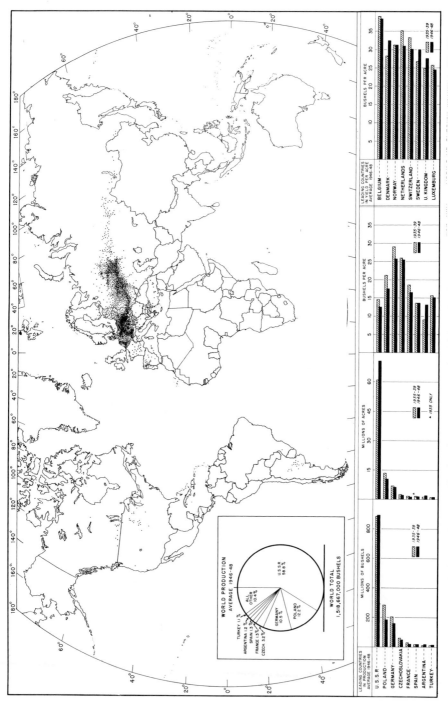

FIGURE 17-1. World rye distribution, average of 1946-1948. Each dot represents 1,000,000 bushels.

(*Courtesy US Department of Agriculture*)

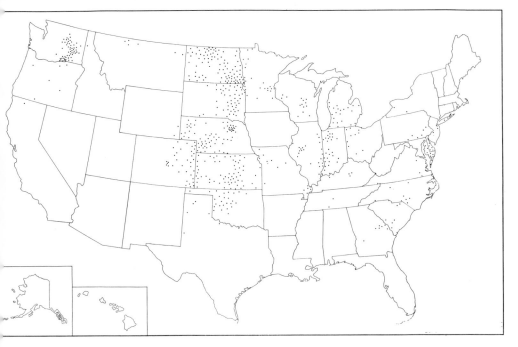

FIGURE 17-2. **Acreage of rye harvested in the United States in 1959. Each dot represents 2,000 acres. The U.S. total was 1,392,072 acres.**

(Courtesy US Department of Agriculture)

grain, but it is also used for hay, pasture, as a companion crop, or sometimes as a smother crop [40]. In the Eastern states, rye frequently is grown for pasture or as a cover or green manure crop.

HISTORY OF RYE CULTURE

Rye appears to have been cultivated for more than 2000 years. There are no records of rye grain in pre-Christian times, but it became widely distributed during the medieval period, particularly in Europe. After the Renaissance, rye was more prominent than was wheat. In fact, it was the predominant world bread grain until the nineteenth century. Since then, rye has been replaced more and more by wheat [74].

Rye was brought to the western hemisphere by the English and Dutch who settled in the northeastern areas of what is now the United States. Rye continued to be of greater importance in these settlements than in the colonies farther south. At the time of the first United States census in 1839, rye production centered in eastern Pennsylvania, southeastern New York, northern New Jersey, and central Maryland. During the next ten years, the rye area moved westward into the North Central states, where a substantial part of the rye crop is still grown [11].

THEORIES OF ORIGIN

Rye was not found in the remains of the Swiss Lake Dwellers or in the tombs of the ancient Egyptians [24]. The cultivation of rye is believed to have originated in Asia Minor, because rye exists there in a great diversity of forms. It is found as a weed widely distributed in fields of wheat and winter barley in southwestern Asia. In Afghanistan, it is a stubborn weed, especially since many of its forms have a tendency to reseed. With the northward movement of wheat from southwestern Asia, mixtures of rye with wheat apparently were selected for growing as an independent cultivated crop [79].

Cultivated rye may have descended from *S. anatolicum,* a wild rye found in Syria, Armenia, Iran, Turkestan, and the Kirghis Steppe [4]. Another view is that rye originated from *S. montanum,* a wild species found in southern Europe and nearby parts of Asia, and also believed to have been cultivated in the Bronze Age. The similarity of species makes it impossible to prove which originated from the other [78].

ADAPTATION

Rye is grown mostly in cool climates. Most of the rye in Europe is grown in regions where the average annual precipitation ranges from 20–30 inches. It is grown more widely than oats in the moist climates of the world. The rye acreage in the drier climates accounts for only 10–15 per cent of the world total. The crop withstands all kinds of adverse weather conditions except heat [22]. Rye sprouts more quickly and grows more vigorously than wheat at low temperatures. Its earliness frequently enables rye to escape injury from drought or rust, although the heads are likely to be blasted if hot dry winds occur when the plants are in blossom. The earliness of winter rye is detrimental in sections where late spring or early summer freezes can cause sterility in flowering plants [5].

Winter rye is the most hardy of all cereals. One of its chief characteristics is its ability to survive temperatures too low for wheat production. Winter-hardy types can be sown in the fall of the year with assurance of a good crop even in regions where winter temperatures frequently fall as low as 40°F below zero, or where the mean winter temperature is about 0°F

[66]. Winter rye is grown beyond the Arctic Circle in Finland and as far north as 60° N. in the Soviet Union. Some rye is grown in North America at the northern limits of the Canadian grain belt [22, 59]. It generally survives the cold winters in northern North Dakota and Montana [28, 40].

The highest yields of rye usually are obtained on fertile well-drained loam soils. However, rye is more productive than other grains on infertile, sandy, or acid soils. More than 75 per cent of the Soviet Russian rye acreage is located in the so-called non-Chernozem region. The forest soils in this region are moderately to strongly leached, and are unadapted to any other major cereal grain except oats. Rye is unable to compete with winter wheat in the Chernozem region of the Soviet Union except on the light soils [22]. It makes a better growth on the poor wind-blown sandhills of south Australia than does any other cereal [68, 20]. Spring rye out-yields spring wheat fairly consistently by 10–12 per cent on the clay soils of Saskatchewan in Canada [7]. Rye is an especially good crop for drained marshlands or newly cleared timberland of the southeastern United States [29]. On the drylands of northeastern Colorado and adjacent states, rye has often outyielded wheat on the sandy lands, but wheat generally out-yields rye on the so-called "hard lands," *i.e.,* loams and clay loams. Under conditions favorable for winter wheat, rye usually yields less grain because of its shorter growth period, heavier straw yield, and lower spikelet fertility. Rye is likely to be sown on less productive land, or with poorer seedbed preparation, than is customary for wheat.

Rye volunteers freely because the grain shatters readily. These grains produce volunteer plants that thrive under adverse culture conditions. Since rye matures earlier than other grains, some of the seed is again shattered before the regular planted crop is harvested. Consequently, it is difficult to eradicate rye in a system of continuous small grain. Mixtures of appreciable quantities of rye in wheat lower the market grade [40].

BOTANICAL DESCRIPTION

Rye is an annual or winter annual grass classified in the tribe Hordeae. The only cultivated species is *Secale cereale*.

Vegetative Characters

The stems of the rye plant (Fig. 17-3) are larger and longer than those of wheat. The leaves of the two plants are similar, except that rye leaves are coarser and more bluish in color. The ligules are short and somewhat rounded; the auricles are white, narrow, and wither early (or they may be absent altogether). The roots of rye branch profusely, especially near the soil surface, and some may penetrate to a depth of 5–6 feet [81].

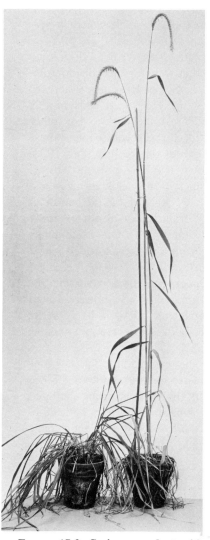

FIGURE 17-3. Spring rye plant with spikes flowering (right). The plant at the left is a winter variety that failed to head because it also was grown under warm greenhouse temperatures. (*Courtesy US Department of Agriculture*)

FIGURE 17-4. Spikes of rye: (left) late blooming stage, and (right) mature. (*Courtesy US Department of Agriculture*)

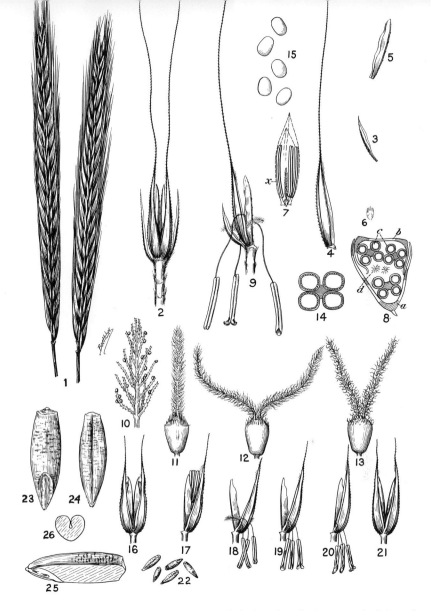

FIGURE 17-5. **1.** Two spikes, lateral view. **2.** Spikelet, dorsal view, attached to node of rachis. **3.** Glume, lateral view. **4.** Lemma, lateral view. **5.** Palea, lateral view. **6.** Lodicule. **7.** Diagrammatic lateral longitudinal view of floret at anthesis, showing position of gynoecium and androecium. **8.** Diagrammatic cross section of spikelet: (a) lemma, (b) palea, (c) stamens, (d) stigma. **9.** Lateral view of floret at anthesis, with one subtending glume. **10.** Portion of stigma with adhering pollen grains. **11, 12, 13.** Pistil (ovary and stigma) before, during, and after anthesis. **14.** Diagrammatic cross section of anther. **15.** Pollen grains. **16.** Two florets, lateral view, at beginning of anthesis. **17, 18, 19, 20.** Floret, lateral view, showing successive stages in anthesis. **21.** Two florets after anthesis. **22.** Caryopses (seeds). **23.** Caryopsis, dorsal view, showing embryo. **24.** Caryopsis, ventral view. **25.** Caryopsis, lateral longitudinal (sagittal) section, showing endosperm and embryo. **26.** Caryopsis, cross section.

(*Courtesy US Department of Agriculture*)

Inflorescence

The inflorescence of rye is a spike with a single spikelet at a rachis joint (Figs. 17-4 and 17-5). The spikelet consists of three florets, two being fertile and one abortive. The spikelet is subtended by two narrow one-nerved glumes. The lemma is broad, keeled, terminally awned, and ciliate on the keel. The caryopsis is narrower than the wheat kernel. It usually is brownish-olive, greenish-brown, bluish-green, or yellow in color. The caryopsis threshes free from the lemma and palea (Fig. 17-6).

FIGURE 17-6. **Kernels (caryopses) of rye.**

(Courtesy US Department of Agriculture)

POLLINATION

Since rye plants are largely self-sterile, they are mostly cross-pollinated. When 84,133 florets were covered to prevent cross pollination, sterility ranged from 96–99 per cent in different varieties in different years [31]. However, some selected strains are rather self-fertile [4]. Rye spikes normally have many empty florets: approximately one-third of the 29,760 florets observed in Wisconsin rye fields during a three-year period failed to set seed [31].

One worker observed two rye varieties to interpollinate to the extent of approximately 50 per cent when grown in adjacent plots. Less than 10 per cent of outcrossing occurred at a distance of 10 feet from the plot border [71], where most of the florets were fertilized by pollen from other plants of the same variety.

The flowering and dehiscence of rye are very similar to those of wheat, barley, and oats.

VARIETIES

Both winter and spring varieties of rye are grown, but by far the larger part of the world production is obtained from winter varieties. Few varieties of rye maintain uniform distinct characteristics because they comprise a mixture maintained by cross pollination. Winter varieties adapted to the northern United States are wholly unsuited to conditions in the South where winter temperatures are not sufficiently low to force true winter varieties into early heading. The so-called winter varieties in the South actually have a partial spring habit of growth. These varieties flower and mature before the advent of unfavorable hot summer weather.

Varieties Grown in the United States

Abruzzes (Abruzzi) rye, introduced from Italy [29], together with its selected strains, is well-adapted to the states south of a line that extends from Maryland to Oklahoma. It is grown primarily as a pasture or cover crop and makes a vigorous upright growth even in cold weather.

The Florida Black variety is suitable for winter and early spring pasture in Florida, where it is earlier, a better seed producer, and more resistant to leaf rust than Abruzzes [36]. Gator, released in Florida in 1956, but also grown in Georgia and South Carolina, is resistant to leaf rust, stem rust, and powdery mildew.

Balbo, a variety introduced from Italy about 1919, was released by the Tennessee Agricultural Experiment Station in 1933. The kernels are extra large, but longer and narrower than those of Abruzzes. Balbo is characterized by a rapid upright growth habit which makes it a highly desirable variety for early pasture [42]. In Tennessee during mild weather, Abruzzes produces pasture as abundantly as Balbo but suffers much worse from freezing [56]. Important in Tennessee, Balbo also is widely grown in Colorado and in all states eastward to New Jersey, Delaware, Virginia, and North Carolina. It is popular among dairymen because of its ability to produce both early fall and spring pasture, its resistance to the Hessian fly, its palatability, and the fact that the milk from cows pastured on it is free from taint.

Rosen rye, introduced from Russia, was distributed by the Michigan Agricultural Experiment Station in 1912. It was adapted to the Corn Belt, the Northeastern states, and several Western states. It yielded about twice as much as common rye in Michigan [69]. Rosen is a rather late variety with large heads. Pure Rosen has large, bluish-green kernels. It was kept pure for many years by growing foundation seed stocks on South Manitou Island in Lake Michigan where it was the sole rye variety grown. Petkus, which is indistinguishable from Rosen, is adapted to the same general conditions [70]. Both varieties have been replaced largely by Balbo, and by the Adams and Imperial varieties that were developed in Wisconsin [5].

Dakold, which originated at the North Dakota Station in 1912 through natural selection, is a very winter-hardy variety in North Dakota, northern

Montana, and some parts of Canada. It has small heads, small dark-colored kernels, and rather slender stems. It matures early [40]. A hardier strain, Dakold 23, was released in Saskatchewan, Canada.

Emerald is a green-seeded mass selection from Minnesota No. 2, made in Minnesota. A yellow-kerneled selection named Imperial—the synthetic progeny of seven bulked superior self-fertile selections [32]—is a vigorous, hardy, productive variety in Wisconsin. Emerald and Imperial are being replaced by Adams and Caribou in these states. Adams, selected from Imperial in Wisconsin, is more vigorous and resistant to diseases. Caribou, developed in Saskatchewan, was released by the Minnesota Station. White Soviet is a variety with light brown grains introduced from Russia to Canada and then into the United States about 1940. It is grown in the Dakotas, but is being replaced by Caribou and Antelope. Antelope was selected from the Korm (Crown) variety in Saskatchewan where it was released in 1953.

Pierre is a winter-hardy variety released by the South Dakota Station. It is a synthetic variety produced from a composite of 16 inbred lines isolated from a population of the Dakold and Swedish varieties which are then allowed to cross-pollinate. The 16 inbreds were selected on the basis of superior winter-hardiness as well as topcross yield performance. While the original hybrid vigor has been lost, the winter hardiness has been retained. Pierre outyields other strains of common rye in South Dakota wherever winter killing is a factor [17]. Caribou, Antelope, and Pierre are the most productive of the hardy varieties. They now lead in the Dakotas as well as in the prairie provinces of Canada. Other hardy varieties formerly grown include Swedish (Minnesota No. 2), Schlanstedt (Wisconsin Pedigree No. 2), Dean, Advance, Ivanof, and Mammoth White.

Raritan, developed by the New Jersey Station, has yielded 10–12 per cent more than other varieties in New Jersey. This variety is the progeny of 98 bulked selected strains [71].

Tetra-Petkus, a tetraploid variety introduced into the United States from Germany after 1950, attracted considerable attention. It produces a vigorous vegetative growth and large grains. Yields in the Northern states are satisfactory, except where sterility is increased by pollen from other varieties nearby. The large kernels of Tetra Petkus are unsuited to the equipment used in cleaning and processing ordinary rye for flour or whiskey, and mixtures of the two sizes are particularly undesirable. It is less popular than formerly.

Kung, a late variety, has been tested in Oregon and California [5].

Spring rye is grown rarely in North America, except in cold northern areas subject to late spring frosts. The best known variety, Prolific, was introduced from Germany into Canada and then into the United States. A very early spring rye, Merced, was released in California in 1947, where it is fall-sown in areas where winters are mild.

Varieties Grown in Other Countries

Steel rye (Stalrag) is a widely grown variety in Sweden. A selection from this variety, named Kung (Kungsrag II) was released in 1939. It has broader and denser spikes and a stiffer straw than does the parent variety. Kung is now the predominant variety on fertile soils, particularly in south-western Sweden [37]. More recent varieties grown in this region are Agro II and Petkus II. The Bjorn variety is grown in northern Sweden. Dubbel-stal, a tetraploid rye, is being tested in comparison with diploid varieties [1].

Among the more important varieties in Finland are Toivo, Oiva, Pekka, and Onni. These varieties were developed from crosses between native and foreign varieties. They have the winter hardiness of Finnish native varieties together with the improved straw, head, and grain qualities of the foreign varieties. These Finnish-bred varieties comprise almost 50 per cent of all rye grown in Finland; native varieties, or selections from them, occupy the remainder of the acreage [62].

The most widely grown varieties of winter rye in the Soviet Union are Byatka, Lisitsina, and Yeliseyevka [59].

Black Winter is the rye variety commonly grown for green fodder in southern Victoria in Australia. Other varieties found there include Emerald and White. The Slave variety is grown in New South Wales [68].

GROWTH OF THE RYE PLANT

Rye will begin to germinate at a temperature as low as 33°F, but optimum temperatures range from 55–65°F. Northern ryes often cease germination above 85°F. Rye grain usually germinates after it has absorbed water equal to about 56 per cent of the grain weight. Under normal conditions winter rye tillers mainly in the fall. Appreciable growth ceases in the fall when mean temperatures drop below 40°F, but begins again in the spring when temperatures rise above 40°F [59]. However, slight growth may occur on sunny winter days when the air temperature in the shade does not exceed 32°F.

Winter rye requires exposure to cool temperatures of about 55°F to induce flowering. Temperatures between 34–39°F for 20–55 days are required to reach a high degree of winter hardening [59]. However, rye in a hardened condition shows less tendency to dormancy than do less hardy winter wheat varieties.

Some northern varieties of rye may require a photoperiod of 14 hours or more, with temperatures of 41–50°F, to induce flowering. Soviet Russian studies indicate that northern varieties require a longer photoperiod than do southern varieties [59].

The shooting stage is favored by cool temperatures of 59–63°F. Ripening normally takes place at temperatures of 60–68°F, while temperatures above 77°F may injure the crop. Winter rye may be scorched by prolonged exposure to temperatures of 100–104°F [59].

CULTURAL PRACTICES

Rye may replace wheat, oats, or barley in crop rotations that include small grains. Cultural requirements for rye are similar to those for wheat.

Seedbed Preparation

In the eastern United States, winter rye is sown on fall-plowed land to follow a close-drilled crop, but also occasionally to follow corn, cotton, or other intertilled crops. The plowed land usually is disked and harrowed before seeding the rye with a drill. When rye follows most clean cultivated crops, the seedbed may be prepared merely by disking and harrowing [29].

Rye grown in the northern Great Plains and Prairie states in the United States often is drilled in small grain stubble without previous preparation. This practice is satisfactory on reasonably weed-free land because of the economy of labor, and because it also leaves the stubble to hold the snow as a protection for the young rye plants. Rye also may be grown on disked corn land, fall-plowed land, or summer fallow in the Western states, but usually such land is reserved for wheat or other crops [40].

Seeding Practices

Winter rye can be sown at almost any time from late summer to late fall, but seeding should be sufficiently early for the plants to become established before winter begins. Early seeding produces the most pasturage. Rye generally should be sown at about the same time as winter wheat, but any delay in seeding is less important because rye grows better than wheat at low temperatures. It may be seeded safely as much as two weeks later than winter wheat in a given area. In the eastern United States, rye may be sown from about September 1 in the North to as late as November 30 in the South. In central Tennessee, the highest grain yields of Balbo rye are obtained from sowing about October 15 [56]. November seeding has resulted in the highest yields in the central Cotton Belt. It may be seeded

2–4 weeks earlier when grown for pasture, as a cover crop, or for green manure. In Florida, winter rye generally is seeded between October 1–November 15 for winter or early spring pasture [36]. In northern North Dakota and Minnesota, as well as in the prairie provinces of Canada, winter rye should be seeded between August 15–September 1. The seeding time in central South Dakota is during September, and grain yields are progressively lower as seeding is delayed after October 1 [21]. The best dates for Nebraska are from September 15–October 1, for Kansas about October 1, and south of Kansas from October 1–November 1.

As in the case of other spring grains, spring rye should be seeded as early as soil conditions are favorable [40].

Rye generally is seeded in the Western states at the rate of 3–6 pecks per acre, the lighter rates being prevalent under semiarid conditions [40]. The usual rate in the Northeastern states is 6–7 pecks, while in the Southeastern states it varies from 4–6 pecks. On sandy loam soils in the central Cotton Belt, the two-peck rate has produced the highest yield of Abruzzes rye, but at least three pecks usually are recommended.

Winter rye, because of its tall rank vegetative growth, is rather unsatisfactory as a companion crop for seeding with perennial cultivated grasses. The yields of perennial grasses in northern Utah were higher when sown alone than when seeded with a rye companion crop [73].

Harvest

Rye usually is harvested for grain like other small grains, except where special use is made of the straw. In that event, special threshers are used to thresh the grain from the heads in such a manner that only the upper portion of the bundle comes in contact with the thresher cylinder. Most of the American rye crop for grain is harvested with a combine.

CULTURAL PRACTICES IN OTHER COUNTRIES

In the Soviet Union, rye sown on fallow or fall-plowed land on the open Siberian prairies yields less than that sown on unplowed stubble land. Stubble catches more snow which protects the rye plants and supplies soil moisture. Drilling on stubble land between September 5–10 is advocated for the prairies or open regions of Siberia, Transural, and northern Kazakstan. Sowing on fallow generally is recommended in other regions [26].

In the British Isles, rye is grown mostly in the eastern counties on sandy acid soils where other cereals are poorly adapted. Rye usually follows either potatoes or wheat in rotations. It usually is sown between September 1–October 15, at the rate of 6–8 pecks of seed per acre. Commercial fertilizers seldom are used for rye. The rye field usually is harrowed and rolled in the spring. Rye is produced primarily for grain or for green fodder.

In the Mallee region of south Australia, rye is grown for pasture or for reclaiming semiabandoned loose sandhill land. It is generally sown at the rate of 40–56 pounds of seed per acre. In some regions, sandhills are sown to rye, allowed to reseed, and then used for grazing. It may be sown in the fall (April to as late as May 15) for sand drift control, but the plants must be established before the end of June [20]. Strict control of grazing is necessary on stabilized soils to prevent a recurrence of soil blowing [68]. In Australia, some rye is cut for hay or grain. In fact, a single rye field may be grazed in July, cut for hay in October, and harvested for grain in February. Rye is regarded as a less satisfactory hay crop than other cereals. In Australia, rye generally is cut for hay either in the blossom stage, or when dead ripe. When cut in bloom and fed to horses, the tough wiry awns may cause sore mouths, or in wet harvest weather the green hay may develop certain molds that have caused the death of horses. The awns break off when dead-ripe rye is cut for hay, but the stems are then tough, unpalatable, and low in digestible nutrients [58].

CHEMICAL COMPOSITION

Rye is similar to wheat in chemical composition, except in having a lower protein content (Table 17-1). The principal proteins in rye are a prolamin (gliadin), a glutelin, an albumin, and a globulin. The prolamin is similar to that found in wheat.

TABLE 17-1. **Proximate Composition of Rye and Winter Wheat.**

Constituents	Rye*	Wheat*	Rye Germ**
	(Pct)	(Pct)	(Pct)
Moisture	13.4	13.4	—
Protein	11.5	12.1	39.76
Oil or fat	1.7	1.9	13.23
Carbohydrates	69.5	69.0	27.37
Crude fiber (cellulose)	1.9	1.9	2.44
Mineral matter	2.0	1.7	4.97
Lignin	—	—	6.82

* After Kent-Jones and Amos, 1957.
** After Schuette and Palmer, 1938. Moisture-free basis.

The mineral matter of the rye germ is principally phosphorus, sulfur, magnesium, and potassium. The germ is particularly high in protein and in phosphorus.

MARKET GRADES

Under the Official Grain Standards of the United States, rye shall be any grain which, before the removal of dockage, consists of 50 per cent or more of rye and not more than 10 per cent of other grains for which standards have been established. Rye is graded in four numerical grades and sample grades (Table 17-2). There also are six special grades: plump, tough, smutty, garlicky, weevily, and ergoty. The word "ergoty" is made a part of the grade designation when rye contains more than 0.3 per cent of ergot [60].

TABLE 17-2. **U. S. Market Grades for Rye.**

Maximum Limits of

Grade No.	Minimum Test Weight per Bushel	Damaged Kernels (Rye and Other Grains)		Foreign Material Foreign Matter other than Wheat
		Total	Heat-Damaged	Total	
	(Lbs)	(Pct)	(Pct)	(Pct)	(Pct)
1*	56	2	0.1	3	1
2*	54	4	0.2	6	2
3*	52	7	0.5	10	4
4	49	15	3.0	10	6

Sample Grade: Sample grade shall include rye which does not come within the requirements of any of the grades from No. 1 to No. 4, inclusive; or which contains more than 16 per cent of moisture; or which contains inseparable stones and/or cinders; or which is musty, or sour, or heating, or hot; or which has any commercially objectionable foreign odor except of smut or garlic; or which contains a quantity of smut so great that any one or more of the grade requirements cannot be applied accurately; or which is otherwise of distinctly low quality.

* The rye in grade No. 1 may contain not more than 10.0 per cent, in grade No. 2 not more than 15.0 per cent, and in grade No. 3 not more than 25.0 per cent of "thin" rye, which "thin" rye shall consist of rye and other matter that will pass readily through a sieve 0.032 inch thick with perforations 0.064 × 0.375 inch.

MILLING

Rye is milled into flour by processes similar to those used for wheat. However, rye bran adheres closely to the endosperm, which makes a clean-cut separation of the middlings impractical. Also the middlings tend to flake rather than pulverize when ground between smooth rolls, so that the reduction rolls for rye are finely corrugated. In milling, 5–7 breaks generally are involved. The chop from the first break generally consists of 25–30 per cent flour which is sifted out. Flour of the highest grade comes from this first break; that from later breaks and reductions becomes darker in color as the purity decreases and has a more distinct rye flavor. Three grades of rye flour generally are produced in the United States: white, medium, and dark. The normal milling yield of rye is 65 per cent light or patent rye flour, and 15–20 per cent of offals [16].

UTILIZATION

About 20–25 per cent of the total rye grain production in the United States is consumed for food. Similar portions are used in making alcohol and distilled spirits (rye whiskey), and for sowing the total rye acreage. The annual per capita consumption of rye flour in recent years has been about two pounds.

Rye bread is widely consumed in northern Europe, partly because it is cheap, but also because many people enjoy it. Rye flour alone produces a heavy, sour, but nutritious bread. The protein content of rye flour is somewhat lower than in wheat flour. Because rye flour dough retains a much smaller quantity of gas than does dough made from wheat flour, rye bread in the United States usually is made from flour that contains an admixture of 25–50 per cent of clear or other grades of wheat flour. The wheat flour provides some gluten to retain the yeast fermentation gases which cause the dough to rise. The result is really a rye-flavored bread. Only 4–5 per cent of American bread is rye bread, and this is used mostly in sandwiches.

Nearly one-third of the rye grain produced is fed to livestock. Rye grain is not regarded highly as a concentrated feed for livestock unless mixed with other cereal grains. When fed alone, it is rather unpalatable as well as difficult to masticate. The proportion of rye in mixed feed usually is less than one-third. Rye shorts, or other rye-feed by-products of flour milling, should be mixed with other feeds. Sheep are reported to eat rye more readily than do other farm animals [58].

Rye pasture is less palatable than that of wheat, oats, or barley but is consumed readily when other pasturage is unavailable.

Rye straw is useful for bedding livestock, and has some feeding value. It formerly was widely used as packing material for nursery stock, crockery, and other products; straight and unbroken rye straw was used to stuff horse collars.

RYE DISEASES
Ergot

Ergot (*Claviceps purpurea*) is a serious disease which attacks rye as well as many grasses. It is prevalent throughout the world in humid and subhumid regions of the temperate zone.

In addition to causing serious losses in grain yield, the ergot bodies are poisonous to livestock and human beings. Rye is considered dangerous for feed or food when it contains more than 0.3 per cent of ergot sclerotia by weight. In large dosages, the ergot alkaloids cause constriction of the capillary blood vessels in certain tissues. Abortion often is caused in pregnant livestock. The effects of the ergot disease are cumulative. Frequently, continued dosages result in a breakdown of tissues in the limbs or extremities, such as ears, hoofs, and toes. Such action finally results in a numbness of the appendages, shrinkage, and finally dropping off. Death often occurred among humans as the result of ergot plagues during the Middle Ages. However, ergot also is a valuable drug, used extensively in obstetrics. It has been used by midwives for centuries in Europe, China, and Arabia [83].

The ergot disease is characterized by large spurlike purplish-black bodies or sclerotia that replace the kernel in the rye spikelet (Fig. 17-7). The spores of the fungus infect the ovaries at the time of flowering, and the honeydew stage becomes evident about 7–14 days later. Conidia formed at this time are disseminated to other plants by insects, rain, or wind. When the honeydew stage has run its course, the infected ovary changes into a horny sclerotium that projects from the spikelets. Many of these sclerotial bodies fall to the ground where they overwinter in the soil, and others may be sown with the seed of the next crop. The sclerotia germinate under favorable temperature and moisture conditions in the spring. Ascospores are formed which may cause the primary infection on rye or other grasses [82, 3].

The use of ergot-free seed or year-old seed is the most feasible method of control, for the ergot sclerotia lose their viability after about a year. The mowing of grasses along roadsides or on wastelands after blooming but just before the ergot develops reduces sources of ergot infection. Rotation of crops also is helpful. Ergot may be removed by pouring the infested grain into 20 per cent solution of common salt in water. Stirring brings the light ergot bodies to the surface where they may be skimmed or floated off. The salt must be washed from the seed and the seed partly dried before it is sown [3]. Resistant varieties of rye are unknown.

Stem or Stalk Smut

Stem or stalk smut caused by *Urocystis occulta* apparently is restricted

FIGURE 17-7. **Two rye spikes infected with ergot (left), ergot sclerotia (right below); rye grains (right above).**

(*Courtesy US Department of Agriculture*)

to rye, but it is common throughout the world. It is found in the rye-growing areas of Minnesota and nearby states. The stem smut of rye is closely related to flag smut of wheat but the hosts are different.

The disease becomes evident just before the rye heads appear. Affected plants are darker green than normal. Long narrow lead-colored streaks appear on the culms, sheaths, and blades. These streaks later turn black. The stems usually are twisted or distorted but finally may split to release the spore masses (Fig. 17-8). The plants are more or less dwarfed while the heads generally fail to emerge from the sheath. Those that do appear are almost always destroyed by smut. Some plants break over as the grain ripens. The spores, which are spread by wind, contaminate the soil as well as the seed of healthy plants [72, 33].

Infection occurs at soil temperatures from 41–77°F, but the optimum temperatures for infection are from 55–63°F. A relatively dry soil favors infection as well as subsequent development of the fungus in the host. High soil moisture—*i.e.,* 65 per cent of water-holding capacity—reduces the amount of infection. Smut infection lowers the winter survival of the plants [34, 35].

Stem smut can be controlled by crop rotation, seed treatment, and resistant varieties. One or more years between rye crops is effective since the spores usually fail to survive in the soil for more than one year. However, the soil may be reinfested by spores from nearby fields. Seed treatment protects smut-infested seed, but is ineffective against smut-infested soil. Seed may be treated for stem smut with Ceresan or other chemicals, as is wheat for protection against bunt [77, 33].

Anthracnose

Anthracnose, caused by *Colletotrichum graminicolum,* is an important rye disease, especially in the humid and subhumid eastern United States.

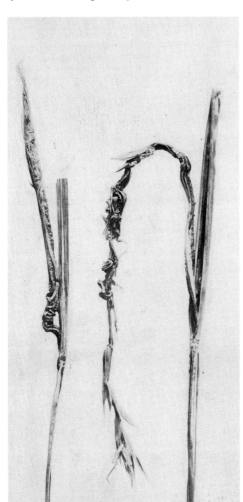

FIGURE 17-8. **Split stems and distorted heads of rye infected by stem smut.** (*Courtesy US Department of Agriculture*)

The disease appears to be associated with infertile soils. Infected plants often ripen or die prematurely. Diseased tissues at first are stained brown, but later the lower portions of the culms are blackened. Head infection, which also occurs, causes shriveled lightweight kernels. Control measures include crop rotation, plowing under crop residues, and improved soil fertility.

Rye Rusts

Leaf rust of rye, caused by *Puccinia recondita* (formerly *P. dispersa*) is widespread. Severe infection reduces tillering and grain yield. Ovate orange-colored uredia on the leaves continue to spread infection, and are followed by black teliospores that remain under the epidermis. It overwinters in the leaves of rye as dormant mycelium. The destruction of volunteer rye containing mycelia is an important control measure. No variety of rye is resistant, although resistant lines have been selected.

Stem rust, caused by *Puccinia graminis secalis,* usually causes only slight damage. The disease also develops on barley as well as on many grasses. The symptoms are similar to those for stem rust of wheat. This rust depends on the common barberry, the alternate host, for its existence in the Northern states. The small amount of rye in the Southern states lessens the danger from wind-blown spores.

Other Diseases

Minor diseases of rye include the wheat smuts, bunt (*Tilletia caries* and *T. foetida*) and loose smut (*Ustilago tritici*). Other diseases that occasionally damage rye are powdery mildew (*Erysiphe graminis secalis*), fusarium blight (*Gibberella* and *Fusarium* spp.), Rhynchosporium leaf scald (*Rhynchosporium secalis*), septoria leaf blotch (*Septoria secalis*), bacterial blight (*Xanthomonas translucens*), and mosaic.

INSECTS

Rye is attacked by many of the same insects, such as grasshoppers, chinch bugs, Hessian fly, jointworm, and sawfly, that attack other small grains. Total losses on rye are seldom serious. The Hessian fly is less harmful to rye than to wheat, but early-sown winter rye provides a favorable environment for the deposition of grasshopper eggs, which may promote grasshopper injury to other crops.

CYTOGENETICS

Aneuploids

Cultivated rye has 7 haploid and 14 diploid chromosomes [38], but occasional plants have an extra pair of fragments of accessory "B" chromosomes. The 16-chromosome strains of rye are probably short-lived, but others arise from normal plants [45]. Rye lacks cytological stability, which is associated with frequent partial sterility [54]. Occasionally additional fragments are present. The larger fragments may undergo postmeiotic nondisjunction, which doubles the fragment number in such progeny [46, 47, 48). The fragments contain fewer active genes than do ordinary chromosomes. The fragments sometimes pair normally at meiosis [18], while their offspring may have 0–8 fragments. Fragment chromosomes reduce fertility more than they restrict vegetative development. Increasing numbers of fragments cause corresponding reductions in pollen fertility and number of kernels per head. Primitive ryes from Anatolia in Asia Minor, the area of the supposed origin of cultivated rye, contain strains with a high frequency of accessory chromosomes [51].

Autotetraploids

An autotetraploid induced in diploid Rosen rye by a heat treatment [13], was highly sterile but increased fertility was obtained by continued selection in Sweden. Another tetraploid rye was obtained from the Ostgota Grarag variety in Sweden. Other tetraploid strains produced from the Stalrag and Wasa II varieties by colchicine treatment in Sweden had stiff straw, good tillering, good kernel quality, and were practically as early as the diploid strains [50].

Meiosis in autotetraploid rye has been characterized by multivalent associations [61], generally with a high frequency of quadrivalents at the first division. The number of quadrivalents in four tetraploid varieties averaged 3.95–4.29 [52]. About 15 per cent of the plants in a population of autotetraploid rye were aneuploids with 27, 29 or 30 chromosomes. These aneuploids had lower seed setting than those plants with 28 chromosomes [43].

Fertility in diploid varieties exceeds that in tetraploids by 10 per cent [43], or more. However, the best tetraploid varieties are equal to their respective diploids in yield, stiffness of straw, earliness, frost resistance, and drought resistance. The kernels are about 53 per cent heavier than in diploid rye, and they germinate better; but the seed-set is 20–25 per cent less, tillering is about 12 per cent less, and there are fewer flowers per spike and a greater tendency to shed the basal spikelets before maturity [52].

Drawbacks to tetraploid rye are tall straw which makes combine harvest difficult, large kernels which necessitate more seed per acre, but especially the need for isolation from ordinary rye to avoid a low seed-set. Tetraploid Stalrag (Steel rye) is grown in Sweden because of its good baking quality.

The 3 possible F_1 hybrids that involve tetraploid strains of the Petkus, Steel, and King varieties yielded about 19 per cent more grain than the parents. The hybrids had more flowers per head, a higher seed set, and more mature plants per plot [53].

Tetraploid ryes pollinated by diploids produced some seed, but reciprocal crosses were sterile because of failure of pollen-tube growth [8]. The seed set of Tetra Petkus was 16.1 per cent and 20.3 per cent when interpollinated with the Emerald and Imperial diploid varieties, respectively. The fertility of Tetra Petkus, when exposed to pollen of diploid varieties, was about one-half to two-thirds of that when isolated from diploids [25]. Seed produced by such crosses usually is shriveled [19].

Haploidy

One haploid (7-chromosome) rye plant that arose in Sweden, apparently as a result of low temperature, grew slowly and died before it headed [44]. Another haploid obtained by heat treatment (105.8°F) of the pollinated flower was stunted, produced few good pollen grains, and failed to dehisce [57].

Wheat-Rye Hybrids

Rye has been crossed with most wheat species [16]. The 42-chromosome wheats are fertilized fairly readily with rye pollen, but the 28-chromosome wheats are difficult to cross with rye [14]. Successful reciprocal (rye × wheat) crosses are rare.

Amphidiploid wheat-rye (*Triticale*) hybrids have 56 somatic chromosomes, the total from both parents (42 + 14). They are fertile, do not segregate, and have characters intermediate between wheat and rye [76, 15]. Such amphidiploids occur occasionally from simple crossing, but they also have been induced by heat treatment [13], and by colchicine treatment of wheat-rye crosses [9, 50]. So far, none of these amphidiploids has proved of practical value [50].

One aim in wheat-rye crossing has been to transfer the winter hardiness of winter rye to winter wheat, but this has not been successful even by backcrossing of F_1 wheat-rye hybrids to winter wheat [14]. Wheats that carry an addition of one or two pairs of rye chromosomes are often unstable, have objectionable rye characters, and show no evidence of great cold resistance. Since rye and wheat chromosomes are not known to pair, it may be impossible to transfer the genes for hardiness in rye into the wheat chromosomes. First generation wheat-rye crosses, except amphidiploids, are almost completely self-sterile [30]. Fertility is increased by backcrossing to wheat, and the progeny become more wheatlike as they lose rye chromosomes. Some with one pair of rye chromosomes have the characteristic hairy neck of rye [14], but this character is unstable because 1 per cent or more of the progeny have smooth necks as a result of a loss of rye chromosomes. Some wheat-rye segregates are fully as fertile as wheat [75]. Hairy-neck is a simple Mendelian character [23]. One wheat variety from China crosses readily with rye and produces a good seed set. This crossability can be transferred to more desirable winter wheats [76]. Wheat-rye segregates can be improved by selection [50], but a true wheat type with desired rye characters of practical value has never been obtained.

Other Intergeneric Rye Hybrids

Crosses between cultivated rye and wild rye (*S. montanum*) are vigorous, partly fertile, and show nearly normal chromosome behavior [38]. Pollen and seed fertilities in the hybrids of only 18.6 and 20.4 per cent, respectively, still permitted recombinations of genes from the two parents [64]. Rye has been crossed with several *Aegilops* species with varied results. When *Haynaldia villosa* was pollinated with cultivated rye, neither embryo nor endosperm was produced, while crosses with *Secale fragile* produced F_1 plants that were completely self-sterile [65].

Squirrel-tail barley (*Hordeum jubatum*) ($n = 14$) and cultivated rye (*Secale cereale*) ($n = 7$) cross readily, but produce almost no seed because the embryo and endosperm develop poorly, and collapse about 6–13 days after fertilization [12]. One excised embryo grown on an artificial medium produced a sterile plant [6].

GENETICS

Self-sterility in rye limits inheritance studies [41].

Green aleurone is a simple dominant to yellow, and is expressed as xenia [71].

Crosses that involve short broad head vs. long narrow head and lax vs. dense head are intermediate in the F_1 generation, while the F_2 segregate as a monogenic 1:2:1 ratio. Short spikes are associated with short culms. Several genes appear to be involved in the inheritance of kernel and culm length.

Hairy culm and sheath of wild rye are dominant over the glabrous condition in cultivated sorts. Brittle plant is a monogenic recessive, while waxiness of stems, leaves, and glumes in wild rye is a simple dominant to the nonwaxy cultivated type.

Yellow seedling, white seedling, yellow-green plant stripe, golden-green blend, and virescent-white are simple recessives to normal green.

Self-sterility has been reported as a simple dominant to self-fertility, but forms with constant intermediate self-sterility indicate that several genes often are involved. Environmental effects make the evaluation of sterility very difficult.

Spring growth habit appears to be partly dominant over winter habit, with monogenic inheritance. Earliness appears to be dominant over lateness, but several genes probably are involved. The perennial habit of wild rye behaves as a dominant over the annual habit of cultivated rye.

In some cases, resistance appears to be dominant over susceptibility to leaf rust, stem rust, and powdery mildew.

RYE BREEDING

Varietal improvement in rye generally has been brought about by mass selection or by compositing inbred lines.

Fertility Problem

Self-sterility is a common phenomenon in rye, but only about half the plants of a Swedish variety were partly self-sterile. Pollen viability ranged from 0–90 per cent. Seed set in the Ostgota Grarag variety was much less than in the Stalrag (Steel) variety. A low seed set is associated with low pollen viability [49].

The fertility of inbred lines usually is low, but has been increased by selection from 6.5 per cent up to 50 per cent [32]. A large proportion of self-pollinated ovaries soon abort [27]. The degree of chromosome pairing, and of fertility also, was reduced by three generations of inbreeding [55].

Self-incompatibility in Steel rye seems to be controlled by the interaction of genetic factors [39].

Rye Improvement by Inbreeding

Self-fertilization of rye plants permitted the isolation of several lines that bred true for uniform grain color, and were nearly pure for several other characters. Most of the lines showed a general reduction in vigor, height, grain plumpness, and yield. Many plant abnormalities were uncovered by selfing. Some lines were nearly self-fertile, but others set only a few seeds. No selfed line was as vigorous as the open-pollinated variety [4].

Some crosses of inbred lines are superior to open-pollinated rye [32], but the progeny of a cross between fertile and sterile inbred lines of rye lost most of the sterility in later generations [63].

Moderate inbreeding has been used in developing new varieties in Sweden. The progeny of selected plants is isolated one or two generations later. The Kungsrag II variety arose from a single plant selected from Stalrag. The moderately inbred strains are uniform enough for practical culture [37]. Pierre rye is a synthetic variety developed in South Dakota as a composite of 16 selected inbred lines that were allowed to interpollinate to produce the commercial variety [17].

Polycrosses have been studied at the Minnesota Station as a means for testing the comparative performance of rye inbreds. The plants were selected on the basis of relatively high seed setting. Colorless aleurone and green aleurone selections of rye of comparatively high self-fertility that had been self-pollinated for 1–19 generations were grown in two separate nurseries and allowed to interpollinate. Most of the lines were derived either from Dakold or from the Emerald variety. Most of the 43 resulting polycrosses tested were superior to the standard varieties in yield and vigor. Apparently, the degree of inbreeding or self-fertility of the selected lines had little effect on the yield of the polycross progenies [80].

Mass Selection Methods

In Sweden, so-called family groups of improved rye varieties have been maintained by mass selection, together with isolation within wheat fields at a distance of about 200 yards from other rye. Some 5000–10,000 seeds within each family group are space-planted. Typical well-developed plants, 10–20 per cent of the total, are selected at harvest. Progenies of some of the very best plants are kept separate within the family group the next year. The remainder are massed for sowing in the isolation plot for the following year. Grain harvested from these larger plots is used for the production of elite seed of the varieties. New elite seed stock is brought out every second year. Repeated mass selection changes the genetic composition of the family, particularly of one derived from a cross between two varieties [37].

Raritan rye was produced in New Jersey by selecting 216 strains from a mass composite of 10 varieties. After continuous selection for several years, 98 lines were bulked and allowed to interpollinate. The grain yield of the new variety exceeded that of common rye by 10–12 per cent [71].

REFERENCES

1. Aberg, E., "Recent changes in Swedish crop production," in *Advances in Agronomy*, Vol. 7. New York: Academic Press, pp 39–74. 1955.
2. "Agricultural Statistics, 1960." USDA, pp 1–633. 1961.
3. Brentzel, W. E., "Studies on ergot of grains and grasses." N. Dak. Ag. Exp. Sta. *Tech. Bul. 348*. 1947.
4. Brewbaker, H. E., "Studies of self-fertilization in rye." Minn. Ag. Exp. Sta. *Tech. Bul. 40*. 1926.
5. Briggle, L. W., "Growing rye." USDA *Farmers Bul. 2145*. 1959.
6. Brink, R. A., D. C. Cooper, and L. E. Ausherman, "A hybrid between *Hordeum jubatum* and *Secale cereale* reared from an artificially cultivated embryo." *J. Hered.*, **35**: 66–75. 1944.
7. Champlin, M. J., "A quarter century of crop rotation experiments." Sask. Ag. *Ext. Bul. 129*. 1951.
8. Chin, T. C., "Cytology of the autotetraploid rye." *Bot. Gaz.*, **104**(4): 627–632. 1943.
9. ———, "Wheat-rye hybrids." *J. Hered.*, **37**(7): 195–196. 1946.
10. Clark, J. A., "Improvement in wheat," in USDA Yrbk. of Ag., pp 207–302. 1936.
11. Collier, G. A., "Grain production and marketing." USDA *Miscel. Publ. 692*. 1949.
12. Cooper, D. C., and R. A. Brink, "Collapse of the seed following the mating of *Hordeum jubatum* × *Secale cereale*." *Genetics*, **29**: 370–390. 1944.
13. Dorsey, E., "Induced polyploidy in wheat and rye." *J. Hered.*, **27**: 155–160. 1936.
14. Florell, V. H., "A genetic study of wheat × rye hybrids and backcrosses." *J. Ag. Res.*, **42**: 315–339. 1931.
15. ———, "Chromosome differences in a wheat-rye amphidiploid." *J. Ag. Res.*, **52**(3): 199–204. 1936.
16. Geddes, W. F., "Technology of cereal grains," in *Chemistry and Technology of Food and Food Products*, 2nd ed., Vol. III. New York: Interscience, pp 2018–2090. 1951.
17. Grafius, J. E., "Pierre rye." S. Dak. Ag. Exp. Sta. *Bul. 406*. 1951.
18. Hakansson, A., "Behavior of accessory rye chromosomes in the embryo sac." *Hereditas*, **34**(1-2): 35–59. 1948.
19. ———, and S. Ellerstrom, "Seed development after reciprocal crosses between diploid and tetraploid rye." *Hereditas*, **36**: 256–296. 1950.
20. Herriot, R. I., "Rye." *J. Dept. Ag. So. Austral.*, **51**(6): 319–326. 1948.
21. Hume, A. N., E. W. Hardies, and C. Franzke, "The date of seeding winter rye." S. Dak. Ag. Exp. Sta. *Bul. 220*. 1926.
22. Jasny, N., *Competition Among Grains*. Stanford U. Food Res. Inst., pp 1–606. 1940.
23. Jones, J. W., and N. F. Jensen, "Behavior of the hairy neck in wheat-rye hybrid." *Agron. J.*, **46**(2): 78–80. 1954.
24. Kent-Jones, D. W., and A. J. Amos, *Modern Cereal Chemistry*, 5th ed. Liverpool: Northern Publ. Co. pp 1–817. 1957.
25. Koo, F. K. S., "Deleterious effects from interpollination of diploid and auto-tetraploid winter rye varieties." *Agron. J.*, **50**: 171–172. 1958.
26. Krimgold, D. B., "Planting winter wheat and rye in unplowed stubble." *J. Am. Soc. Agron.*, **37**: 655–660. 1945.
27. Landes, M., "The causes of self-sterility in rye." *Am. J. Bot.*, **26**: 567–571. 1939.

28. Laude, H. H., "Cold resistance of winter wheat, rye, barley, and oats, in transition from dormancy to active growth." *J. Ag. Res.*, **54**(12): 899–917. 1937.
29. Leighty, C. E., "Rye growing in the southeastern states." USDA *Farmers Bul. 894.* 1917.
30. ———, and J. W. Taylor, "Hairy neck wheat segregates from wheat-rye hybrids." *J. Ag. Res.*, **28**: 567–576. 1924.
31. Leith, B. D., "Sterility in rye." *J. Am. Soc. Agron.*, **17**: 129–132. 1925.
32. ———, and H. L. Shands, "Fertility as a factor in rye improvement." *J. Am. Soc. Agron.*, **30**: 406–418. 1938.
33. Leukel, R. W., and V. F. Tapke, "Cereal smuts and their control." USDA *Farmers Bul. 2069.* 1954.
34. Ling, L., "Factors affecting infection in rye smut and subsequent development of the fungus in the host." *Phytopath.*, **31**: 617–633. 1941.
35. ———, and M. B. Moore, "Influence of soil temperature and soil moisture on infection of stem smut of rye." *Phytopath.*, **27**: 633–636. 1937.
36. Litzenberger, S. C., W. H. Chapman, and W. A. Carver, "Oat and rye recommendations for northern Florida for 1948–1949." Fla. Ag. Exp. Sta. *Bul. 653.* 1948.
37. Ljung, E. W., "The rye breeding work of the seed association," in *Svalof 1886–1946*, Lund, Sweden: Carl Bloms Boktryckeri A.-B., pp 127–134. 1948.
38. Longley, A. E., and W. J. Sando, "Nuclear divisions in the pollen mother cells of Triticum, Aegilops, and Secale and their hybrids." *J. Ag. Res.*, **40**(8):683–719. 1930.
39. Lundqvist, A., "Studies on self-sterility in rye, *Secale cereale*, L." *Hereditas*, **40**: 278–294. 1954.
40. Martin, J. H., and R. W. Smith, "Growing rye in the western half of the United States." USDA *Farmers Bul. 1358.* 1923.
41. Matsuura, H., *A Bibliographical Monograph on Plant Genetics.* 2nd ed. Hokkaido Imp. U., Japan. pp 395–399. 1933.
42. Mooers, C. A., "Balbo rye." Tenn. Ag. Exp. Sta. *Cir. 45.* 1933.
43. Morrison, J. W., "Chromosome behavior and fertility of Tetra Petkus rye." *Can. J. Ag. Sci.*, **36**: 157–165. 1956.
44. Muntzing, A., "Note on a haploid rye plant." *Hereditas*, **23**: 401–404. 1937.
45. ———, "Genetical effects of duplicated fragment chromosomes in rye." *Hereditas* **29**: 91–112. 1943.
46. ———, "Cytological studies of extra fragment chromosomes in rye. I: Iso-fragments produced by misdivision." *Hereditas*, **30**: 231–248. 1944.
47. ———, "Cytological studies of extra fragment chromosomes in rye. II: Transmission and multiplication of standard fragments and iso-fragments." *Hereditas*, **31**: 457–477. 1945.
48. ———, "Cytological studies of extra fragment chromosomes in rye. III: The mechanism of non-disjunction at the pollen mitosis." *Hereditas*, **32**: 97–119. 1946.
49. ———, "Sterility in rye populations." *Hereditas*, **32**: 521–549. 1946.
50. ———, "Experiences from work with induced polyploidy in cereals," in *Svalof 1886–1946*, Lund, Sweden: Carl Bloms Boktryckeri A.-B., pp 324–337. 1948.
51. ———, "Accessory chromosomes in rye populations from Turkey and Afghanistan." *Hereditas*, **36**: 507–509. 1950.

52. ——, "Cyto-genetic properties and practical value of tetraploid rye." *Hereditas*, **37**: 17–84. 1951.

53. ——, "An analysis of hybrid vigor in tetraploid rye." *Hereditas*, **40**: 265–277. 1954.

54. ——, and R. Prakken, "Chromosomal aberattions in rye populations." *Hereditas*, **27**: 271–308. 1941.

55. ——, and S. Akdik, "Cytological disturbance in the first inbred generation of rye." *Hereditas*, **34**(4): 485–509. 1948.

56. Neel, L. R., "Rye for pasture and seed in Tennessee." Tenn. Ag. Exp. Sta. *Cir. 52*. 1935.

57. Nordenskiold, H., "Studies of a haploid rye plant." *Hereditas*, **25**: 204–210. 1939.

58. Norman, L. S., "Rye growing." *S. Austral. Dep. Ag. J.*, **47**(1): 43–45. 1943.

59. Nuttonson, M. Y., "Rye-climate relationships and the use of phenology in ascertaining the thermal and photothermal requirements of rye." Washington, D.C.: Am. Inst. Crop Ecol. pp 1–219. 1958.

60. "Official grain standards of the United States." USDA *SRA-AMS-177*. pp 1–93. 1960.

61. O'Mara, J. G., "Meiosis in autotetraploid rye." *Bot. Gaz.*, **104**: 563–575. 1943.

62. Pesola, V. A., "Rye and wheat breeding in Finland." *Heredity*, **2**: 141–143. 1948.

63. Peterson, R. F., "Improvement of rye through inbreeding." *Sci. Ag.*, **14**: 651–668. 1934.

64. Price, S., "Irradiation and interspecific hybridization in Secale." *Genetics*, **40**: 651–667. 1955.

65. Sando, W. J., "Intergeneric hybrids of Triticum and Secale with *Haynaldia villosa*." *J. Ag. Res.*, **51**(9): 759–800. 1935.

66. Schaben, L. J., "Rye—a source of daily bread." *For. Ag.*, **12**: 163–168. 1948.

67. Schuette, H. A., and R. C. Palmer, "The chemistry of the rye germ. IV: Its proximate composition." *Cer. Chem.* **15**: 445–450. 1938.

68. Simms, H. J., "Ryecorn—a cereal for winter grazing and drift control in the Mallee." *Victoria Dep. Ag. J.*, **42**(3): 151–154. 1944.

69. Spragg, F. A., "Red Rock wheat and Rosen rye." *J. Am. Soc. Agron.*, **10**: 167–171. 1918.

70. ——, "Rosen rye." Mich. Ag. Exp. Sta. *Spec. Bul. 105*. 1921.

71. Sprague, H. B., "Breeding rye by continuous selection." *J. Am. Soc. Agron.*, **30**: 287–293. 1938.

72. Stakman, E. C., and M. N. Levine, "Rye smut." Minn. Ag. Exp. Sta. *Bul. 160*. 1916.

73. Stoddart, L. A., "Rye nurse crops in range reseeding." *Ecology*, **27**: 61–64. 1946.

74. Taylor, A. E., "Rye in its relation to wheat." Stanford U. Food Res. Inst. *Wheat Studies*, **4**(5): 181–234. 1928.

75. Taylor, J. W., "Irregularities in the inheritance of the hairy-neck character transposed from Secale to Triticum." *J. Ag. Res.*, **48**(7): 603–617. 1934.

76. ——, and K. S. Quisenberry, "Inheritance of rye crossability in wheat hybrids." *J. Am. Soc. Agron.*, **27**: 149–153. 1935.

77. Taylor, R. E., and W. A. R. Dillion Weston, "Seed disinfection. VI: Stripe smut of rye." *J. Ag. Sci.*, **35**: 116–118. 1945.

78. Vavilov, N. I., "On the origin of cultivated rye." *Bul. Appl. Bot.*, **10**: 561–590. 1917.

79. ——, "The origin, variation, immunity, and breeding of cultivated plants." (Trans. by K. Starr Chester). *Chronica Botanica*, **13**(1-6): 1949–50.

80. Warren, F. S., and H. K. Hayes, "Correlation studies of yield and other characters in rye polycrosses." *Sci. Ag.*, **30**: 12–29. 1950.
81. Weaver, J. E., *Root Development of Field Crops*. New York: McGraw-Hill, pp 162–166. 1926.
82. Weniger, Wanda, "Ergot and its control." N. Dak. Ag. Exp. Sta. *Bul. 176*. 1924.
83. Youngken, Jr., H. W., "Ergot—a blessing and a scourge." *Econ. Bot.*, **1**(4): 372–380. 1947.

18. BARLEY[1]

ECONOMIC IMPORTANCE

Barley is grown in nearly all cultivated areas of the temperate zones, in many subtropical areas, and in high altitude sections of the torrid zones of both hemispheres. It is an important crop in Europe, North Africa, much of Asia, North America, Argentina, and Australia. In the Old World barley is grown largely for human food; in the New World, it is produced mainly for livestock feed [36].

The world barley acreage for the period from 1950–54 averaged approximately 121.18 million acres annually, with a yield of 22.2 bushels per acre. The average production for these years was about 2.69 billion bushels. The principal producers were the U.S.S.R., China, United States, Canada, Turkey, India, and the United Kingdom (Fig. 18-1).

In the United States, barley is most widely grown in the North Central states and in California. Much of the barley acreage is north and west of the region in which corn is the dominant crop. The average annual production in the United States from 1952–61 was 377 million bushels on 12.9 million acres. The average yield was 29.2 bushels per acre. The states that led in barley production during this period were California, North Dakota, Minnesota, Montana, and South Dakota [7] (Fig. 18-2). Practically all of the commercial barley was of the covered or hulled type.

HISTORY OF BARLEY CULTURE

Barley is regarded by many as the most ancient cultivated grain. Heads, carbonized grains, and impressions of grains on vessels have been

---

[1] The authors have received valuable suggestions on barley in California from Dr. Coit A. Suneson, Agricultural Research Service, U.S. Department of Agriculture, Davis, California.

unearthed in several countries. Barley grains have been found in straw-lined pits in the Fayum in Egypt, about 60 miles southwest of Cairo. These excavations disclosed the remains of a Neolithic race that cultivated barley there some 5000–10,000 years ago. The Fayum Neolithic grain was identified as six-rowed barley, but the sample contained a mixture of about 25 per cent of emmer [11]. Six-rowed cultivated barley, similar to that known to-day as "Manchuria" barley, was also obtained from an excavation at the Saqqara Pyramid in Egypt [4]. Monuments of ancient Babylon contained figures of six-rowed barley. There is also evidence that the crop was grown by the Swiss Lake Dwellers of the Stone Age—*i.e.,* between 2000–3000 BC [11]. Prehistoric remains in China contain tortoise-shells and bone fragments engraved with idiographs that represented barley. Such idiographs are also found in some Chinese archives that date back to about 200 BC. Barley probably was introduced into Japan from Korea at the dawn of Japanese history (circa 100 BC). It is generally recognized that six-rowed barley was cultivated earlier than were the two-rowed forms. The oldest authentic records of two-rowed barley were found in Greek-Roman archives dated about 300 BC [108]. There are indications that barley was once more highly esteemed than wheat, as a staple food, although it has generally been replaced in more recent times by the extended cultivation of wheat and rye. Barley has maintained its eminent place in agriculture largely because of its malting properties [92].

Barley was brought to North America by the early colonists. Some English barley was grown on the islands off the south coast of Massachusetts in 1602. In Canada, barley was sown at Port Royal in Nova Scotia in 1606. The crop was under cultivation in Virginia in 1611, and the Dutch settlers on Manhattan Island harvested barley in 1626. It was carried West by the early settlers. Spanish settlers from Mexico introduced Coast barley into Arizona in 1701, and into California in 1771. The winter barleys were introduced into the southeastern United States, probably from Switzerland or the Balkans, at an early but unknown date. Hooded barley was introduced into the United States from Nepal in 1840. The Manchuria-Oderbrucker barleys became established in the upper Mississippi Valley between 1860–90. Several of the present two-rowed varieties were brought in from Sweden and Germany about 1900 [119].

ORIGIN OF CULTIVATED BARLEY

Geographical Centers of Origin

Some of the early investigators considered Mesopotamia to be the center of origin of cultivated barley, but N. I. Vavilov [115, 116] considered that Abyssinia was the principal center, because many diverse forms grow

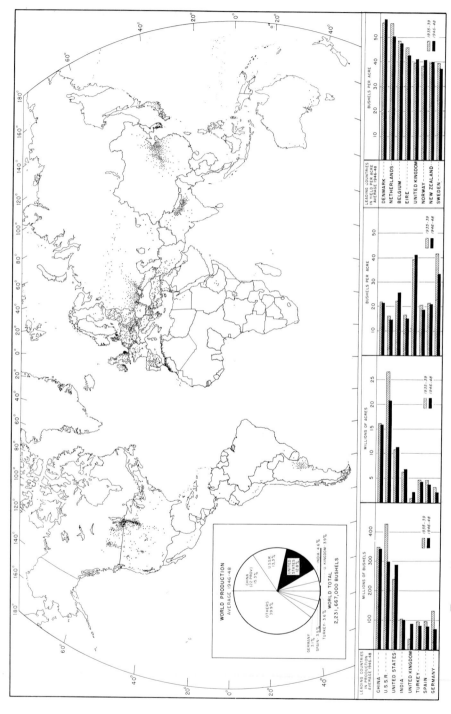

FIGURE 18-1. World barley production; average of 1946-48. Each dot represents 1,000,000 bushels.

(*Courtesy US Department of Agriculture*)

wild there. This region is particularly rich in hulled, awned types. Another possible center of origin is southeastern Asia, particularly China, Tibet, and Nepal, which is characterized by hull-less six-rowed varieties and by short-awned, awnless, and hooded forms. The first cultivation of wild six-rowed barley may have started in East Asia [108], the southeast valleys of the Himalaya Mountains [15], or in the Hindu-Kush Mountains of West Pakistan [67].

Theories of Botanical Origin

Until rather recently, it was generally assumed that cultivated barley originated from *Hordeum spontaneum,* a wild two-rowed species with a brittle rachis which crosses readily with cultivated barleys. This theory still has its supporters [96].

A monophyletic origin of cultivated barley, postulated by Aberg (1938, 1940, 1948), is based on the discovery of a wild six-rowed spring barley, *H. agriocrithon,* in Tibet. This species crosses readily with cultivated types, and also has a brittle rachis. Cultivated barley, through a genetic change, developed a tough rachis. Three possible schemes of phylogenetic development of cultivated barleys were listed:

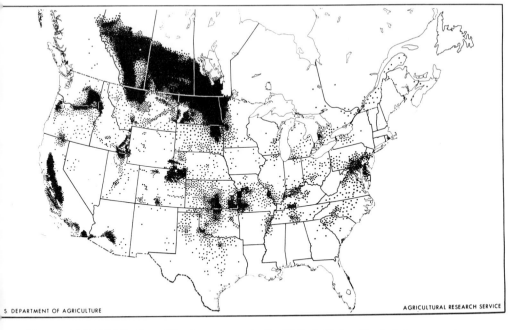

S DEPARTMENT OF AGRICULTURE   AGRICULTURAL RESEARCH SERVICE

FIGURE 18-2. **Distribution of barley acreage in the United States. Each dot represents 2,000 acres.**

(Courtesy US Department of Agriculture)

1. The six-rowed brittle-eared forms developed into six-rowed, tough-eared types, from which two-rowed, tough-eared forms evolved.
2. The six-rowed, brittle-eared forms developed into two-rowed, brittle-eared types, which then gave rise to two-rowed, tough-eared species.
3. The two-rowed, tough-eared forms arose from hybrids between two-rowed, brittle-eared and six-rowed, tough-eared barleys. The two-rowed, brittle-eared species developed by reduction from the six-rowed, brittle-eared forms, and thus would not have produced two-rowed, tough-eared types. The species *H. irregulare* was considered to be a cross between *H. vulgare* and *H. distichum*.

It was concluded that the phylogenetic development was partly a process of reduction. Thus, the shortening of branches produced a spike or head from a panicle, the several spikelets were reduced to one at the rachis nodes, and the several flowers in the spikelets were reduced to one. The three possible schemes of phylogenetic development of cultivated barley are given in Fig. 18-3.

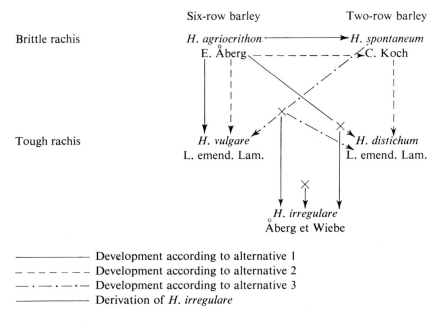

            Development according to alternative 1
– – – – – –   Development according to alternative 2
— . — . — . —   Development according to alternative 3
            Derivation of *H. irregulare*

FIG. 18–3 : **Three possible schemata of phylogenetic development within Cerealia Ands [3].**

A hypothesis of diphyletic origin of cultivated barley [108] assumes that some primitive cultivated forms of *H. agriocrithon* became differentiated by mutation from brittle to tough rachis (Bt2 to bt2) in eastern Asia. These or their derivatives gradually spread over various parts of the world.

Later, two-rowed cultivated forms appeared by mutation from brittle to tough rachis (Bt to bt) in *H. spontaneum* that grew in southwestern Asia. These two-rowed cultivated forms crossed repeatedly with six-rowed varieties of genotype Bt Bt bt2 bt2 to give rise to new two-rowed and six-rowed forms that became the cultivated varieties of Asia and Occidental countries. This hypothesis is diagramed in Fig. 18-4.

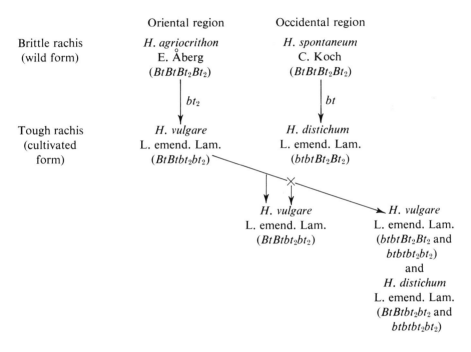

FIG. 18–4: **Phylogeny and geographic differentiation in cultivated barleys.**

GENERAL ADAPTATION

Barley is grown from the Arctic Circle to the tropical plains of northern India. It is found beside pools of frozen water in Ethiopia as well as beneath date palms in the Sahara Desert. Barley adapted itself to the high plateaus of Bolivia, South Africa, and Tibet; to the hills of western China; and to the alkaline desert lowlands of Egypt, Turkestan, and Australia. One form of barley with recurved stalks grows on the slopes of the Himalaya Mountains, well above 15,000 feet in elevation. Barley is one of the most dependable crops where drought, frost, and alkali are to be encountered [36, 119].

Climatic Conditions

Barley grows particularly well where the ripening season is long and cool. While it will withstand much dry heat, it does not thrive in hot humid climates, probably due to the greater prevalence of disease in such climates. It grows better with moderate rather than excessive rainfall. In areas where the crop is adapted, barley usually matures early enough to escape serious drought and rust attacks [36].

Some varieties of spring barley mature in 60–70 days, or even earlier than spring types of rye, wheat, or oats [90]. Certain strains of naked spring barley from Tibet are characterized by remarkable resistance to cold as well as by early ripening [15]. Consequently, spring barley is grown farther north and at higher altitudes than any other cereal. In the United States, from western Iowa eastward to the Atlantic seaboard, the 70°F isotherm of average summer (June, July, August) temperature approximates the southern limit of dependable growth of spring barley. Farther west, this isotherm swings northward in South Dakota, but ultimately, under the influence of increased elevation, it swings southward in the Great Plains through western Nebraska, eastern Colorado, and eastern New Mexico. There is, however, no large-scale spring barley production in the United States in regions where the average annual rainfall exceeds 35 inches [118].

Since about 1940, spring barley has been largely replaced by other crops in southern Michigan, eastern Wisconsin, and southeastern Minnesota, where much of the malting barley formerly was grown. In the same period, spring barley production increased correspondingly in the drier areas of North Dakota and Montana.

Winter-hardy forms are generally associated with a winter habit of growth [43, 6]. Barley grown in the subtropics or other warm regions consists of varieties of spring growth habit seeded in the fall. The crop grows under cool winter conditions, and then matures in time to escape the humid summer climate. Spring-type barleys are fall-seeded in Japan [54], India, Mexico, California and Arizona, and in the Mediterranean countries of Europe, Africa, and Asia. Only winter barleys are generally adapted to the southeastern United States. True winter barleys are less hardy than either winter rye or winter wheat. Spring barley varieties fall-sown in Tennessee winter-killed frequently, even where the minimum temperature is never below 12°F [32]. The northern limit of winter barley production formerly followed closely the isotherm of 30°F for average winter (December, January, February) temperature. Extensive winter barley production was unsuccessful where the average winter temperature was much below the freezing point. South of the winter isotherm of 30°F, the cultivation of winter barley extended westward to about the position of the 25-inch rainfall line. Beyond this area, increased dryness added to low temperatures brings about a greater likelihood of winter killing [118].

Since 1945, hardier winter varieties—such as Kearney, Dicktoo, and Hudson—have been released. This has extended winter barley production northward into New York, as well as northward and westward from southeastern Kansas into Nebraska, Colorado, and South Dakota. Thus, winter barley now succeeds where the average winter temperature is less than 25°F.

SOIL CONDITIONS

Barley is best adapted to well-drained, fertile, deep-loam soils with a pH of 7–8. It generally produces low yields on sandy soils. Moderately fertile soils favor a rapid vigorous growth, but barley grown on soils high in nitrogen often lodges with consequent low grain yields. Some varieties have a very high salt tolerance, an important factor in stand establishment as well as in grain yield on much of the saline land in the western United States. The California Mariout variety, for instance, is very tolerant: more than 50 per cent of its seeds germinated and emerged within ten days where the soil solution had a concentration of approximately 19 atmospheres, whereas there was no emergence of the sensitive Arivat variety under similar conditions [10]. In general, the barley plant is considered to be more tolerant to soil salinity and alkalinity, but more sensitive to soil acidity, than are the other cereals.

CHARACTERISTICS OF GENUS HORDEUM

The genus *Hordeum* was described by Linnaeus in 1754, and also by Aberg and Wiebe [6]:

> Genus *Hordeum:* Spike indeterminate, dense, sometimes flattened, with brittle, less frequently tough awns. Rachis tough or brittle. Spikelets in triplets, single-flowered, but sometimes with rudiments of a second floret. Central florets fertile, sessile or nearly so, lateral florets reduced, fertile, male or sexless, sessile or on short rachillas. Glumes lanceolate or awnlike. The lemma of the fertile flowers awned, awnleted, awnless, or hooded. The back of the lemma turned from the rachis. Rachilla attached to the kernel. Kernels oblong with ventral crease, caryopsis usually adhering to lemma and palea. Annual or perennial plants.

There are four sections in the genus *Hordeum,* but section Cerealia, which includes all of the cultivated types, is delimited as follows [6]:

> Summer or winter annuals, spikes linear or broadly linear, tough or brittle. The central florets fertile, the lateral ones fertile, male, or sexless. Glumes lanceolate, narrow or wide, projecting into a short awn. The lemma in fertile florets awned, awnleted, awnless, or hooded, the lemma in male or sexless florets without awns or hoods. Kernel weight 20 to 80 mg. The chromosome number in the diploid stage 14.

FIGURE 18-5. Barley plant showing:
(a) spike; (b) exposed upper peduncle;
(c) flag leaf; (d) sheath; (e) leaf blade,
third from top; and (f) internode below
peduncle.

(*Courtesy US Department of Agriculture*)

FIGURE 18-6. Young winter barley
plants with several tillers that show
different early growth habits: (A)
prostrate, (B) erect, and (C) semiprostrate.

(*Courtesy US Department of Agriculture*)

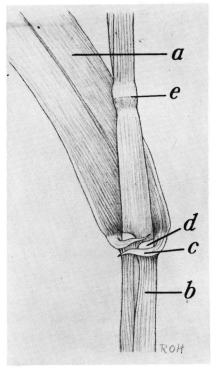

FIGURE 18-7. **Portion of barley culm with: (a) leaf blade, (b) leaf sheath, (c) auricle, (d) ligule, and (e) node.**
(*Courtesy US Department of Agriculture*)

FIGURE 18-8. **Spikes of barley: (Left) 2-row, (Right) 6-row.**
(*Courtesy US Department of Agriculture*)

DESCRIPTION OF THE CULTIVATED BARLEY PLANT

The cultivated forms of barley are either summer or winter annuals.

Vegetative Parts

The lateral spread of barley roots is usually 6–12 inches, while the depth of penetration varies from 3.0–6.5 feet [120].

The barley culm consists of 5–7 hollow cylindrical internodes, separated by solid swollen joints or nodes at which the leaves arise (Fig. 18-5). The culm length ranges from 8 inches in short types under dry conditions to 60 inches in tall varieties under good growing conditions. The usual number of culms per plant is from 3–6 when seeded at the normal rate (Fig. 18-6).

487

The leaf sheath is generally glabrous, but in a few varieties it is covered with hairs. The ligule is short (0.5–3.0 mm.), truncate, or somewhat advanced in the middle but obtuse and slopes away at both ends. The auricles, which partly or entirely clasp the stem, are larger than those of wheat or rye (Fig. 18-7). The leaf blade is lanceolate-linear, but the upper or flag leaf is curled or rolled in some varieties. The surface of the blade is harsh, usually being covered by a white, waxy bloom.

Inflorescence

The barley spike (Fig. 18-8) has a zig-zag rachis from 1–5 inches long that is strongly compressed. The rachis internodes range in length from 2 mm. or less in dense-headed varieties to 4–5 mm. in lax-headed sorts. The margins of the rachis are hairy, except in a few varieties. Three spikelets are attached at each of the 10–30 nodes of the rachis. The groups of spikelets are arranged alternately at notches on opposite sides of the rachis so that the head appears to have six rows of spikelets. In six-rowed varieties all three spikelets at a rachis joint are fertile, whereas in two-rowed sorts only the central spikelet is fertile (Fig. 18-9). Six-rowed varieties usually have from 25–60 kernels, while two-rowed varieties have from 15–30 kernels per spike.

In the cultivated barleys each spikelet contains a single floret, subtended by two linear, flat, weakly nerved, pointed glumes. The floret of the central spikelet is sessile, whereas in the lateral ones it may be sessile in six-rowed varieties, or elevated on a short stalk in two-rowed varieties.

The lemma of the floret is oblanceolate, and, at its apex, is drawn out into a stiff straight awn (Fig. 18-10). The awn may be rough or smooth, reduced to a point, or be completely absent. In some varieties the awn is replaced by a trifurcate appendage called a hood (Fig. 18-11). The palea is obtuse, two-nerved, arched inward between the nerves, and turned inward at the margins. The rachilla is a continuation of the axis of the spikelet. It lies within the crease of the kernels. The rachilla is covered with either long or short hairs (Fig. 18-12). The sexual organs consist of three stamens, and a pistil with a single ovule and a forked stigma. Two lodicules at the base of the pistil face the lemma, and serve to open the flower by swelling during pollination.

The barley kernel consists of the caryopsis, lemma, palea, and rachilla, but the caryopsis of naked or hull-less varieties threshes free (Fig. 18-13). The lemma and palea adhere to the caryopsis of the more numerous hulled varieties. The caryopsis is composed of the pericarp, endosperm, and embryo, which is located on the dorsal side of the caryopsis. The barley kernel may be creamy white, black, red, purple, or blue. The last three colors are the

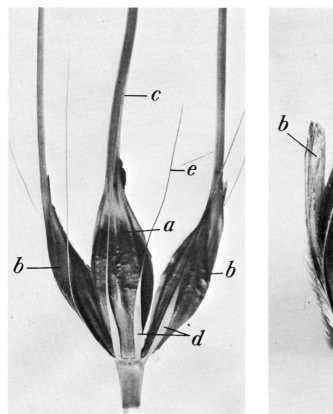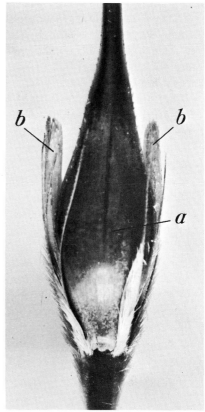

FIGURE 18-9. **Barley spikelets; 6-row (left), 2-row (right): (a) central kernel; (b) lateral kernels on 6-row barley, and empty (sterile) spikelet on 2-row barley; (c) awn; (d) glumes; and (e) glume awn.**

(Courtesy US Department of Agriculture)

result of anthocyanin pigments. When these pigments occur in the barley hulls, the kernels are red or purple, but when they occur in the aleurone layer, they are blue. The white and blue varieties are the only ones grown extensively in this country [36].

POLLINATION

Blooming of a barley spike usually begins slightly above the middle and proceeds from this point upward and downward. All of the spikes on a plant usually complete blooming within 7–9 days.

Most smooth-awned varieties grown in the United States were derived from the Lion variety which also has a stigma with only a few hairs. They show a tendency toward partial sterility because the few stigma hairs fail to catch and hold enough pollen. Pollination may fail when stigma hairs are entirely lacking. In extreme cases, nearly 50 per cent of the florets may be empty [125].

Barley is largely self-fertilized since the flowers usually are pollinated before the spike emerges from the boot. In one set of nursery trials, only one natural hybrid was observed in six years [34]. Some natural cross-pollination does occur however: several natural hybrids of barley were collected in 1915. In Colorado, investigators [82] collected intermediate forms which, when tested in 1927, were found to be F_1 hybrids. Black and white varieties were alternated in rows six inches apart, and all plants were harvested separately. Single head rows were grown the next year, and the hybrid and normal plants in the progeny were counted. Seasonal conditions had less effect on natural crossing than did variety. The commercial American varieties had only one natural cross among 37,295 plants. However, a variety of *H. deficiens* var. *nudideficiens* had 3.3 per cent of natural crossing in 1927, 20.7 per cent in 1928, and 5.6 per cent in 1929. The florets of this variety often stand open for several days. Other varieties tested showed less than 0.15 per cent of natural crossing. In California, about 1 per cent of natural crossing has been reported.

BARLEY SPECIES

The principal differences between the wild and cultivated forms of barley are the delayed germination and brittle rachis in the wild forms as compared with normal germination and tough rachis in the cultivated forms [2].

Cultivated Species

The cultivated barley species all have 14 diploid chromosomes. Three cultivated species are described as follows [5, 6]:

1. *Hordeum vulgare*: Six-row barley with a tough rachis. All florets are fertile and develop kernels of normal germinating capacity. Within *H. vulgare* there are two groups: the typical six-rowed group in which the lateral kernels are only slightly smaller than the central ones, and the intermedium group in which the lateral kernels are markedly smaller than the central ones (Fig. 18-14). Intermedium barleys may have lateral spikelets that

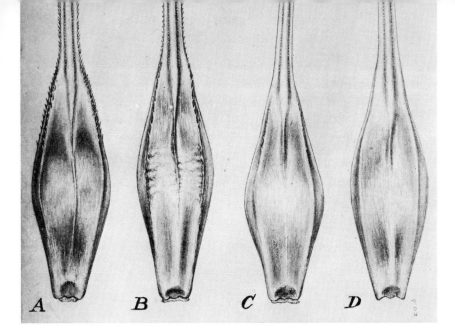

FIGURE 18-10. Barley lemmas that show veins toothed in different degrees (A, B, and C) and smooth (D). Also the basal portion of the corresponding rough and smooth awns.

(Courtesy US Department of Agriculture)

FIGURE 18-11. Types of barley spikes without awns: (A) awnless, (B) elevated hoods, (C) sessile hoods.

(Courtesy US Department of Agriculture)

range from completely fertile to completely sterile. These two groups overlap, since there is a gradual change from one type to the other.

    2. *H. distichum*: Two-rowed barley with a tough rachis. All of the
central florets are fertile, while the lateral florets are either male or all sexless. Only the florets in the central rows develop kernels with normal germination capacity. Within *H. distichum* there are two groups: the typical
two-rowed group with lateral florets consisting of lemma, palea, rachilla,

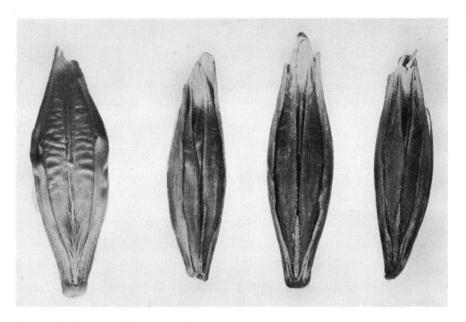

FIGURE 18-12. (Left) Two-rowed Hannchen barley kernel showing long rachilla hairs
and wrinkled palea. (Right) The 2 lateral kernels and 1 central kernel of a 6-rowed
barley with short rachilla hairs. The lateral kernels are curved and asymmetrical.

(Courtesy US Department of Agriculture)

FIGURE 18-13. Kernels (caryopses) of naked barley.

(Courtesy US Department of Agriculture)

FIGURE 18-14. Spikes of barley species. I. Hordeum vulgare: (A) Typical 6-row barley, (B) Intermedium barley, II. Hordeum distichum: (A) Typical 2-row, (B) deficiens barley, III. Hordeum irregulare.

(*Courtesy US Department of Agriculture*)

and reduced sexual parts; and the deficiens group with lateral florets reduced and consisting of lemma and rarely palea and rachilla, but with no sexual parts. These two groups overlap, as there is a gradual change from one type to the other.

3. *H. irregulare*: Irregular barley with a tough rachis. The central florets are fertile, while the lateral florets are reduced to a rachilla in some cases and these distributed irregularly on the spike. The rest of the lateral florets are fertile, sterile, or sexless. The irregular barleys all seem to have originated in Ethiopia [5].

The cultivated barley species may be distinguished from the key prepared by Aberg and Wiebe [6]:

Key to Cultivated Species

   A. Six-rowed barley with tough rachis; all florets fertile.....*H. vulgare*
      B. Lateral kernels only slightly smaller
         than central ones.................*Typical six-rowed group*
      BB. Lateral kernels markedly smaller
         than central ones.....................*Intermediate group*

    AA. Two-rowed barley with tough rachis; the lateral florets
       either all male or all sexless......................*H. distichum*
        B. Lateral florets consist of lemma, palea,
           rachilla, and reduced sexual parts...*Typical two-rowed group*
        BB. Lateral florets reduced to lemma and rarely
           palea and rachilla, but with no sexual parts...*Deficiens group*

   AAA. Central florets fertile; lateral florets reduced to
       rachilla in some cases and these irregularly dis-
       tributed on spike, the rest of the lateral florets
       fertile, sterile, or sexless.........................*H. irregulare*

Wild Barley Species

Two wild species of barley located in the section Cerealia of the genus *Hordeum,* namely, *H. spontaneum* and *H. agriocrithon,* have 14 diploid chromosomes and are readily crossed with the cultivated species.

H. spontaneum is a two-rowed form with a brittle rachis. The central florets are fertile and the lateral ones staminate. All glumes are rather long and drawn out to awnlike points.

H. agriocrithon, a wild six-rowed spring barley found in the eastern highlands of Tibet, has a brittle rachis and fully fertile florets in both central and lateral spikelets. The lemmas are long awned, and the kernels adhere to the lemma and palea [1].

Several other wild species of barley, remotely related to the cultivated forms, are found in the United States. All furnish forage when young, but many are aggressive weeds. The sharp-pointed joints of the mature spikes of *H. jubatum* are injurious to livestock. The perennial species are *H. montanense, H. jubatum,* and *H. nodosum.* The annual species are *H. murinum, H. pusillum, H. gussoneanum,* and *H. adscendens.* Pastures in the southwestern states are badly overrun with *H. jubatum, H. murinum,* and *H. pusillum* [46].

CULTIVATED BARLEY GROUPS

Among the important barleys in the United States are those of the Manchuria-OAC 21-Oderbrucker group which is believed to have come originally from Manchuria or nearby countries. These varieties, which are used most widely for malting, are grown chiefly in the humid and subhumid regions of the upper Mississippi Valley. They are six-rowed, awned, spring-type barleys with medium-sized kernels, most of which mature in midseason, The plants are inclined to be tall; the spikes, long, lax, and nodding. The seeds possess sufficient postharvest dormancy to safeguard them against the danger of germination while in the shock. These varieties shatter badly when grown in a dry climate.

The varieties in the Coast group are of North African origin. They have a spring growth habit, but are widely grown from fall or winter sowing in the mild climate of California and southern Arizona. These barleys are spring-seeded in areas of limited rainfall in the intermountain region and in the Great Plains. They are six-rowed, awned, with large kernels, and have short to midtall culms. The spikes are midlong to short, dense, and held erect or semierect in most varieties. The Coast varieties do not shatter readily, and they mature early.

The most probable place of origin of the varieties of the Tennessee Winter group is either the Balkans-Caucasus region, or Korea. These winter varieties are grown in the southeastern quarter of the United States. The plants are midtall, and midseason in maturity. The spikes are six-rowed, awned, midlong, lax, and tend to nod; kernels are medium to small in size; leaves are narrow. The fall growth of these plants is prostrate, typical of their winter growth habit. Only winter barleys are adapted to Tennessee, and all hardy varieties grown there trace their ancestry to the old Tennessee Winter variety [32].

Two-rowed varieties are grown mostly in the Pacific Northwest, the Intermountain region, and the northern half of the Great Plains. Hooded spring varieties are scattered throughout the Intermountain area where they are used chiefly for hay, while hooded varieties of winter barley are grown in the South.

CULTIVATED VARIETIES

Probably 150 varieties of barley are grown in the United States. More than 40 new varieties were released between 1938–47. They yield an average of 3–5 bushels of grain per acre more than did the older varieties and often have other advantages, such as resistance to diseases, insects, and drought; greater winter hardiness; stiff straw; and smooth awns [121].

The six-rowed spring varieties generally outyielded the two-rowed types, particularly in the subhumid to humid Upper Mississippi Valley. The two-rowed barleys outyield the six-rowed types in limited areas of the Eastern states [90]. The most important spring barley varieties in the United States in 1961 are listed in Table 18-1.

TABLE 18-1. **Important Spring Barley Varieties Grown in the United States in 1961.**

Variety	General Type	Head Type	Awns	Kernels	Utilization	Area of Production
Traill	Manchurian	6-row	Rough, long	Hulled	Malting	N. Dakota, So. Dakota, Minnesota
Kindred	"	"	"	"	"	North Central States
Compana	———	2-row	Semi-smooth	"	Feed	Montana on dryland
California Mariout	Coast	6-row	Rough, long	"	Feed	California, Arizona
Vantage	Manchurian	6-row	Smooth, long	"	Feed	Minnesota, N. Dakota, Montana
Hannchen	———	2-row	Rough, long	"	Malting	Oregon, California
Betzes	———	2-row	Rough	"	Malting	Montana, Idaho
Arivat	Coast	6-row	Semi-smooth	"	Feed	Arizona, So. California
Gem	Coast	6-row	Smooth, long	"	Feed	Idaho, Washington
Atlas	Coast	6-row	Rough, long	"	Malting	West Coast
Trebi	Coast	6-row	Rough, long	"	Feed	Western States
Tregal	———	6-row	Smooth	"	Feed	Minnesota, N. Dakota
Forrest	Manchurian	6-row	Smooth, long	"	Malting	Minnesota, N. Dakota
Club Mariout	Coast	6-row	Rough	"	Feed	Colorado, Kansas, Nebraska, Pacific Coast

Winter or Semiwinter Varieties

Winter barleys are grown for soil cover, but primarily to obtain the higher production associated with earlier maturity. The principal winter barley region of the United States lies south of a line that extends from west-central New York State to the northeastern portion of Colorado. True winter types are grown from fall-sowing in this area. Some winter barley is grown in the milder portions of the Pacific Northwest. In the Gulf Coast area, for a distance of 100 to 150 miles inland, disease-resistant spring or semiwinter varieties seeded in the fall can be grown successfully. Spring varieties are fall-sown in California and southern Arizona, where warm weather and short winter days retard the flowering of winter types, so that they would ripen a month later than do spring varieties.

About 50 winter or semiwinter varieties of barley, all six-rowed types, are grown commercially in the United States. The more important ones in 1961 are listed in Table 18-2. In general, winter types have a prostrate habit of growth in the fall, are less leafy, and fail to head from late spring seeding. Most of the semiwinter varieties will head from early spring seeding. In some areas they are sown either in the fall or early spring.

Derivatives of the Tennessee Winter variety are the most widely grown winter barleys in the United States. These include Tennessee Winter 52, Jackson 1 [32], Dayton, Kentucky 1, Reno, and Ward.

Wong is a six-rowed, extremely stiff-strawed, awnletted variety with short spikes that originated in China [59], but Hudson is superior to Wong both in yield and winter hardiness.

TABLE 18-2. **Important Winter Barley Varieties Grown in the United States in 1961.**

Variety	Head Type	Awns	Kernels	Utilization	Area of Production
Hudson	6-row	Rough, long	Hulled	Feed	Eastern States
Wong	6-row	Awnletted	"	"	"
Kenbar	6-row	Semi-smooth	"	"	"
Dicktoo	6-row	Rough	"	"	Nebraska, South Dakota
Kearney	6-row	Rough	"	"	Southern Nebraska
Reno	6-row	Rough	"	"	Kansas
Mo. B-475	6-row	Rough	"	"	Missouri
Rogers	6-row	Rough	"	"	Oklahoma
Dayton	6-row	Semi-smooth	"	"	Ohio, Kentucky
Cordova	6-row	Smooth	"	"	Texas
Daire	6-row	Awnletted	"	"	North Carolina South Carolina

Harbine is a stiff-strawed combine type with considerable resistance to the leaf diseases [49], but it is less hardy than Rogers in Oklahoma. Cordova is a stiff-strawed, smooth-awned, semiwinter variety grown in central Texas where it is well suited for winter grazing [8].

The most winter-hardy barley varieties are grown primarily in the central Great Plains region. They all are rough-awned. Kearney is grown in Nebraska, Colorado, Illinois, and in the Texas Panhandle. Dicktoo is grown in Kansas, Nebraska, and South Dakota. Pueblo is restricted to Colorado, where it is less hardy than Kearney under severe winter conditions [84].

Rough-awned winter barley varieties grown in the Pacific Northwest and the Intermountain region include Cascade, White Wonder, Winter Club, Idaho Club, and Alpine.

TYPES OF BARLEY GROWN IN OTHER COUNTRIES

Spring barleys are much more widely grown than winter varieties over most of the world. Hulled varieties predominate in Occidental countries, while hull-less (naked) varieties are important in some Oriental countries.

Spring Varieties

The common nodding type of six-rowed spring barley is widely distributed in Russia, Syria, Asia Minor, Manchuria, Turkestan, Europe, and Canada. The six-rowed types also are grown in South America. There are erect six-rowed types in southern Europe, the Alpine regions, the Mediterranean area, eastern Asia, and Japan.

Six-rowed spring barleys predominate in Canada.[2] The principal rough-awned varieties in the Prairie Provinces, where most of the crop is grown, are OAC 21, Olli, and Traill. Smooth-awned barleys grown in the region are Montcalm, Vantage, Vantmore, Husky, Wolfe, Gateway, Parkland, and Swan. In eastern Canada, Brant and Nord are grown. The chief malting varieties are Montcalm, OAC 21, Olli, Parkland, and Gateway. Two-rowed spring barley is of minor importance in Canada. The principal two-rowed varieties in the prairie provinces are Hannchen, Compana, and Herta, while Charlottetown 80 is widely grown in the maritime provinces [41].

Two-rowed spring barley is the most prevalent type in northern and central Europe. In Great Britain, Plumage Archer and Spratt-Archer—lax-headed, chevalier-type varieties—are widely grown for malting while Kenia and Maja are popular as feed barleys. In Sweden, the principal two-rowed varieties include Ymer, Primus II, Maja, and Svanhals. Brio is the chief six-rowed variety grown in south Sweden, while Vega, Dora, Stella, and Edda are grown in north Sweden [44]. Kenia and Herta are two rowed varieties grown in Denmark. The *deficiens* two-rowed type is found in Ethiopia and Arabia [90].

In North Africa and the Mediterranean countries of Europe, most of the barley consists of six-rowed spring varieties sown in the fall.

[2] List modified from information supplied July 15, 1957, by A. E. Hannah, Senior Cerealist, Department of Agriculture, Ottawa, Canada.

In northern Japan, the most common spring barleys are varieties of the tall, hull-less type, such as Marumi and Mitsukiko [54].

Winter Varieties

Winter or semiwinter barley types are grown in China, Korea, Japan, Kashmir, Transcaucasia, and Europe.

Almost all of the fall-sown barley grown in Japan is of the six-rowed awned, semiwinter type, with short stems and awns. About 60 per cent of the total crop is naked barley. In northern Japan, the hulled, tall types with winter growth habit are most widely grown, while in central and southern Japan short-stemmed, hull-less types are grown almost exclusively. The principal six-rowed naked barley varieties grown in Japan are Akashinriki, Kobinkatagi No. 1, Wasehadaka, Kagawa, Marumi, Yanehadaka, and Shinriki-Hadaka. The chief hulled varieties include Sekitori, Saitama No. 1, Tochigi Sekitori No. 1, Sekitori No. 2, Sekitori No. 3, Tanikaze No. 5, and Tanikaze No. 2 [107, 54].

GROWTH OF THE BARLEY PLANT

The minimum temperature for germination of barley lies between 37.4–39.2°F, the optimum at approximately 68°F, and the maximum between 82.4–86°F [43].

With the entry of water, the radicle begins to swell. Almost simultaneously, starch begins to appear in the coleorhiza, the periblem of the root, and in the plumule. Finally, the starchy endosperm cells next to the epithelium show a partial dissolution. A similar effect is observed on the starch cells farther inward. The starch is converted to maltose which is transformed to sucrose as it enters the scutellum through the action of the enzyme diastase which is secreted by the epithelial cells.

In the early growth of barley, the internodes of the stem remain short, the growing point produces only leaf initials and the undifferentiated portion of it elongates. With the elongation of the stem internodes, double ridges appear on the growing point and soon the spike and its parts differentiate and develop. The number of fertile spikelets formed toward the tip of the spike is determined in part by environment [13].

The most rapid pollen tube growth in barley occurs at 80–95°F. The egg and polar nuclei may suffer injury when exposed to 104°F for one hour. Thus, blast following high temperatures may be due as much to ovule injury as to pollen killing. Optimal growth of both endosperm and embryo is approximately 86°F, with less rapid growth at 95°F, and death at 104°F. Between 50–86°F, growth as measured by the number of generations in endosperm and embryo, conformed to the Van't Hoff rule[3] [74]. In hot climates, barley approaching maturity may survive field temperatures as high as 110–120°F with little apparent injury.

The period from flowering to physiologic maturity requires 26 days in barley grown under irrigation in Idaho (Fig. 18-15). The average water content of the ovaries at flowering time is about 80 per cent, and the water content of the growing kernel decreases gradually to about 42 per cent, when the deposit of dry matter ceases. The kernels dry rapidly thereafter [33]. The dry matter content of the kernel increases very little between the 25th and 30th days after flowering, when the moisture content may drop from 47 to 25 per cent [39]. Under good growing conditions, the period from flowering until the grain is ready for harvest commonly exceeds 40 days, and it may extend to 55 days.

[3] Van't Hoff rule is that the velocity of a chemical reaction in homogeneous systems is doubled or trebled with each increase of temperature of 10°C (18°F). This rule applies to many vital processes at temperatures below the thermal death point.

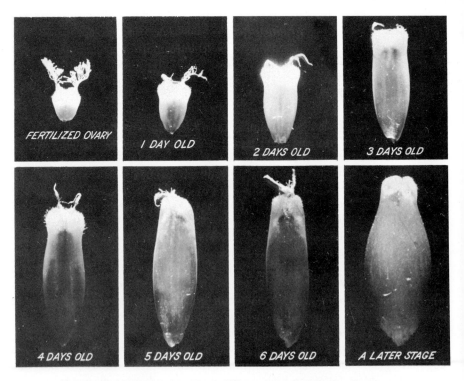

FIGURE 18-15. **Barley kernels at different ages in their development.**

(*Courtesy US Department of Agriculture*)

CULTURAL PRACTICES

Cultural practices for barley production in the United States are similar to those for wheat.

Rotations

Barley generally is grown in rotation with other crops, particularly after cultivated row crops such as corn, soybeans, beans, potatoes, or sugar beets. Sometimes barley follows other small grains. Barley following a meadow crop may be subject to lodging because of excessive soil nitrates.

In the humid regions, the most practical rotation is one that includes corn, barley, and a legume hay or pasture crop, with barley used as a companion crop for the legume or legume-grass mixture. In the Corn Belt, barley often follows oats, wheat, or soybeans in order to avoid losses from the scab disease which is carried on corn. In California, barley often follows oats to lessen damage from the take-all disease.

In Missouri, a one-year winter barley-lespedeza or soybean sequence is widely followed. Winter barley also is grown in two-year rotations with red clover or sweetclover [73].

In the semiarid Great Plains, a common practice is to grow barley on corn-stubble land or summer fallow. Satisfactory Kansas rotations that include spring barley are sorghum, barley, wheat; and sorghum, barley, fallow, and wheat [106]. Barley is sometimes alternated with fallow or field peas in eastern Washington and Oregon. In the irrigated areas of the Western states, barley often is used as a companion crop for seeding alfalfa or pasture mixtures. In general, barley is most productive under irrigation in Colorado when grown after cultivated crops such as corn, sugar beets, potatoes, or beans [83].

In the Southern states, winter barley occupies the same position in rotations as does wheat. A satisfactory sequence is to sow barley after a summer legume, usually cowpeas plowed under about September 1. In the Piedmont region, a satisfactory three-year rotation is corn with Crimson clover later seeded among the stalks, cowpeas, and barley. This may be modified to include a second year of barley or a pasture crop.

Fertilizers

Fertilizer requirements for barley are about the same as those for wheat. In the more humid regions, barley generally responds to applications of nitrogen and phosphorus, and to potash also on light-textured soils that tend to be leached. On poor soils barley often benefits from topdressing with nitrogen. Most of the spring crop is produced on rather fertile soils, but nitrogen and phosphorus often are applied.

Barley usually produced higher yields in Minnesota when 50 pounds per acre or more of available P_2O_5 were applied. The smallest increase was obtained on sandy soils; the largest on heavy soils. Barley also responded to applications of nitrogen with phosphorus in all soil areas of Minnesota. However, it was considered undesirable to apply more than 30 pounds of nitrogen per acre because of the danger of lodging, especially when legumes were seeded with the crop [16]. Phosphorus improved the quality of malting barley in fertilizer trials in Michigan, Iowa, and Illinois. In these areas, nitrogen and phosphorus, or phosphorus and potash, produced beneficial effects [47].

Fertilizers applied to spring barley varieties in northeastern Illinois showed that Oderbrucker responded much less favorably than did the Moore variety. Average yields of nine barley varieties from four fertilizer treatments at Woodstock, Illinois, 1947–50, were as follows:

Fertilizer Treatment			Average Yields per Acre
N	P_2O_5	K_2O	All Varieties
(Lb per acre)			(Bu)
0	0	0	30.5
0	60	60	34.5
60	0	60	42.0
60	60	0	43.7
60	60	60	45.6

Nitrogen was the primary nutrient that limited the barley yields, even on productive land with a rotation that included legumes. The yield from the complete fertilizer was 11.1 bushels per acre more than the treatment without nitrogen, but the nitrogen caused most of the varieties to lodge [71].

Winter barley produced an average increase of 8.3 bushels per acre from an annual application of 150 pounds of superphosphate per acre in Missouri. Winter killing was nearly always less severe where fertilizer was applied [73].

An application of 25–50 pounds per acre of nitrogen to Hannchen barley under dryland conditions in Oregon gave significant increases in yield in two years, but no response was obtained in the third year, an abnormally dry season. Nitrogen gave the best response when applied at seeding time, or when the plants were six inches tall. Higher yields were obtained from applications of ammonium nitrate to the soil than from the same rates of urea nitrogen applied as a foliar spray [28]. In the Palouse area of eastern Washington, high rates of nitrogen fertilization (80 and 120 pounds of nitrogen per acre) on barley decreased kernel size; increased barley, malt, and wort nitrogen; and reduced malting quality [79].

Seedbed Preparation

In the humid spring barley region, the land often is fall-plowed in October or November and then disked early in the spring before seeding barley. Spring plowing often results in delayed seeding. Plowing usually is necessary when there is plant residue, barnyard manure, or sod to be turned under. When barley follows a clean-cultivated row crop, the seedbed often is merely disked and harrowed.

Under semiarid conditions in Kansas, a suitable seedbed on corn or sorghum land can be prepared for spring barley by a light cultivation with a one-way plow followed by a subsurface packer. Land plowed in the spring often is too loose or cloddy for a good seedbed for barley, in which case the yields are likely to be lower than on fall-plowed or fall-listed land. At the Hays (Kansas) Station, barley yielded about 40 per cent more on summer-fallow than on fall-plowed stubble land or spring-disked corn or kafir land. Fall-plowing gave higher barley yields than fall-listing or spring-plowing of barley stubble land [106]. On the drylands of eastern Colorado, summer fallow is the most effective tillage practice for the production of winter barley on the hard-land soils [84].

Seeding Practices

Maximum yields of spring barley are obtained when the crop is seeded as early as the land can be worked in the spring, usually sometime between March 1–May 15 in different parts of the country. This usually is early April in Wisconsin, where malting barley is produced. Late seeding may result in low yields of lightweight kernels when the crop matures in hot dry weather [90]. On the northern Great Plains, the most favorable seeding period is from April 1–25. In Montana, North Dakota, and South Dakota, the loss from seeding after April 25 is more than 1 per cent per day. In the central Great Plains, spring barley usually can be sown between March 1–April 10. Yields are nearly always reduced by seeding as late as April 15 in west-central Kansas [106]. In the higher altitude regions of Colorado, barley is sown between April 1–May 15, or earlier when conditions are suitable [83]. In California and southern Arizona, spring barley varieties are sown as a winter crop from late October to as late as January 15. In the South, as well as in the Midwest, most winter barley is sown in September or October. It should be sown early enough to produce at least four inches of top growth before it goes into the winter. In Missouri, winter barley for fall pasture is seeded in late August or early September, while that grown solely for grain may be seeded later from September 15–30 [73]. Winter barley in northern Colorado is seeded from September 1–15 [84].

The average rates of seeding barley range from 1.2–2.2 bushels per

acre in the different states (Appendix Table A-9). In the humid spring
barley region, 6–8 pecks (72–96 pounds) per acre generally provide sufficient plants for a satisfactory crop. On the Northern Great Plains, 4–6 pecks
is the usual seeding rate, the lower rate being sown in the drier localities.
Spring barley is generally sown at the rate of 5–6 pecks on the drylands
of western Kansas, while the common rate is four pecks under somewhat
drier conditions in eastern Colorado. In the drier localities of the Great
Basin, the seeding rate may be as low as three pecks. The usual rate of
seeding barley under irrigated conditions in Colorado is 90 pounds per acre
[83]. Winter barley is commonly seeded at the rate of 6–8 pecks per acre,
but 10 pecks may be sown when the seeding date is delayed [73].

Barley is generally sown with a grain drill because it assures uniform
depth and spacing of the seeds. The furrow drill is advocated for winter
barley sown under dryland conditions in Colorado [84]. The seed should be
placed in moist soil. The seeding depth varies from 1–2 inches in the humid
regions or under irrigation, but usually is 2–3 inches under semiarid
conditions.

Chemical Weed Control

Spraying barley or other grain crops with various formulations of 2,4-D
for weed control has become a widespread practice.

The 2,4-D applied to Velvon barley in salt, amine, or ethyl-ester formulations at the rate of 0.5 or 1 pound of acid equivalent per acre killed the
annual weeds with no injury to the crop. The yield of barley was materially
reduced with the two-pound per acre application of the amine or ester,
and the ester caused weakened or bent stems and sterile spikes [70].

The 2,4-D caused reduced yields of barley when applied to plants
1–5 inches tall, or when the plants were well into the boot stage before
heading. Applications between these two stages caused little or no damage
to the barley [68]. In other experiments vegetative abnormalities occurred
when barley was treated before the five-leaf stage with one pound per acre
acid equivalent of the butyl ester form. Barley plants treated between the
pre-heading and late-heading stages may produce blasted florets and reduced yields [22].

Barley generally is sprayed with 2,4-D when the plants are between
the tillering (6–8 inches tall) and jointing stages to control susceptible broad-
leaf weeds. The normal rate of application is 0.50–0.75 pound acid equivalent per acre in the amine form.

Harvesting

Most of the domestic barley crop is harvested with a combine. In the
Western states, barley is combined directly when the grain is ripe and dry.

This is the cheapest method, but it may result in shattering of the malting types. The windrow-pickup combine method eliminates the danger of this loss. The grain is windrowed when the heads have turned a golden yellow, but the straw still may be slightly green, and is picked up and threshed after drying for three or more days. The moisture content of the grain should be 14 per cent or less before it is threshed [106]. The windrow-pickup method occasionally is used for harvesting barley in the humid states, but malting barley is windrowed only after it is fully ripe.

Some barley in the United States and other countries is cut with a binder and threshed with a combine or separator. It can be cut with a binder when physiologically mature—*i.e.*, when it arrives at the hard-dough stage. Harvesting with a header has been almost completely discontinued.

Malting barley must contain few or no broken or skinned kernels in order to meet the requirements of the trade. Mechanical injury may be minimized during threshing by proper adjustment of the cylinder. High percentages of skinned or broken kernels result from machines that operate at cylinder bar speeds in excess of 600 feet per minute. In many cases, it is possible to reduce the proportion of damaged kernels from 15–20 per cent to below 5 per cent by a reduction of the cylinder bar speed to 300–400 feet per minute [117]. Too little clearance between the concave and cylinder teeth, crooked teeth, and end play in the cylinder also damage the kernels.

PRODUCTION IN SOME OTHER COUNTRIES

More than 90 per cent of the barley in Canada is produced in the prairie provinces, for feed or malting. In Saskatchewan, the crop generally is sown in early May at the rate of 1.5–2 bushels per acre. Sometimes seeding is delayed until after May 15 in order to eradicate wild oats before barley seeding. Most of the Canadian barley is harvested with a combine, either directly or after the crop has been windrowed [40].

Barley in Great Britain generally is grown for malting, with substandard lots used as livestock feed. Light loam soils are preferred and the Norfolk rotation—roots, barley, clover, and wheat—is widely used. Barley also is grown after sugar beets or after clover, and occasionally after wheat. Barley after root crops has produced higher yields but is more likely to lodge than that grown after wheat. Lime applications sometimes are beneficial on very acid soils. Except on very infertile soils, commercial fertilizers seldom are applied to spring barley that follows roots or grass. Fertilizers sometimes are applied to barley that follows another cereal crop. Fertilizers recommended for very light soils are: ammonium sulfate, 100 pounds; superphos-

TABLE 18-3. **Grade Requirements for Subclass Barley of the Class Barley.**

| Grade | Minimum Limits, Per Cent | | Maximum Limits, Per Cent | | | | | |
	Test Weight per Bushel, Lb	Sound Barley	Total Damaged Kernels	Heat-Damaged Kernels	Foreign Material	Broken Kernels	Thin Barley	Black Barley
1	47	97	2.0	0.2	1.0	5.0	10.0	0.5
2	45	94	4.0	0.3	2.0	10.0	15.0	1.0
3	43	90	6.0	0.5	3.0	15.0	25.0	2.0
4*	40	80	8.0	1.0	4.0	20.0	35.0	5.0
5	36	70	10.0	3.0	6.0	30.0	75.0	10.0

Sample Grade: Sample grade shall include barley of the class Barley, which does not come within the grade requirements of any of the grades from No. 1 to No. 5, inclusive; or which contains more than 16.0 per cent of moisture; or which contains stones; or which is musty, or sour, or heating; or which has any commercially objectionable foreign odor except smut or garlic; or which contains a quantity of smut so great that any one or more of the grade requirements cannot be applied accurately; or which is otherwise of distinctly low quality.

* Barley that is badly stained or materially weathered, shall not be graded higher than No. 4.

phate, 300 pounds; and potash salts, 200–300 pounds per acre. Spring barley is sown as early as possible—often in March, but in February in southern England. The seed is drilled at the rate of 2.5–3 bushels (140–168 pounds) per acre [11]. The barley is harvested with a binder or combine, and most of the combined grain requires artificial drying.

Barley has a long history of cultivation in China, where it is the most important winter crop next to wheat. The principal region of barley production is adjacent to the Yangtze River. There, barley matures 2–3 weeks earlier than wheat, which permits the growing of a transplanted rice crop on the land during the summer. Barley is better suited to the poorly drained rice lands of the Yangtze rice region than are other winter crops. Most of the barley grown in China consists of six-rowed hulled or hull-less types. It usually is interplanted with legumes such as field peas, broadbeans, or lentils. In the rice belt, south of the Hwai River and Tsinling Range, barley is sown in October or November after the rice harvest. The land is plowed, harrowed, and bedded with drainage furrows between beds. Stable manure or "night soil" generally are applied as fertilizers, but wood or straw ashes also are used on noncalcareous rice soils. The seed is dropped in hills or drills. Barley fields are usually cultivated twice. The crop is harvested between April 1 and May 15. Barley is sown in September in the winter wheat belt, from north of the Tsinling Range to south of the Great Wall. It generally follows summer crops, such as kaoliang (grain sorghum) or millets. The crop is usually drilled, but occasionally it is broadcast. It is harvested from late May to early June. North of the Great Wall, barley is sown from late March to early May and harvested in July or August.[4]

Barley is one of the most important crops in Japan, where it is grown for human food as well as for livestock feed. The crop is cared for intensively on small fields almost entirely with hand labor. Most of the barley is grown alternately with another crop in the same season. When barley follows paddy rice, the field often is ridged and the barley sown on top of the ridges. On upland fields, sweet potatoes, soybeans, or upland rice often are planted between the rows before the barley is harvested. Japanese farmers ordinarily apply about 450 pounds of lime per acre in preparation for the fall seeding of barley because most of their soils are acid. In addition to heavy applications of manure or compost, commercial fertilizer applications may include from 71–89 pounds of nitrogen (N), 45–89 pounds of phosphates (P_2O_5), and 71–80 pounds of potash (K_2O) per acre. Barley is fall-sown between September 15–November 30, while spring barley generally is sown in April in northern Japan. Both covered and naked barley are sown at rates of 48–74 pounds per acre, in drills or in bands about four inches wide. The rows usually are spaced from 12–24 inches apart. Most of the

[4] Most of this information was supplied by T. H. Shen, Commissioner, Joint Commission on Rural Reconstruction, Taipei, Taiwan, in a letter dated July 15, 1957.

TABLE 18-4. **Grade Requirements for the Subclasses Malting Barley and Blue Malting Barley of the Class Barley.**

| | Minimum Limits, Per Cent | | Maximum Limits, Per Cent | | | | | |
| | Test Weight per Bushel, Lb | Sound Kernels | Damaged Kernels | Foreign Material | Skinned and Broken Kernels | Thin Barley | Black Barley | Other Grains |
Grade*								
1	47	79	2.0	1.0	4.0	7.0	0.5	2.0
2	45	94	3.0	2.0	7.0	10.0	1.0	3.0
3	43	90	4.0	3.0	10.0	15.0	2.0	5.0

* Barley of the class Barley which does not meet the requirements of any of the grades 1–3, inclusive, for the subclasses Malting Barley and Blue Malting Barley shall be classified and graded according to the grade requirements for the subclass Barley.

barley crop in Japan is harvested in June with hand sickles, laid in swaths to dry for several days, and then threshed with a small foot-powered or motor-driven thresher. The threshed grain is cleaned in fanning mills or occasionally winnowed in a breeze. The cleaned grain then is spread out on straw mats to dry, after which it is packed in rice-straw bags [54].

ANALYSIS OF BARLEY YIELDS

Within a variety, yield is more closely associated with the number of heads per unit area than with the number of plants, number of kernels per head, or size of kernel. Small-seeded varieties may outyield the large-seeded ones because they produce a larger number of plants and heads per unit area [14]. Grain yields are not directly proportional to the thickness of stand, because of the increased development of individual plants in thin stands. Irregular stands with spacings that vary as much as 40 per cent may produce as much as uniform stands having the same total plant population [95].

In England, about 1.4 million barley grains are sown per acre, or approximately 290 per square yard. From these, about 100 plants per square yard may survive until harvest [11].

Partial spikelet sterility, which tends to be inherent in some varieties, may not cause reduced yields unless the sterile florets exceed 25–30 per cent. Later seeding (March 29 vs. April 25) may decrease sterility but reduce the yield also. Increases in kernel weight in strains with 30 per cent or more of sterile florets failed to compensate fully for the loss in yield due to sterility [125]. Kernels adjacent to empty florets are no larger than other kernels on the same spike [52].

COMMERCIAL CLASSES OF BARLEY

Barley, like other cereal grains produced in the United States, is marketed largely by grades under the Grain Standards Act. Barley must contain 50 per cent or more barley before the removal of dockage, and it must not contain more than 25 per cent of other grains for which standards have been established. Hull-less barley is excluded from all commercial classes [66].

Barley is divided into three classes: Barley, Western Barley, and Mixed Barley. Under the classes, barley is graded into five numerical grades and sample grade.

The class Barley, which includes white-hulled types grown east of the Rocky Mountains, must not contain more than 10 per cent of black barley

TABLE 18-5. **Grade Requirements for Western Barley.**

| Grade | Minimum Limits, Per Cent | | Maximum Limits, Per Cent | | | |
	Sound Barley	Heat-Damaged Kernels*	Wild Oats	Foreign Material	Broken Kernels	Black Barley
1	98	0.1	1.0	0.5	3.0	0.5
2	96	0.2	2.0	1.0	6.0	1.0
3	93	0.3	3.0	2.0	10.0	2.0
4	88	0.5	5.0	3.0	15.0	5.0
5	80	1.0	10.0	4.0	25.0	10.0

Sample Grade: Sample grade shall include barley of the class Western Barley which does not come within the grade requirements of any of the grades from No. 1 to No. 5, inclusive; or which contain more than 15 per cent of moisture; or which contain stones; or which is musty, or sour, or heating; or which has any commercially objectionable foreign odor except of smut or garlic; or which contains a quantity of smut so great that any one or more of the grade requirements cannot be applied accurately; or which contains the seeds of wild brome grasses of a character and in a quantity sufficient to cause the grain to be of low quality for feeding purposes; or which is otherwise of distinctly low quality.

* Includes barley, other grains, and wild oats.

or Western Barley. It is divided into three subclasses: Malting Barley, Blue Malting Barley, and Barley. The grade requirements for the class Barley are given in Table 18-3.

The subclass Malting Barley is six-rowed barley of the class Barley which has 90 per cent or more of the kernels with white aleurone layers. It must not be semisteely in mass. After the removal of dockage, it must not contain more than 5 per cent of two-rowed types or varieties unsuitable for malting, such as Trebi. The subclass Blue Malting Barley is similar in requirements, except that 90 per cent or more of the kernels have blue aleurone layers. The subclass standards for the malting barleys are given in Table 18-4.

Western Barley is white-hulled barley grown west of the Great Plains region. It may contain not more than 10 per cent of black barley or of barley of the class Barley, single or in combination. The grade requirements for Western Barley are given in Table 18-5.

Mixed Barley is graded on the basis of the class of Barley that predominates in the mixture. It includes black barley.

COMPOSITION OF THE BARLEY KERNEL

Chemical Composition

The protein content of most barley varieties may vary from 7.5–15.0 per cent of the dry weight of the grain, while the starch content varies from about 50–60 per cent. The moisture content when threshed may vary from 10–20 per cent [51], but barley grown in California or other areas with a dry summer climate often contains less than 10 per cent moisture. Mealy or mellow kernels usually are high in starch, while translucent ones tend to be high in protein. Chemical composition is given in Table 18-6.

TABLE 18-6. **Percentage Chemical Composition of Barley.**

Type of Barley or Product*	Mois- ture	Ash	Crude Protein	Ether Extract	Crude Fiber	Nitrogen- Free Extract	Cal- cium	Phos- phorus
Barley	9.6	2.9	12.8	2.3	5.5	66.9	0.07	0.32
Feed Barley	7.9	4.9	15.0	4.0	13.7	54.5	0.03	0.41
Malt	7.7	2.9	12.4	2.1	6.0	68.9	—	—

* From U.S. Department of Agriculture Yearbook of Agriculture, 1939.

The protein in the barley kernel is comprised of about 3 per cent leucosin, an albumen; about 18 per cent edestin, a globulin; about 38 per cent hordein, a prolamin; and about 41 per cent glutelin [51].

Sugars and other carbohydrates in the developing barley kernel are mostly converted to starch in a fully mature kernel. Any barley kernel in which starch deposition is interrupted before it has reached full size will be "steely"—*i.e.,* hard or flinty, with fewer starch granules in the protein matrix. Growth interruption may come from disease, drought, hot weather, or frost [36].

Diastatic power is a measure of the ability of the kernel to convert starch to maltose (malt sugar). Some barleys have enough diastase to convert readily much more starch than is contained in the kernel. Diastatic power is relatively greater in the smaller barley kernels of a sample because the scutellum, which secretes the diastase, is nearly as large as that of large kernels which contain much more starch.

Protein content is increased by an abundance of soil nitrates and by environmental factors that retard starch synthesis and deposition. Much of the protein is in the embryo and in the aleurone layer just beneath the hull. These constitute a greater percentage of the total seed in small-kerneled barleys than in large-kerneled barleys. Thin barley has a higher protein content and a lower starch content than does plump barley.

Kernel Quality for Malting

Six-rowed barleys are used by most maltsters in North America, whereas two-rowed barleys are preferred in Europe, as well as by some American brewers.

A barley suitable for malting must be clean, bright, and free from foreign material as well as from other cereals or objectionable varieties. Maltsters generally prefer barleys with uniform, medium-sized, mellow, plump kernels instead of very large or slender kernels. Barley of high bushel weight, or high kernel weight, usually is well filled. Straw-colored hulls indicate that the barley was well ripened, and free of damage from weather, storage, or disease. (Heat damage is indicated by a faint chocolate brown color under the hull.) Maltsters also desire barley with a high germination capacity. American maltsters prefer a barley with about a 12 per cent protein content and a high diastatic power. Some undesirable characteristics in barley for malting purposes are weathered, underripe, shriveled, scabbed, skinned, broken, and steely kernels. Mealiness is almost always associated with high starch and low protein, but steeliness does not necessarily indicate a high protein content. Underripe barley with a green tinge is unsuitable for malting.

Average kernel weight and bushel weight are positively associated with the amount of malt extract. Protein content and diastatic power also are associated [21]. Medium test weight barley may be more desirable for malting purposes than one with a high test weight because the latter is more likely to contain an abundance of skinned, frayed, and broken kernels [26].

MALTING, BREWING, AND MILLING PROCESSES

Barley probably was the first cereal used by the ancients for making beverages. About 30 per cent of the barley crop in the United States is used for malting. Approximately 80 per cent of the malt is used in beer; 14 per cent in distilled alcoholic products; and 6 per cent in malt syrups, malted milk concentrates, breakfast foods, and coffee substitutes [90]. Malting is a controlled germination or sprouting of barley, or other cereals, during which the enzymes are activated whereby the ingredients are changed to facilitate later brewing, distilling, or malt syrup production. Insoluble and nondiffusible substances are transformed into simpler compounds through the action of enzymes.

Malting

Malting comprises several operations: steeping the barley in water, germination, and the drying of the malt. The entire process requires about 12 days. The barley generally is stored for 4–6 weeks after harvest to undergo after-ripening, which assures prompt germination later. The barley then is cleaned of impurities, broken kernels, and foreign seeds. Next, it is graded into 2–3 different-sized kernels which are malted separately [86, 50].

The cleaned barley is conveyed to the malt house where it is dumped into large iron tanks, funnel-shaped at the bottom, and partly filled with cold clean water. The tanks are equipped for aeration as well as for water overflow to clean the barley. The light kernels float to the surface and are removed. After 45–65 hours of steeping, the barley has absorbed from 45–48 per cent water, enough to start germination [86].

The steeped barley then is conveyed to drums or compartments for germination. The malting drum consists of a closed cylinder with the capacity of a steep tank, or up to 650 bushels. In the compartment system, the barley germinates in long perforated-bottom compartments which have a capacity up to 5000 bushels. In both containers, moist, temperature-controlled air is drawn through the grain as it germinates. The barley is turned periodically by mechanical devices to prevent the rootlets from matting as well as to assist in temperature control. In floor malting, still practiced in some European countries, the grain is spread out on floors of cool ventilated rooms. As the grain germinates, it is hand-turned with forks to cool it and to control rootlet growth. The germination period usually is 5–7 days at temperatures from 60–70°F. During this period, the rootlets develop while the plumule or acrospire grows under the hull of the barley kernel. The ideal end-point of growth is when the acrospire just reaches the length of the kernel [86, 90].

At the end of the germination period, the green malt is conveyed to large kilns where the moisture is reduced to 4–7 per cent to avoid undesirable changes. This operation is known as drying or kilning. The kilns usually consist of two floors, one above the other. The green malt is spread in layers 2–3 feet deep on the upper floor where drying is started at a relatively low temperature. Hot air is drawn through the malt. After about 24 hours, the malt is dropped to the lower floor where drying is completed. The process requires from 48–72 hours. The malt then is removed from the kiln, cleaned to remove rootlets, and conveyed to storage [86, 90].

Two general types of malts are produced commercially in the United States: brewers malts and distillers malts. Brewers malts are germinated at moisture contents of 43–46 per cent, kilned at high temperatures of 160–180°F, and finally dried down to about 4 per cent moisture. This produces malts high in flavor and aroma. Distillers malts are germinated at a moisture content of 45–49 per cent, kilned at temperatures of 120–140°F, and finally dried down to 5–7 per cent moisture. These conditions favor the production as well as the conservation of high enzymatic activities [29, 90].

During germination, enzymes are produced or liberated in an active state, primarily in the epithelial layer of the scutellum. This structure is located between the germ and endosperm of the kernel. As germination proceeds, the enzyme cytase changes the cell-wall material to make it more permeable. The extent of this enzymatic action determines the mellowness and friability to the finished malt. The amylase enzymes, which convert starch into maltose sugars and dextrins in brewing operations, probably are the most important enzymes in barley malt. Ungerminated barley contains bound beta-amylase, which is liberated or activated during germination by proteolytic enzymes. Alpha-amylase is produced during germination, probably by synthesis. Only a small amount of starch is converted to maltose or other sugars during germination. The major conversion of starch takes place during the subsequent mashing of malt. Several other enzymatic systems, particularly those that transform the proteins, are either produced or activated during the malting process [45, 29, 90].

Brewing

Most of the malt produced in the United States is used in the manufacture of beer. Mashing is an intermediate step in the use of malt in the brewing process. In the mashing operation, the malt is crushed between rollers to avoid injury to the barley hulls which serve later as a filtering medium.

A weighed quantity of crushed malt is then dropped into a metallic cylindrical vessel, the mash-tun, which is provided with an agitator, a perforated false bottom, and pipe connections for warm or cold water. Adjuncts such as cracked corn or rice grits are added to the malt. Water at about 120°F is added and the mixture stirred thoroughly. The enzymes formed during malting become active. Starch is converted by amylase into maltose, or into intermediate products called dextrins. Under favorable conditions, the starch produces 80 per cent maltose and 20 per cent dextrins. The most favorable temperatures for maltose formation are 135–143.5°F, and a pH of 5–5.5. Other enzymes break down the complex protein molecule. The optimum conditions for this proteolytic enzyme activity are a temperature of about 118–122°F, and a pH of 4.3–5. The temperature in mashing is raised to about 175°F with hot water and steam. After mashing is completed, the insoluble material settles to the bottom where it serves as a filtering medium. The solution (wort) is drawn off, and the residue of sprouting grains is dried for sale as feed. This method of mashing, known as the infusion method, is used almost universally in the United States [86].

The filtered extract of malt and adjuncts (the clear wort), is boiled with hops, which are added to give flavor to the beer. Boiling extracts desirable products from the hops, and renders certain undesirable constituents harmless. The wort is strained into coolers after boiling. Yeast is then added to the cooled, filtered, and hopped wort to induce the transformation of the fermentable sugars in the wort into alcohol and carbon dioxide. The hop resins and proteins are then eliminated. The resulting product, the beer, is then aged, chill-proofed, filtered, bottled, and pasteurized. Keg beer is handled in a similar manner except that it is neither bottled nor pasteurized [89, 90].

Milling

Pearled barley is used for human food in the United States and other countries. A barley pearler consists of 6–8 abrasive disks that revolve within a perforated cylinder to grind the hulls and bran off the kernel. The disks, which are usually coated with carborundum or emery, revolve at about 450 rpm. The cylinder is designed to keep the barley turning so as to obtain a uniform removal of material. The machine operates on the batch principle, which is often controlled automatically. The barley is pearled for a few minutes, after which it is transferred to a screen, sifted, aspirated to remove the hulls and fine particles, and then cooled. The cooled grain is rerun through the same steps. After three pearlings, all the hull and most of the bran will have been removed. At this stage, the dehulled barley may be graded for size for sale as pot barley. After 5–6 pearlings, the bran as

FIGURE 18-16. **Steam-rolled barley for feed.**

(*Courtesy US Department of Agriculture*)

well as most of the embryos are removed, and the product that remains is marketed as pearled barley. Barley flour is sifted from the ground material, and the residue is used for animal feed. White two-rowed varieties with large kernels are generally used for pearling [29, 90].

Most of the barley flour is obtained from the fourth, fifth, and sixth pearlings, which consist largely of starchy endosperm. This material may be milled further, or bolted and aspirated to obtain pure flour. Pearled grains also may be milled to produce highly refined patent barley flour. The hulls usually are removed from the grain before producing barley flour by the roller milling process [29, 90]. In Oriental countries, large quantities of barley are utilized as flour or grits and hull-less barleys often are milled because they yield a larger percentage of flour than do the hulled types.

UTILIZATION OF BARLEY AND ITS PRODUCTS

More than 50 per cent of the barley crop in the United States is used for feed; nearly 30 per cent is used for malted products; 6 per cent is used for seed; and the remainder is exported, destroyed, or used in pearled barley and other food products.

Feed and Food

From one-fourth to one-third of the barley grown in the United States is fed on the farms where it is produced. Barley has about 95 per cent of the feeding value of corn grain. It is a popular feed for hogs because its use results in desirable proportions of firm white fat and lean meat. It is ground or steamrolled before feeding (Fig. 18-16). Malt sprouts from the malting process, as well as dried and wet brewers grains—by-products of brewing— are used as livestock feed.

Only a small amount of unmalted barley grain is used as human food in North America. The average annual per capita consumption in the United States is 1.1 pounds. Large quantities of the grain are consumed by human beings in some Asiatic countries. In Japan, from 65–75 per cent of the crop is used directly as human food, generally as pearled barley cooked with rice [54]. In China, barley often is ground into flour with either broad beans or lentils for human consumption. In Tibet, the grain generally is roasted or parched, ground, and mixed with yak milk to form a dough which is eaten directly.

Processed Products

Pearled and pot barleys are used in soups or in dressings in the United States. Barley flour is used in baby foods and breakfast cereals. It also may be mixed with wheat flour for making bread when wheat is scarce. A mixture of up to 20 per cent of barley flour produces a satisfactory bread.

Other Uses of the Crop

Barley is cut for hay in the western United States, particularly in California. It is harvested for hay while the plants are still green but the heads well formed. The protein content of the hay is higher before the grain is mature [90.]. Smooth-awned or hooded varieties often are grown for hay.

In winter barley areas, the crop often is pastured in the fall after the plants are well established. In some cases, barley is pastured again in the spring for a short period, after which it is allowed to produce a grain crop. Barley also is used in these areas as a winter cover crop. Sometimes the crop is plowed under as a green manure [90]. In the lower Yangtze Valley of China, barley is used extensively as a green manure crop in rice fields.

Barley straw in the United States is plowed under or utilized for bedding or roughage. In Japan, the straw is used for straw ropes, roof thatching, litter, and mulches for vegetables [54].

BARLEY DISEASES[5]

Diseases reduce the annual barley crop in the United States by at least 5 per cent [57].

Covered Smut

Covered smut, caused by *Ustilago hordei,* is a fungus disease that causes considerable losses. It is distributed widely throughout the world. This disease first becomes noticeable when smutted heads emerge from the boot. Hard, black spore masses, each covered with a grayish membrane, replace the kernels, and may be carried over in the threshed grain.

Some covered smut spores lie dormant on the surface of the seed. Others are carried under the hulls or send slender infection hyphae beneath the hulls before or after threshing, thus producing most of the infection [113]. The barley seedling becomes infected between germination and emergence from the soil. Soil temperatures of 50–70°F during this period result in the highest percentage of infection. Mild temperatures for 2–4 weeks after seedling emergence favor later smut development. More smut develops in plants grown in acid soil than in those grown in neutral or alkaline soil [57].

---

[5] For a more detailed account of barley diseases, see J. G. Dickson, *Diseases of Field Crops,* 2nd ed. (New York: McGraw-Hill, 1956), pp. 517.

Seed-borne covered smut spores may be controlled by seed treatment with organic mercury compounds. For example, Ceresan M may be applied to barley seed as a dust or slurry at the rate of one-half ounce per bushel. The seed should be stored for a few days before sowing. Some barley varieties are resistant to the disease, but resistance is complicated by the occurrence of different physiologic races, thirteen of which were identified before 1945 [112, 113].

Nuda Loose Smut

Nuda loose smut of barley, caused by *Ustilago nuda,* occurs generally wherever barley is grown, but it is more prevalent in the humid and sub-humid regions than in dry regions. Total losses are small, but they may be heavy in some fields.

This smut causes the entire head, except the rachis, to be replaced by a brown spore mass enclosed in a thin membrane which soon ruptures. The spores then blow away to leave a naked rachis. Smutted heads emerge from the boot slightly earlier than healthy ones and frequently are taller.

Nuda loose smut spores from diseased barley heads are blown by wind or carried by rain to the flowers of healthy heads. The spores normally germinate at once to form long slender infection hyphae which grow deeply within the young seed as it develops. The fungus resumes growth when the barley seed germinates. Infected kernels appear normal, but the infected plants produce smutted heads.

Seed treatments with chemical disinfectants are ineffective because the fungus is deeply imbedded in the seed. The disease is best avoided by sowing certified smut-free seed or seed of resistant varieties. Hot water or anaerobic seed treatments with water give fair control but usually reduce germination somewhat. In the hot-water treatment, the seed is placed in loose-mesh burlap bags and soaked for five hours in water at approximately 70°F. The bags are then removed from the water, drained, and placed in a water bath at 120°F for about one minute. They are then placed in water at exactly 126°F for 11 minutes, and then plunged into cold water. The seed is then spread out to surface-dry before it is sown. The hot-water treatment generally is applied only to small seed lots [57]. One anaerobic treatment involves soaking the seed four hours, draining it one-half hour, and then holding it in full tight drums for 30 hours at 90°F to 80 hours at 65°F. (or with a two-hour time difference for each 1°F average temperature difference between 65–90°F) [93].

Many commercial barley varieties are susceptible to this loose smut, but Trebi—as well as some varieties derived from it—are resistant to the most common physiologic races of the fungus [24].

Nigra Loose Smut

Nigra loose smut, caused by *U. nigra,* sometimes called black or semi-loose smut, is rather generally distributed on cultivated barley wherever it is grown [110, 24]. It causes considerable loss to the barley crop in the United States.

The nigra loose smut is evident when the barley heads appear. The spore masses are dark-brown to black. Diseased heads usually emerge somewhat later than do those of nuda loose smut. Sometimes some intact awns or hulls are evident in the spore masses of smutted heads.

The spores are disseminated by the wind usually when the healthy heads are in bloom. Some of the spores come in contact with the flowers or the embryonic seeds of healthy plants. Seed infection occurs in much the same manner as for covered smut. Infection of the young seedling takes place at the time of seed germination. Temperatures of 60–70°F and a relatively dry soil at the time of emergence favor infection. Mild weather conditions for 2–4 weeks after the seedlings appear results in a higher percentage of smut [111, 57].

Nigra loose smut can be controlled by ordinary chemical seed treatments. A few barley varieties particularly those of the Manchuria group, are somewhat resistant to the disease. Smooth-awned varieties with considerable resistance include Newal, Wisconsin Barbless, and Glabron. Resistance is complicated by the existence of at least nine physiologic races [24].

Stem Rust

Barley stem rust is caused by the same fungi, *Puccinia graminis tritici* and *P. graminis secalis,* that attack wheat and rye. It is found in most regions of the world where cultivated barley is grown, but particularly in the humid and subhumid areas of North America, Europe, and Asia. Stem rust causes serious barley losses in the United States in some years, as in 1937. Serious outbreaks of the disease sometimes occur in southwestern Japan because of the hot humid weather conditions prevalent as the crop approaches maturity.

Stem rust on barley is characterized by red pustules that break through the epidermis of the stems, leaves, leaf sheaths, glumes, and awns. Black spores develop later in the season. The kernels shrivel, the rusted stems turn brown, dry out, and soon break over.

The life history of stem rust of barley is the same as that for stem rust of wheat (see Chap. 15).

Some practices such as planting early varieties, early seeding, and the use of phosphate fertilizers to hasten maturity may help the barley to escape stem rust damage. The most practical control measure is the use of resistant varieties. Kindred is a resistant variety that has been grown extensively in the North Central states. Other commercial varieties resistant to stem rust include Peatland, Mars, Plains, Feebar, and Moore [30, 57].

Leaf Rust

Leaf rust of barley, caused by *Puccinia hordei,* is found in most countries of the world where barley is grown. It occurs in the eastern and central United States, and sometimes causes severe local damage on winter barley, but is seldom serious on spring barley. Severe leaf rust reduces the yield as well as the quality of the grain [57].

Pustules of the summer or uredial stage of leaf rust appear on the leaf blades and sheaths, but rarely on the floral bracts of barley plants. The pustules are small, round, and yellow or yellowish-brown in color. The black or telial stage follows the summer stage with lead-gray pustules that are covered by the epidermis.

The life history of leaf rust of barley is similar to that of leaf rust of wheat. This rust survives the winters in the uredial stage, particularly in the southern winter barley regions. It spreads northward with the advance of spring. Infection in northern barley areas frequently is not evident until late spring or early summer. Secondary spread of the urediospores is favored by warm, humid, summer weather. The aecial stage, which occurs infrequently in the United States, develops on the Star-of-Bethlehem (*Ornithogalum umbellatum*) and closely related species [60].

This rust is controlled most economically by growing resistant varieties, such as Goliad, which also is resistant to stem rust. Breeding for leaf rust resistance is complicated by the existence of 52 known physiologic races that can be differentiated on nine barley varieties. The most prevalent race in North America is UN Race 4 which was found in 29.7 per cent of the leaf rust collections. New races also have been reported to arise by mutation [58].

Stripe Rust

Stripe rust, caused by *Puccinia glumarum,* commonly known as yellow rust, is seldom found on barley in the United States. The disease is destructive on barley in Europe, and also occurs in Africa, South America, Japan, China, and India. Considerable damage is likely to result from a heavy attack of the disease, particularly when the plants are rusted in the milk stage or earlier. The kernels may be shriveled and the yields considerably reduced.

Stripe rust is characterized by conspicuous yellow or yellow-orange pustules of the uredial or summer stage that develop primarily on the leaves,
leaf sheaths, and floral bracts. The pustules often unite in rows of various
lengths to give the appearance of fairly narrow yellow stripes. They occur
from early spring until midsummer. The uredial stage is followed, usually
in late summer, by the black or telial stage. The black pustules also are
produced more or less in rows that look like long, narrow, dark-brown, or
black stripes [60].

Stripe rust winters over as spores or as mycelium. The aecial stage is
unknown. Epidemics are most likely to occur after abundant infection in
the late summer or fall of the previous year when abundant inoculum has
survived the winter. The disease is favored in the spring and early summer
by cool nights, warm days, heavy dews, and abundant sunshine.

Resistant varieties are the only practical control for the disease. A
large number of barley varieties, including Hannchen and Wisconsin Pedigree
38, are resistant to stripe rust[12].

Powdery Mildew

Powdery mildew, caused by *Erysipha graminis,* does more damage to
barley than to any other cereal crop. It is found throughout the humid and
subhumid regions of the world. In the United States, it is particularly troublesome in the Atlantic and Southeastern states where winter barleys generally
are grown. Occasionally, it causes serious losses in the North Central states
and on the Pacific coast. When severe, it may reduce yields 25 per cent
or more by the impairment of the green-leaf tissue of the barley plant. In
California tests, heavy mildew infection in 1948 caused a maximum yield
reduction of 27.4 per cent. The loss was accounted for by an average reduction of 6.4 per cent in kernel weight and 21.5 in kernel number [88].

The first indications of infection by powdery mildew are small, white,
or light-gray spots of cottony threads (mycelia) on the upper surface of the
leaves. The spots or lesions enlarge, darken, and become powdery with age
as they produce millions of spores. These lesions may involve large areas
of the leaf which become yellow, then brown, and finally dry out. Powdery mildew grows primarily on the upper surface of the leaves, but in severe
attacks it may also be found on the stems and floral bracts.

Primary infection of powdery mildew occurs from conidia or ascospores
which are disseminated by the wind. As the barley plant approaches maturity,
small, black, reproductive bodies (perithecia) of the fungus develop in the
infected areas. These may aid the disease to overwinter. The disease may
persist from year to year as mycelium in areas where the winters are mild
enough for the infected leaves to live over. However, ascospores are the
primary source of infection in the spring barley regions [57, 24].

Powdery mildew is more severe on barley plants that have made a rank growth. Heavy applications of nitrogen fertilizer or other factors that promote a heavy leafy growth should be avoided. The disease can be controlled by dusting the plants with sulfur, but the method is uneconomical. The most practical control measure is the growing of resistant varieties. Numerous barley varieties are resistant to one or more races of the fungus. Atlas 46 is a resistant California variety [88]; Missouri Early Beardless was found to be mildew-resistant; while Kentucky 1, Poland, Wong, Calhoun, Sunrise, and Tucker were moderately resistant to physiologic Races 2 and 10 found in Missouri [72].

Fusarium Head Blight or Scab

Fusarium head blight or scab is a disease of barley as well as of wheat and rye. It also damages corn and sorghum. The disease is caused by *Fusarium graminearum* whose sexual perithecial stage is known as *Gibberella zeae*. Two other species, *F. culmorum* and *F. avenaceum,* also incite the disease. These fungi also cause seedling blights of corn and sorghum. Fusarium head blight causes heavy losses to barley in the Corn Belt of the United States, and is common on barley in the humid and subhumid regions in Europe, Asia, and Africa. Head blight causes a reduction in grain yield as well as a deterioration in grain quality. The head blight fungus also causes a foot rot and seedling blight of barley [23].

The head blight develops in warm, humid, weather at any stage from the formation to the ripening of the kernels. Infection begins in the flowers but frequently spreads to other parts of the spike. In barley, the diseased area turns light brown. Pink mold growth often develops around the base of the infected flower. Black fruiting bodies (perithecia) may be found on the glumes. Blighted kernels are grayish-brown and light in weight. The interior of the kernels becomes floury and discolored. The fungus produces toxins that cause acute vomiting when the grain is eaten by hogs, dogs, or man.

The head blight fungus overwinters on barley seed, as well as on plant residues of barley, corn, and other affected crops of the previous season. Infected seed, when sown, produces infected seedlings. Spores borne on diseased plant residues, such as corn stubble, also may cause seedling infection, but later the spores may cause floral infection of the barley heads. The crown tissues of barley plants are invaded by fungus mycelium from diseased plant residue in the soil [57].

Fair control is achieved by crop rotation so that barley does not follow corn, barley, wheat, or rye. The use of disease-free seed, or treatment of diseased seed with an organic mercury compound, restricts seedling infection. Another control measure involves the completely turning under of crop residues. Nearly all commercial varieties of barley are susceptible to head blight, although Svansota, Chevron, and Peatland are partly resistant.

Stripe

Stripe disease, caused by *Helminthosporium gramineum,* occurs only on barley, and in nearly all countries where barley is grown. Grain losses of 10–25 per cent are frequent on susceptible varieties [56]. The disease is now relatively unimportant in the spring barley region of the United States and Canada, but it causes considerable damage in California as well as in the winter barley areas of the South Central states. In California, stripe has been reported to cause an aggregate yield reduction of 0.75 per cent for each 1.0 per cent of disease [97].

Stripe originates from infected seed. It first appears as long, pale-green stripes on the leaves. Later, the stripes turn brown or even black, at which time the leaves may split along the stripes. Usually all the leaves of diseased plants are affected. Striped plants usually are stunted, and the heads frequently fail to produce seed or even to emerge from the boot [57].

Diseased leaves produce abundant spores (conidia) which are blown to healthy barley plants during or after the flowering period. Seed infection occurs from these wind-borne spores. When the seed germinates, the fungus mycelium invades all plant parts, with the ultimate reproduction of the spores during the period of barley flowering.

Sufficient moisture to wet the spores is necessary for floral infection, so seedling infection is favored by a cool, moist soil. Growing temperatures of 15°C (59°F), or lower, during the period of emergence favor the development of stripe in plants from naturally inoculated seed [56].

When available, resistant varieties offer the most practical method for the control of stripe. Varietal resistance is complicated by the existence of numerous physiologic races of the pathogen [19]. Among the commercial barley varieties grown in the North Central states, Spartan is highly resistant, while Hannchen, Regal, Trebi, and Wisconsin Barbless are resistant only to certain races. In California, the varieties Vaughn, Arivat, Wisconsin Barbless, Trebi, Coast, and Hannchen showed resistance to the disease [102]. Seed treatment with an effective organic mercury fungicide will control seed-borne infection.

Spot Blotch

Spot blotch, caused by the fungus *Helminthosporium sativum,* attacks barley as well as wheat, rye, and many grasses. The sexual stage of the fungus is *Cochliobolus sativus.* The same organism also causes seedling blight, root rot, stem rot, head blight, and kernel blight. Spot blotch is widely distributed in the United States and Canada, and also in other countries of the world where barley or other susceptible crops are grown. It may cause severe damage to barley.

Spot blotch affects all parts of the barley plant. Infected seedlings have dark-brown to black blades and sheaths and often die. The roots of diseased seedlings show darkened areas, and dark-brown spots appear on the leaves. These spots fuse to form blotches that may cover large areas of the leaf blade. Heavily infected leaves dry out and mature early; heads often fail to emerge completely; and diseased plants also may be stunted and produce excessive tillers. Numerous dark-brown spots appear on the germ end of diseased barley kernels, a condition commonly called black point [18, 57].

Initial infections arise from the causal fungus which may be carried on the seed or on plant remains in the soil. Numerous secondary infections may occur up to the time the barley plant matures. The disease is favored by warm wet weather.

Spot blotch borne on the seed may be controlled by seed treatment with an organic mercury fungicide, but resistant varieties are a more practical control measure. Barleys of the Manchuria type and many two-rowed barleys are rather resistant [42]. Peatland, Velvet, and Wisconsin Barbless [48], and Mars and Moore varieties are resistant [23]. It is unsafe to grow successive barley crops in areas where the disease is likely to be serious. In the spring-grain area of the United States, crop rotation is ineffective because a large percentage of the acreage is seeded to other cereals or grasses that also harbor the disease [57].

Net Blotch

Net blotch, caused by the fungus *Helminthosporium teres,* apparently infects only cultivated barley. The sexual stage is *Pyrenophora teres.* Net blotch is found on barley in the temperate regions of the world. The disease usually is of minor importance in the United States, but may cause considerable damage under some conditions.

The characteristic symptoms are brown netted blotches or irregular stripes on the leaves, brown discoloration of the stem, and light-brown indistinct blotches on the kernels. The size of the kernels also is reduced. The netted areas enlarge and fuse in the course of the growing season [23].

Spores produced on diseased leaves are wind-borne to other leaves. Repeated secondary infections occur, particularly in cool humid weather. The fungus overwinters on infected seed as well as on old straw or stubble in the field. The sexual stage of the fungus (ascospores) is produced abundantly on old plant remains.

The principal controls for net blotch are the growing of resistant varieties, clean cultivation, and crop rotation. Varietal resistance is complicated by the existence of at least two distinct races of the pathogen in the United States. Resistance to the western race is found in the Manchuria-Oderbrucker group of barleys, which includes Peatland. Resistance to the eastern race is concentrated in the North African and Abyssinian barleys [23]. Kindred is one of a few commercial varieties resistant to both races. Barley sown on or near fields with diseased stubble may become heavily infected. Seed treatment with organic mercury dusts controls the fungus carried on the seed [57].

Bacterial Leaf Blight

Bacterial leaf blight of barley, caused by *Xanthomonas translucens,* is widely distributed throughout the western hemisphere, and is also found in Europe, Asia, and Australia. In the United States, the disease is found particularly in the spring barley area where it is generally of minor importance. Occasional serious outbreaks on susceptible varieties result in reduced yields [57].

Bacterial blight infection on barley is characterized by irregular, narrow, glossy-surfaced stripes on the leaves. The first symptoms are small water-soaked areas on the leaves which later enlarge to yellowish or brownish somewhat translucent blotches. Small gray drops of bacterial exudate may appear on the lesions. Similar diseased areas may develop on the leaf sheaths and floral bracts, and even the heads may be blighted in severe late attacks.

Bacterial blight is favored by wet weather. It is spread by rain and by insects. The bacteria are carried over from season to season on the seed, in crop residues, and in the soil.

The principal control measures, crop rotation and seed treatment with organic mercury fungicides, reduce but may not prevent occasional outbreaks of the disease. Some barley varieties are partly resistant [57].

Scald

Scald of barley, rye, and some grasses, is a fungus disease caused by *Rhynchosporium secalis*. It occurs widely in northern Europe, North America, Australia, Tunis, Argentina, and Peru [17]. In the United States, scald is a serious disease chiefly in the Pacific coast states, but it also occurs in the winter barley areas in the Eastern and Southeastern states. Losses in yield up to 20 per cent have resulted from severe attacks [57].

Scald primarily attacks the leaves and sheaths, causing oval or lens-shaped blotches which, at first, are water-soaked and gray-green. The blotches later appear as pale or white central areas surrounded by rings of brown tissue. The plants are almost completely defoliated by severe infection.

Scald is spread during the growing season by spores (conidia) produced on diseased leaves. The fungus which infects both seedlings and mature plants, overwinters on infected dead leaves and probably also on other crop residues and spreads to barley seedlings the next spring. The disease is favored by a cool growing season.

Control measures for scald consist of growing resistant varieties, rotating crops, and turning under or destroying crop residues. Atlas 46 is resistant to scald in California. Its resistance was derived from the variety Turk. Trebi also is resistant [80]. Many varieties of rough-awned Tennessee Winter type barleys were resistant to natural infections of scald in Missouri tests [72]. Six physiologic races have been reported but only one attacks barley [17].

Virus Diseases

Stripe mosaic, a virus disease, occurs to some extent in all barley regions in the United States and Canada, and sometimes causes considerable reduction in spring barley yields. The most frequent symptoms observed are bleached, yellow or light-green stripes, light-green to yellow mottling, and sometimes almost complete yellowing of the leaves. Virulent strains of the virus may cause brown stripes in the leaves. Barley plants become severely stunted when much of the green chlorophyll of the leaves is destroyed. The stripe mosaic virus is seed-borne, but is now known to overwinter in the soil. Healthy plants become infected when whipped against diseased plants by wind. Some barley varieties show signs of resistance to the disease. As a control measure, it is desirable to avoid sowing infected seed. Seed treatment is ineffective [61, 57].

The yellow-dwarf disease of barley was first observed in California in 1947, and was identified as a virus disease in 1951 when the state suffered a 10 per cent loss of the crop. The virus is transmitted by five widely distributed species of aphids. Wheat and oats also are susceptible to the disease. In barley, this virus causes a brilliant golden yellowing of the leaves, as well as moderate-to-severe stunting of the plants. Plants become infected at all stages. Stunting is less when the plants are older at the time of infection, but young plants frequently die. Yellow-dwarf infection of barley tends to reduce lodging, tiller development, size and fertility of heads, kernel weight, and yield [105]. The disease is spread from plant to plant by aphids. It is not transmitted through the seed or soil. Severity of the disease is somewhat decreased by early seeding so that the barley plants are well established by the time the weather is warm enough for aphid activity.

Barley sown in November or December in California tends to evade serious damage from natural yellow-dwarf infections. The disease can be eliminated by complete control of aphids, while the development of resistant varieties offers the most satisfactory means for control. The Rojo variety is considered tolerant to the disease [61, 69, 57, 100, 105].

Other Diseases

Several other diseases of barley that sometimes cause losses include ergot (*Claviceps purpurea*), anthracnose, Septoria leaf spot, downy mildew, and pythium root rot.

INSECT PESTS

Important insects that damage barley include the greenbug (*Toxoptera graminum*), Hessian fly (*Phytophaga destructor*), chinch bug (*Blissus leucopterus*), and grasshoppers (*Melanoplus* spp.).

The greenbug is a serious pest on winter barley in the central and southwestern United States as well as in other parts of the world. Severe outbreaks occur in some years. Many barley varieties showed a high degree of resistance to greenbug in Oklahoma, but all except Dicktoo and Kearney were from China, Korea, or Japan and were not adapted to the United States [20]. Some other species of aphids occasionally kill barley.

Tests of 5144 varieties of barley for Hessian fly resistance in the eastern United States revealed seven varieties with low plant infestation. These varieties, Dinar, Nile, Burgarab, Abusir, Besert 13, Besert 14, and Delta, are all of North African origin [44]. Studies on the California-Mexico border indicated that California Mariout was comparatively resistant to the insect in 1951 [103].

Barley is very attractive to the chinch bug and frequently is damaged in some of the Central states. There is no satisfactory control for chinch bug infestation in barley or other small grains.

Grasshoppers are controlled by poison baits, or chlordane and toxaphene dusts or sprays.

CYTOLOGY-CYTOGENETICS

All cultivated species of barley have 7 pairs of chromosomes, but wild species may have 7, 14, or 21 pairs. Wild species with 7 chromosome pairs are *Hordeum caput-medusae, H. maritimum, H. spontaneum,* and *H. agrio-crithon.* Species with 14 chromosome pairs are *H. jubatum, H. bulbosum,* and *H. silvaticum.* Three species, *H. murinum, H. gussoneanum,* and *H. secalinum* have 7 and 14-chromosome forms. *H. nodosum* has 7, 14, and 21-chromosome forms [94].

Interspecies Hybrids

Hybrids between cultivated species of barley apparently are almost completely fertile without evident meiotic irregularities, even though the parents came from widely separated regions. Crosses between the cultivated species and the 7-chromosome wild species, *H. spontaneum,* have shown no marked sterility or abnormal segregation. With the exception of hoods, most of the characters of *H. spontaneum* are dominant over their alleles in cultivated barley. Similar results have been observed for the cross between *H. vulgare* and *H. agriocrithon.* Thus, all species in Section Cereale appear closely enough related to give fertile F_1 plants and regular Mendelian ratios [94].

Relatively few wide interspecific hybrids have been studied in barley. Hybrids have been obtained between cultivated barley species and the 14-chromosome wild species. In a cross of *H. jubatum* × *H. vulgare,* only 10 per cent of the seeds germinated, although 70 per cent of the florets set seed. In a *H. jubatum* × *H. distichum* cross, about 54 per cent of the seeds grew vigorously to produce plants twice as tall as the female parent [76]. Some seed set also has been obtained from the crosses, *H. vulgare* × *H. bulbosum* and *H. distichum* × *H. nodosum* [94]. Crosses between the cultivated barleys and other wild barley species generally have failed to produce viable seed.

Polyploids

Relatively few haploids or triploids have been reported in barley. Those found were generally members of twin seedlings.

Several autotetraploids have been reported in barley, some of which occurred spontaneously, while others were induced by heat or colchicine treatments. Various morphological changes occur in barley plants when the chromosomes are doubled. Tetraploids generally have stronger, and thicker culms and produce higher yields of straw than the diploid. Their leaves also are longer, broader, and thicker. The number of seeds per spike is lower in tetraploids because of partial sterility, but the seeds usually are larger than those of comparable diploids [94].

Meiosis in autotetraploid barley is irregular. About 50 per cent of the progeny may have aberrant chromosome numbers. Tests of ten autotetraploids in Sweden indicate that the grain yield averaged only 40 per cent of that of the comparable diploids. The highest yields were obtained from selections in the offspring of crosses. Some selections yielded 80 per cent as much as the diploids [62, 94].

MUTATIONS

The barley plant is remarkably stable genetically, although numerous spontaneous hereditary changes have occurred. Chlorophyll deficiencies are the most common mutants. Studies of mutation frequency have shown that 0.5 per cent or less of the barley spikes produced new mutants [94]. About one new chlorophyll mutant has appeared in the progeny of every 10,000 plants of the Golden variety of barley [31].

Induced Mutations

Most induced mutations are deleterious recessives. High temperatures increase the frequency of chromosomal aberrations and other mutations; a number of tetraploid barleys have been produced by heat treatment [94].

Irradiation with X-rays induced certain mutations that occur in approximately the same relative proportions as they occur spontaneously, but at a lower frequency. In Swedish experiments, mutation frequency was increased about 5000 times by X-ray treatment [44]. Exposure to atomic-bomb-induced radiations produced effects comparable to exposure to X-ray dosages of 16,000 roentgens [94]. Irradiation with gamma rays, radiophosphorus, or neutrons also produce mutations.

Colchicine treatment has been particularly effective in altering chromosome number, especially in producing tetraploids.

Role in Breeding Programs

Several early, male-sterile, and naked spontaneous mutations collected in California have some potential value for breeding. Mutants of practical value have been isolated in Sweden from Golden, Maja, and other barley varieties. One Maja mutant (Erectoides 12) yields more and has a stiffer straw than the parent variety. Another mutant has a stiffer straw and ripens two or three days earlier [31]. Other induced mutants of potential value include variations in number of kernel rows, plant height, leaf breadth, spike density, and awn length. In fact, almost any genetic changes sought by plant breeders may be induced as new mutations [65].

GENETICS

The genetics of more than 180 characters of the barley plant have been reported [94, 83]. Many of these have been assigned to specific linkage groups.

Chaff or Grain Colors

Black hull color, which is dominant to nonblack, segregates in a 3:1 ratio in many crosses. There is evidence of an allelic series of three genes for degree of pigmentation of lemma and pericarp: black, gray, and white. In each combination, the darker color is dominant over the lighter one, with segregation in single-factor ratios [94].

Purple chaff color is dominant to white. The character often has been reported to be conditioned by one or two gene pairs. Two complementary genes (P_bC_c) also have been identified. Crosses between purple and nonpurple stocks may segregate with either a 3:1 or a 9:7 ratio in the F_2 generation. Some crosses between nonpurple stocks have given purple F_1 plants, with a 9:7 ratio in F_2 [126].

Brownish-yellow chaff color has been reported as caused by a single gene dominant to white, whereas orange chaff is conditioned by a single gene recessive to the factor for white chaff.

Two pigments are responsible for seed colors in barley: anthocyanin, which is violet in acid but blue in alkaline solutions; and a melaninlike black pigment. These pigments may occur in the hulls, pericarp, aleurone layer, and occasionally deeper in the endosperm. The seeds are white when neither pigment is present, violet when anthocyanin is present only in the pericarp, and blue when anthocyanin occurs only in the aleurone layer. Anthocyanin in an acid condition in the pericarp and in an alkaline condition in the aleurone results in a purple color [94].

Black color in the hulls is associated with color of grain which is localized in the pericarp. Crosses between black and white-grained types generally have given a 3:1 ratio in F_2 with black dominant.

Most reports indicate that blue aleurone is caused by a single dominant gene. However, a 9:7 ratio has been obtained in F_2 in a cross of two white-aleurone varieties, an indication of two complementary factors for blue vs. white aleurone [63]. Since blue occurs in the aleurone, xenia may be observed when the cross is made on the white-seeded parent, but the expression of the character frequently is influenced by environmental conditions.

Purple pericarp color is reported as dominant to white or yellow and produced by a single gene. Red pericarp has been reported to be dominant to white pericarp and to be caused by one gene in some cases, but by two genes in others. Red is recessive to black pericarp. The difference between purple and red is conditioned by two genes in some crosses, but in other crosses by two additional complementary genes that affect the expression of the two primary genes [94].

Head or Spike Characters

Cultivated barley species have been classified largely on the basis of fertility of the lateral florets. Many crosses have been made between six-row, two-row, intermedium, and deficiens types. The genetics of row number has been attributed to one factor pair. In some crosses of *H. vulgare* and *H. distichum,* a 1:2:1 segregation for two-rowed, intermediate, and six-rowed is obtained in the F_2 generation. Other workers have reported that fertility of the lateral florets is due to two factor pairs. In some *H. vulgare* × *H. distichum* crosses, seven classes have been differentiated on their breeding behavior in F_3. The present concept is that two series of multiple alleles are involved in the fertility of the lateral florets. A multiple allelic series of row factors has been described, that is, v, V^d, V, and V^t. This series interacts with the independent intermedium allelic series, I^h, I, and i, to give different degrees of fertility of the lateral florets [123, 124]. Environmental conditions affect fertility expression.

Most of the so-called awnless types have short awns on the lower florets. The awnless character generally is dominant to hooded, and both are dominant to the awned condition. Awn inheritance is simple in some cases, but complicated in others. Many workers have reported a monofactorial segregation of 3:1 hooded to awned in the F_2 generation. Crosses between short-awned varieties and hooded strains result in a two-factor segregation for hoods, long awns, and short awns in a 9:3:4 ratio [127].

Two gene pairs generally are responsible for the difference between certain long- and short-awned (or awnless) varieties. Three or four genes may be involved in awn length in some crosses. Appendages (awns or hoods) on the lateral florets may be determined by one gene pair. Normal appendages, which occur only on six-rowed types, are dominant to reduced appendages [94].

Crosses between rough and smooth-awned varieties usually segregate in a 3:1 ratio, with rough awns dominant. In some crosses, two gene pairs appear to be involved with a 12:3:1 ratio of rough, intermediate-smooth, and smooth-awned F_2 plants [94].

Vegetative Characters

Plant height may involve several genes. Four dwarf mutations are brachytic (br), many-noded dwarf (m), and "Uzu" (uz), all recessive; and a dominant dwarf (D) mutant. Another factor pair, tall vs. short (Hh) also has been reported. Plant height in different crosses between tall and short plants indicate that from one to four genes are involved, with tall usually dominant [94]. Crosses between two short varieties indicate that two gene pairs (Br br and Uz uz) have complementary affects on plant height, with each parent dominant for one height gene but recessive for the other [55].

Pubescence on leaf sheaths is conditioned by one gene pair with pubescence dominant. Several genetic factors may be involved in strength of straw, with weak straw often dominant. Transgressive segregation in straw stiffness also has been reported [94]. Earliness may be determined by one, two, three, or many genes in different crosses. In some crosses, earliness is dominant, whereas in others it is recessive [94].

In growth habit, the spring type is dominant to winter with one gene pair involved in some crosses, but two, three, or more genes are involved in others [94]. At least three major genes, Sh, sh_2, and sh_3 are necessary for the expression of winter habit [109]. The Sh gene is dominant.

Disease Reaction

Reaction to spot blotch (*Helminosporium sativum*) has been reported as controlled by one-factor pair with susceptibility dominant, but resistance was dominant and controlled by more than one gene in some crosses. One variety, Svanhals, was believed to have at least three genes for resistance [94].

Resistance to the stripe disease (*H. gramineum*) usually appears to be at least partly dominant, but all grades of dominance from resistance to susceptibility also have been reported. One to three genes are involved in stripe reaction in different crosses [94].

Twelve genetic factors for reaction to Race 3 of powdery mildew (*Erysiphe graminis hordei*) have been identified in the United States. Nine of these factors are dominant or incompletely dominant, while three are recessive. Two factor pairs seem to control the reaction to mildew (predominately Race 6) in a cross that involved susceptible Manchuria and resistant Chevron. The genes appeared to be additive for increased resistance [94].

Resistance to leaf rust (*Puccinia hordei*) appears to be conditioned by one gene in some crosses and by two genes in others. Resistance is either dominant or incompletely dominant. Some crosses segregate in a ratio of 15:1 for resistance vs. susceptibility in the F_2 generation [94].

Stem rust (*P. graminis*) resistance apparently is inherited as a single dominant gene in some crosses. One variety (Peatland) has a single gene that determines both seedling and mature-plant resistance to Races 19, 39, and 56. Susceptibility to some races of stem rust is dominant. Seedling reaction to stem rust generally indicates mature-plant reaction to the pathogen [94].

Resistance to stripe rust (*P. glumarum*) appears to be dominant and conditioned by one or two gene pairs.

Resistance to loose smut (*Ustilago nuda*) appears to be dominant over susceptibility in most barley crosses. Resistance is conditioned by one gene in some crosses, but by two genes in others. In a Brachytic × Newal cross, resistance was controlled by one incompletely dominant and one recessive gene. Three genes for resistance were identified in several crosses [87]. A total of five genes for loose smut resistance have been identified in different varieties.

Resistance to Race 6 of covered smut (*Ustilago hordei*) is conditioned by one major factor pair in the crosses, Chevron × Brachytic and Colsess × Brachytic. Resistance was dominant in the F_1 generation of the Chevron × Brachytic cross, while the F_2 segregations fit 1:2:1 ratios in both crosses [91].

In several barley varieties there appears to be one dominant gene for resistance to scald (*Rhynchosporium secalis*). In crosses with the susceptible Atlas variety, monohybrid ratios have been obtained for resistance vs. susceptibility.

CHROMOSOME NUMBERS — LINKAGE GROUPS

Of the seven linkage groups previously reported in barley studies with chromosome translocations indicate that groups III and VII should be considered as one [53]. Recently, the chromosomes have been designated to correspond to the linkage groups as follows [78]:

New Chromosome Number and Linkage Group	Previous Designation Translocation Stock	Linkage Group	Key Marker Gene Pair
1	b	III–VII	Nn
2	f	I	Vv
3	c	VI	Uz uz
4	e	IV	Kk
5	a	II	Bb
6	g	———	Oo
7	d	V	Rr

Some of the genetic factors of economic importance have been summarized [94, 85, 81].

Chromosome 1: Includes covered vs. naked caryopsis (N, n); blue vs. non-blue aleurone (Bl_2, bl_2); red vs. green stem (Rs, rs); lax vs. dense spike (L, l); normal vs. brachytic plant height (Br, br); resistance vs. susceptibility to stem rust (T, t); and normal vs. waxy endosperm (Wx, wx).

Chromosome 2: Includes genes for chlorophyll abnormalities; purple vs. nonpurple stem (Pr, pr); nonsix-rowed vs. six-rowed (V, v); awned vs. awnless (Lk, lk); lax vs. dense spikes (Rin, rin); tall vs. short plants (H, h); purple vs. nonpurple grain color (complementary factors) (Re, re); and early vs. late heading (Ea, ea).

Chromosome 3: Includes genes for chlorophyll abnormalities; normal vs. "uzu" (semibrachytic) plant height (Uz, uz); and lax vs. dense spikes (Lc, lc).

Chromosome 4: Includes genes for hooded vs. awned (K, k); blue vs. non-blue aleurone (Bl, bl); fertile intermedium vs. nonintermedium (I^h, i); infertile intermedium vs. nonintermedium (I, i); and resistance vs. susceptibility to mildew Race 3 (Mlg, mlg).

Chromosome 5: Includes genes for black vs. white lemma and caryopsis (B, b); normal vs. brittle rachis (Bt, bt); resistance vs. susceptibility to *Helminthosporium sativum:* susceptibility vs. resistance to mildew Race 3 (Ml_d, ml_d); and resistance vs. susceptibility to mildew (Mlp, mlp).

Chromosome 6: A gene pair for late vs. early maturity (Ec, ec) has been located in this chromosome [77]. Green vs. orange lemma (O, o) also occurs in this chromosome.

Chromosome 7: Includes genes for rough vs. smooth awns (R, r); lax vs. dense spike (L_3, l_3); long vs. short-haired rachilla (S, s); spring vs. winter habit (Sh_2, sh_2); and tall vs. short plants (H_2, h_2).

BREEDING METHODS

Among the qualities sought in barley improvement are high yields, nonshattering, suitability for combine harvest, smooth awns, good malting quality, stiff straw, disease resistance, and winter hardiness among winter varieties [36]. Selection from hybrids for improved malting quality often involves type and color, tight hull, stiff straw, smooth awn, and resistance to smut, stripe, and scab [25].

Standard Breeding Methods

The standard breeding procedures for barley are similar to those used in wheat. Artificial cross-pollination techniques have been described in detail [75].

Among the important barley introductions are the varieties Manchuria, Oderbrucker, Club Mariout, California Mariout, Hannchen, Tennessee Winter, and Coast.

Many new varieties were selected from Manchuria, Oderbrucker, and Tennessee Winter. The winter-hardy varieties, Reno and Ward, were selected from Tennessee Winter. Important varieties that arose as selections include Atlas and Trebi [121].

Hybridization, followed by pedigree selection, is the most widely used method of barley improvement. Backcrossing also has been popular, particularly in California. The smooth-awned varieties, Velvet, Flynn, Vaughn, Wisconsin Barbless, Velvon, and Lico were developed by hybridization. In Sweden, the Ymer variety represents the peak of achievement of the development of a good malting barley by hybridization [44]. Many other varieties have been developed from crosses to meet specific requirements such as drought resistance, disease resistance, and winter hardiness.

Bulk Variety Mixtures

When pure varieties are mixed, natural selection tends to eliminate most poor varieties and to preserve most of the well-adapted ones. A mixture of 11 varieties was grown at eight stations in the United States for 5–13 years. Trebi, Coast, and one other variety comprised 62–99 per cent of the mixture in the last year grown. At all places there was a rapid elimination of the less-adapted sorts. A variety dominant at one station was eliminated at another. Only five of the 11 varieties remained among the best three survivors at any of the eight locations [37, 35]. In a California study, the survival of Atlas, Club Mariout, Hero, and Vaughn in a mixture was studied for 16 years. Two of the varieties were brought to practical extinction. The percentages of plants of each variety in the mixture after 16 years were as follows: Atlas, 88.0 per cent; Club Mariout, 10.5 per cent; Hero, 0.7 per cent; and Vaughn, 0.4 per cent. It was concluded that survival in a mixture is not always related to either yield or disease resistance [98].

Bulked Hybrid Method

Composite crosses, conceived by the late H. V. Harlan, combine hybridization with natural selection. The seed of 379 barley crosses that involved 28 varieties were mixed in equal amounts in the F_2 generation, after which they were grown as a mixture in the field through the F_7 generation. Later, the F_7 pedigree lines and the F_7 composites were compared for yield. The results indicate that a bulk population is as effective as pedigree selection for perpetuating superior genetic combinations [58, 35].

In a comparison of the pedigree and bulk methods of barley improvement of 11 hybrid populations in Iowa, selection in F_2, F_3, and F_4 for vigorous plants with large, well-filled, and disease-free heads usually resulted in somewhat higher yields than did bulk culture. Selection did not isolate appreciably higher yielding lines. Selected lines averaged approximately two days later in heading, one day later in maturity, and 1.5 inches taller than the comparable bulk populations. Lodging resistance of selected lines did not differ from nonselected populations [9].

Six different composite crosses of barley were grown from 6–24 generations in California. As with varieties, genetic characters failed to survive equally in mixtures or at different locations. At the more selective locations, progenies recovered from prolonged natural selection were predominantly like the few best adapted parents. The characters that showed low survival were two-rowed, hoods, smooth awns, and black seeds. The study also revealed a continuous improvement in yield level when composite crosses are grown over long periods [104].

A bulked hybrid population that includes broadly diversified germ plasm can be subjected to competitive natural selection through many generations at a low cost. Fifteen generations of natural selection were suggested to be followed by continued natural selection, cyclic hybrid recombinations with intervening natural selection (a form of recurrent selection), or conventional selection procedures [101].

Other Methods

A proposed plant breeding procedure involves early testing for performance in crosses, which incorporates some of the desirable features of both the bulk hybrid and pedigree methods. In two crosses, the performance of F_2 derived lines gave a good indication of the performance of the F_3 derived lines selected from them. Selection for date of heading and plant height were the most effective, while test weight and yield were the least. Selection between the F_2 derived lines, with final selections made within superior F_2 derived lines in the F_6–F_{10} generations was suggested [27].

Male-sterility, conditioned by a simple recessive gene, provides a method for perpetuating synthetic barley hybrids. Male-sterile plants are characterized by partially open glumes that expose the stigmas, which are receptive to pollen for 6–10 days. In California, F_1 barley hybrids yielded 21 per cent more than the average of the parents. Since heterosis makes the seeds larger, it has been suggested that seed from open-pollinated bulk populations be graded for size in order to increase the proportion of both male-sterile and F_1 plants in the next generation. Hybrid vigor was utilized in composite hybrid populations, wherein the male-sterile portion of each generation produces hybrid seed. In California tests, the full benefit of extant heterosis was not realized because of poor pollen extrusion and dissemination which resulted in seed production on only 25–49 per cent of the male-sterile flowers in the pupulation. This poor seed set in turn minimized the effective use of grading for seed size to increase the proportion of F_1 seeds sown. Yields of the hybrids tested generally were equal to but not superior to those of established varieties [99].

REFERENCES

1. Aberg, E., "*Hordeum agriocrithon*, nova sp., a wild-six-rowed barley." Ag. Coll. of Sweden *Ann.*, Vol. 6. pp 159–216. 1938.
2. ———, "The taxonomy and phylogeny of *Hordeum* Section Cerealia with special reference to Tibetan barleys." Uppsala, Sweden: Almqvist and Wiksells Boktryckeri–A–B. pp 1–156. 1940.
3. ———, "Cereals and peas from eastern Tibet and their importance for the knowledge of the origin of cultivated plants." Ag. Coll. of Sweden *Ann.*, **15:** 235–250. 1948.
4. ———, "Barley and wheat from the Saqquar Pyramid in Egypt." Ag. Coll. of Sweden *Ann.* **17:** 59–63. 1950.
5. ———, and G. A. Wiebe, "Irregular barley, *Hordeum irregulare*, sp. nova." *J. Wash. Acad. sci.*, **35**(5): 161–164. 1945.
6. ———, and G. A. Wiebe, "Classification of barley varieties grown in the United States and Canada in 1945." USDA *Tech. Bul. 907.* pp 1–190. 1946.
7. *Agricultural statistics, 1958.* USDA. pp 41–46. 1959.
8. Atkins, I. M., "Cordova barley." Tex. Ag. Exp. Sta. *Bul. 760.* 1953.
9. Atkins, R. E., "Effect of selection upon bulk hybrid barley populations." *Agron. J.*, **45**(7): 311–314. 1953.
10. Ayers, A. D., "Germination and emergence of several varieties of barley in salinized soil cultures." *Agron. J.*, **45**(2): 68–71. 1953.
11. Beaven, E. S., *Barley: 50 Years of Observation and Experiment.* London: Duckworth. pp 1–394. 1947.
12. Bever, W. M., "Reaction of wheat, barley, and rye varieties to stripe rust in the Pacific Northwest." USDA *Cir. 501.* 1938.
13. Bonnett, O. T., "The development of the barley spike." *J. Ag. Res.*, **51:** 451–457. 1935.

14. ——, and C. M. Woodworth, "A yield analysis of three varieties of barley." *J. Am. Soc. Agron.*, **23**: 311. 1931.

15. Brucher, H., and E. Aberg, "Die Primitiv-Gersten des Hochlands von Tibet, ihre Bedeutung fur Zuchtung und das Verstandnis des Ursprungs und der Klassifizierung der Gersten." Kgl. Landw. Hochschule Schevedens *Ann.* **17**: 247–319. (Eng. summary.) 1950.

16. Burson, P. M., "Commercial fertilizers for malting barley." Barley Improvement Conf. *Rpt.* pp 6–7. 1951.

17. Caldwell, R. M., "Rhyncosporium scald of barley, rye, and other grasses." *J. Ag. Res.*, **55**: 175–198. 1937.

18. Christensen, J. J., "Studies on the parasitism of *Helminthosporium sativum*." Minn. Ag. Exp. Sta. *Tech. Bul. 11.* 1922.

19. ———, and T. W. Graham, "Physiologic specialization and variation in *Helminthosporium gramineum*." Minn. Ag. Exp. Sta. *Tech. Bul. 95.* 1934.

20. Dahms, R. G., *et al.*, "Reaction of small-grain varieties and hybrids to greenbug attack." Okla. Ag. Exp. Sta. *Tech. Bul. T-55.* 1955.

21. Den-Hartog, G. T., and J. W. Lambert, "The relationships between certain agronomic and malting quality characters of barley. *Agron. J.*, **45**(5): 208–212. 1953.

22. Derscheid, L. A., "Physiological and morphological responses of barley to 2,4-Dichlorophenozyacetic acid." *Pl. Phys.*, **27**: 121–134. 1952.

23. Dickson, J. G., "Leaf and head blights of cereals," in *Plant Diseases*. USDA Yrbk. of Ag. pp 344–349. 1953.

24. ———, *Diseases of Field Crops*. 2d. ed., New York: McGraw-Hill. pp 1–517. 1956.

25. ———, *et al.*, "Barley and malt studies. I: Development of new varieties of barley for malting and their properties." *Cer. Chem.* **12**: 596–609. 1935.

26. Frey, K. J., "Relationships between test weight and certain malting quality criteria in barley." Mich. Ag. Exp. Sta. *Quart. Bul.*, **35**: 430–432. 1953.

27. ———, "The use of F_2 lines in predicting the performance of F_3 selections in two barley crosses." *Agron. J.*, **46**: 541–544. 1954.

28. Foote, W. H., and F. C. Batchelder, "Effect of different rates and times of application of nitrogen fertilizers on the yield of Hannchen barley." *Agron. J.*, **45** (11): 532–535. 1953.

29. Geddes, W. F., "Technology of cereal grains," in Jacobs, M. B., *The Chemistry and Technology of Food and Food Products*, 2d. ed., Vol. 3. pp 2018–2090. 1951.

30. Grafius, J. E., "Feebar barley." S. Dak. Ag. Exp. Sta. *Cir. 67.* 1947.

31. Gustafsson, A., and J. MacKey, "Mutation work at Svalof." In *Svalof, 1886–1946: History and Present Problems*. Lund, Sweden: Carl Bloms Boktryckeri A.-B. pp 338–357. 1948.

32. Hancock, N. L., and O. H. Long, "Barley variety studies in Tennessee." Tenn. Ag. Exp. Sta. *Bul. 203.* 1947.

33. Harlan, H. V., "Daily development of kernels of Hannchen barley from flowering to maturity at Aberdeen, Idaho." *J. Ag. Res.*, **19**: 393–430. 1917.

34. ———, "The identification of varieties of barley." USDA *Bul. 622.* pp 1–15, 25–30. 1918.

35. ———, *One Man's Life With Barley*. New York: Exposition Press. pp 1–223. 1957.

36. ——, and M. L. Martini, "Problems and results in barley breeding," in USDA Yrbk. of Ag. pp 303–346. 1936.

37. ——, and M. L. Martini, "The effect of natural selection in a mixture of barley varieties." *J. Ag. Res.*, **57**: 189–200. 1938.

38. ——, M. L. Martini, and H. Stevens, "A study of methods of barley breeding." USDA *Tech. Bul. 720.* 1940.

39. ——, and M. N. Pope, "Water content of barley kernels during growth and maturation." *J. Ag. Res.*, **23**: 333–360. 1923.

40. Harrington, J. B., and L. H. Shebeski, "Barley production in Saskatchewan." Sask. Ag. Ext. *Bul. 99.* 1948.

41. Harrison, T. J., "Barley varieties for western Canada." Barley Improvement Inst. *Bul. 2.* 1950.

42. Hayes, H. K., *et al.*, "Reaction of barley varieties to *Helminthosporium sativum*." Minn. Ag. Exp. Sta. *Tech. Bul. 21.* 1923.

43. Hector, J. M., *Introduction to the Botany of Field Crops.* Vol. I: *Cereals.* Johannesburg, So. Africa: Central News Agency Ltd. pp 234–271. 1936.

44. Hill, C. C., W. B. Cartwright, and G. A. Wiebe, "Barley varieties resistant to the Hessian fly." *Agron. J.*, **44**: 4–5. 1952.

45. Hills, C. H., and C. H. Bailey, "The nature of the increase in amylase activity of germinating barley." *Cer. Chem.*, **15**: 273–281. 1938.

46. Hitchcock, A. S., *Manual of the Grasses of the United States.* USDA *Misc. Publ. 200.* pp 264–268. 1935.

47. Hunt, L. A., "Commercial fertilizers for malting barley. II: Malting quality." Barley Improvement Conf. *Rpt.* pp 7–16. 1951.

48. Immer, F. R., *et al.*, "Barley in Minnesota." Minn. Ag. Exp. Sta. *Spec. Bul. 135.* 1934.

49. Johnston, T. H., and A. M. Schlehuber, "Harbine, a new combine barley." Okla. Ag. Exp. Sta. *Bul. 367.* 1951.

50. Kaufman, D. S., "Barley malt: Its manufacture and use." Can. Soc. Tech. Ag. *Rev. No. 11.* pp 120–126. 1936.

51. Kent-Jones, D. W., and A. J. Amos, *Modern Cereal Chemistry*, 4th ed. Liverpool: Northern Publ. Co. pp 1–651. 1947.

52. Kramer, H. H., and R. Veyl, "Intra-spike kernel competition in barley." *Agron. J.*, **44**: 156. 1952.

53. ——, R. Veyl, and W. D. Hanson, "The association of two genetic linkage groups in barley with one chromosome." *Genetics*, **39**: 159–168. 1954.

54. Leonard, Warren H., "Barley culture in Japan." *J. Am. Soc. Agron.*, **39**(8): 643–658. 1947.

55. ——, D. W. Robertson, and H. O. Mann, "Complementary factors for height inheritance in barley." *Jap. J. Gen.*, **31**: 229–240. 1956.

56. Leukel, R. W., J. G. Dickson, and A. G. Johnson, "Effects of certain environmental factors on stripe disease of barley and the control of the disease by seed treatment." USDA *Tech. Bul. 341.* 1933.

57. ——, and V. F. Tapke, "Barley diseases and their control." USDA *Farmers Bul. 2089.* 1955.

58. Levine, M. N., and W. J. Cherewick, "Studies on dwarf leaf rust of barley." USDA *Tech. Bul. 1056.* 1952.

59. Love, H. H., and W. T. Craig, "Wong, a winter barley for New York." Cornell U. Ag. Exp. Sta. *Bul. 796.* 1943.

60. Martin, J. H., and S. C. Salmon, "The rusts of wheat, oats, barley, rye," in *Plant Diseases.* USDA Yrbk. of Ag. pp 329–343. 1953.

61. McKinney, H. H., "Virus diseases of cereal crops," in *Plant Diseases.* USDA Yrbk. of Ag. pp 350–360. 1953.

62. Muntzing, A., "Experiences from work with induced polyploidy in cereals." In *Svalof, 1886–1946: History and Present Problems.* Lund, Sweden: Carl Bloms Boktryckeri A.-B. pp 324–337. 1948.

63. Myler, J. L., and E. H. Stanford, "Color inheritance in barley." *J. Am. Soc. Agron.,* **34**: 427–436. 1942.

64. Nilsson-Ehle, H., "The future possibilities of Swedish barley breeding." Svalof, 1886–1946, Lund, Sweden: Carl Bloms. pp 113–126. 1948.

65. Nybom, N., "Mutation types in barley." *Acta Ag. Scand.,* **4**: 430–456. 1954.

66. "Official grain standards of the United States." USDA *SRA-AMS-177.* pp 1–93. 1960.

67. Oinuma, T., "Karyomorphology of cereals." *Biol. J. Okayama U.,* **1**: 12–71. 1952.

68. Olson, P. J., *et al.*, "Sensitivity of wheat and barley at different stages of growth to treatment with 2,4-D." *Agron. J.,* **43**(2): 77–83. 1951.

69. Oswald, J. W., and E. R. Houston, "The yellow-dwarf virus disease of cereal crops." *Phytopath.,* **43**: 128–136. 1953.

70. Overland A., and L. W. Rasmussen, "Some effects of 2,4-D formulations in herbicidal concentrations on wheat and barley." *Agron. J.,* **43**(7): 321–324.

71. Pendleton, J. W., A. I. Lang, and G. H. Dungan, "Responses of spring barley varieties to different fertilizer treatments and seasonal growing conditions." *Agron. J.,* **45**(11): 529–532. 1953.

72. Poehlman, J. M., "Agronomic characteristics and disease resistance of winter barleys tested in Missouri, 1943 to 1948." Mo. Ag. Exp. Sta. *Res. Bul. 442.* 1949.

73. ———, and C. A. Helm, "Winter barley in Missouri." Mo. Ag. Exp. Sta. *Bul. 508.* 1947.

74. Pope, M. N., "The temperature factor in fertilization and growth of the barley ovule." *J. Ag. Res.,* **66**(11): 389–402. 1943.

75. ———, "Some notes on technique in barley breeding." *J. Hered.,* **35**: 99–111. 1944.

76. Quincke, F. L., "Interspecific and intergeneric crosses with *Hordeum.*" *Can. J. Res.,* **18**(C): 372–373. 1940.

77. Ramage, R. T., and C. A. Suneson, "A gene marker for the g chromosome of barley." *Agron. J.,* **50**: 114. 1958.

78. ———, C. R. Burnham, and A. Hagberg, "A summary of translocation studies in barley." *Crop Sci.,* **1**(4): 277–279. 1961.

79. Reisenauer, H. M., and A. D. Dickson, "Effects of nitrogen and sulfur fertilization on yield and malting quality of barley." *Agron. J.,* **53**(3): 192–195. 1961.

80. Riddle, O. G., and C. A. Suneson, "Sources and use of scald resistance in barley." *J. Am. Soc. Agron.,* **40**: 926–928. 1948.

81. Robertson, D. W., "Summary of linkage studies in barley, 1953–56." Third Barley Impr. Conf. *Abs.* pp 37–46. 1957.

82. ———, and G. W. Deming, "Natural crossing in barley at Fort Collins, Colorado." *J. Am. Soc. Agron.,* **23**: 402–406. 1931.

83. ———, *et al.*, "Culture of barley in Colorado." Colo. Ag. Exp. Sta. *Tech. Bul. 39.* 1948.

84. ———, *et al.*, "Winter barley in eastern Colorado." Colo. Ag. Exp. Sta. Ext. *Bul. 438-A.* 1954.

85. ———, G. A. Wiebe, and R. G. Shands, "A summary of linkage studies in barley: Supplement II, 1947–1953." *Agron. J.*, **47**: 418–425. 1955.

86. Rohde, H. W., "Malting and mashing." *Cer. Chem.*, **12**: 610–620. 1935.

87. Schaller, C. W., "Inheritance of resistance to loose smut, *Ustilago hordei*, in barley." *Phytopath.*, **39**: 959–979. 1949.

88. ———, "The effect of mildew and scald infection on the yield and quality of barley." *Agron. J.*, **43**: 183–188. 1951.

89. Schuck, H. G., "Brewing barley malt." *Can. Soc. Tech. Ag. Rev.*, No. 11. pp 127–129. 1936.

90. Shands, H. L., and A. D. Dickson, "Barley-botany, production, harvesting, processing, utilization, and economics." *Econ. Bot.*, **7**: 3–26. 1953.

91. Shands, R. G., "Inheritance of covered smut resistance in two barley crosses." *Agron. J.*, **48**: 81–86. 1956.

92. Shellenberger, J. A., and C. H. Bailey, "Biochemical distinctions between barley varieties." *Cer. Chem.*, **13**(6): 631–655. 1936.

93. Smith, F. H., "Control loose smut by the anaerobic (without air) method." *Clemson* Ag. Coll. Ext. *Cir. 461:1–8.* 1959.

94. Smith, L., "Cytology and genetics of barley." *Bot. Rev.*, **17**: 1–51, 133–202, 285–355. 1951.

95. Sprague, H. B., and N. F. Farris, "The effect of uniformity of spacing seed on the development and yield of barley." *J. Am. Soc. Agron.*, **23**: 516–534. 1931.

96. Staudt, G., "The origin of cultivated barleys: A discussion." *Econ.. Bot.*, **15**(3): 205–212. 1961.

97. Suneson, C. A., "Effect of barley stripe, *Helminthosporium gramineum* Rab., on yield." *J. Am. Soc. Agron.*, **38**: 954–955. 1946.

98. ———, "Survival of four barley varieties in a mixture." *Agron. J.*, **41**(10): 459–461. 1949.

99. ———, "Male-sterile facilitated synthetic hybrid barley." *Agron. J.*, **43**(5): 234–236. 1951.

100. ———, "Breeding for resistance to yellow dwarf virus in barley." *Agron. J.*, **47**: 283. 1955.

101. ———, "An evolutionary method cf plant breeding." *Agron. J.*, **48**: 188–191. 1956.

102. ———, and S. C. Santoni, "Barley varieties resistant to stripe, *Helminthosporium gramineum* Rabh." *J. Am. Soc. Agron.*, **35**: 736–737. 1943.

103. ———, and B. J. Hall, "Resistance reactions to the Hessian fly on the California-Mexico border." *Agron. J.*, **45**: 172–174. 1953.

104. ———, and H. Stevens, "Studies with bulked hybrid populations." USDA *Tech. Bul. 1067.* 1953.

105. ———, and R. T. Ramage, "Studies on the importance of the yellow-dwarf virus." *Agron. J.*, **49**: 365–367. 1957.

106. Swanson, A. F., and H. H. Laude, "Barley production in Kansas." Kans. Ag. Exp. Sta. *Bul. 318.* 1943.

107. Takahashi, R., "Studies on the classification and the distribution of the Japanese barley varieties. I: Significance of the bimodal curve of the coleoptile length." *Berichte Ohara Institut für Landwirtschafliche Forschung*, **9**: 71–90. Kurashiki, Japan. 1942.

108. ———, "The origin and evolution of cultivated barley," in *Advances in Genetics*, Vol. VII. New York: Academic Press. pp 227–266. 1955.

109. ———, and S. Yasuda, "Genetic studies of spring and winter habit of growth in barley." *Berichte Ohara Institut für Landwirtschafliche Forschung*, Bd. X, Haft 4. pp 245–308. 1956.

110. Tapke, V. F., "An undescribed loose smut of barley." *Phytopath.*, **22**: 869–870. 1932.

111. ———, "A study of the cause of variability in response of barley loose smut control through seed treatment with surface disinfectants." *J. Ag. Res.*, **51**: 491–508. 1935.

112. ———, "Physiologic races of *Ustilago hordei.*" *J. Ag. Res.*, **55**: 683–692. 1937.

113. ———, "Studies on the natural inoculation of seed barley with covered smut (*Ustilago hordei*)." *J. Ag. Res.*, **60**: 787–810. 1940.

114. ———, "New physiologic races of *Ustilago hordei.*" *Phytopath.*, **35**: 970–976. 1945.

115. Vavilov, N. I., "Studies on the origin of cultivated plants." *Bul. Appl. Bot., Genetics, and Plant Breed.*, **16**: 1–248. (Russ. with Eng. summary.)

116. ———, "The origin, variation, immunity, and breeding of cultivated plants." *Chron. Bot.*, **13**(1–6). 1949–50.

117. Vogel, S. L., "Threshing barley for malting purposes." Barley Improvement Conf. *Rpt.* pp 16–21. 1951.

118. Weaver, J. C., "Climatic relations of American barley production." *Geog. Rev.*, **33**: 569–588. 1943.

119. ———, *American Barley Production*. Minneapolis, Minn.: Burgess Publ. Co. pp 1–115. 1950.

120. Weaver, J. E., *Root Development of Field Crops*. New York: McGraw-Hill. pp 175–179. 1926.

121. Wiebe, G. A., "Improved varieties of barley," in *Science in Farming*. USDA Yrbk. of Ag., 1943–47. pp 403–413. 1947.

122. ———, and D. A. Reid, "Classification of the barley varieties grown in the United States and Canada in 1958." USDA *Tech. Bul. 1224*. pp 1–234. 1961.

123. Woodward, R. W., "The I^h, I, and i in *Hordeum deficiens* genotypes of barley." *J. Am. Soc. Agron.*, **39**: 474–482. 1947.

124. ———, "The inheritance of fertility in the lateral florets of four barley groups." *Agron. J.*, **41**: 317–322. 1949.

125. ———, "Sterility in Velvon barley and its relationship to yield, kernel weight, and date and rate of seeding." *Agron. J.*, **41**(9): 430–434. 1949.

126. ———, and J. W. Thieret, "A genetic study of complementary genes for purple lemma, palea, and pericarp in barley." *Agron. J.*, **45**: 182–185. 1953.

127. ———, and D. C. Rasmussen, "Hood and awn development in barley determined by two gene pairs." *Agron. J.*, **49**: 92–94. 1957.

19. OATS

ECONOMIC IMPORTANCE

Oats rank as the fourth most important cereal in the world, after wheat, rice, and maize. Approximately 4.15 billion bushels were harvested from 129,050,000 acres annually from 1950–54 [6]. More than 80 per cent of the world acreage lies in moist, temperate areas, particularly in North America, northern Europe, and Soviet Russia. The United States, the U.S.S.R., Canada, France, United Kingdom, and West Germany lead in oat production (Fig. 19-1). Nearly one-half of the world crop is produced in the United States and Canada. Most of the oat crop is fed to livestock on home farms, less than 5 per cent of it being used as human food.

Oats rank third among the cereal crops of the United States. During the period 1952–61, oats were harvested each year on an average of 33 million acres. The average annual production was 1.231 billion bushels, with a yield of 37 bushels an acre. About 80 per cent of the national crop is produced in the North Central states; Iowa, Minnesota, Illinois, Wisconsin, South Dakota, and Nebraska lead in oat production (Fig. 19-2).

Oats have held their place in American agriculture largely because of their high feed value, their usefulness in crop rotations, and the ease of growing and handling them. Oats often follow corn or another row crop where the seedbed is prepared without plowing, and are often used as a companion crop for legume and grass seedings. The spring sowing of oats on corn land in the Corn Belt seldom conflicts with other field work [126].

HISTORY OF OAT CULTURE

The writers of classical antiquity appear to refer the use of oats for medicinal purposes only. Oats grew as weeds, particularly in barley fields,

544

and were domesticated later [123]. Oat grains have been found in the Swiss Lake Dwellings of the Bronze Age (1500–500 BC) [124, 126].

Writers of the early Christian era indicate that common oats were grown by the Europeans for grain, while the red oats were grown for fodder, particularly in Asia Minor. Oats were a staple agricultural product in Germany at the time of the Roman invasion [73]. The earliest record of cultivated oats in China is found in a historical work on the period AD 618–907 [126]. The oat crop was established extensively in Western Europe by AD 1600.

Oats were grown on the Elizabeth Islands in Massachusetts in 1602, and in the Massachusetts Bay area in 1629. The first oats in Virginia were sown as early as 1603, and in the Jamestown colony by 1607 [33]. Oats were grown in Newfoundland in 1622. It is believed that oats were introduced into Canada by the first Scottish settlers [43]. George Washington is said to have planted 400 acres of oats at Mount Vernon in 1787. Expansion of oat production generally has coincided with the settlement of new areas. At the close of the Revolutionary War, oat production moved across the Appalachian Mountains into the Ohio Valley, and then into the Corn Belt by 1850.

ORIGIN OF CULTIVATED OATS

The origin of cultivated oats is lost in obscurity. The common oat (*Avena sativa*), in its cultivated form is believed to be of Asiatic origin. Vavilov (1949–50) placed its center of origin in the Near East, but others believe that both the common cultivated oat and the common wild oat (*A. fatua*) extended from that region far to the north and northeast [116]. The centers of origin for cultivated red oats (*A. byzantina*), as well as for wild red oats (*A. sterilis*), seem to be the Mediterranean and the Near East. The Mongolian naked oat probably developed in northeastern Asia from the wild form of *A. fatua* ssp. *septentrionalis* to the naked form of the subspecies *nodipilosa*. This oat is reported chiefly from the mountainous region of northeastern China westward to Mongolia and Siberia to the Ural Mountains [98].

For nearly 100 years, it was believed that the common wild oat (*A. fatua*) is the progenitor of the common cultivated oat (*A. sativa*). C. Haussknecht, in Germany in 1885, assumed that the wild oat was the progenitor because of its primitive characteristics. Later writers supported this theory on the basis of similarities of morphological characters and probable centers of origin of the two species. It also has been generally agreed—and for similar reasons—that cultivated red oats (*A. byzantina*) arose from wild red oats (*A. sterilis*) [116]. However, Coffman [27] accumulated a mass of evidence from genetics, plant pathology, and plant physiology in

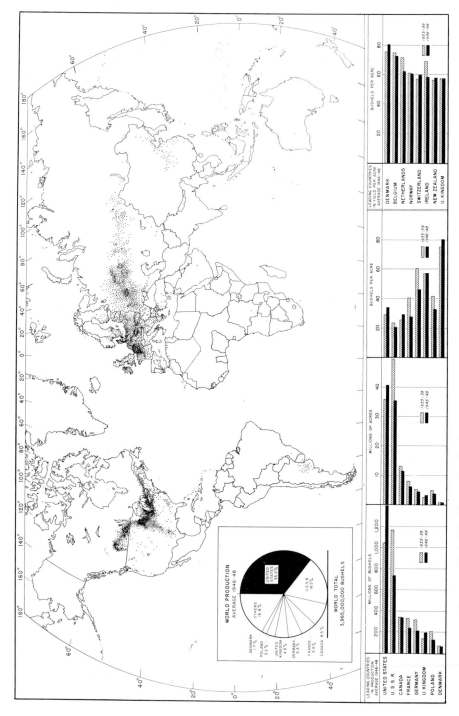

Figure 19-1. World oat distribution, average of 1946-48. Each dot represents 1,000,000 bushels.

(*Courtesy US Department of Agriculture*)

support of the theory that the common oat may be a derivative of the wild red oat rather than of the common wild oat. He suggested that *A. sterilis* probably is the progenitor of all oats with 21 chromosome pairs, which include *A. byzantina, A. sativa, A. orientalis, A. fatua,* and *A. nuda.* Oats similar to *A. nuda* have been obtained from *A. sterilis* derivatives in this country. Oats that somewhat resemble plants of *A. orientalis* also have been observed in progeny of crosses that involve *A. sterilis* derivatives. Therefore, it is postulated that *A. sativa* arose from the polymorphous *A. byzantina* oats taken into Europe by Slavonic migrants from Asia Minor [29, 41].

ADAPTATION

Common oats make their best growth in cool, moist regions such as northern United States, southern Canada, and northern Europe. Red oats are grown primarily in regions with warm climates such as those found in the southern United States, the Mediterranean region of Europe and Africa, Australia, and Argentina. Common oats generally are poorly adapted to these regions [124, 126].

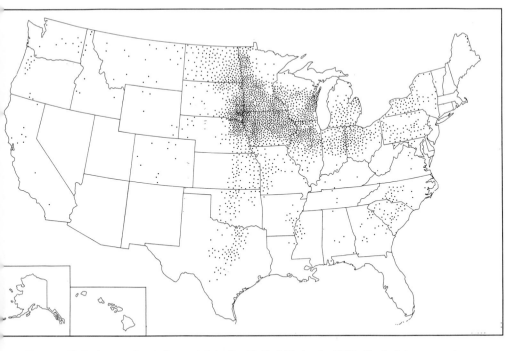

FIGURE 19-2. **Acres of oats harvested in the United States in 1959. Each dot represents 10,000 acres. United States total: 26,572,824 acres.**

The oat plant requires more water for its development than does any other small grain, but it will do better with less sunshine. High temperatures at blooming time increase the proportion of empty spikelets, a condition called "blast." Hot dry weather at the time of grain development causes premature ripening, whereas hot humid weather during this period favors the development of diseases that frequently reduce grain yields [126]. Oat yields generally are inferior to those of barley when moisture is scarce [75].

Heat-tolerant varieties of red oats have made oats an important crop in the warm countries. Some common oat varieties also are heat-resistant. Heat resistance apparently is not correlated with time of maturity, with resistance to any of the major oat diseases, with after-harvest dormancy, or with any of the observed morphological characters of the oat kernel [25]. Later research indicates that the most highly heat-resistant oat varieties have awned dark kernels [30].

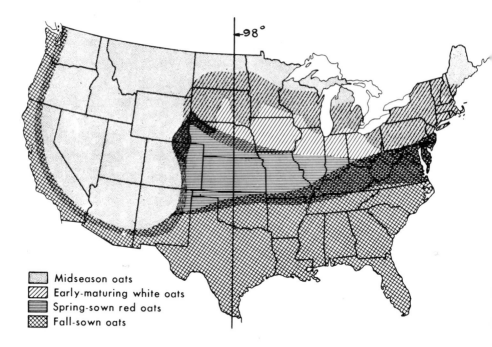

Midseason oats
Early-maturing white oats
Spring-sown red oats
Fall-sown oats

FIGURE 19-3. **Distribution of the principal types of oats in the United States. The northern border of winter oat production corresponds closely with the isotherm of $-5°$ F. average minimum winter (December-February) temperature. Midseason oats are grown in cool climates of the northern States and the intermountain region. Early white and red oats are grown between the winter oat and midseason oat regions.**

(*Courtesy US Department of Agriculture*)

Winter oats are less winter-hardy than are the hardier winter forms of barley, wheat, and rye [80]. The development of more hardy winter oat varieties in recent years has extended winter oat production northward, and has made the crop more certain in the colder portions of the southern United States [126]. Winter killing is negligible in the most mild southern zone of the Southern states where the average minimum winter temperature is 20°F, or higher. It is seldom serious in the zone with 20–10°F minimum temperature, but it usually was severe or complete in the northern zone of the Southern states where the average minimum winter temperature is 0°F, or lower [26]. Hardier varieties have been developed, however. By 1960 winter oats were being grown north of the Ohio River as well as in other areas where the average minimum temperature in winter is about −5°F (Fig. 19-3).

Oats are a satisfactory crop on a wide range of soil types so long as they are well drained and reasonably fertile. Oats are less sensitive than wheat or barley to soil conditions, particularly in regard to acidity. Oats generally make their best growth on loam soils, but they produce fair yields on very heavy soils or on light sandy soils in the presence of sufficient moisture. The crop generally responds well to phosphatic fertilizers in moist northern climates [75]. In general, at the same absolute minimum temperatures, winter killing in fall-sown oats increases as the soils become progressively heavier [26].

BOTANICAL DESCRIPTION OF THE OAT PLANT

Oats belong to the genus *Avena* of the tribe Aveneae of the grass family, *Gramineae*.

Vegetative Characters

The oat plant is an annual grass with hollow jointed stems, flat blades, and a terminal panicle. Under average conditions, the oat plant produces 3–5 hollow stems, or culms, that vary from ⅛–¼ inch in diameter and from 2–5 feet in height. The culm usually has 4–5 nodes and internodes. The upper internode is called the peduncle. The leaf consists of the blade, sheath, and ligule. The leaf blades average about 10 inches in length and about ⅝ inch in width. The ligule usually is well developed and characterized by a number of small teeth, whereas in other cereals the ligule is more or less blunt. The roots are small, numerous, fibrous, and densely covered with fine hairs. They may penetrate the soil to a depth of several feet [124, 126]. The roots increase in length in direct proportion to the

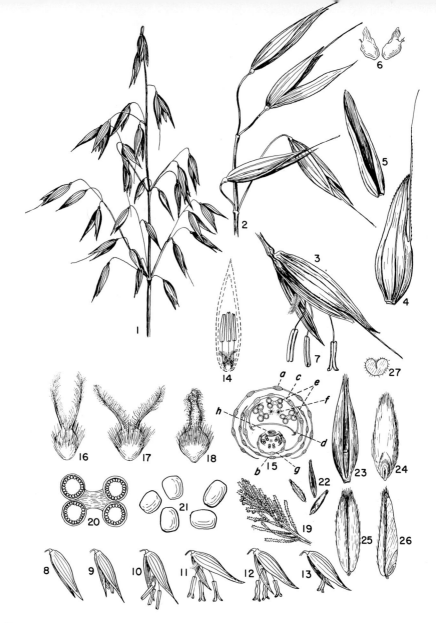

FIGURE 19-4. **Oat inflorescence: (1) panicle; (2) distal or top part of panicle branch with 4 spikelets attached to pedicels; (3) floret at anthesis; (4) lemma, showing dorsal awn attachment; (5) ventral view of palea; (6) lodicules; (7) anthers; (8-13) florets showing successive stages of anthesis; (14) floret before anthesis, showing position of stamens and pistil; (15) cross section of 3-flowered spikelet, showing (a and b) glumes, (c) lemma, (d) palea, (e) anthers, (f) stigma, (g) secondary floret of spikelet, (h) rudimentary third or tertiary floret; (16-18) pistil—before, during, and after anthesis; (19) portion of stigma with adhering pollen grains; (20) cross section of anther showing 4 lobes; (21) pollen grains, enlarged; (22) kernel and caryopses, smaller than natural size; (23) oat kernel; (24-26) caryopsis or groat, enlarged; (27) cross section of caryopsis.**

lateness of maturity: midseason oats penetrate deeper than do early oats [141].

Inflorescence

The inflorescence of the oat plant is a panicle, composed of the rachis, rachis branches, and spikelets (Fig. 19-4). Many lateral axillary branches arise from alternate sides of the rachis at its nodes [14]. The rachis or main axis and each of the lateral branches terminate in a single apical

FIGURE 19-5. Oat panicles: (Left) unilateral, "side", or "horse-mane" oat with 7 whorls of branches; (Right) equilateral, or spreading, or "tree" panicle with 5 whorls of branches.
(*Courtesy US Department of Agriculture*)

spikelet. The average number of whorls of branches on the panicles of some oat varieties may range from 5–7. The panicles are either spreading (equilateral) or one-sided (unilateral) (Fig. 19-5). By far the greater number of cultivated varieties are the type with spreading panicles. The spikelets separate from their pedicels and the florets from their rachilla segments. The glumes often persist after the lemma and palea have fallen [124, 127].

The floret or oat grain is produced on many branches in spikelets that vary in number from 20–150 per panicle. The spikelets are pedicellate, be-

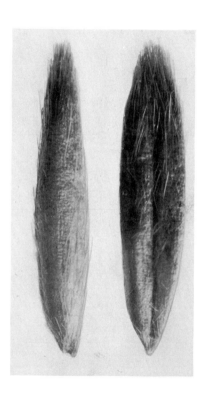

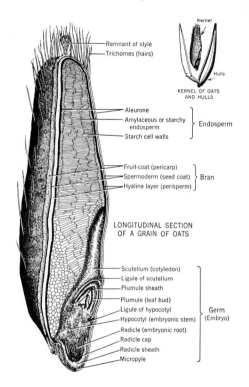

FIGURE 19-6. **Caryopses of oats: Side view (left), ventral or crease view (right).**
(*Courtesy US Department of Agriculture*)

FIGURE 19-7. **The oat caryopsis: Other names used for its structure include: Starch cell walls — endosperm cells that contain starch grains; speroderm — testa; perisperm — nucellus; plumule sheath — coleoptile; ligule of hypocotyl — epiblast; hypocotyl — subcrown internode; radicle cap — rootcap; and radicle sheath — coleorhiza.**
(*Courtesy The Quaker Oats Company*)

ing subtended by two glumes that usually are pale yellow or reddish in color. The glumes are membranous, many-nerved, and generally longer than the spikelet. The oat floret includes the rachilla segments, lemma, palea, and the sexual organs or later the caryopsis or kernel. The oat flower consists primarily of the three stamens with their filaments and anthers, the single ovary within its style, and bifid stigma (Fig. 2-7). The florets in each spikelet, except in hull-less oats, are tightly enclosed within the lemma and palea. The lemma is bifid or entire and varies in color from white, yellow, gray, and red to black. The lemma may be awned or, as in some of the best cultivated varieties, practically awnless. When present, the awn arises dorsally on the lemma—*i.e.,* it is an extension of the midrib. In most cultivated forms the awn is found only on the lower grain of the spikelet, usually being small, curved or straight, and untwisted. In the wild forms, the awn is found on nearly all grains of the spikelet; it is strongly developed, geniculate (bent like a knee), and twisted [127].

The oat kernel or caryopsis is spindle-shaped and furrowed on one side (Figs. 19-6 and 19-7). It usually is a light buff color and covered with moderately long, fine, silky hairs. The caryopsis ranges from $\frac{5}{16}$–$\frac{7}{16}$ inch in length, and from $\frac{1}{16}$–$\frac{3}{16}$ inch in width. The kernel constitutes about 65–75 per cent of the total weight of the whole grain [124, 127]. The kernel consists of two main parts, the endosperm and embryo. In a cross section of the endosperm, the tissues are trichomes or hairs, pericarp, spermoderm or seedcoat, perisperm or hyaline layer, aleurone layer, and starchy endosperm. The oat caryopsis is usually called the "groat" [20].

POLLINATION

When the plant blooms, the lemma and palea open slightly, the filaments elongate, and the extruded anthers shed their pollen. The pollen grains that fall on the stigma germinate instantly; the pollen tube may reach the egg nucleus within 30 minutes [58]. The flowers close within an hour after pollination [90]. Blooming begins at the apex of the panicle and progresses downward for 3–4 or up to about 8 days [90, 16]. All panicles of a single plant usually complete blooming in about 10 days, but plants with many late tillers may bloom for a month when the weather is cool. Oats usually bloom when the temperature starts to drop in the afternoon, but when a drop in temperature occurs in the forenoon, they bloom then.

Oats are naturally self-pollinated. Only one natural cross was found in the progeny of 7742 plants in West Virginia [60]. In other cases, cross-pollination between adjacent rows has ranged from 0.19–6.62 per cent [35, 60, 61]. The greatest number of natural hybrids was found among plants that came from secondary seeds on the panicle [69].

CHARACTERISTICS OF OAT SPECIES

A key based on available information on the species and subspecies of *Avena* is as follows [127]:

Key to the Species and Subspecies of Oats

	Common name of species and subspecies	Chromosome No. (2n)

1a. Paleas loose.

  2a. Second floret and successive rachilla segments very long.

    3a. Spikelets multiflorous (with 3 to 7 florets).

4a. Panicles midsized to large, equilateral; glumes 15 to 28 mm long (*Avena nuda* L.)	Large Naked Oat	42
4b. Panicles very small, semiunilateral; glumes 16 to 26 mm long (*A. nudibrevis* Vav.) (*A. nuda* L. ssp. *biaristata* (Alef.) Asch. & Graeb.).	Small Naked Oat	14

1b. Paleas tight.

  2a. Second floret rachilla segments short to long.

    3a. Spikelets usually with 2–3 florets.

      4a. Second floret of spikelets separating from first floret by basifracture.

5a. Lemmas large, hairy, awns very strong, twisted and geniculate (*A. sterilis* L.).	Wild Red Oat	42

      4b. Second floret of spikelets separating from first floret consistently by basifracture, or not separating consistently either by basifracture, heterofracture (intermediate), or by disarticulation.

5a. Lemmas midlarge, glabrous; awns weak, nontwisted (*A. byzantina* C. Koch).	Red Oat	42

      4c. Second floret of spikelets separating from first floret by disarticulation.

        5a. Apex of lemmas with 2 glume points (teeth).

          6a. Lemmas short to very long, lanceolate, with midlong to long lemma (glume) points (teeth).

            Lemmas hairy; pedicels of spikelets short; spikelets separating by fracture or abscission, deciduous.

Lemmas short to long, hairy (*A. wiestii* Steud.).	Desert Oat	14
Lemmas midlong to very long, very hairy (*A. barbata* Brot.).	Slender Oat	28

Lemmas glabrous; pedicels of spikelets long; spikelets separating by fracture, not deciduous.		
Lemma (glume) points (teeth) long, distinct; second floret rachilla segments slightly hairy (*A. strigosa* Schreb.).	Sand Oat	14
Lemma (glume) points (teeth) mid-long, less distinct; second floret rachilla segments very hairy (*A. abyssinica* Hochst.).	Abyssinian Oat	28
6b. Lemmas very short, blunt with short lemma (glume) points (teeth) (*A. brevis* Roth.).	Short Oat	14
5b. Apex of lemmas entire or slightly 2-toothed.		
6a. Spikelets separating by abscission, leaving distinct basal scars, deciduous; lemmas usually hairy (*A. fatua* L.).	Wild Oat	42
6b. Spikelets separating by fracture, not leaving distinct basal scars, not deciduous; lemmas usually glabrous (*A. sativa* L.).		
Panicles equilateral (*A. sativa* L. ssp. *diffusa* (Neils.) Asch. & Graeb.).	(Common) Tree Oat	42
Panicles unilateral (*A. sativa* L. ssp. *orientalis* (Schreb.).	(Common) Side Oat	42

Descriptions of Cultivated Oat Species

The cultivated oat species generally grown are common oats, *Avena sativa;* red oats, *A. byzantina*; and naked or hull-less oats, *A. nuda*. The common oat is divided into two subspecies: the tree oat, *A. sativa* ssp. *diffusa*; and the side oat, *A. sativa* ssp. *orientalis*. The common oat includes the bulk of the oats grown today. These species have been fully described [49, 73, 124, 127].

In the common oat (*A. sativa*), the second floret separates from the first by distafracture near the tip of the rachilla segment, which always remains attached to the first floret (Fig. 19-8F). The spikelet separates from its pedicel by fracture without leaving a basal scar. The second floret of the spikelet is almost never awned; in many varieties even the first floret is nearly awnless. Basal hairs are sparse. The lemmas are black, gray, yellow, or white. The common tree oat, *A. sativa* ssp. *diffusa,* is characterized by panicle branches that spread outward in various directions from the rachis as an axis, which gives the panicle a pyramidal or treelike form; the whorls of branches usually vary from 4–7. The common side oat, *A. sativa* ssp. *orien-*

talis, has a unilateral panicle in which the panicle branches and spikelets generaly turn to one side of the rachis and extend more distinctly upward, or appressed [127].

The cultivated red oat (*Avena byzantina*) is differentiated chiefly by the mode of floret separation, in which the second floret adheres tightly to the first floret and separates from it by basifracture of the rachilla segment (Fig. 19–18E). In some varieties of red oats that are intermediate between red and common oats, many of the florets separate by heterofracture (breakage of the rachilla segment) at various points. In general, red oats are prostrate or semiprostrate in early growth, although some of the more distinct spring types are erect. The culms usually are slender, rather stiff, and of a reddish color. The panicles generally are small, narrow, and erect with relatively few spikelets. The glumes and caryopses generally are some-

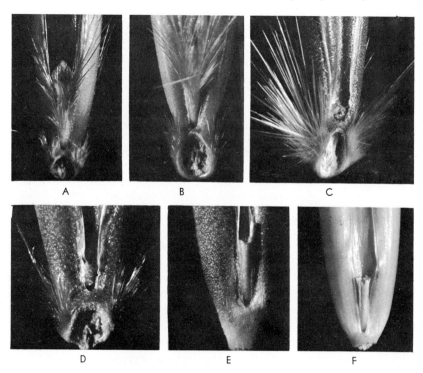

FIGURE 19-8. Types of floret separation: (A) fatuoid from Fulghum oat, Avena byzantina; (B) A. fatua; (C) A. sterilis; (D) A. byzantina; (E) Burt oat, A. byzantina, showing broken rachilla segment where second floret became detached by basifracture; (F) A. sativa, showing rachilla segment attached to first floret from which the second floret separated by disarticulation. The first florets of (A) (B) (C) and (D) were separated from the pedicel by disarticulation, which left a scar or "suckermouth." The florets of the cultivated species (E) and (F) became detached from the pedicels by basifracture.

(*Courtesy US Department of Agriculture*)

FIGURE 19-9. **Spikelet, naked kernels (caryopses) and panicle of Liberty hull-less oats.**
(Courtesy US Department of Agriculture)

what longer, and the lemmas larger, than those of common oat varieties. Both florets of the spikelet of the more typical varieties bear weak nontwisted awns. Basal hairs usually are more numerous than in the common oat. The lemmas may be red, grayish red, black, dark brown, brownish-yellow, or yellow in color [124, 127].

In the naked oat or hull-less oat (*Avena nuda*), the kernels, or caryopses, are loose within the enclosed lemmas and paleas. In addition, the rachilla segments of the second, third, fourth, and successive florets are extremely long, while the glumes, lemmas, and paleas are alike in texture [127]. (Fig. 19-9).

Descriptions of Wild Oat Species

Two important species of wild oats, *Avena fatua* and *A. sterilis,* frequently are noxious weeds in many parts of the world.

The wild oat or common wild oat (*Avena fatua*) is prevalent in the western half of the United States, where it is difficult to eradicate because of its shattering and seed dormancy characteristics. The common wild oat differs from the desert, slender, and sand oat forms primarily by the absence of the two distinct awnlike points at the apex of the lemma, and by its larger florets. In the field, the plants usually can be distinguished from cultivated oats by their greater vigor and frequent shattering as well as by the whitish straw and chaff at the time of maturity. The panicles are large and drooping. The spikelets separate from their pedicels by abscission so as to leave distinct basal scars or suckermouths. The callus that results from the abscission layer is surrounded with a dense growth of hair. The florets separate from each other by disarticulation of their respective rachilla segments. As a result, the wild oat drops its seeds as soon as they ripen. All florets bear a rather long, twisted, and geniculate awn. The lemmas generally are hairy, although they are nearly glabrous in a few strains. The lemma color may be white, gray, yellow, reddish-brown, or black [124, 127]. Dormancy of the wild oat may persist for several years when buried in the soil. Ripe seeds from different localities may show a dormancy of 0–87 per cent after 9–11 months of storage in the laboratory [138].

The wild red oat (*Avena sterilis*) occurs in the Mediterranean region of Europe, North Africa, and Asia Minor. The lemma usually is covered with a dense growth of hairs. Both florets of the spikelet bear long, strong, twisted, and geniculate awns. The second floret adheres firmly to the first one and is separated only by basifracture of the rachilla segment that supports it. The abscission method of spikelet separation is even more pronounced in the wild red oat than in the cultivated red oat. A very marked callus or suckermouth is evident on separation of the lower floret of the spikelet from its pedicel. Three botanical varieties or types of wild red oats have been described under the names of *Ludoviciana, Maxima,* and *Macrocarpa* [127].

VARIETIES

General Characteristics of Varieties

Many oat varieties are difficult to distinguish. The Burt variety of red oats (*Avena byzantina*) is highly variable in spikelet disarticulation, basal hairs, awns, and lemma color. Red is the most stable lemma color [34]. Clinton oats repeatedly have given rise to a wide variety of off-types, particularly tall plants with open, "lacy" panicles. These often are susceptible to crown and stem rusts and usually have a weaker straw than the parent variety. These changes are thought to be due to mutations rather than to natural crossing or mechanical mixtures. Tall types were found to be unstable cytologically. Clinton is a selection from a cross between *A. sativa* and *A. byzantina*. These two parental species apparently have been differentiated in nature so long that their chromosomes are no longer entirely homologous [91].

Early oat varieties have slender culms and tend to lodge and shatter more readily than do midseason varieties. Some midseason varieties lodge badly, but seldom shatter. The older red-kernelled varieties of *A. byzantina* shattered more than did the *A. sativa* varieties [130].

Most of the oat varieties grown in the United States since 1940 are resistant to one or more diseases. Markton [13] and its derivatives, such as Marion, Bannock, Bridger, and Shasta, are resistant to most races of the smuts.

Victoria derivatives generally are resistant to some races of crown rust, stem rust, and smut fungi. This is particularly true of varieties that originated from a Victoria-Richland cross, which include Vicland, Overland, Ventura, and Cedar. These, however, are particularly susceptible to Victoria blight.

Bond-derived varieties generally are resistant to Victoria blight and crown rust, while some of them are also resistant to many races of stem rust and the smuts. Among these varieties are Clinton, Cherokee, Nemaha, and Andrew. Clinton was grown on approximately 67 per cent of the oat acreage of the United States in 1950.

Since 1950, some previously obscure rust races, particularly Races 45 and 57 of crown rust and Race 7 of stem rust, have caused losses on Bond-related varieties. Varieties such as Santa Fe, Landhafer, and Trispernia are resistant to Races 45 and 57 of crown rust; Richland, and also some Hajira-Joanette strains from Canada, were resistant to Race 7 of stem rust; White Russian is resistant to Race 8. New varieties (such as Minhafer), developed for resistance to these races, have been released to growers [32].

American Oat Varieties

Oat varieties grown in the United States may be grouped as spring or winter, midseason or early, and white or red. Spring oats are midseason or early varieties grown from spring seeding, except in mild climates. Winter oats are grown primarily from fall seeding, although under some conditions they may be sown in late winter or very early spring. The terms *white* or *red* have been loosely used to differentiate white or yellow common oats

(*Avena sativa*) from the prevalent varieties of red oats (*A. byzantina*). Some varieties of common oats have gray or black lemmas, while some "red oat" varieties are gray, black, or yellowish or reddish white.

Oat varieties with white or yellow seeds are more commonly grown in the northern states, whereas red or gray oats are grown chiefly in the Southern states. The central or spring-sown red oat region is the transition zone between the fall-sown red oat region in the South and the northern common white oat region.

In the Great Plains region, midseason common oat types are grown in the northern part and early red oats in the southern part.

Common oats of midseason maturity are most widely grown in the Rocky Mountain region, particularly in areas under irrigation.

On the Pacific coast, varieties of the red oat group are grown in California, while midseason varieties are prevalent in Washington and Oregon.

In the Southern or fall-sown oat region, a number of hardy crown rust-resistant varieties are grown for grain or grazing. Victoria-derived varieties grown in the lower South were largely replaced after 1947 or 1948 by Bond-derivatives resistant to Victoria blight. Derivatives of the old Red Rustproof variety, resistant to Victoria blight and somewhat tolerant to Race 45 of crown rust, are still being grown in the old Cotton Belt. Nortex is one of these varieties. The Red Rustproof type of oat persisted in this area for more than 100 years because of its superiority over other types in vigor and resistance to or tolerance of disease [126].

In uniform winter hardiness nurseries conducted over a 20-year period in the South, the most hardy varieties were Hairy Culbertson, Bicknell, Fulghum (winter type), Tech, Wintock, and Fulwin. All were more winter-hardy than Winter Turf, the earlier standard hardy oat. Hardy varieties resistant to crown rust and smut were derived from a Lee × Victoria cross. All of the more hardy oats grown in the United States seem to include certain red oats in their parentage [24, 28]. Atlantic and Arlington, winter-hardy varieties grown in the northern Piedmont area, have demonstrated good resistance to crown rust and mosaic [39].

Oat types grown in different regions in the United States are shown in Fig. 19-3. Suitable varieties now grown east of the 98th meridian are resistant to crown rust, stem rust, and Helminthosporium blight. Those grown west of this line must have smut resistance. The more important oat varieties —including the leading oat varieties grown in the United States in 1961— have been described by several researchers [11, 22, 31, 32, 40, 92, 96, 108, 113, 126, 127].

Midseason oats grown in the United States in 1961 are white spring varieties of common oats (*Avena sativa*). The most widely grown varieties east of the 98th meridian were Garry and Ajax, while the chief varieties west of this line are Overland and Park.

Almost all early-maturing white spring varieties are common oats (*Avena sativa*). Clintland is the most widely grown variety east of the 98th meridian, while the principal varieties grown west of this line in 1961 were Cherokee, Minhafer, Clinton, Andrew, Beedee, and Newton. Cherokee is a red oat derivative that is accepted as a common white oat on the market.

The most widely grown spring-sown red oat varieties and their derivatives are Missouri 0-205, Cherokee, Andrew, and Kanota. Missouri 0-205 and Kanota are marketed as red oats, whereas Cherokee and Andrew are sold as white oats.

Fall-sown oats may be common oats or red oats (*A. byzantina*). The most widely-grown varieties east of the 98th meridian in 1961 were Moregrain (red), Suregrain (red), Arlington (white), Victorgrain 48-93 (red), Dubois (white), and Nortex (red). Nortex is a Red Rustproof derivative. The chief oat varieties grown west of the 98th meridian were Alamo (white), Mustang (red), and Cimarron (gray to red). California Red (red) is grown along the Pacific coast, particularly in California. Fall-sown oats usually have some degree of winter hardiness.

Types and Varieties in Other Countries

Canada ranks second to the United States in oat production in the western hemisphere. The varieties grown are almost exclusively common oats (*Avena sativa*) of types which are mostly midseason to late, rather tall, and white-grained. Newer varieties in Canada, mostly resistant to some of the prevalent races of stem rust, include Garry, Abegweit, Ajax, Beaver, Exeter, Fortune, Roxton, and Vanguard. Older varieties with little or no stem rust resistance include Alaska, Abundance, Banner, Cartier, Eagle, Erban, Gopher, Larain, Legacy, Mabel, and Victory [126].

Some oats are grown in Argentina, Uruguay, and Chile. The varieties in these countries are strains of the Red Algerian oat (*A. byzantina*) or similar types, such as Argentina, La Prevision No. 13, La Estanzuela No. Bid., Klein Victoria, and Klein Mar. Common oats (*A. sativa*), being poorly adapted, are seldom grown in these countries [126].

Northern Europe, because of its cool moist climate, is very favorable for oat production, particularly in the United Kingdom and in the Scandinavian countries. In the British Isles, winter oat varieties include Picton, Aberystwyth White Winter S. 147 and S. 81, and Gray Winter. Spring oat varieties include Eagle, Marvellous, Onward, Early Miller, Supreme (black grain), Golden Rain, Victory, and Black Tartarian (black grain). Common oats (*A. sativa*) are grown exclusively in Sweden. Some of the white or yellow oat varieties grown in recent years include Segar, Guldregn I, Sol II, Blenda, Trio, and Rex. Black oat varieties grown in central Sweden are

Stormogul II and Englebrekt II, whereas very early types adapted to northern Sweden are Orion III and Same [1]. Common oat varieties are grown almost exclusively in the rather cool climate of northern France and Germany. While oat rusts occur in these countries, they are less destructive than those in North America. Oats also are well adapted to many parts of the U.S.S.R. [126].

In the warm countries that border the Mediterranean Sea, varieties of red oats (*A. byzantina*) are the most important. Red oats also predominate in South Africa as well as in Australia. Oats are relatively unimportant in Asia. The varieties grown in India are short fine-stemmed types similar to some American varieties that are intermediate between common and red oats [126].

GROWTH OF THE OAT PLANT

Stages in Development

In the seedling stage, the growing point remains short, the leaf initials differentiate, the leaves grow, and the tiller buds develop in the axis of the leaves at the base of the stem. Later, the internodes of the culms elongate and the panicle branches, spikelets, and floral parts differentiate and develop [14, 15].

A germinating oat kernel usually has three potential culm buds, two branch buds, and the main culm. Secondary and tertiary tillers may arise subsequently until a plant may have as many as 30–40 tillers. The number of such buds that initiate growth varies with the environment and variety [148].

Spikelet differentiation begins first with the spikelet at the tip of the central axis and proceeds basally in succession at the tips of the primordia of the branches of the first order, and follow on the branches of the second and third orders. The glumes are the first of the spikelet parts to differentiate. The basal flower of the spikelet is always more advanced in development than are the flowers above it. In oats, the basal flower and the next one above it usually are fertile, but the third flower often does not produce a kernel. The flower parts differentiate in the following order: lemma, anthers, palea, lodicules, and pistil [14].

Pollen grains may germinate on the stigmas of common oats (*Avena sativa*) within five minutes after pollination. The pollen tubes pass between the cells of the conducting tissue near the center of the style and into the ovary. The male generative nuclei may be near the egg nucleus and polar nuclei within 30 minutes, with the male gamete entering the egg within four hours. The fertilized egg may reach the prophase stage 13.5 hours after pollination. A two-celled proembryo was observed 19 hours after pollination [18]. The cellular tissue of the endosperm has formed within 72 hours after anthesis [79].

The kernels in the lowest whorl are still in the late dough stage when the apical kernels are ripe. The green weight of a developing kernel increases rapidly for thirteen days, with a pronounced decline after the fifteenth day. Dry weight increases more rapidly than green weight until after the fifteenth day. Kernel growth may then continue for a few days until the glumes of the apical spikelets become straw color. During the 2–4 days of final ripening the lemma and palea assume their mature color, while the moisture content of the grain may decrease from about 40 per cent down to about 20 per cent [16].

In a Minnesota study, oats increased in kernel weight up to four days before maturity, or when the kernels in the terminal spikelets were in hard dough stage [7]. Kernel development ceases when senescence sets in with chlorophyll disintegration and tissue desiccation [151]. Iowa studies indicate that oat seeds reach a near-maximum dry weight when they contain as high as 45 per cent moisture. Very little dry matter was laid down after they dried to this moisture content. Germination increased with maturity up to 20–28 days after anthesis [57]. Materials are not translocated to any extent from the straw to the grain after the crop is cut.

Factors that Influence Tillering

In Iowa tests, the number of tillers per plant was greater in the winter varieties than in most of the spring varieties. There was little relationship between heading date of spring oat varieties and their tillering capacity [56].

The number of head-bearing culms per plant decreases as the seeding rate increases [150]. In general, variations in seeding rate around the optimum seem to cause only minor variations in tillering as well as in subsequent yield [63].

Photoperiodic and Temperature Responses

Light and temperature influence the number of head-bearing tillers. All varieties tested needed more than 12-hour photoperiods to produce heads within 90 days. Plants grown at a temperature of 58°F required 4–9 days longer to head than did those grown at 70°F. Oats sown the first week in May produced more heads per plant than did those sown in early April and considerably more than those sown after the first week in May [149]. Long day-lengths reduced plant height slightly [148]. The use of photoperiods of 18–24 hours, with a temperature of 70°F, make it possible to mature four crops of oats in a greenhouse in one year [147].

In Japan, there was a close relation between the blooming time and the time of highest temperature during the day. Oat flowers always commenced to bloom after the temperature had started to decline from the maximum reached in the course of the day. The flowers never opened while the temperature continued to rise. The temperature drop at the time of blooming varied from 0.2–7.5°C (0.36–13.5°F). When the highest temperature was reached early in the day, the oat flowers bloomed early, and vice versa. The optimum temperature for blooming was 24–26°C (75.0–78.8°F). The optimum humidity was from 50–60 per cent. Rainfall, wind velocity, and sunlight had little or no direct influence on blooming [90].

Winter Hardiness

Winter killing in oats is caused by low temperatures as well as by heaving of the soil during freezing and thawing. Other environmental factors also contribute to the effect [5].

Rising temperatures break the winter dormancy to reactivate growth in oats and other winter cereals. Cold resistance decreased very rapidly as soon as the plants resumed growth. In a hardened condition, the Sporen oat variety was less resistant to cold than were Tennessee barley, Kanred wheat, and Dakold rye. All of these cereals had lost their cold resistence after nine days under a favorable growth environment, after which little difference in hardiness remained. During the transition, the water content of the plants increased, whereas the total solids in the sap decreased [80].

Heat Resistance

Oat varieties differ widely in heat resistance when exposed to temperatures of 48–51°C (118.4–124.7°F) for 45 minutes. Red oats (*Avena byzantina*) as a group are not more heat resistant than certain varieties of common oats (*A. sativa*). Oats seem to resist heat better after prior exposure to bright sunlight, and to relatively warm temperatures in the case of winter oats. Plants about 50 days old are more heat resistant than either younger or older plants. Oats appear to be most heat resistant in the early boot stage. Heat resistance also is greater in slow-growing winter oats with rather small culms than in rapid-growing large-culmed varieties. There appears to be no absolute correlation between morphological characteristics and heat resistance in oats, although most varieties that are highly resistant to heat have awned dark-colored kernels. Early maturing spring or winter varieties usually are more heat resistant than are midseason or late varieties. There is a high positive association between heat resistance and winter hardiness in oats. Winter varieties appear to be more heat resistant than are spring or semiwinter varieties [25, 30].

Seed Dormancy

Certain varieties of oats usually fail to germinate promptly for 7–10 weeks or more after harvest. Such dormancy is undesirable in the South, where oats often are sown for summer pasture soon after threshing, but oats should have enough dormancy to prevent sprouting in the shock during wet harvest seasons.

Freshly harvested seed of all varieties of *Avena byzantina, A. fatua,* and *A. sterilis* showed either slow or delayed germination, but varieties of common oats (*A. sativa*) exhibit all degrees of prompt, slow, and delayed germination. All varieties except Fulghum, Victoria, and a variety of *A. sterilis,* showed a high germination after storage for 7–10 weeks after harvest [37].

In other tests, the more dormant varieties were strains of the Red Rust-proof type, followed by strains of Fulghum and Fulgrain [19]. Most dormant oats are completely afterripened when stored for 1–6 months at 104°F. Freshly harvested seed of dormant oats kept at a low temperature (36°F) in a relatively high humidity maintained dormancy for a period of three years. Newly harvested dormant oat seeds germinated at a temperature slightly above freezing (36°F) when moisture conditions were favorable, but failed to germinate at a relatively high temperature of 86°F. In Iowa experiments, a pregermination chilling treatment of oat seeds at 4°C (39.2°F) for 10 days considerably increased the germination of prematurely harvested seeds, especially in the Garry variety which showed postharvest dormancy [57].

Vernalization

Some of the cultivated red oats (*Avena byzantina*), particularly Red Rust-proof and Fulghum and their various strains and hybrids, can be grown from both fall and spring seeding in the southern half of the United States. Such varieties require a period of cool temperatures to ensure normal heading. Numerous field experiments have demonstrated that Fulghum, and especially Red Rustproof oats, require early spring seeding for satisfactory growth and normal maturity. In a date-of-seeding test in Missouri, Fulghum showed a greater low temperature requirement than did Kherson, a true spring variety. When seeding was delayed a month, Fulghum suffered a reduction in grain yield of 45 per cent, whereas Kherson, a variety of *A. sativa,* suffered only a 10 per cent reduction [122].

Artificial vernalization of the seed hastened the heading date of oats from 2–10 days and increased the yield of varieties with a low temperature requirement when sown in midspring in Virginia. True spring oats showed decreased yields from artificial vernalization and, when sown early in the spring, outyielded all of the vernalized oats. Fall-sown oats yielded about 20 per cent more grain than did the highest yielding vernalized variety sown in the spring [135].

CULTURAL PRACTICES

Rotations

Oats seldom are grown in continuous culture, and usually follow a row crop in rotations. In the Corn Belt, oats often follow corn but are often used as a companion crop in which to establish legumes or grasses. A widely followed Corn Belt rotation is corn (two years), oats (one year), wheat (one year), and clover-timothy (two years). Winter oats in the South usually follow such row crops as cotton, corn, or soybeans in order to provide a winter cover crop [133].

A common rotation in the northeastern states is corn (one year), spring oats seeded to clover or grass (one year), and clover or grass (two years) for hay or pasture. A similar rotation often is followed in the North Central states, except that alfalfa may replace the clover. In Missouri, oats are used in short rotations where they are followed by sweetclover, lespedeza, or other legumes. A one-year rotation of oats and lespedeza is common. Oats are seeded in lespedeza sod of the previous year. Lespedeza volunteers each year from seed shattered to the ground in the previous year. A two-year oat rotation also is popular in Missouri, *i.e.,* corn is followed by oats seeded to sweetclover. The next spring, the sweetclover is plowed under in time to plant corn [110].

As a companion crop for legumes, oats often had deleterious effects in Connecticut. When measured at the time the oats were removed for silage, legume yields were lowest when seeded with oats. Recovery during a favorable year (1959) was rapid for alfalfa, red clover, and ladino clover. Yields of birdsfoot trefoil remained depressed. During a dry year (1957), alfalfa regrowth was satisfactory following seeding competition with weeds, but not with oats. Oats frequently were more competitive than weed growth, which flourishes in their absence [107].

Some effects of legumes in oat rotations were compared in Arkansas. Oats following after corn, with annual legumes planted in the corn row, showed gains of only 2–11 per cent more than did oats following corn alone. Oats after legumes planted in corn middles showed no gain. When oats followed corn that in turn followed a legume crop plowed under, the oat yields were increased about 7–9 per cent. However, where the legume had been cut for hay, oat yields were 5–15 per cent under the check yields [86].

In central Texas, the most common sequence is to follow corn or cotton with fall-sown oats. A combination of spring-sown oats and Madrid biennial sweetclover is a desirable sequence in three-year or four-year rotations in the north Texas area. The oats are seeded with sweetclover in January or February. After the oats are harvested for grain, the clover produces considerable hay or pasture the first season, followed by a hay or a seed crop in the second year [10].

In northern Florida, fall-sown oats commonly follow such row crops as corn, cotton, peanuts, or tobacco. It is desirable for oats to follow a legume because of the additional nitrogen provided by the latter. The oat crop is sometimes plowed under for green manure before planting tobacco or vegetables [92].

Oats are sown on fallowed land in the drier areas of the Western states. Where a crop can be produced each year, oats usually follow corn, sorghum, or potatoes. Under irrigation, oats often are used as a companion crop for alfalfa or clover. A typical rotation is alfalfa, (three years), sugar beets or potatoes or corn (one or two years), and oats seeded with alfalfa.

In the humid Pacific Coast area, oats frequently occupy the season between row crops and legumes.

Fertilizers

Oats respond well to liberal applications of commercial fertilizers, but on fertile soils it usually is more economical to apply fertilizers to other crops in the rotation.

Well-rotted manure at the rate of 10–15 tons per acre may be applied safely to poor soils before oats are sown, but barnyard manure seldom is applied to fertile soils before oats because it may produce excessive straw growth with consequent lodging. The use of some superphosphate with the manure generally is advisable. Where legumes are used in the rotation to supplement the nitrogen in the soil, applications of 200–250 pounds of superphosphate at seeding time is an effective fertilizer treatment for oats [132, 126].

Even on the poorer soils, applications of more than 30 pounds of actual nitrogen per acre for oats are inadvisable, because of the risk of lodging. In cold wet springs, light applications of nitrogen fertilizer will be beneficial to the oat crop until the soil becomes warm enough to bring about nitrification. In Iowa experiments, yield increases of 50–65 per cent were due to nitrogen stimulation of more heads per plant and more seeds per head when

20, 40 and 80 pounds of nitrogen per acre were used. However, the Bond variety failed to increase in any yield component [52].

Complete fertilizers often are necessary for good yields of oats, particularly in the Eastern states. Some widely used fertilizer formulas are 5-10-5, 6-12-6, or similar combinations [126]. In some areas of the Corn Belt, oats have responded with high yields from applications of 200–300 pounds of an 8-8-8 or similar formula [132]. Oat yields on Wisconsin soils of medium or low productivity have been increased by the use of 250–500 pounds of 0-20-20 or 0-10-30 fertilizer [119].

On the light soils of the Georgia coastal plain, fall-sown oats respond to potash more than to phosphate. About 400 pounds per acre of a complete fertilizer, such as 4-8-6 or 4-8-8, often is applied at seeding time. This is followed in the spring by an additional top-dressing application of 16–32 pounds of actual nitrogen per acre [133]. In Florida, recommended fertilizers for fall-sown oats are 6-6-6, 4-10-7, or similar combinations applied at the rate of 300–500 pounds per acre. When the oats are grazed, additional nitrogen is top-dressed on the growing plants in February. Oats need copper applications for maximum growth on certain Florida soils. When the soil is known to be deficient in this element, a 15-pound application of copper sulfate per acre usually will correct the difficulty [93].

Seedbed Preparation

A moist friable seedbed is desirable for oats. It should contain sufficient moisture to insure prompt germination followed by satisfactory early growth.

FIGURE 19-10. **This type of end-gate seeder, which operated from a drive chain passing over a sprocket attached to a wagon wheel, was widely used for sowing spring oats before broadcast seeders drawn by trucks or tractors became available.**

(Courtesy US Department of Agriculture)

In most sections of the Corn Belt, where oats usually follow corn, the seed-bed generally is prepared by disking before the crop is seeded. A field cultivator also may be used in seedbed preparation when the oat crop follows corn, Korean lespedeza, or soybeans [110]. When oats follow cotton in Texas, the land usually is worked down to a level seedbed by a disk harrow or other surface implement [10].

Plowing is necessary for seedbed preparation when oats follow a sod crop or when heavy residues need to be turned under. Ordinarily, fall plowing is preferable to spring plowing for spring oats, because it permits earlier spring seeding.

Seeding Practices

Oats generally are seeded with a grain drill, although broadcast seeders are still extensively used for sowing oats on disked corn land in the spring (Fig. 19-10). The drill is preferable because it requires less seed, insures a more uniform stand, and provides for a more complete soil coverage of the seed [126]. The small five-disc drill, once commonly used in the South, is satisfactory for sowing winter oats between cotton rows [133].

Plump or high test-weight oat seed generally is advocated. In some experiments in Iowa, oats that ranged in test weight from 17–38 pounds per bushel were sown. The dry weight of the seedlings was positively correlated with the test weight of the seed oats, and the plants from light seed were smaller for 7–10 weeks or longer. Usually the plant weights from light test-weight seed reached those from heavy seed by the time that the oats were mature. Oat kernels produced on plants from light test-weight seed weighed less than did those from heavy seed [55].

The average rate of seeding oats in the United States is 2.5 bushels (10 pecks) per acre (Appendix Table A-9). The optimum seeding rate for oats generally ranges from 8–10 pecks per acre when sown in 6–8-inch drills. Arkansas tests of oats for grain production indicate that 7–9 pecks per acre provide sufficient seed for winter oats, whereas 10 pecks is the optimum rate for spring oats [86]. Under dryland conditions, the rate of seeding for oats usually is reduced to 5 or 6 pecks. Seeding rates under irrigation frequently are 10–12 pecks per acre. Where oats are used for fall or winter pasture, the rate of seeding often is 12 pecks or even 16 pecks for large-seeded varieties such as Letoria, Traveler, New Nortex, or Stanton [133]. In experiments in Illinois, oats seeded in 16-inch rows yielded 80 per cent as much grain per acre as oats sown in conventional 8-inch rows; those grown in 24-inch rows, 66 per cent; and those in 32-inch rows, 54 per cent [106]. The test weight of oats sown in wide rows also was reduced, probably because of a greater number of late tillers.

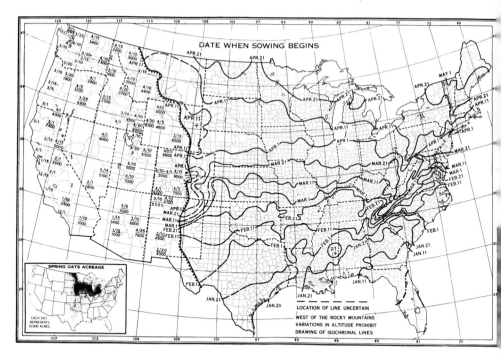

FIGURE 19-11. **Dates for starting to sow spring oats.**

(*Courtesy US Department of Agriculture*)

Under nearly all conditions in the United States, spring oats are seeded as early as the land can be prepared, but seldom later than May 15. Seeding should be completed before the mean daily temperature reaches 50°F (Fig. 19-11). The crop generally is seeded by March 15 in the spring-sown red oats area. In Iowa tests, there was a definite decrease in yield from oats seeded after April 16. Oats sown over an eight-week period in early spring, when temperatures are relatively cool, generally ripened during a two-week period in July at Ames. Thus, three or four days of delay in seeding represented approximately a one-day delay in maturity [146]. In earlier Iowa tests, deferred sowing after the optimum date decreased the acre yield as much as three bushels per day for each day of delay [132]. In Missouri experiments with eleven varieties, oat seedings made in April produced only 65–90 per cent as large a grain yield as that obtained from seedings made in March, while seedings delayed until May yielded only one-third as much as did the March seedings [117]. The optimum date for seeding spring oats in central Texas is January 15, but it may be as late as March 15 on the High Plains [10].

Winter oats should be sown three to four weeks before the first killing frost for the area [126]. In general, fall-sown oats are seeded in the South sometime between September 1 and December 31 (Fig. 19-12). In Arkansas experiments, late September seeding seemed to be optimum for winter oats in the higher elevations of the state, while October 1–10 was most satisfactry in the Cotton Belt of the state [86]. In central Texas, the optimum date for fall seeding is October 15, but in the Rolling Plains area oats generally are sown between September 15 and October 15 [10]. November is the optimum time for sowing oats in Florida. Earlier seeding is somewhat hazardous because of drought or diseases, whereas late-sown oats are more likely to be damaged by cold weather [93].

Chemical Weed Control

Oats may be sprayed with 2,4-D for the control of broad-leaved weeds, such as the mustards and Canada thistle, when they are in the early boot stage. The recommended applications for 3 formulations of 2,4-D are: sodium salt, 0.5 pound; amine salt, 0.5 pound; or butyl ester, 0.25 pound per acre. Iowa tests indicate no significant yield reductions in ten oat varieties that received the above treatment. However, the yields of six of the ten varieties of oats were reduced significantly when given the same treat-

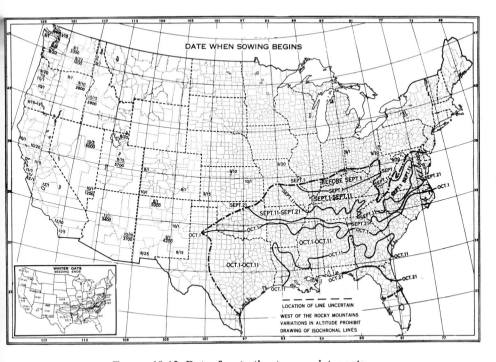

FIGURE 19-12. **Dates for starting to sow winter oats.**

(Courtesy US Department of Agriculture)

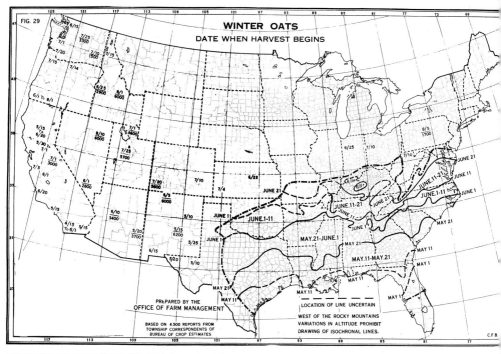

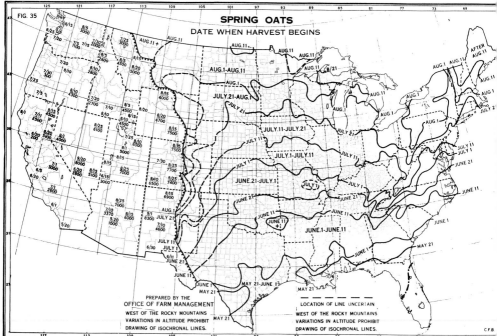

FIGURE 19-13. **Dates when oat harvest begins; winter oats (top), and spring oats (bottom).**
(Courtesy US Department of Agriculture)

ments during the initiation of the floral primordia in the central culms. The butyl ester treatment was the most injurious while the amine salt caused the least damage [123].

Tests in New Jersey indicate that a low or a high fertility level results in less injury to oats from 2,4-D sprays than does a medium fertilizer treatment of 250–300 pounds of 10-10-10 fertilizer per acre. Yields at the high fertility level were reduced significantly only by treatment during anthesis. Reductions in number of seeds per tiller were consistently associated with reductions in yield [4].

In North Carolina, treatments with the amine salt of 2,4-D were applied to 29 winter-oat varieties on November 26 (early tillering) and on March 1 (fully tillered) at 0.5- and 2-pound rates. Oats were least injured by the 0.5-pound treatment on March 1. Both yield and height at maturity were severely reduced in most varieties by the 2-pound treatment on November 26 [112].

Harvest for Grain

Oat harvest for grain in the southern half of the United States begins early in May with winter oats and in June with spring oats. Most of the spring oats in the United States are harvested in July or August (later at northern latitudes and higher altitudes) (Fig. 19-13). However, oats sown late owing to cold wet spring weather may be harvested even after September 1 at high altitudes and in the more northern oat areas [126].

The cradle is still used occasionally for harvesting oats in small fields on rough land in the South [133]. Some oats also are cut with a binder and fed without threshing. The self-binder is still used to harvest some oats, particularly in humid regions. In 1955, nearly one-half the oat crop in Wisconsin was cut with a binder, shocked, and threshed with a grain separator [119]. Binders are used principally where the straw is saved for roughage, bedding, or litter. Binders also are used on some irrigated farms where they are better suited than combines to small fields crossed by irrigation ditches [42]. Oats are harvested with a binder, generally when most of the kernels are in the hard-dough stage and nearly all traces of green have disappeared from the grain and straw.

The combine has replaced the binder to a large extent for harvesting oats. For satisfactory combine harvest, oat kernels should be dead ripe, dry, and contain not more than 13 or 14 per cent moisture. In the more humid regions, oats generally are combined two weeks or more after the grain reaches the binder-ripe stage. This period may be only a week in hot dry seasons. When oat harvest is delayed to allow the kernels to become dead ripe for the combine, losses of 15–20 per cent in grain yields sometimes occur as a result of lodging or shattering [110]. Such losses often are avoided when oats are windrowed at the binder-ripe stage, cured for two or three days in the windrow, and then threshed from the windrow with a combine with a pick-up attachment. The windrow-pickup method also has advantages in fields that are weedy or that ripen unevenly, during wet periods, and where the stems are likely to break over after ripening [132, 133].

Harvest for Forage

Oats can be made into high quality hay for farm animals. The crop generally is cut for hay in the soft-dough stage. In experiments in Arkansas the protein percentages in oat hay harvested at different stages of maturity were as follows: boot, 13.14; full head to flower, 10.37; flower to milk, 10.22; milk, 8.59; soft dough, 8.62; and hard dough, 8.67. The pounds of protein per acre were 505, 496, 540, 629, 612, and 635, respectively, for the six stages of maturity. It was concluded that oat hay harvested when the grain was in the milk, soft-dough, and hard-dough stages of maturity was about equal in feeding value [137]. Hay yields of up to eight tons per acre were obtained from spring oats of the Markton variety grown as a winter annual in Arizona [136]. Oats usually are cut for hay with a mower, windrowed with a side-delivery rake, and allowed to cure. The hay may be baled with a pickup baler or stored loose in the barn. Winter oats for hay sometimes are grown in mixtures with legumes such as vetch or field peas in many sections of the South as well as in the Pacific Coast and Rocky Mountain areas [133, 42].

Fall-sown oats may supply considerable grazing in late fall and winter, and then are harvested for hay or grain in late spring or early summer. Grazing is likely to reduce grain yields, except possibly where a rank vegetative growth otherwise would cause lodging [133]. In Florida, oats often are grazed when the plants are 6–8 inches tall. Rotational grazing is regarded as a good practice. One area may be grazed rather closely for two or three weeks while other areas are allowed to grow for subsequent grazing. A good grain crop can be harvested in most seasons when the livestock are removed from the oats by February 15 [92]. Winter pasture yields equivalent to 18 tons per acre were obtained from spring oats under irrigation in Arizona. Markton was the variety most suitable for sustained winter pasture production when grazed at the onset of the jointing stage throughout the winter pasture season [136].

Oats also have been harvested for silage. Experimental results in Arkansas indicate that oats for silage should be harvested in the boot or in the milk stages of maturity for high quality silage. Such silage has a higher protein content as well as a lower percentage of crude fiber than that harvested at a later stage. However, oats harvested for silage when the grains are in the milk stage will return the highest yield of nutrients per acre. Oat plants cut for silage when the grains are in the hard-dough stage of maturity are difficult to pack in the silo because their stems are hard and dry and their moisture content lower [137]. In the Western states, oats often are cut for silage with a forage harvester when the kernels are in the soft-dough stage [42].

PRODUCTION IN SOME OTHER COUNTRIES

Oats rank second in total value among grain crops in Canada, where they are used for livestock feed almost exclusively. Most of the oats are produced in Manitoba, Saskatchewan, and Alberta. The highest yields have been obtained when oats were sown early in the spring at approximately 10 pecks (80 pounds) per acre under normal moisture conditions, with a reduced rate of seeding in the drier regions. Midseason or early varieties of common oats (*Avena sativa*) generally are grown. Oats often are sown in mixtures with barley, particularly in Ontario, Quebec, and the Maritime provinces. Mixtures of wheat or peas with oats are common in some areas as a means of increasing the protein content of the feed. Oats often are used as an emergency or supplementary hay or pasture crop in eastern Canada. They produce a high quality hay when cut in the milk or early-dough stage of kernel development. For pasturing, oats often are seeded at different times during the summer where feed is required throughout the season. Rust-resistant varieties generally are used when oats are seeded for pasture or hay in late spring or early summer [43].

Oats are grown throughout the British Isles, but most of the crop is grown in northern and western England, Wales, and Scotland. In these moist cool regions, oats usually follow potatoes, roots, or pastures in rotation. In the drier areas of eastern and southern England, oats generally follow wheat or barley. When oats follow well-grazed pastures, 200–300 pounds per acre of superphosphate fertilizer generally is applied for the crop. When oats are grown after another small grain, it is a common practice to apply 200–300 pounds of superphosphate, 100 pounds of potash salts, and 100 pounds of ammonium sulfate. The land is usually fall-plowed in preparation for oats. Spring oats generally are seeded before March 15, while winter oats are sown in September or October. The usual rate of seeding oats is 12 pecks per acre.

Oats are an important crop in Sweden as a feed for livestock. They are grown primarily in upland areas, on relatively infertile soils, on many organic soils, and on poorly drained land. Oats often are grown between crops of wheat and barley because they are less susceptible to foot-rot diseases. Oats sometimes are sown in mixtures with barley or peas. Oat-pea mixtures usually consist of 75–85 per cent oats and 15–25 per cent peas, calculated on normal seeding rates for the two crops [1].

Oats are a major cereal crop in the U.S.S.R. They are grown chiefly for livestock feed, but considerable quantities have been used since World War II for the manufacture of alcohol and as a cereal and flour for human consumption. They occupy 25–50 per cent of the grain acreage in the northern half of the country, largely because oats are better suited than wheat or barley to the cool humid climate and acid soils found there. Oats extend to the northern limits of agriculture in some parts of Siberia and European Russia. They are less important in the southern drier regions. The Russian oat crop is almost entirely spring sown.

Oats are a minor crop in Australia, where they are grown primarily for hay as a feed reserve for sheep after pastures have become exhausted. Oat hay production is concentrated particularly in the Wagga-Wagga District of New South Wales and in the Ballarat-Maryborough region in Victoria. Algerian oats (*Avena sterilis*), or their selections, are largely grown because of their early maturity. Common oat varieties (*A. sativa*) generally mature too late to avoid the summer dry period, except in Tasmania and the cold upland regions [140].

COMMERCIAL STANDARDS

Under the federal grain standards, oats are defined as any grain that consists of 50 per cent or more of cultivated oats, with not more than 25 per cent of wild oats and other grains for which standards have been established.

Classes of Oats

Oats are divided into five commercial classes, primarily on the basis of color: White, Red, Gray, Black, and Mixed. White oats include yellow oats, but often it is impossible to separate reddish or ivory-pink white oats from Red oats. Red oats vary from a light to a deep brownish-red color. They also include oats with tinges of white, brown, or black on the kernels. Mixed oats include all mixtures of oats not provided for in the classes White oats, Red oats, Gray oats, and Black oats [104].

Grades

Oats are graded as No. 1, No. 2, No. 3, No. 4, and Sample Grade. Grades are based on test weight, soundness, brightness, foreign material, and contamination with other grain or wild oats.

TABLE 19-1. **Grade Requirements for the Classes White Oats, Red Oats, Gray Oats, Black Oats, and Mixed Oats.**

	Minimum Limits			Maximum Limits	
Grade No.	Test Weight per Bushel, Lb	Sound Cultivated Oats	Heat-Damaged Kernels	Foreign Material	Wild Oats
		(%)	(%)	(%)	(%)
1[1]	34	97	0.1	2.0	2.0
2[2]	32	94	0.3	3.0	3.0
3[3]	30	90	1.0	4.0	5.0
4[4]	27	80	3.0	5.0	10.0

Sample Grade: Sample grade shall be oats which do not meet the requirements for any of the grades No. 1 to No. 4, inclusive; or which contain more than 16.0 per cent of moisture; or which contain stones; or which are musty, or sour, or heating; or which have any objectionable foreign odor except of smut or garlic; or which are otherwise of distinctly low quality.

[1] The oats in grade No. 1 White oats may contain not more than 5.0 per cent of red oats, gray oats, and black oats, singly or in combination, of which not more than 2.0 per cent may be black oats.

[2] The oats in grade No. 2 White oats may contain not more than 3.0 per cent of black oats.

[3] Oats that are slightly weathered shall be graded not higher than No. 3.

[4] Oats that are badly stained or materially weathered shall be graded not higher than No. 4.

The grade designation for oats includes the number of the grade or the words *sample grade,* as the case may be; the name of the applicable class; and the name of each applicable special grade. Special grades are provided for bright, heavy, extra heavy, tough, thin, weevily, smutty, ergoty, garlicky, and bleached oats [104].

COMPOSITION OF THE OAT KERNEL

The oat grain usually is comprised of about 70–75 per cent kernel (groat) and 25–30 per cent of hull. Naked or hull-less oats are grown only rarely. The hulls contain about 31 per cent of crude fiber.

Chemical Composition

The composition of oats and their chief milled products are given in Table 19-2 [20]:

TABLE 19-2. **Percentage Composition of Oats and Their Milled Products.**

Item	Grain with Hull	Kernel Without Hull; (Groats, Oatmeal, or Rolled Oats)
Moisture	10.1	8.7
Protein	12.2	16.0
Fat	4.3	5.6
Crude fiber	12.1	1.2
Carbohydrates	57.8	66.7
Ash	3.5	1.9
Calories per 100 grams	319.0	380.0
Calories per ounce	90.0	108.0

The approximate mineral constituents of oats and oat products are given in Table 19-3 [115].

TABLE 19-3. **Percentage Composition of Oats and Oat Products.***

Item	Ash	Iron	Calcium	Phosphorus	Manganese
Dry oats	3.4	0.0051	0.065	0.341	32
Finished groats	1.9	0.0044	0.053	0.466	32
Hulls	6.0	0.0112	0.092	0.100	16
Oat shorts	6.7	0.0120	0.178	0.329	74
Oat flour, chips and meal, ppm	2.1	0.0047	0.51	0.414	45

* Basis 7 per cent moisture. Source: Quaker Oats Company.

Oats are a good source of certain vitamins, particularly thiamine, niacin, and pantothenic acid. Vitamin content is given in Table 19–4.

TABLE 19-4. **Vitamin Content (Milligrams) of Oats and Oat Products.***

Item	Thiamine	Riboflavin	Niacin	Pantothenic Acid	Folic Acid	Choline Chloride	Pyridoxine
Dry oats	0.65	0.14	1.15	0.86	0.034	107	0.20
Finished groats	0.77	0.14	0.97	1.36	0.057	120	0.12
Hulls	0.15	0.16	1.04	0.31	0.030	43	——
Oat shorts	0.44	0.35	1.62	0.78	0.060	90	——
Oat flour, chips and meal	0.78	0.17	1.25	1.19	0.060	120	——

* Milligrams per 100 grams on dry basis. Source: Quaker Oats Company.

Apparently, the thiamine content of oats is not impaired by roasting during milling, but a slight loss on cooking to a porridge has been reported [20].

Rolled oats and oatmeal are high in protein, fat, and energy value, and are the richest source of calcium, phosphorus, iron, and thiamine among the cereal foods. Their high nutritive value is partly due to the fact that they are essentially whole-grain products which include the germ [62].

Winter oats often are superior in feeding value to spring oats grown in the same areas because they are more plump and thus have less hull [67].

Factors that Influence Grain Quality

Oats with a heavy test-weight and a low percentage of hulls are desirable for both milling and livestock feed. The hull normally comprises about 28 per cent of the oat grain, but it may vary from 20 per cent in plump oats to 45 per cent in light thin oats.

Test weights average from 32–36 pounds, but may range from 20–50 pounds in extreme cases. A high test-weight usually is an indicator of a low percentage of hull [134], but the length and thickness of the hull also affect the hull percentage. Long thin-hulled oats may weigh less per bushel than short plump thick-hulled oats with a lower groat percentage [152].

Double or "bosom" kernels have a high hull percentage. The hull percentage of primary kernels averages 4–6 per cent higher than that of secondary kernels. Varieties differ in quality as measured by hull percentage, kernel weight, percentage of bosom kernels, and test weight [8], but cool temperatures and ample moisture during kernel development are conducive to good quality.

OAT MILLING

Oats for milling should be free from heat damage, foreign odors, smut, mustiness, or molds. Weathered, underdeveloped, or germinated grain is undesirable. Oats with a low percentage of hull give the highest yields of groats. White oats are perferred for human consumption because fragments of colored hull in the milled product are considered unattractive.

Preparation for Milling

Oats received at the mill are cleaned in order to remove foreign materials such as dust, chaff, weed seeds, and other cereal grains. Double

(bosom) oats, slim oats, pin oats, light oats, and groats are also removed
[20, 62, 115, 145].

After cleaning, the milling oats are conveyed to the dryer where the
moisture content is reduced from about 11–13 per cent down to 7.0–8.5
per cent, which makes the hulls more brittle and thus more easily removed.
The drying (roasting or kilning) is accomplished in a vertical stack of
large open steel pans, 10–12 feet in diameter, placed one above the other
in stacks of 7–14. The bottom of each pan is steam-jacketed. Oats are fed
to the center of the top pan where they are slowly stirred outward by sweeps
which move them toward the edge of the pan where they drop into chutes
which carry them to the middle of the next lower pan. The process is repeated as the oats pass to lower pans. Roasting requires one to one and a
half hours at a temperature of about 180°F. The dried grain passes through
a cooler in which air at room temperature is drawn through the product.
This aeration further reduces the moisture content of the grain down to 6.5–
7.5 per cent.

Hulling

For removal of the hulls, the oats are passed between two large circular carborundum or emery-stone discs, mounted horizontally one immediately above the other. The upper surface of the lower stone is almost flat,
whereas the lower surface of the upper stone is slightly conical. The upper
stone revolves rapidly, but the lower one is stationary.

The dry oats flow by gravity through an opening in the center of the
upper stone and then pass between the pair of stones to the outer edge.
The stones are adjusted precisely so that the intervening space is slightly
greater than the length of the groats in the grain to be hulled. The grains
are turned on end while moving toward the outer edge of the stones, and
the hulls are shattered and torn from the groat.

The mixture of loosened hulls, whole-oat groats, and bits of floury
pieces broken from the groat are directed from the hulling stones through
sieves, reels, and purifiers which separate the various fractions. The oat
groats obtained at this point are ready to be processed.

Processing the Groats

Whole groats destined for large standard flakes are steamed directly
with live steam at atmospheric pressure for a few minutes to soften the kernels so that pulverization is kept at a minimum when the groat is flattened as it passes between precisely adjusted heavy steel rolls.

For quick-cooking or small flakes, the groats are steel-cut into pieces of the desired size with rotary-type granulators. Each granule of medium steel-cut oats comprises about one-third of a groat. For medium steel-cut oats, the rolls are set close together to make thin flakes.

Yield of Milled Products

About 13.5 bushels (or 432 pounds) of medium-good to good quality oats are required to produce a barrel, or 180 pounds, of high quality rolled oats. The milling yield ranges from 35–65 per cent. A barrel of ground oatmeal of steel-cut oats is 196 pounds. Heavy, plump, dry and clean commercial oats give the highest extraction of rolled oats. Thin-hulled high-test-weight oats of the Cherokee, Clinton, and Bonda varieties have given high milling extraction [20, 126].

UTILIZATION OF OATS AND THEIR PRODUCTS

Nearly 90 per cent of the oats grown in the United States are used for feed, some 3 per cent is used in making breakfast foods, and the remainder is used for seed. Usually about 75 per cent of the oats produced are kept for feed and seed on the farm where they are grown.

Livestock Feed

Oats are a valuable feed grain for all classes of livestock, particularly for horses, poultry, young animals, and breeding stock. High test-weight oats are highly regarded as feed for race horses. More oats are now fed to dairy cattle and poultry than were fed to horses in the United States in 1918 (when the horse population was at its height). Oat groats are sometimes utilized as feed for young fowls. A small acreage of oats is used for pasture, hay, or silage [126].

Oat hulls are fed either as ground hulls in the mash, or in the form of whole oats, in the poultry ration to protect against slipped tendons, cannibalism, and feather-picking in chickens [126].

Food Products

Oat groats were ground into meal before steel-cut oats were developed. Later, large rolled flakes became popular, and more recently the smaller or quick-cooking types of flakes have been processed to a considerable extent. Rolled oats, the chief product of an oat mill, are used for breakfast food, cookies, bread, and pudding.

Oat flour, a by-product of rolled oats manufacture, is used in prepared breakfast foods. Since it contains no gluten, oat flour can be used in bread making only when mixed with about four parts wheat flour to one part oat flour. Oat flour contains an antioxidant, and is used to preserve quality in foods that contain fat. The antioxidant delays the development of rancidity. For this purpose, oat flour is infused with lard, margarine, or peanut butter. It also is dusted on potato chips as well as on salted nuts. The flour is also used to coat paper containers of certain foodstuffs such as bacon or coffee [126].

Other Uses

Furfural, a liquid aldehyde, is the most valuable industrial product made from oat hulls. It is made from the hulls by destructive distillation in the presence of acid and steam under regulated conditions. About 200 pounds of furfural are obtained from 2000 pounds of hulls. Furfural is a major solvent or chemical intermediate in the processing and refining of mineral and vegetable oils. It also is used in plastics. Its solvent properties make it valuable in paint removers and lacquer solvents. Furfural also is used in the purification of wood resin as well as in the production of synthetic resins, such as bakelite. It is a raw material in the production of adiponitrile, an intermediate product in the manufacture of nylon.

Oat hulls are also used to make pharmaceutical products. These are synthesized from furan resins. They include Furmethide and furacin. Furacin is an antiseptic which is a possible supplement for penicillin or streptomyacin [126].

Oatmeal soap and bath packs have been used for many years. As a constituent of certain soaps, oatmeal adds pleasant as well as effective detergent qualities.

A very small quantity of high-quality oats, usually of the Victory variety, are used for plant growth studies that involve the bending of the coleoptile by light, auxins, or other external stimuli [126].

OAT DISEASES

The most important oat diseases are loose smut, covered smut, stem rust, crown rust, Victoria blight, Helminthosporium leaf blotch, Septoria leaf blotch, halo blight, and mosaic diseases.

Smuts

Smuts of oats are worldwide, but cause an annual loss of somewhat less than one per cent of the crop in the United States. Oats are attacked by two smuts: loose smut, caused by *Ustilago avenae,* and covered smut, caused by *U. kolleri.* Loose smut is the most common species in the South Atlantic states, whereas covered smut occurs often in the Western states [81].

Loose smut is more conspicuous than covered smut when the oat panicles first emerge from the boot because it destroys the floral bracts as well as the kernels. The smut mass in each spikelet may be surrounded at first by a delicate white membrane which soon ruptures to release the spores. They are disseminated by the wind to flowers of healthy plants where they lodge under the lemma and palea. The spores germinate within the flowers to produce a mass of fungus mycelium which becomes established between the embryo kernel and the floral bracts. The mycelium becomes dormant as the kernel matures. When the oat kernel germinates, the fungus infects the oat seedling, develops systemically in the host, and replaces the oat kernel with masses of smut spores [68, 81].

Covered smut emerges from the oat plant with the spores enclosed in the floral bracts. The branches are shortened so that the panicle has a compact appearance. The smut mass that replaces the oat kernel is covered by a thin grayish membrane which usually ruptures when the crop is threshed. The spores then are spread over the surface of the threshed grain and some spores lodge beneath the oat hulls where they germinate to form a mat of fungus mycelium over the seed coat. Other spores remain dormant on the outer surface of the oat hulls until the seed germinates [81].

Oat smut infection may occur at temperatures between 41° and 86°F, but it generally occurs between 59° and 68°F. Infection may occur when the soil moisture content is between 5 and 60 per cent, but most often when it is between 35 and 40 per cent of its field carrying capacity. Neutral or slightly acid soils seem to favor infection [68].

Both species of oat smut can be controlled by seed treatment with volatile fungicides since the fumes will reach the spores as well as the mycelium beneath the oat hulls. Effective dust seed treatments include Ceresan M or Agrox applied at the rate of 0.5 ounce per bushel, or Mergamma applied at the rate of 1.5–2.5 ounces per bushel. Among the quick wet treatments, Panogen has been an effective fungicide when applied at the rate of 0.75 of a fluid ounce per bushel of seed in a slurry treater [81]. The disease is now largely prevented by the use of resistant varieties.

Oat smuts can hybridize and produce new races of smut. About 25 races of the oat smut fungus species have been recognized in the United States by their reaction on 10 differential oat varieties. All major commercial oat varieties grown in 1953 were susceptible to one or more races of these smuts [68]. Some of the more resistant varieties include Benton, Boone, Clinton, Huron, Marion, Markton, Marvic, Neosho, and Rangler [128, 45]. Smut-resistant varieties reported in Kansas are Kanota, Fulton, Osage, and Neosho [60].

Crown Rust

Crown or leaf rust, caused by *Puccinia coronata* Cda., is the most destructive rust on oats. It also attacks several species of grasses and its alternate host is buckthorn (*Rhamnus* spp.). Crown rust is virtually coextensive with oat culture, but is is generally most destructive in the humid to subhumid areas of the temperate zone. In the United States, crown rust is particularly serious in the Southern and North Central states. Yields of susceptible varieties may be reduced from 20–50 per cent [84]. In Iowa tests, Idamine oats with 24 per cent crown rust infection yielded 74.1 per cent as much grain as nearly rust-free oats [94].

Crown rust occurs as pustules principally on the leaves, although they frequently are found on the leaf sheaths, stems, and panicles. The orange-yellow pustules of the uredial or summer stage are usually more or less round, but often they coalesce to form irregular patterns. The black telial or winter stage appears later in the season.

Oats that are heavily infected with crown rust usually produce low yields, have low test-weights, lodge badly (Fig. 19-14), and ripen prematurely. Heavily rusted winter oats also become more susceptible to winter killing [114]. In Iowa experiments, the winter hardiness index of 21 varieties infected with 20–80 per cent of crown rust was 13–68 per cent lower than were comparable rust-free plants [95]. Susceptible plants first infected in the seedling stage were found in Iowa experiments to use 290.8 per cent more water per unit of dry matter than did rust-free plants [94].

The life history of crown rust is similar to that of stem rust, except that the aecial or cluster-cup stage develops on the buckthorn (*Rhamnus* spp.) instead of on the barberry. In the spring, aeciospores are wind-borne from the buckthorn to oats and grasses, where the uredial stage develops. When weather conditions are favorable, the urediospores cause secondary infections. As the oat plant matures, the teliospores develop and these overwinter on the old oat-plant remains. In the spring, the teliospores germinate to produce sporidia which infect the buckthorn. In the South, the uredial stage develops throughout the year on oats and grasses. In the Northern states, the uredial stage generally does not overwinter. Epidemics result from urediospores blown in from the South, or from the development of the aecial stage on the buckthorn.

Warm moist weather is most favorable for rapid development and spread of crown rust, and moisture—as from dews or rains—is likely to be

FIGURE 19-14. **The badly rusted varieties of oats have lodged or broken over. Rows of resistant strains are still erect.**

(*Courtesy US Department of Agriculture*)

held longer in dense stands of oats. In the South, the amount of crown rust infection largely depends on the amount of inoculum that overwinters. Mild winters are particularly favorable for the survival of crown rust [84].

The principal control measures for crown rust involve the growing of resistant varieties and eradication of the buckthorn. Resistance to crown rust is independent of resistance to stem rust [82]. The development of crown rust-resistant varieties of oats has been complicated by the identification of more than 100 physiological races of the fungus. Victoria and Bond were found to be resistant to crown rust, and were used widely in breeding suitable resistant varieties. Victoria was introduced from Uruguay in 1927; Bond was obtained from Australia in 1929 [131]. About 1946, Victoria-derived oat varieties were found to be susceptible to Victoria blight, a Helminthosporium disease. Fortunately, some of the Bond-derived varieties proved to be resistant to Victoria blight as well as to crown rust. Among the Bond-derived varieties are Clinton, Bonda, Andrew, Benton, and Mindo which are widely grown in the Corn Belt. Camellia, Taggart, and Belair are Grown to some extent in the Southern states. It was soon found that

crown rust Races 45, 57, and 101 attack Bond, Victoria, and their derivatives. As a result, new resistant varieties similar to Clinton and Benton
were developed from the Landhafer and Santa Fe varieties [77, 126], and
were being grown in 1961.

Stem Rust

Stem rust of oats, caused by *Puccinia graminis avenae,* occurs on some
varieties of all species of oats as well as on many grasses. The forms found
on oats normally do not attack wheat, barley, or rye. The disease is found
wherever oats are grown and causes reduction in yields. It is now less
destructive than in former years in the United States because of the widespread growing of resistant varieties since the 1930's [126].

Symptoms of stem rust on oats are similar to those of stem rust on
wheat. The disease attacks both the stems and leaves of the oat plant. The
pustules of the uredial or summer stage of stem rust are brick-red in color,
whereas those of crown rust are bright yellow or yellow-orange. The telial
stage is apparent on fully grown oat plants late in the season.

The life history, methods of dissemination, and control measures for
stem rust of oats are similar to those for stem rust on wheat.

The White Tartar, Green Russian, and Richland varieties are resistant
to certain races of the stem rust fungus. Bond and its derivatives are resistant to many stem rust races and also to Victoria blight as well as to
crown rust and the smuts. Some of these varieties are Clinton, Mohawk,
Advance, Bonham, Kent, Benton, Bonda, and Mindo. However, most of these
Bond-derived varieties are susceptible to Races 6 and 7 of the stem rust
fungus, which have appeared in epiphytotic proportions since 1950. New
strains have been developed that are resistant to these races [126].

There are at least 14 known physiologic races as well as several subraces in the United States and Canada [121, 142]. No oat can resist all these
races and subraces. Seedling reaction appears to be a reliable index of reaction on adult plants to some races of the fungus [83]. Minhafer oats, resistant to Races 7A and 8, were obtained from the cross:

Bond-Rainbow × Hajira-Joanette × Landhafer

Victoria Blight

Victoria blight (known also as Helminthosporium blight), caused by
Helminthosporium victoriae, was discovered in Iowa in 1945 in widely distributed fields of the Boone, Tama, and Vicland varieties. By 1946, the
disease was prevalent in every important oat-growing state. Some of the
newer varieties of oats derived from Victoria were nearly wiped out [126].

FIGURE 19-15. **Severe attack of Victoria blight on a susceptible variety (center). The varieties at left and right are resistant.**

(Courtesy US Department of Agriculture)

Victoria blight is primarily a seedling and culm disease. Infected leaves are characterized by reddish-brown stripes or spots. The straw breaks over as the oats head out (Fig. 19-15). The grain is shriveled or chaffy largely because of the infection at the base of the culm. The straw and stubble of susceptible varieties is darkened by masses of conidia which are produced at the nodes as the plants are killed [44].

The pathogen is carried over from year to year on the seed, as well as on crop residues of susceptible varieties.

Seed treatment with volatile organic mercury compounds reduces seedling losses of susceptible varieties, but fails to control the later culm blight. With a few exceptions, only oats derived from Victoria hybrids are susceptible to the disease [121]. The resistant Bond-derived varieties include Clinton, Mohawk, Advance, Bonham, Kent, Benton, Bonda, Mindo, Andrew, Zephyr, Colo, Shelby, Nemaha, and Cherokee. These varieties are productive, early, stiff-strawed, and of high test-weight [125, 126].

Helminthosporium Leaf Blotch

Helminthosporium leaf blotch, caused by *Pyrenophora avenae* (Conidial stage: *Helminthosporium avenae*), is widely distributed on cultivated oats. In recent years, severe damage to the oat crop has been reported in local areas in the United States, particularly in the more humid areas that border the Gulf of Mexico. Some damage has also been reported in Virginia, Arkansas, and Wisconsin [46]. Nevertheless, the disease generally is of minor importance.

Characteristic symptoms are brown spots or irregular blotches, which spread over the entire leaf blade. Defoliation frequently occurs. Diseased leaf blades turn yellow and dry out as the amount of infection increases. Yields are reduced when the leaf blotch is severe [44].

Leaf blotch is carried over from one oat crop to the next as seed-borne inoculum, mycelium, or conidia, but also as ascospores on crop residues. Primary infection occurs on the seedling leaves, whereas secondary infection occurs throughout the growing period of the oat plant [45].

Control measures consist of rotating crops, plowing under crop residues, treating seed with organic mercury compounds, and using resistant varieties.

Septoria Leaf Blotch

Septoria leaf blotch of oats is caused by *Septoria avenae,* which is the imperfect stage of *Leptosphaeria avenaria.* The disease also occurs on several grasses. It has become important in the spring and winter oat areas of the United States since the 1940's.

The leaf spots caused by the disease are typically chocolate-brown-to-tan lesions surrounded by flesh-to-yellow-colored halos of necrotic tissue which blends into the green leaf tissue. The spots often coalesce to form irregular blotches. When the spots become older, they turn light tan-to-gray as the pycnidia develop throughout the lesions. About 10–12 days after the leaf spots are noticed, lesions appear on the leaf sheaths as well as on the culms. The culm lesions develop into the black-stem phase. It results from inoculum that originated from pycnidia borne in the leaf lesions [72]. Perithecia develop on the old diseased straw. The damage caused by the Septoria disease on susceptible varieties results largely from shriveled kernels and lodging.

The Septoria leaf blotch is carried over from one season to the next as mycelium and pycnidia on diseased oat straw or stubble. The micropycnidia occur early in the spring which cause the initial leaf lesions on oat plants. The perithecia develop later. Leaf infections are favored by cool wet weather.

The only practical control measures are rotating crops, plowing under old straw, and using resistant varieties. Bond-derived varieties are relatively susceptible to culm rot by the Septoria disease. Most other commercial oat varieties are relatively resistant [44]. Some resistant varieties are Ajax, Bever, Branch, Clintafe, Clinton, Shelby, and Spooner.

Mosaic Diseases

Several mosaic diseases occur on oats in various countries. The most common ones in the United States are the soil-borne mosaics and the yellow-dwarf virus.

Soil-borne mosaics are found primarily on fall-sown oats in the Southeastern United States. When abundant, these mosaics reduce the yields of susceptible oat varieties, such as Bond, Camellia, Victoria, and Letoria. Two viruses have been isolated. One virus, *Marmor terrestre* var. *typicum,* causes apical mosaic, a light-green mottling that tends to be prominent toward the leaf tips. The other virus, *M. terrestre* var. *oculatum,* causes eye-spot mosaic which is characterized by light-green or yellow, nearly elliptical sports with green centers. Some plants in certain oat strains develop a typical rosette. These viruses overseason in the soil, but are not carried on the seed of diseased plants. Infection is favored by cool autumn temperatures of near 60–65°F for 35–60 days. Consequently, these mosaics are likely to be of little importance on spring-sown oats. The use of resistant varieties is the most practical means of control. Some resistant or tolerant varieties are: Anderson, Atlantic, Appler, Arlington, Ballard, Custis, Fulgrain, Fulwin, Lee, Victorgrain, and Winter Resistant [87, 88].

The barley yellow-dwarf virus also attacks oats. It has been referred to for years as the "red leaf" disease. It is an aphid-transmitted virus that may cause considerable or heavy damage to susceptible varieties. Since 1945, the disease has caused sporadic damage to the oat crop, particularly in the North Central states. It was very destructive in California in 1951. Leaves of infected plants turn light-green or yellow from the tips down. The chlorotic foliage tends to redden in oats. Plants become infected at all stages. The main effects of the disease on oats are blasted florets, shriveled kernels, and reduction in test weight. Grain yields are reduced most when the oat plants are infected in early growth, such as the three-leaf stage. Most oat varieties are highly susceptible to the yellow-dwarf virus, but Albion and Fulghum are tolerant. In the spring-oat region, early seeding of early varieties might afford partial control until adapted resistant varieties are developed [87, 48].

Other Diseases

Some of the minor diseases that occasionally cause considerable damage to oats, together with their causal organisms, are: halo blight (*Pseudomonas coronafaciens*), bacterial stripe blight (*Pseudomonas striafaciens*), downy mildew (*Sclerospora macrospora*), powdery mildew (*Erysiphe graminis avenae*), Fusarium blight (*Gibberella* and *Fusarium* spp.), Scolecotrichum leaf blotch (*Scolecotrichum graminis* var. *avenae*), snow mold

(*Fusarium nivale*), and anthracnose (*Colletotrichum graminicolum*). Varietal resistance has been reported for halo blight and bacterial stripe blight [97]. Oat blast, a nonparasitic ailment resulting in floret sterility, is most prevalent where high temperatures occur at flowering time. Snow mold may retard the northward advance of hardy winter oats, although the Norline variety appears to tolerate the disease.

INSECT PESTS

Fortunately, oats generally are less subject to insect attack than are either wheat or barley. The Hessian fly does not attack oats and the chinch bug greatly prefers wheat or barley, although it does damage oats. The various stem borers cause little damage to oats. The fruit fly is a common pest of oats in England, but it has been controlled by the distribution of resistant varieties [126].

The spring grain aphis or greenbug (*Toxoptera graminum*) sometimes damages oats severely, especially in the South Central states. Infestations of the greenbug have been unusually abundant in recent years. Aphids transmit the virus that causes the barley yellow dwarf disease of oats. Oats also are readily attacked by the bluegrass billbug (*Calendra parvulus*), certain leafhoppers, the grain bug (*Chlorocroa sayi*), grasshoppers, and Mormon crickets. Insects also cause an average annual loss of at least 5 per cent of oats in storage on farms, in elevators, or in warehouses. (For discussion of control measures for most of these insects, see Chap. 15).

CROSSES WITHIN AND BETWEEN SPECIES

Oats that belong to the 7, 14, and 21 chromosome groups are referred to as diploid, tetraploid, and hexaploid species, respectively. The species usually cultivated most extensively are hexaploids with three sets (genomes) of seven chromosomes each. The genome constitution of the hexaploid species has been reported to be AABBCC.

Crosses Within Species

Crosses within species usually are fully fertile. Some notable irregularities have been reported in England in crosses between spring and winter types of *Avena sativa*. Argentine and Victory spring varieties, crossed with the Gray Winter and Avoine d'hiver winter varieties, produced about 20 per cent of pollen mother cells that contained univalent chromosomes. The spring × spring and the winter × winter variety hybrids showed only about one per cent of such irregularity. Thus, the chromosomes in these spring and winter oats were only partly homologous [70]. Picton, a winter-hardy variety of oats selected from the cross Argentine × Gray Winter, contains plants which have chromosome irregularities. Within this variety, it was possible to select plants that produced offspring with a low frequency of such irregularities [71].

Partial sterility has been observed in crosses between white and black *A. sativa* oats in Sweden, and more than one-half of the pollen mother cells showed irregularities [3].

Interspecific Crosses Within Groups

Crosses between species with the same chromosome number usually have been made rather easily. In four crosses of four hexaploid interspecies hybrids in Japan (*Avena fatua* × *A. sativa, A. fatua* × *A. sterilis, A. sativa* × *A. byzantina,* and *A. sterilis* × *A. byzantina*), the hybrids were equally as fertile as the parents, but occasional chromosomal irregularities were observed [99]. Other observations of meiotic behavior in the F_1 of crosses which involved *A. sativa, A. sterilis,* and *A. fatua* (from Asia Minor) indicate from 2.45–12.81 per cent of irregularities in the pollen mother cells. However, all F_1 hybrids of the above species with *A. byzantina* as one parent had from 59–88 per cent of such irregularities. Other hexaploid species crosses with a high frequency of pollen mother cell irregularities were *A. nuda* × *A. fatua* (from Asia Minor), 46 per cent; and *A. fatua* (from Afghanistan) × *A. sativa* (Gray Winter variety), 33.5 per cent. The most common irregularity of meiosis was the occurrence of univalents [76].

Hybrids between two diploid species (*A. brevis* and *A. strigosa*) have been reported as perfectly normal with a high degree of fertility. Hybrids between the tetraploid species, *A. barbata* and *A. abyssinica,* have shown some chromosome irregularities, with quadrivalents in 15 per cent of the pollen mother cells. This indicates structural differences in the chromosome sets [47].

A cross between *A. sativa* and *A. fatua* produced some plants with 41 chromosomes instead of the normal 42. These chromosome-deficient plants were deficient in one member of the "L" pair of chromosomes which carried genes necessary for the formation of broad leaves. Narrow-leaved 40-chromosome plants also isolated were less fertile than were the broad-leaved plants [109].

Interspecific Crosses Between Groups

Interspecific crosses have been made between diploid and tetraploid oats, for example, *Avena barbata* ($n = 14$) × *A. wiestii* ($n = 7$) and *A.*

barbata ($n = 14$) × *A. strigosa* ($n = 7$). The F_1 plants of the latter hybrid had seven bivalents and seven univalents in most of the pollen mother cells, but there were other combinations. The pollen grains formed were nearly empty. The F_1 plants closely resembled *A. barbata* in almost all characters, except for fertility and time of flowering. Some plants contained viable pollen and produced seed. In the F_2 and later generations, the progeny tended to approach either the 14- or 28-diploid chromosome level in stabilization. Those progenies with intermediate chromosome numbers tended to disappear due to sterility [99, 100]. The cross, *A. abyssinica* ($n = 14$) × *A. strigosa* ($n = 7$), produced a few weakly developed kernels and most of them gave rise to hybrid plants [79]. The panicle type of F_1 plants of this cross was similar to that of *A. abyssinica,* but the plants inherited crown rust resistance from *A. strigosa* [17].

An amphidiploid hybrid with 21-chromosome pairs has been produced from the cross, *A. abyssinica* × *A. strigosa,* after the chromosomes were doubled by the use of colchicine. When eight F_2 amphidiploid plants were grown in the field, seven were highly resistant to crown rust and one was susceptible. Attempts to cross the amphidiploid ($n = 21$) with common oat varieties were unsuccessful [17].

Interspecies crosses also have been made between tetraploid and hexaploid oat species to produce so-called pentaploid hybrids. Two of these hybrids were *A. barbata* ($n = 14$) × *A. fatua* ($n = 21$), and *A. barbata* ($n = 14$) × *A. sterilis* ($n = 21$). The pentaploid hybrids were highly sterile [99]. These hybrids usually show an unstable pairing of chromosomes. In fact, hybrids with high or low numbers of chromosomes usually are unstable. Plant segregates with 21 or 22 bivalents were highly fertile, whereas those with 24 or 25 chromosome pairs were semisterile. Most of the plants with more than the normal hexaploid chromosome number had a semidwarf growth habit [102].

Tetraploid F_1 hybrids, produced from *A. sativa* ($n = 21$) × *A. strigosa* ($n = 7$) and from *A. fatua* ($n = 21$) × *A. strigosa* ($n = 7$), were completely sterile when self-pollinated [79].

From their behavior in hybrids, the genomes of *A. fatua* have been designated as AABBCC, whereas those in *A. barbata* are AAB'B'. The homology between the BB and B'B' genomes is not fully determined [102]. The genomes of the hexaploid species apparently are closely related, except for possible differences in one or two chromosomes.

FATUOIDS

Fatuoids or false wild oats have been observed in cultivated oat varieties for many years. They arise suddenly in varieties of both common and red cultivated oats. Fatuoid kernels have a prominent basal cavity; dense and often very long hairs on the base of the lemma; and a long, twisted, geniculate awn on all florets of the spikelet [124]. Otherwise they closely resemble the variety in which they arise. For example, fatuoids that occur in black oats are black, like the parent.

Fulghum produces more fatuoids than any other important American variety. An average of 0.19 per cent of fatuoids was found in 119,246 seeds or plants observed. Fatuoids are detrimental chiefly because their presence may discredit a strain [36]. Approximately 0.2 per cent of fatuoids appeared spontaneously in lines of normal Fulghum self-pollinated for four generations. When fatuoids were open-pollinated, they cross-fertilized an average of 11.6 per cent in five years. Normal Fulghum, under similar conditions, contained less than 0.5 per cent of crosses in any season. Thus, the persistence of fatuoids in normal oats is increased by natural crossing [129]. Fatuoids have no more dormancy than the varieties in which they arise [38].

Mutation appears to explain the origin of fatuoids [74], but crossing with *Avena fatua* also has been suggested as a cause. Alpha heterozygous fatuoids behave as though they are the result of gene mutation, usually with a deficiency of homozygous mutant progeny. When self-fertilized, they produce normal plants, heterozygous fatuoids, and homozygous fatuoids in a ratio which is theoretically 1:2:1, but often is nearer to 1:1:0.

Beta heterozygous fatuoids result from the loss of one chromosome from the C genome, in which case the affected pollen grain may not be functional and sterile fatuoid progeny are produced. When self-fertilized, the characteristic ratio is one normal to more than four heterozygous fatuoids [101, 74].

Gamma heterozygous fatuoids, characterized by the loss of a part of a C-genome chromosome, also produce many sterile pollen grains. Upon self-fertilization, they produce normal and heterozygous fatuoid progeny in a ratio of about 1:1 [74].

The origin of steriloids associated with articulation in an *Avena barbata* × *A. strigosa* cross has been explained as due to substitution between partially homologous chromosomes [103]. Hybrid segregates of a cross between *A. sativa* and *A. fatua* often are mistaken for fatuoids [74], but many of these do not resemble the cultivated variety, and they segregate for various characters.

GENETICS

Grain Characters

Black grain (lemma and palea) color is inherited in a monogenic 3:1 ratio or as a digenic 15:1 ratio with black dominant over nonblack [64,

85, 124]. A yellow-grained *Avena sativa* crossed with *A. sterilis* with brown to reddish-black grains gave F_2 ratios of 12 black: 3 red: 1 yellow, or 15 black: 1 nonblack [89]. F_2 segregation for other grain colors are as follows: Gray vs. white, 3:1: yellow vs. white, 3:1 or 15:1: and red vs. nonred (Yellow or white), 3:1 [124].

Crosses with fatuoid kernels that arise from a gene mutation segregate into an F_2 ratio of 1 normal:2 intermediate:1 fatuoid. The heterozygous intermediates have the geniculate awn and the *A. fatua* type of callus only on the lower grain [85]. In a cross of *A. sativa* varieties with Bond (*A. byzantina*), the *sativa* type of articulation was dominant over the *byzantina* type with a 3:1 segregation [65].

Hulled vs. hull-less crosses segregate into a monogenic ratio of 1 hulled:2 intermediate:1 hull-less. Both hulled and hull-less grains may occur in the panicles of F_1 and intermediate F_2 plants [85, 124].

Awnless vs. strong awn segregates in 1:2:1 ratio for awnless, intermediate, and strong awns. A similar ratio has been reported for awnless vs. weak-awned types [124].

Other Plant Characters

Open vs. side panicle has segregated into 3:1 or 15:1 ratios in different crosses, with open panicle dominant. Duplicate factors are involved in the 15:1 ratio, that is, either dominant gene produces an open panicle [85, 124].

Early vs. late heading has segregated into a 15:1 ratio in some crosses [124], but other crosses involve multiple factors having a cumulative effect. In such cases, earliness appeared to be either completely or incompletely dominant to lateness [117].

Some crosses involving normal and dwarf oat plants give a 3:1 ratio in the F_2 generation [124], but multiple factors also have been reported. In crosses between *A. sativa* and *A. byzantina,* transgressive segregation in F_2 indicates the presence of multiple factors for plant height [120].

Segregation for niacin, riboflavin, and protein content has been studied in the F_2 generation of two oat crosses. Transgressive segregation for niacin content was indicated in both. Low niacin content was dominant in the C.I. 5298 × Huron cross. Transgressive segregation for high ribo-flavin content was observed in both crosses. Low protein percentage was dominant in the C.I. 5298 × Huron cross. It appeared that each of these components was determined by a large number of genes [53].

Disease Reaction

Stem rust resistance is inherited as a simple dominant in some crosses [59, 64, 65], but a 13:3 ratio for susceptibility vs. resistance to stem rust also has been reported [124]. Later studies indicate that resistance to the various races of stem rust is conditioned by three genes. Gene A, present in varieties such as Richland, Vanguard, Ajax, and Green Russian, conditions resistance to Races 1, 2, 3, 5, 7, 7A, and 12. Gene B, present in such varieties as Canuck and Rodney, conditions resistance to Races 1, 2, 3, 5, 7, and 12, but is ineffective against Race 7A. Gene C conditions resistance to Races 4, 6, 8, 10, 11, and 13. Gene A is independent of Genes B and C, but there is some evidence of association between B and C [143].

Resistance to crown rust is inherited as a simple dominant to susceptibility in many oat crosses [124]. In the cross, Bond × Rainbow, a monohybrid segregation occurs in F_2 with resistance dominant. Other crosses between Bond and susceptible *Avena sativa* varieties gave a segregation of resistant to susceptible in a 9:7 ratio, which indicates that two major factors were involved [65]. The resistance of Victoria to Races 4, 5, 34A, and 57 appears to be governed by a single dominant major gene, but resistance to Races 1, 2, 3, 6, 24, 38, and 45, appears to be conditioned by three dominant genes [144]. Apparently, three factors, C, D, and S, condition the resistance of Santa Fe to the 14 races of crown rust studied [105]. Two dominant linked genes determine the resistance of Santa Fe to Races 57 and 109 of crown rust [50].

Resistance vs. susceptibility to loose smut and to covered smut often has been reported as being conditioned by single genes, with F_2 segregation of three resistant:1 susceptible [124]. In a Markton (resistant) × Colorado 37 (susceptible) cross, a 9:7 ratio was reported for smutted and nonsmutted plants [12]. At least two major factors seem to be necessary to explain the resistance of Black Mesdag [65]. In other crosses, smut resistance was conditioned by one, two, or three factors [23].

Inheritance studies indicate that susceptibility to Victoria blight is governed by a single dominant major gene [144].

Induced Mutations

A number of desirable mutant strains of oats have been isolated from irradiated seed of the Huron variety [51], but some of these may have resulted from outcrossing of the partly sterile irradiated progenies with other varieties. Of 61 strains tested, only one appeared to contain a mutation for stem rust that was different from known genes [54].

Linkage Relations

A genetic linkage is indicated between spikelet disarticulation and basal hair development with a crossover value of 2.7 per cent [65].

The genes $M_1M_1U_1U_1$ for resistance to crown rust Races 57 and 109 are linked with 28.8 per cent recombination [50].

OAT IMPROVEMENT

Oats have been bred for higher yields and resistance to diseases, lodging, and shattering [124]. Varieties that are resistant to the smuts, stem rust, and crown rust have been developed [97]. Resistance to Victoria blight also has been incorporated into some new varieties.

Introductions

The first oats grown in the United States were introductions brought in by the early colonists from their native countries. Many new varieties also were introduced during the ninteenth century by the federal government. Swedish Select was introduced in 1899 [21]. The Kherson and Sixty-Day varieties came from Russia in 1898 and 1901, respectively. The Algerian red oat was introduced from Algeria in 1903. Victory oats were introduced from Sweden a few years later. Most of the later introductions, such as Victoria and Bond, were never grown commercially, but many have proved valuable in crosses [126].

Selections

Oat improvement by selection started soon after 1900, although the method was used in Sweden as early as 1891 [2]. Victory originated in Sweden as a pure-line selection from the old Probsteier variety. The Markton, Richland, Gopher, and Rainbow varieties originated as selections in the United States. Selection within the old Red Rustproof variety, grown in the southern United States since 1875, has resulted in many varieties, including Fulghum, Appler, Bancroft, Delta Red, Ferguson 922, Nortex, and New Nortex [126].

Hybridization

Hybridization of oat varieties began in the United States in Vermont about 1870. In England, the Abundance variety, a product of hybridization, was released in 1892.

Oat improvement by hybridization has been used extensively in the

United States since 1920. Oat varieties resistant to the smuts, crown rust, and stem rust, such as Richland, Markton, Victoria, Bond, Landhafer, and Santa Fe, have been crossed with varieties having other desirable characters [97].

The backcross method of hybridization is being used more and more [126]. Bulk hybrids also have been tried [9].

In breeding for disease resistance, artificial epidemics are developed in order to eliminate susceptible progenies [124].

REFERENCES

1. Aberg, E., "Recent changes in Swedish crop production," in *Advances in Agronomy*, Vol. 7. New York: Academic Press. pp 39–74. 1955.
2. Akerman, A., "The breeding of oats," *Svalof, 1886–1946: History and Present Problems*. Lund, Sweden: Carl Bloms Boktryckeri A.–B. pp 98–112. 1948.
3. ———, and A. Hagberg, "Intraspecific sterility in oats." *Hereditas*, **40**: 438–452. 1954.
4. Aldrich, R. J., "Effect of 2,4-D on the growth and yield of oats grown under three levels of fertility." *Agron. J.*, **50**(3): 145–148. 1958.
5. Amirshahi, M. C., and F. L. Patterson, "Development of a standard artificial freezing technique for evaluating cold resistance in oats." *Agron. J.*, **48**: 181–188. 1956.
6. Agricultural statistics, 1960. USDA. pp 1–633. 1961.
7. Arny, A. C., and C. P. Sun, "Time of cutting wheat and oats in relation to yield and composition." *J. Am. Soc. Agron.*, **19**: 410–39. 1947.
8. Atkins, R. E., "Factors affecting milling quality of oats." *J. Am. Soc. Agron.*, **35**: 532–539. 1943.
9. ———, and H. C. Murphy, "Evaluation of yield potentialities of oat crosses from bulk hybrid tests." *Agron. J.*, **41**(1): 41–45. 1949.
10. Atkins, I. M., and E. S. McFadden, "Oat production in Texas." Tex. Ag. Exp. Sta. *Bul. 691*. 1947.
11. ———, and F. A. Coffman, "Mustang, a hardy winter oat." *Agron. J.*, **43**(6): 287–291. 1951.
12. Austin, W. W., and D. W. Robertson, "Inheritance of resistance to *Ustilago levis* (K. and S.) Magn. (covered smut) in cross between Markton and Colorado 37 oats." *J. Am. Soc. Agron.*, **28**: 467–471. 1936.
13. Barbee, O. E., "Markton and other varieties of oats." Wash. Ag. Exp. Sta. *Bul. 314*. 1935.
14. Bonnett, O. T., "The development of the oat panicle." *J. Ag. Res.*, **54**: 927–931. 1937.
15. ———, "The oat plant: Its histology and development." Ill. Ag. Exp. Sta. *Bul. 672*. pp 1–112. 1961.
16. Booth, E. G., "Daily growth of the oat kernel and effect on germination of immaturity and controlled low temperatures." Minn. Ag. Exp. Sta. *Tech. Bul. 62*. 1929.

17. Brown, C. M., and H. L. Shands, "Behavior of the interspecific hybrid and amphidiploid of *Avena abyssinica* X *A. strigosa.*" *Agron. J.*, **46**: 357–359. 1954.

18. ———, and H. L. Shands, "Pollen tube growth, fertilization, and early development in *Avena sativa.*" *Agron. J.*, **49**: 286–288. 1957.

19. Brown, E., *et al.*, "Dormancy and the effect of storage on oats, barley, and sorghum." USDA *Tech. Bul. 953.* 1948.

20. Brownlee, H. J., and F. L. Gunderson, "Oats and oat products: culture, botany, seed structure, milling, composition, and uses." *Cer. Chem.*, **15**: 257–272. 1938.

21. Carleton, M. A., *The Small Grains.* New York: Macmillan. pp 87–114, 171–174. 1916.

22. Casady, A. J., E. G. Heyne, and F. W. Smith, "Oats in Kansas." Kans. Ag. Exp. Sta. *Bul. 386.* 1957.

23. Cochran, G. W., "Inheritance of reaction to smut, stem rust, and crown rust in four oat crosses." *J. Ag. Res.*, **70**: 43–61. 1945.

24. Coffman, F. A., "Specific hybridization, a probable method for producing hardier winter oats." *J. Am. Soc. Agron.*, **29**: 79–81. 1937.

25. ———, "Heat resistance in oat varieties." *J. Am. Soc. Agron.*, **31**: 811–817. 1939.

26. ———, "The comparative winter-hardiness of oat varieties." USDA *Cir. 622.* 1941.

27. ———, "Origin of cultivated oats." *J. Am. Soc. Agron.*, **38**: 983–1002. 1946.

28. ———, "Results from uniform winterhardiness nurseries of oats grown from 1942 to 1946." *J. Am. Soc. Agron.*, **39**: 1027–1035. 1947.

29. ———, "*Avena sativa* L., probably of Asiatic origin." *Agron. J.*, **47**: 281. 1955.

30. ———, "Factors influencing heat resistance in oats." *Agron. J.*, **49**: 368–373. 1957.

31. ———, "Culture and varieties of spring-sown red oats." USDA *Farmers Bul. 2115.* 1958.

32. ———, "Oat varieties in the Western States." USDA *Handbook 180.* pp 1–19. 1960.

33. ———, *Oats and Oat Improvement.* Agronomy Monographs, Vol. 8. *Am. Soc. Agron.* pp 1–650. 1961.

34. ———, J. H. Parker, and K. S. Quisenberry, "A study of variability in the Burt oat." *J. Ag. Res.* **30**: 1–64. 1925.

35. ———, and G. A. Wiebe, "Unusual crossing in oats at Aberdeen, Idaho." *J. Am. Soc. Agron.*, **22**: 245–250. 1930.

36. ———, and J. W. Taylor, "Widespread occurrence and origin of fatuoids in Fulghum oats." *J. Ag. Res.*, **52**: 123–131. 1936.

37. ———, and T. R. Stanton, "Variability in germination of freshly harvested *Avena.*" *J. Ag. Res.*, **57**: 57–72. 1938.

38. ———, and T. R. Stanton, "Dormancy in fatuoid and normal oat kernels." *J. Am. Soc. Agron.*, **32**(6): 459–466. 1940.

39. ———, H. A. Rodenhiser, and J. W. Taylor, "New varieties for the northern winter oat regions." *Agron. J.*, **41**: 551–554. 1949.

40. ———, H. Stevens, and C. S. Holton, "Overland and Cody, two new short-strawed oats for the Northwest." *Agron. J.*, **43**(7): 325–328. 1951.

41. ———, and J. MacKay, "Hafer (*Avena sativa* L.)," in *Handbuch der Planzenzuchtung*, II Band, 2 Aufl. pp 427–531. 1958.

42. ———, H. Stevens, and T. R. Stanton, "Culture of oats in the Western States." USDA *Farmers Bul. 2134.* 1959.

43. Derick, R. A., and D. G. Hamilton, "Oats in Canada." Can. Dep. Ag. *Farmers Bul. 27.* 1948.

44. Dickson, J. G., "Leaf and head blights of cereals," in *Plant Diseases.* USDA Yrbk. of Ag. pp 344–349. 1953.

45. ———, *Diseases of Field Crops*, 2d ed. New York: McGraw-Hill. pp 1–517. 1956.

46. Earhart, R. W., and H. L. Shands, "Oat varietal response to infection by *Helminthosporium avenae.*" *Agron. J.*, **44**: 234–238. 1952.

47. Ellison, W., "The occurrence of quadrivalents in certain diploid and tetraploid *Avena* hybrids." *J. Gen.*, **36**: 515–522. 1938.

48. Endo, R. M., and C. M. Brown, "Effect of yellow-dwarf on the yield of oats." *Agron. J.*, **49**: 503–505. 1957.

49. Etheridge, W. C., "A classification of the varieties of cultivated oats." Cornell U. Ag. Exp. Sta. *Memoir 10.* 1916.

50. Finkner, R. E., R. E. Atkins, and R. C. Murphy, "Inheritance of resistance to two races of crown rust in oats." *Ia. State Coll. J. Sci.*, **30**: 211–228. 1955.

51. Frey, K. J., "Agronomic mutations in oats induced by X-ray treatment." *Agron. J.*, **47**: 207–210. 1955.

52. ———, "Yield components in oats. II: The effect of nitrogen fertilization." *Agron. J.*, **51**(10): 605–610. 1959.

53. ———, *et al.*, "Inheritance of niacin, riboflavin, and protein in two oat crosses." *Agron. J.*, **46**: 137–139. 1954.

54. ———, and J. A. Browning, "Mutations for stem rust resistance induced in oats by X-ray treatment." *Phytopath.*, **45**: 490–492. 1955.

55. ———, and S. C. Wiggans, "Growth rates of oats from different test weight seed lots." *Agron. J.*, **48**: 521–523. 1956.

56. ———, and S. C. Wiggans, "Tillering studies in oats. I: Tillering characteristics of oat varieties." *Agron. J.*, **49**: 48–50. 1957.

57. ———, E. Ruan, and S. C. Wiggans, "Dry weights and germination of developing oat seeds." *Agron. J.*, **50**(5): 248–250. 1958.

58. ———, and R. M. Caldwell, "Oat breeding and pathological techniques," in *Oats and Oat Improvement*, Am. Soc. Agron. Monographs, Vol. 8. pp 227–260. 1961.

59. Garber, R. J., "Inheritance and yield with particular reference to rust resistance and panicle type in oats." Minn. Ag. Exp. Sta. *Tech. Bul. 7.* 1922.

60. ———, and K. S. Quisenberry, "Natural crossing in oats at Morgantown, West Virginia." *J. Am. Soc. Agron.*, **19**: 191–197. 1927.

61. ———, and M. M. Hoover, "Natural crossing between oat plants of hybrid origin." *J. Ag. Res.*, **38**: 647–648. 1929.

62. Geddes, W. F., "Cereal Grains," in *Food and Food Products*, 2d. ed. Vol. II. M. B. Jacobs, Ed. New York: Interscience. pp 1022–1133. 1951.

63. Grafius, J. E., "The relationship of stand to panicles per plant and per unit area in oats." *Agron. J.*, **48**: 460–462. 1956.

64. Hayes, H. K., *et al.*, "Correlated studies in oats of the inheritance of reaction to stem rust and smuts and other differential characters." *J. Ag. Res.*, **36**: 437–457. 1928.

65. ———, M. B. Moore, and E. C. Stakman, "Studies of inheritance in crosses between Bond, *Avena byzantina*, and varieties of *A. sativa.*" Minn. Ag. Exp. Sta. *Tech. Bul. 137.* 1939.

66. Heyne, E. G., *et al.*, "Osage and Neosho oats." Kans. Ag. Exp. Sta. *Cir. 242.* 1947.

67. Hill, D. D., "The chemical composition and grades of barley and oat varieties." *J. Am. Soc. Agron.*, **25**: 301–311. 1933.

68. Holton, C. S., and V. H. Tapke, "The smuts of wheat, oats, and barley," in *Plant Diseases.* USDA Yrbk. of Ag. pp 360–368. 1953.

69. Hoover, M. M., and M. H. Snyder, "Natural crossing in oats at Morgantown, West Virginia." *J. Am. Soc. Agron.*, **24**: 784–786. 1932.

70. Howard, H. W., "Meiotic irregularities in hexaploid oats. I: Univalent frequencies in spring × winter variety hybrids of *Avena sativa.*" *J. Ag. Sci.*, **37**: 139–144. 1947.

71. ———, "Meiotic irregularities in hexaploid oats. II: A cytological survey of the variety Picton." *J. Ag. Sci.*, **38**: 332–338. 1948.

72. Huffman, M. D., "Disease cycle of Septoria disease of oats." *Phytopath.*, **45**: 278–280. 1955.

73. Hunter, H., *Oats: Their Varieties and Characteristics.* London: Benn. pp 1–131. 1924.

74. Huskins, C. L., "Fatuoids, speltoid, and related mutations of oats and wheat." *Bot. Rev.*, **12**(8): 457–514. 1946.

75. Jasny, N., *Competition Among Grains.* Stanford U. Food Res. Inst. pp 531–543. 1940.

76. Joshi, A. B., and H. W. Howard, "Meiotic irregularities in hexaploid oats. IV: Hybrids between *Avena sativa* (spring and winter varieties), *A. fatua, A. sterilis, A. byzantina,* and *A. nuda.*" *J. Ag. Sci.*, **46**(2): 183–190. 1955.

77. Kehr, W. R., *et al.*, "The present status of breeding rust resistant oats at the Minnesota station." *Agron. J.*, **42**: 356–359. 1950.

78. ———, and H. K. Hayes, "Studies of inheritance in crosses between Landhafer, *Avena byzantina* L., and two selections of *A. sativa* L." *Agron. J.*, **42**(2): 71–78. 1950.

79. Kihara, H., and I. Nishiyama, "Genetics and cytology of certain cereals. III: Different compatability in reciprocal crosses of *Avena*, with special reference to tetraploid hybrids between hexaploid and diploid species." *Jap. J. Bot.*, **6**: 245–305. 1932.

80. Laude, H. H., "Cold resistance of winter wheat, rye, barley, and oats in transition from dormancy to active growth." *J. Ag. Res.*, **54**: 899–917. 1937.

81. Leukel, R. W., and V. F. Tapke, "Cereal smuts and their control." USDA *Farmers Bul. 2069.* 1954.

82. Levine, M. M., *et al.*, "Field studies on rust resistance of oat varieties." USDA *Tech. Bul. 143.* 1930.

83. ———, and D. C. Smith, "Comparative reaction of oat varieties in the seedling and maturing stages to physiologic races of *Puccinia graminis avenae* and distribution of these races in the United States." *J. Ag. Res.*, **55**: 713–729. 1937.

84. Martin, J. H., and S. C. Salmon, "The rusts of wheat, oats, barley, rye," in *Plant Diseases.* USDA Yrbk. of Ag. pp 329–343. 1953.

85. Matsuura, H., "Genic analysis in *Avena.*" Hokkaido Imp. U. Fac. Sci., Series V, Vol. 1, No. 2. 1931.

86. McClelland, C. K., "Oat variety and production studies." Ark. Ag. Exp. Sta. *Bul. 301.* 1934.

87. McKinney, H. H., "Virus diseases of cereals," in *Plant Diseases*. USDA Yrbk. of Ag. pp 350–360. 1953.

88. ———, *et al.*, "Mosaics of winter oats and their control in the southeastern states." USDA *Cir. 809*. 1949.

89. Middleton, G. K., "Inheritance in a cross between *Avena sativa* and *Avena sterilis* L." *J. Am. Soc. Agron.*, **30**: 193–208. 1938.

90. Misonoo, G., "Ecological and physiological studies on the blooming of oat flowers." *J. Fac. Agr.*, Hokkaido Imp. U., **37**(4): 211–337.

91. Morey, D. D., "The extent and causes of variability in Clinton oats." Ia. Ag. Exp. Sta. Res. *Bul. 363*. 1949.

92. ———, "Sunland and Seminole, two new oats for Florida." Fla. Ag. Exp. Sta. *Cir. S-63*. 1953.

93. ———, W. H. Chapman, and R. W. Earhart, "Growing oats in Florida." Fla. Agr. Exp. Sta. *Bul. 523*. 1953.

94. Murphy, H. C., "Effect of crown rust infection on yield and water requirement of oats." *J. Ag. Res.*, **50**: 387–411. 1935.

95. ———, "Effect of crown and stem rusts on the relative cold resistance of varieties and selections of oats." *Phytopath.*, **29**: 763–782. 1939.

96. ———, "Registration of oat varieties, XX." *Agron. J.*, **47**: 535–538. 1955.

97. ———, T. R. Stanton, and F. A. Coffman, "Breeding for disease resistance in oats." *J. Am. Soc. Agron.*, **34**(1): 72–89. 1942.

98. Nakao, S., "On the Mongolian naked oats with special reference to their origins." Naniwa U. Fac. Ag. *Spec. Rpt. No. 1*, Japan. 1950.

99. Nishiyama, I., "The genetics and cytology of certain cereals. I: Morphology and cytological studies on triploid, pentaploid, and hexaploid *Avena* varieties." *Jap. J. Gen.*, **5**: 1–48. 1929.

100. ———, "The genetics and cytology of certain cereals. VI: Chromosome behavior and its bearing on inheritance in triploid *Avena* varieties." Coll. Ag. Kyoto U. *Mem.*, **32**: 1–157. 1934.

101. ———, "The genetics and cytology of certain cereals. VII: Genetical significance of the C-chromosome in hexaploid *Avena* species." *Jap. J. Bot.*, **7**: 453–469. 1935.

102. ———, "Cytogenetical studies in *Avena*. III: Experimentally produced eu- and hyper-hexaploid aberrants in oats." *Cytologia*, **10**: 101–104. 1939.

103. ———, "Cytogenetic studies of *Avena*. V: Genetic studies of steriloids found in the progeny of a triploid *Avena* hybrid." Kyoto U. Res. Inst. Food Sci. *Mem. No. 5*. pp 14–24. 1953.

104. "Official grain standards of the United States." USDA *SRA-AMS-177*. 1960.

105. Osler, R. D., and H. K. Hayes, "Inheritance studies in oats with particular reference to the Santa Fe type of crown rust resistance." *Agron. J.*, **45**: 49–53. 1953.

106. Pendleton, J. W., "Effect of clover, row spacing, and rate of planting on spring oat yields." *Agron. J.*, **49**: 555–558. 1957.

107. Peters, R. A., "Legume establishment as related to the presence or absence of an oat companion crop." *Agron. J.*, **53**(3): 195–198. 1961.

108. Petr, F. C., and H. Stevens, "Park oats for Idaho." Ida. Ag. Exp. Sta. *Bul. 290*. 1958.

109. Philp, J., "Aberrant leaf width in polyploid oats." *J. Gen.*, **36**: 405–431. 1938.

110. Poehlman, J. M., "Growing good crops of oats in Missouri." Mo. Ag. Exp. Sta. *Bul. 644*. 1955.

111. ———, "0–200, a new early variety of oats for Missouri." Mo. Ag. Exp. Sta. *Bul. 534.* 1949.

112. Price, C. D., and G. C. Klingman, "Wheat and oats varietal responses to applications of alkanolamine salt of 2,4-D." *Agron. J.*, **50**(4): 200–204. 1958.

113. Reitz, L. P., "Oats in Nebraska." Nebr. Ag. Exp. Sta. *Bul. 408.* 1951.

114. Rosen, H. R., L. M. Westman, and C. K. McClelland, "Winter injury as related to fall and winter growth and crown-rust infection in oat varieties and their hybrids." Ark. Ag. Exp. Sta. *Bul. 418.* 1942.

115. Rupp, E. G., "Facts on oats." Quaker Oats Co. 1955.

116. Sampson, D. R., "On the origin of oats." Harvard U. Bot. *Mus. Leaflets,* **16**: 265–303. 1954.

117. Sappenfield, W. P., and J. M. Poehlman, "Effect of date of seeding on the yield and test-weight of oat varieties." Mo. Ag. Exp. Sta. Res. *Bul. 499.* 1952.

118. ———, "Inheritance of earliness among six common varieties of oats." Mo. Ag. Exp. Sta. Res. *Bul. 514.* 1952.

119. Shands, H. L., and D. C. Arny, "Oats, culture and varieties." Wisc. Ag. Ext. *Cir. 418.* 1955.

120. Shaw, F. J. F., and R. D. Bose, "Studies in Indian oats. II: Inheritance of some characters in interspecific crosses between *Avena sativa* L. and *Avena sterilis* var. *Culta.*" *Ind. J. Ag. Sci.*, **3**: 771–807. 1933.

121. Simons, M. D., and H. C. Murphy, "Oat diseases," in *Oats and Oat Improvement.* Am. Soc. Agron. Monographs, Vol. **8.** pp 330–390. 1961.

122. Stadler, L. J., "Fulghum oats in Missouri." Mo. Ag. Exp. Sta. *Bul. 229.* 1925.

123. Staniforth, D. W., and R. E. Atkins, "Effect of 2,4-D on yield and bushel weight of oats." *Agron. J.*, **44**: 587–589. 1952.

124. Stanton, T. R., "Superior germ plasm in oats," in USDA Yrbk. of Ag. pp 347–414. 1936.

125. ———, "Disease-resistant oats," in *Science in Farming.* USDA Yrbk. of Ag. 1943–1947. pp 395–402. 1947.

126. ———, "Production, harvesting, processing, utilization, and economic importance of oats." *Econ. Bot.*, **7**: 43–64. 1953.

127. ———, "Oat identification and classification." USDA *Tech. Bul. 1100.* 1955.

128. ———, D. E. Stephens, and E. F. Gaines, "Markton, an oat variety immune from covered smut." USDA *Misc. Cir. 324.* 1924.

129. ———, F. A. Coffman, and G. A. Wiebe, "Fatuoid or false wild forms in Fulghum and other oat varieties." *J. Hered.*, **17**: 153–226. 1926.

130. ———, D. E. Stephens, and B. B. Bayles, "Relative resistance of oat varieties to shattering at Moro, Oregon." *J. Am. Soc. Agron.*, **20**: 304–305. 1928.

131. ———, and H. C. Murphy, "Oat varieties highly resistant to crown rust and their probable agronomic value." *J. Am. Soc. Agron.*, **25**: 674–683. 1933.

132. ———, and F. A. Coffman, "Grow disease-resistant oats." USDA *Farmers Bul. 1941.* 1943 (rev. 1949).

133. ———, and F. A. Coffman, "Winter oats in the South." USDA *Farmers Bul. 2037.* 1951.

134. Stoa, T. E., R. W. Smith, and C. M. Swallers, "Oats in North Dakota." N. Dak. Ag. Exp. Sta. *Bul. 287.* 1936.

135. Taylor, J. W., and F. A. Coffman, "Effects of vernalization on certain varieties of oats." *J. Am. Soc. Agron.*, **30**: 1010–1019. 1938.

136. Thompson, R. K., and A. D. Day, "Spring oats for winter forage in the Southwest." *Agron. J.*, **51**(1): 9–12. 1959.

137. Thurman, R. L., *et al.*, "When to harvest oats for hay and silage." Ark. Ag. Exp. Sta. *Bul. 586.* 1957.

138. Toole, E. H., and F. A. Coffman, "Variations in the dormancy of seeds of the wild oat, *Avena fatua.*" *J. Am. Soc. Agron.*, **32**(8): 631–638. 1940.

139. Vavilov, N. I., "The origin, variation, immunity, and breeding of cultivated plants." *Chron. Bot.*, **13**: 1–364. 1949–50.

140. Wadham, S. M., and G. L. Wood, *Land Utilization in Australia*, 2d. ed. Melbourne: Melbourne U. Press. pp 261–262. 1950.

141. Weaver, J. E., *Root Development of Field Crops.* New York: McGraw-Hill. pp 167–174. 1926.

142. Welsh, J. N., and T. Johnson, "The source of resistance and inheritance of reaction to 12 physiologic races of stem rust, *Puccinia graminis avenae* (Erikss. and Henn.)." *Can. J. Bot.*, **29**: 189–205. 1951.

143. ———, and T. Johnson, "Inheritance of reaction to race 7A and other races of stem rust, *Puccinia graminis avenae.*" *Can. J. Bot.*, **32**: 347–357. 1954.

144. ———, B. Petersen, and J. C. Machacek, "Associated inheritance of reaction to races of crown rust, *Puccinia coronata avenae* Erikss., and to Victoria blight, *Helminthosporium victoriae* M. and M., in oats." *Can. J. Bot.*, **32**: 55–68. 1954.

145. Western, D. E., and W. R. Graham, Jr., "Marketing, processing, uses, and composition of oats and oat products," in *Oats and Oat Improvement.* Am. Soc. Agron. Monographs, Vol. 8. pp 552–578. 1961.

146. Wiggans, S. C., "The effect of seasonal temperatures on maturity of oats planted at different dates." *Agron. J.*, **48**: 21–25. 1956.

147. ———, and K. J. Frey, "The effect of increased day lengths on the production of greenhouse grown oats." *Agron. J.*, **47**: 387. 1955.

148. ———, and K. J. Frey, "Photoperiodism in oats." Ia. Acad. Sci. *Proc.*, **62**: 125–130. 1955.

149. ———, and K. J. Frey, "Tillering studies in oats. II: Effect of photoperiod and date of planting." *Agron. J.*, **49**: 215–217. 1957.

150. ———, and K. J. Frey, "Tillering studies in oats. III: Effect of rate of planting and bushel weight." *Agron. J.*, **49**: 549–551. 1957.

151. Wilson, H. K., and S. M. Raleigh, "Effect of harvesting barley and oats at different stages of maturity." *J. Am. Soc. Agron.*, **21**: 1057–1078. 1929.

152. Zavitz, C. A., "Forty years experiments with grain crops." Ontario Dep. Ag. *Bul. 332.* 1927.

PART V Rice, Sorghum, and Millets

20. RICE

ECONOMIC IMPORTANCE

Rice (*Oryza sativa*) is the principal food crop of about one half of the population of the world. It is the staple food of a large majority of the people in China, India, Pakistan, Japan, Korea, Formosa, Ceylon, Indochina, Thailand, Indonesia, Philippine Republic, Malaya, and Madagascar. Nearly one-third of the cultivated area in India is planted to rice [112].

Probably 92 per cent or more of the world rice crop is produced and consumed in Monsoon Asia. This area extends across southeastern Asia from India to Japan, and includes practically all of the adjacent tropical or subtropical islands [134].

The world area in rice during the five-year period 1950–54 averaged about 257 million acres, with an average production of 197 million short tons of rough rice (Fig. 20-1). The average yield was about 1500 pounds per acre. China, India, Pakistan, Japan, Indonesia, Thailand, and Burma led in production. Other important rice-producing countries include Indochina, Philippine Republic, Brazil, United States, Taiwan, Egypt, Madagascar, French West Africa, and Italy. The highest average acre yields of rough rice were obtained in Spain, that is, about 4700 pounds, compared with about 4600 pounds in Italy, 4600 pounds in Australia, 3800 pounds in Portugal, 3400 pounds in Japan, and 2400 pounds in the United States. However, the acre yield in the United States in 1960 and 1961 was 3400 pounds. By 1959-61 the average world production was 255 million tons on 290 million acres, a yield of 1750 pounds per acre.

Rice yields in Japan average from 50–200 per cent more than in other Asiatic countries. The average yield in Japan was nearly 60 per cent higher from 1948–52 than from 1883–87 [84]. These high yields are due mainly to the heavy use of commercial fertilizers, the development of improved varieties, and efficient cultural methods [123, 84]. Similar yields are obtained in Taiwan [44].

607

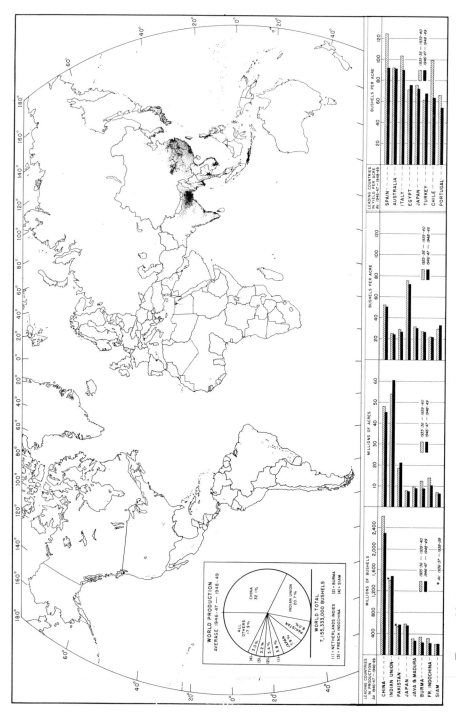

FIGURE 20-1. World rough rice production, average of 1946-47 and 1948-49. Each dot represents 2,500,000 bushels.
(*Courtesy US Department of Agriculture*)

Comparatively low average yields of about 1100 pounds of cleaned rice per acre are obtained in India, with similar low yields in Burma, Thailand, Malaya, Ceylon, and Indochina. In India more than 75 per cent of the area is without irrigation facilities, thus being subject to the vicissitudes of the monsoon rains. The need for rice is so great that much of it is grown on unsuitable land. Fertilizers seldom are applied to the soil, with the result that soil productivity is stabilized at a very low level. Similar conditions prevail in other rice-producing countries of southeastern Asia [112]. Since 1953, however, the better features of the Japanese methods of culture have been gradually adopted in India and other Asiatic countries.

Thailand, Burma, and Indochina normally supply 90 per cent of the rice that moves in international trade. Other important export countries are the United States, Brazil, Italy, and Egypt.

Rice is a minor crop in the United States, although it is a major crop in areas where grown. The average annual harvested acreage during the 10-year period 1952–61 was 1,764,000 acres. The average annual production for this period was 2,613,000 short tons of rough rice, or a yield of

*Data available only for principal States (California, Texas, Louisiana, Arkansas, and Mississippi).

FIGURE 20-2. **Acreage of rice harvested in the United States. One dot represents 2,000 acres. (Data were available only for the principal rice-producing states, California, Texas, Louisiana, Arkansas, and Mississippi.) United States total in 1959: 1,616,962 acres.**

(Courtesy US Department of Commerce)

2500 pounds per acre. Nearly all of this crop was produced in Louisiana, Texas, California, Arkansas, and Mississippi, but some was harvested in Missouri, South Carolina, and Florida [8]. (Figs. 20-2 and 20-3).

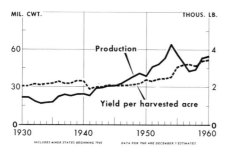

FIGURE 20-3. **Production and yield of rice in the United States. Acre yields increased 70 per cent between 1930 and 1960.**

(*Courtesy US Department of Agriculture*)

The western hemisphere is a surplus rice region because of low per-capita consumption and a rapid expansion of production after 1942, particularly in the United States, Brazil, Ecuador, British Guiana, and Mexico [32, 33, 34].

HISTORY OF RICE CULTURE

In China, the sowing of rice was an important religious ceremony nearly 5000 years ago. Differences among rice varieties were recognized in India as early as 1000 BC. Rice probably spread to Java from India as early as 1084 BC [59, 112]. It was introduced into Japan from China as early as 100 BC. The crop had spread from Kyushu to all of Honshu by AD 1200, but did not become established on the island of Hokkaido until just before AD 1800 [84].

Rice advanced westward from India to Iran, Iraq, Turkestan, and Egypt. It was introduced into Europe from India by Alexander the Great by AD 300, but it was not cultivated there until about AD 700 [112]. It was taken to Spain by the Moors in AD 711 [25].

In the United States, the Virginia colonists experimented with rice production as early as 1622, but without marked success [23]. Rice was first produced commercially in this country in South Carolina about 1685. Later, the crop moved into North Carolina, Georgia, Florida, Alabama, and Mississippi. For 200 years, most of the American rice crop was produced on the delta lands of the South Atlantic states. The Civil War curtailed rice production in that region, and by 1890, it was of little importance there. The production of rice developed along the Mississippi River in Louisiana after the Civil War, and that state led all others by 1889. Rice culture extended to southeastern Texas about 1900, to the prairies of eastern Arkansas about

1905, to California in 1912, and to the delta lands of Mississippi by 1949. The crop has been grown intermittently in Missouri since about 1925.

ORIGIN OF CULTIVATED RICE

The cultivated rice plant probably originated somewhere in the area between southern India and Indochina. Wild rices still persist in this region [59]. India sometimes is regarded as the native home of rice because of the presence there of a large number of wild forms. Moreover, the varietal diversity of cultivated rice found there is the greatest in the world and the nearest known wild relative of cultivated rice, *Oryza fatua* (*O. spontanea*), occurs in abundance. This or some other wild rice is believed to be the progenitor of the cultivated rices found in India and Indochina [20]. There also is a prevalence of dominant genes in Indian rice varieties [130, 112].

Mutations, natural cross-pollination in cultivated rice, and crosses between cultivated rice and wild rice might account for the great diversity of cultivated rice in India [112]. Louisiana workers concluded that *O. sativa* originated directly or indirectly from *O. balunga*, but that in the process of domestication, intermediate forms occurred that would have been classified as *O. fatua* (or *O. sativa* var. *fatua*) [137].

ADAPTATION

Rice production is restricted to areas having warm temperatures and sufficient moisture. The principal rice-producing countries lie between the 30° N. and 30° S. Exceptions are Japan, Korea, Southern Australia, Europe, and California. In these tropical or subtropical regions rice is by far the most productive cereal that can be grown. Rice is grown in Asia from below sea level to an elevation of 8000 feet. Most of the rice crop is grown on submerged land by lowland or paddy culture by intensive methods, often on land that is too wet for other cereals. Paddy rice land is submerged throughout most or all of the crop season [59].

Climate

Rice can be grown successfully only where the mean temperature is 70°F, or above, during the entire growing season of 4–6 months. In the southern United States rice region, the mean temperature is about 70°F in late spring and early fall and about 82°F or above in the summer. The ger-

mination of rice seed at warm temperatures promotes earlier flowering because of the increased rate of growth during the early stages of plant
development [92]. The annual precipitation in the southern United States
ranges from 36–56 inches and is well distributed throughout the year.

The water requirement for rice varies from 8–35 inches per month.
Most of the world rice is grown where the annual rainfall is 40 inches or
more. However, rice thrives in dry hot regions where there is ample irrigation water, as in the rice fields of the Po, Nile, and Sacramento valleys
[134]. Moist tropical or subtropical regions are favorable to rice culture
when the rainfall distribution provides a relatively dry period for harvesting the crop.

Rice is generally grown on flooded land in China, Japan, Egypt, Italy,
and the United States. A dependable supply of fresh irrigation water is
essential for maximum yields. It may be obtained from mountain streams,
from a well-distributed annual rainfall on the watersheds or streams that
pass through the rice areas, or from underground sources. Upland (rain-fed)
rice is grown in many tropical countries with high rainfall where it is impossible to provide fields with water artifically. The rice field must be kept
wet or submerged by natural precipitation during most of the season if good
yields are to be attained.

Soils

Rice is grown on light, medium, or heavy soils, but the heavier soils
require less irrigation because there is less seepage into the subsoil. Most
good rice soils contain a high proportion (generally about 70 per cent) of
fine clay and silt particles. Most rice soils have a pH value between 4 and
6 [38], but the soils in Egypt and California are alkaline. The optimum
reaction for rice on cropped Arkansas soils is about pH 6.5 [70]. Rice on
very acid Arkansas soils (pH 4.0) had poor root growth, considerable floret
sterility, and low grain yields.

Rice culture in the United States is almost entirely confined to comparatively flat prairie, river valley, and delta lands that are easily leveled
for flooding. Most of the soils are of heavy texture generally underlaid by
an impervious subsoil at from 1.5 or less to 5.0 feet below the surface. The
fields should have good surface drainage so that the water can be removed
readily to permit rice harvest [61]. In the prairie of southern Louisiana and
the Grand Prairie of Arkansas, much of the rice acreage is on Crowley silt
loam. Lake Charles and Beaumont clays are typical rice soils in the prairies
of southeastern Texas. Most of the rice in California is grown on a heavy
adobe soil. These soils hold water well.

Some rice is grown on organic or peat soils, which have a high nitrogen
content and high water-holding capacity. The organic soils, as in Florida,

 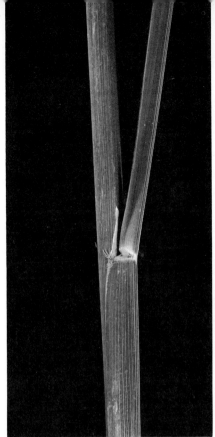

FIGURE 20-4. **A mature rice plant with about 20 tillers.**
(*Courtesy US Department of Agriculture*)

FIGURE 20-5. **Section of culm showing its characteristic long ligule.**
(*Courtesy US Department of Agriculture*)

require heavy applications of phosphorus, potassium, and sometimes other mineral elements. Iron is reduced to toxic compounds in some very acid peat soils in Nigeria, and in Indonesia where it is termed *Hampa*. Other organic soils are slightly acid to neutral peats in which iron is in short supply. In such soils, the rice crop is benefited by additions of iron salts or soil that contains large amounts of iron oxides. This condition prevails in Japan where it causes a deficiency disease called *akiochi*. It occurs also in the Everglade soils of Florida in the United States, particularly in those derived from saw-grass [37].

In Louisiana, Crowley silt loam soil that has produced lowland rice for many years is lower in nitrogen, total phosphorus, and available phosphorus, and definitely more alkaline than similar soil not cropped to rice [115]. The higher pH resulted from flooding with water that contained the equivalent in alkaline salts of 1500 pounds per acre of limestone each year. Soil with 5700 ppm of sodium chloride has reduced the germination of rice seed and prevented grain formation [71].

FIGURE 20-6. **Panicle of Zenith (medium-grain) rice more than six inches long.**

(*Courtesy US Department of Agriculture*)

FIGURE 20-7. **Spikelets (top), seeds (middle), and kernels (bottom) of four types of rice: first column, Rexoro—slender grain; second column, Fortuna —long grain; third column, Blue Rose—medium grain; and fourth column, Caloro—short grain.**

(*Courtesy US Department of Agriculture*)

GENUS ORYZA

Rice belongs to the grass tribe Oryzeae, characterized by one-flowered spikelets, laterally compressed, and which have two very short glumes. Plants of the genus *Oryza,* to which cultivated rice belongs, have six stamens and a basic diploid number of 12 chromosome pairs [41, 112].

Some of the 20–25 wild species of *Oryza,* which include *O. alta* and *O. grandiglumis,* have either diploid or tetraploid chromosome complements. The species *Oryza latifolia, O. eichingeri, O. sylvestris, O. granulata,* and *O. redleyi* have 24 chromosome pairs. Other species have 12 chromosome pairs [75]. *O. glaberrima,* which sometimes is cultivated in Africa (particularly in Nigeria), has dark-colored grains of inferior quality [38]. This species crosses readily with cultivated rice [112]. *O. spontanea* resembles cultivated rice but has long stout reddish awns, and dark-red kernels that shatter before they are ripe. *O. minuta* has small grains [41].

Rice is cultivated as an annual, although it has a perennial growth habit and sometimes is harvested twice or more without reseeding. A plant can be maintained as a perennial for many years when rooted tillers are reset occasionally.

BOTANICAL DESCRIPTION OF THE RICE PLANT

Vegetative Characters

The rice seedling has one seminal root, but adventitious roots arise from the first, second, and third nodes. The plant tillers freely in many varieties, usually bearing four or five culms that grow from 2–6 feet in height. Plants with ample space on fertile well-watered soil may produce as many as 50 tillers (Fig. 20-4). The hollow rice culm has 10–20 internodes. Early varieties have fewer internodes than do late varieties. The leaf sheaths are open and the ligule is long (Fig. 20-5), acute or obtuse, and easily split into two parts. The nodes, internodes, sheaths, blades, and other parts, may be colored with anthocyanin pigments [59, 112].

Inflorescence

The rice inflorescence is a loose terminal panicle, 3–15 inches (usually 4–10 inches) long. The panicle branches arise singly or in whorls. At maturity, the panicle in different varieties may be well exserted, partly exserted, or rarely entirely enclosed in the sheath. Each branch bears several spikelets, each usually with a single floret (Fig. 20-6). The panicle usually bears from 75–150 spikelets, but the number may vary from a few to 500.

The flower consists of two lodicules, six stamens, and two plumose stigmas on two styles, surrounded by the floral bracts—*i.e.,* the lemma and palea (or flowering glumes) and two small outer glumes. The floral bracts may be straw color, yellowish-gold, red, brown, or purplish-black. The lemma may be fully awned, partly awned, tip awned, or awnless.

The mature rice grain or caryopsis is enclosed by the lemma and palea (Fig. 20-7). These structures are called the "hull." Rice enclosed in the hull is called "rough" rice or "paddy," while that with the hull removed is known as "brown" or "husked" rice. The kernels usually range from 3.5–8.0 mm in length, 1.7 to over 3.0 mm in breadth, and from 1.3 to 2.3 mm in thickness. The caryopsis consists of the epidermis, mesocarp or parenchyma, cross cells, tube cells, and inner integuments. The endosperm consists of a single layer of polygonal aleurone cells with a central mass of thin-walled starchy parenchyma [41].

POLLINATION

In lower Bengal in India, the flowers commence to bloom between 7:00 and 8:00 AM and continue to bloom until about 10:00 AM in May and June, but blooming begins two hours later and continues until midday during late October and early November. Flowers of varieties that bloom early in the season seldom remain open longer than half an hour, whereas those of late varieties remain open from 1.0–1.5 hours. During wet weather the flowers may either fail to open, or open and then fail to close. Blooming sometimes occurs on the same day that a spikelet emerges above the sheath. Ordinarily, the entire panicle completes blooming in 4–7 days [40, 112].

In California, more than 75 per cent of the rice flowers bloomed between noon and 2:00 PM. More flowers bloomed between 2:00 and 4:00 PM than between 10:00 AM and noon. Varieties appear to differ in time of blooming [51]. In Texas, rice usually began to bloom the first day after the full boot stage. Either the terminal floret or one midway down the panicle branch bloomed first. In the latter case, blooming proceeded both ways, upward and downward, from the floret that opened first. Blooming was restricted entirely to the period between 8:00 AM and 4:00 PM, but the maximum number of florets bloomed between 11:00 AM and noon. The blooming of one floret usually required from 1–2 hours. The majority of rice panicles observed completed blooming within 6 or 7 days [82].

The hours of blooming are governed largely by temperature. Uniform temperatures favor rapid blooming. Blooming starts early in the day when temperatures are high, but it slows down materially when the sky becomes cloudy and the temperature drops. Most varieties bloom earlier in the day when the humidity is high, but the effect of humidity is less than that of temperature [1].

Cultivated rice normally is self-pollinated, but some natural crossing occurs. Much more natural crossing occurs in the warm, humid southern states of the United States than under the higher daily maximum temperature and lower humidity conditions that prevail in California. The amount of natural crossing ranged from 0–3.39 per cent, while the average at four rice stations was 0.45 per cent [13]. One per cent of natural crossing between plants at a distance of one foot probably is rather common [48]. Considerable natural cross-pollination occurs in Java, where the panicles must be bagged to isolate or maintain pure strains [78].

RICE GROUPS, TYPES, AND CLASSES

Major Groups

The two major groups of cultivated rice are *Oryza sativa* var. *indica,* grown largely in the tropical zones, and *O. sativa* var. *japonica,* which is confined to the more northern subtropical conditions. The *Indica* group consists mostly of long-grain varieties, but there are also many medium-grain and short-grain varieties. This group comprises all of the cultivated rices of India, Indochina, Philippine Republic, and southern China. The *Japonica* group of short-grain rices includes all of the varieties indigenous to Japan, Korea, and northern China, as well as the American, Italian, and Spanish rices that came originally from northern China or Japan.

About 95 per cent of the rice grown in California belongs to the *Japonica* group, while most of that grown in the southern United States belongs to the *Indica* group or is a hybrid derivative of the two types. Many varieties of the Ponlai group, grown in Taiwan, were derived from crosses between the two groups. The haploid chromosome complement in both groups is 12, but a marked degree of sterility often occurs in crosses between the two groups [112]. Hybrids between Japanese and Chinese varieties often are largely sterile, but some fertile progenies can be selected from nearly all of them [54]. The Bulu group of rices of Indonesia resembled the *Indica* type in grain length and plant height, but they have stiff stalks like the *Japonica* rices and produce fertile progeny when crossed with them.

The *Japonica* (short grain) rices generally are adapted to cooler climates and longer photoperiods than the *Indica* rices. They often tiller more freely, and are reputed to respond better to heavy fertilization, although some *Indica* rices also give a good response to fertilizers. The *Japonica* rices also have shorter, stronger stalks which makes them less subject to lodging under heavy fertilization. Many of the native *Indica* varieties in India seem able to tolerate adverse conditions, such as infertile soil and limited water supply, but may lack the capacity for maximum yield under very favorable conditions.

Grain Classification

Size and shape of kernels, a characteristic little affected by environmental conditions, is widely used to classify grain types. Average kernel dimensions for short-grain medium-grain and long-grain rice in the United States are as follows [66]:

Grain Classification	Unhulled (Rough)		Hulled (Husked)	
	Length	Thickness	Length	Thickness
	(mm)	(mm)	(mm)	(mm)
Short	7.2	3.7	5.5	3.2
Medium	8.0–8.7	3.2–3.4	6.0–6.7	2.6–2.9
Long	9.0–9.8	2.4–3.4	6.6–7.7	2.0–2.6

In 1960, approximately 48 per cent of the United States rice production was long-grain, 35 per cent was medium-grain, and 17 per cent short-grain varieties.

Long-grain types predominate in the tropical regions of Asia, except for coarse grain types for home use, whereas the short-grain types prevail in the northern subtropical region. Rice varieties in the Bengal province of India have a wide range of variation in size and shape of kernels. Unhulled grains range in length from 5.15–11.27 mm., and in thickness from 1.61–2.59 mm. A few short-grain varieties similar to *Japonica* rice are found in India (Bengal), Burma, and Indochina [103].

Most of the short-grain rices, as well as some of the medium- and long-grain varieties, have a rather sticky texture when cooked. The sticky type is perferred by some people, especially those who eat rice with chopsticks, because the grains cling together. The long-grain varieties grown in the United States (except Toro and C.P. 23), and many of those in southeast Asia, have a dry flaky texture when boiled. This type is perferred by most consumers.

Type of Starch

The rice endosperm starch may be common (nonglutinous) or waxy (glutinous). The mature, dry common rice grain is more or less translucent, whereas that of waxy rice is opaque or waxy hard. "Waxy" or "glutinous" refers to the gluelike or waxy structure, not to the protein present. The starch in waxy rices consists entirely of amylopectin, a branched-chain starch, while ordinary (straight-chain) starch is about one-fourth amylose and three-fourths amylopectin. Waxy rice is more sticky than common rice when boiled and is used in special puddings, pastries, or confections. Common rice is grown on from 90–100 per cent of the total rice area in different countries. Waxy rice comprised about 10 per cent of the total rice in China and about 8.4 per cent in Japan between 1938–42. Only a few hundred acres of waxy rice are grown in the United States.

Ecological Types

Lowland or paddy rice is grown on land that is artifically flooded. Upland rice is grown without flooding and is entirely dependent upon seasonal rainfall. The yields of lowland rice generally are much higher than those of upland rice because the fields are less weedy and the rice does not suffer from moisture deficiency. Lowland rice, grown under rain-fed or artificial systems of irrigation, is far more important than upland rice. All of the United States commercial rice is flooded, while lowland rice accounted for about 95.4 per cent of the total rice area in Japan from 1938–42.

Upland rice varieties are merely those that best tolerate unflooded culture, but some varieties are adapted to both lowland and upland culture. A few hundred acres of upland rice are grown for local consumption in small fields very widely scattered over the southeastern United States outside the commercial rice areas. Perhaps 75 per cent of the rice area of India is not flooded, except by impounded rainfall in many fields, because of inadequate irrigation development for the large area sown to the crop. In most countries, upland rice is grown on sloping land where the impounding of water is not feasible.

Floating or deep-water rices consist of varieties that have the ability to elongate the culms rapidly to keep the tops above the water surface when flooded by rapidly deepening water. Such varieties may have culms 6–15 feet long or even longer. Floating rices are grown in valleys subject to flooding, mostly in parts of Cambodia and Thailand, but they are also found in India (in the Assam and Bengal provinces) and in Pakistan. The upper part of the culms float on the water with the two top nodes turned upward. When the water recedes, the floating culms may develop new roots, shoots, and panicles at the nodes. When all the water drains away, the culms lying on the mud may root and tiller at the nodes to form new stools and the lower parts of the culms may then decay [24].

Floating rice is sown directly before the flood season without transplanting. The rice is harvested by hand from boats, provided it is still floating when the grain is ripe. However, the water often has drained away and the lodged crop must be cut by hand with some difficulty.

VARIETIES

More than 8000 botanically different rice varieties exist in the world, more than 4000 of which have been identified in India alone. Fully twice that number of named varieties is grown, but many varieties are grown under more than one name. Some 300–500 varieties are grown in the Philippines and a similar number is grown in Thailand. The large number of varieties in Oriental countries results from the belief that a variety often thrives only under limited local or specific conditions [112]. However, differences in water supply, altitude, and season of cultivation, as well as differences in consumer demands, necessitate the growing of many varieties.

Varieties in the United States

In the southern United States, the rices grown include short-, medium-, and long-grain types of early, midseason, and late varieties. Early varieties require 120–139 days from seeding to maturity, midseason varieties about 140–155 days, and late-maturing varieties 155 days or more. Short-grain rice comprises less than 1.0 per cent of the total production in the Southern states, most of which is grown in Arkansas. The principal short-grain varieties are Cody and Caloro (65, 66, 50). About 36 per cent of the total rice in the Southern states was of the medium-grain type in 1960. The principal varieties are Nato, Zenith, Arkrose, and Magnolia. More than 50 per cent of the acreage in Louisiana has been sown to Nato, Zenith, and Magnolia [49]. About 64 per cent of the rice produced in the Southern states in 1951 was of the long-grain type. The chief long-grain varieties in this region are Bluebonnet, Century Patna, Rexoro, Texas Patna, and Toro [65]. Toro is a new long-grain Louisiana variety [46]. Varieties with smooth (nonhairy) hulls, such as Bluebonnet, Rexoro, and Texas Patna, are preferred to those with rough (hairy) hulls for harvest by the combine-drier method. Varieties with smooth hulls disperse much less dust during drying [60].

In California, the principal short-grain rice varieties are Caloro and Colusa; the most important medium-grain variety is Calrose. In 1960, approximately 69 per cent of the California rice crop consisted of short-grain varieties; 31 per cent consisted of medium-grain varieties. The medium- and long-grain rices of the Southern states either do not thrive or else fail to mature in California where the nights are cool and much of the irrigation water is cold.

Descriptions of the major rice varieties grown in the United States are given in Table 20-1 [66].

Varieties Grown in Other Countries

In Japan, a large number of improved varieties adapted to particular

TABLE 20-1. **Characteristics of Rice Varieties Grown in the United States.**

Variety	Maturity Type	Grain Type	Remarks
1. Arkrose	Midseason	Medium	Tall plants; apt to lodge on fertile soils; hairy hulls.
2. Bluebonnet	"	Long	Combines well. Bluebonnet 50 has a shorter stiffer straw. Sunbonnet is a higher milling selection.
3. Caloro	Early to midseason	Short	Inclined to lodge; partly awned; hairy hulls.
4. Calrose	—	Medium	———
5. Century Patna	Early	Long	Short straw; productive.
6. Cody	"	Short	Stiff straw; awnless; hairy hulls.
7. Colusa	"	"	Frequently lodges; awnless; hairy hulls.
8. Magnolia	"	"	Stiff straw; threshes easily; hairy hulls; mills well.
9. Nato	Early	Medium	Slightly shorter stiffer straw than Zenith; threshes easily; smooth hulls.
10. Rexoro	Very late	Long	Stiff straw. Used for parboiling processes.
11. Texas Patna	Late	"	Inclined to lodge; combines well; used for parboiling processes.
12. Toro	Midseason	"	High milling variety.
13. Zenith	Early	Medium	Widely adapted; clear grain.

regions, or for special conditions, have been produced in recent years. All varieties are short-grain *Japonica* types. The improved "Norin" and other varieties, developed by the National Agricultural Experiment Station, are grown on about 69 per cent of the rice area [83]. Late varieties are grown in southern Japan (Kyushu) and very early 100-day varieties (which are better adapted to low temperatures) are grown in the northern latitudes or at higher altitudes. [84].

In the Philippines, the lowland varieties range from 135–210 days from seeding to maturity, whereas the upland varieties range from 128–145 days. Most of the late varieties are more sensitive to photoperiodism than are the early varieties.

In Burma, the Kaukyn group of early rice varieties matures in 100–150 days, the Kauklat medium-maturity group requires 150–170 days, and the Kaukkyi or late group matures in 170 days or more after seeding [38].

PHYSIOLOGICAL FACTORS IN PLANT GROWTH

Germination

Seed of most early rice varieties germinates promptly after maturity or is dormant for only 2–6 weeks, but some late varieties may require a rest period of 3–4 months before germination occurs [112]. Germination tests in Japan of about 300 rice varieties from various parts of the world showed that those from subtropical regions, such as Japan, Korea, and Italy, germinated promptly, but those from tropical regions—*i.e.,* India, Philippine Republic, and Taiwan—germinated slowly. The varieties from China and the United States generally showed intermediate dormancy [102].

The optimum germination temperature for the seed of most varieties is about 85–86°F, but rice may germinate at temperatures ranging from 42–117°F. Germination is limited at 108°F, while the seed is killed beyond 122°F [112].

Rice seed germinates in typical soils when the soil moisture content is 27 per cent or more [112]. Rice can germinate under as much as six inches of water because it requires less free oxygen for germination than do other cereal seeds. The rice seed is capable of releasing oxygen by enzymatic processes that occur during germination. Seedlings can be kept alive under water for nearly 50 days before they die.

Rice sown under water germinates best when it is sown on the soil surface. Any soil cover under water reduces the oxygen supply for the seed and germination decreases as the soil covering increases up to 1.5 inches deep or deeper when no seedlings emerge. Early seeding is preferable to late seeding in water because more oxygen is dissolved in cool water than in warm water [52, 57].

Photoperiodic Reactions

All rice varieties are classed as short-day plants, but they show marked differences in their sensitivity to different photoperiods. All varieties are characterized by an insensitive period in the early stages of growth that ranges from 2–10 weeks after germination in different varieties. Short photoperiods (4–12 hours) generally hasten floral initiation and heading, while long photoperiods (13–24 hours) tend to prolong the vegetative period. The optimum photoperiod for floral initiation appears to vary between 9 and 12.5 hours [16].

Date-of-seeding experiments in the United States show a reduction in the time required for rice to mature as seeding is delayed [59, 2], when the variety is "sensitive" to photoperiod. A shortened growing period also decreases plant height. Varieties that are insensitive or "indifferent" to photoperiod have nearly as long a growing period when sown late as when sown early [2].

Many rice varieties introduced into the southern United States from the tropics often fail to head or else head so late that they fail to set seed or mature before the plants are killed by cold. This behavior in the United States is caused by long days which delay heading, and by cool weather which retards both growth and maturity [12].

Lowland rice in Trinidad usually is sown in June or July, transplanted a month later, and harvested in November. The Joya variety produced 4080 pounds yield of rough rice per acre under such conditions. A second crop, sown in November, and harvested in March, yielded only 1380 pounds per acre, even though grown under apparently favorable conditions. The Joya variety is sensitive to photoperiod. The growing period and consequently the plant growth of the winter crop was reduced by the shorter days [101].

In Texas, sensitive rice restricted artifically to 10-hour daylight periods beginning 30 days or longer after emergence, headed earlier with fewer tillers and panicles, shorter panicles and culms, and reduced grain and straw weights than did plants grown under natural day lengths. Later treatments were less effective. The sensitive varieties were Caloro and Kameji which are of Japanese origin, or from a latitude above 30°N. The less sensitive varieties, Shoemed, Nira, and Rexoro, which are later and of Philippine derivation, showed no response except to treatment begun in the later stages of development [12].

In India, the summer or autumn (aus) rice is sown from March to May and harvested from July to September. Winter (amen) rice is sown in May, transplanted in June or July, and harvested about November. Some rice also is sown in June, July, October, November, and December [24]. Flowering of the summer varieties normally takes place when the seasonal day length is above 12 hours, while winter varieties flower when the day length is below 12 hours [100].

Eight-hour photoperiods are detrimental to rice growth, and when applied to early varieties in India they delayed panicle emergence and also reduced grain yield per plant [88, 94]. Early varieties subjected to 24-hour photoperiods also showed delayed panicle emergence [87, 89, 90, 91]. Photoperiod treatments of late varieties before the plants are 6–8 weeks old are relatively ineffective.

Mineral Nutrition

Nitrogen is the element most often required for high yields of rice. In submerged soils, the plant takes up its nitrogen in ammonium forms and not as nitrates. Some nitrate nitrogen is absorbed while the fields are drained, but this form is seldom applied to rice fields. Nitrogen fertilization increases tillering and vegetative growth, but does not delay flowering [93], unless the application is excessive. Increases in plant height, grain and straw yield, and number of heads usually are proportional to the amount of nitrogen added [68]. Where little chemical fertilizer is applied, the rice plant depends for its nitrogen largely upon the decomposition of organic matter under anaerobic conditions, and upon nitrogen fixed by blue-green algae (which usually are present in paddy fields) [108]. Controlled experiments in India indicate that the yields of rice are consistently higher where algae are present. A considerable increase in nitrogen occurred in fields in which algae grew abundantly, whereas there was a loss of nitrogen on similar soils where algal growth was absent [29].

The rice plant absorbs considerable quantities of phosphorus from the soil, and phosphate applications give increased yields on some soils but not on others. Phosphorus tends to increase the yield of grain but not of straw, while a severe phosphorus deficiency reduces both plant growth and tillering [38].

Potash often is not required on heavy rice soils, which usually contain considerable potassium. However, potash applications on light-textured (sandy) soils frequently increase rice yields.

Calcium applications improve the growth of rice on some soils. In Arkansas, the addition of calcareous carbonate and calcium chloride to very acid soils reduced the sterility in rice plants [70].

Heavy applications of organic amendments to flooded soils may increase the iron uptake by the plant, but decrease the manganese absorption and thus reduce yields. The iron levels in submerged or unsubmerged plants without organic amendments may be comparable, but submergence increases both rice yields and manganese uptake. The better growth of submerged rice on some soils may be partly owing to the greater availability of manganese in submerged soil [22]. A marked response to manganese sometimes has been obtained in upland rice. The rice plant has a high requirement for manganese as well as an exceptionally high tolerance to it.

WATER REQUIREMENTS

Rice thrives only on wet soils and requires from 2.5–15 feet of water during the growing season to produce a good crop.

Upland or Nonsubmerged Rice

If water for flooding is not available, upland rice is grown only in humid regions with more than 40 inches of annual rainfall. It yields only one-third to two-thirds as much as lowland rice, even in countries with high rainfall. Many weeds thrive on wet soils that are not submerged, and thus are difficult to control on upland rice fields. Upland rice also is likely to suffer from moisture shortage at some time during the growing season, even where the average annual rainfall is 60 inches or more. Furthermore, submerged rice plants yield more than do those grown in soil that is kept wet constantly but not submerged.

Many nonirrigated rice fields in the high rainfall areas of monsoon Asia are submerged from much or part of the growing season by the construction of dikes to retain all of the rainfall. A limited acreage formerly grown by this method in the United States was called "providence" rice.

Lowland or Submerged Rice

Lowland or paddy rice fields are submerged during most or all of the growing period. The depth of water on a field generally is increased as the plants grow until it reaches 4–8 inches or more. The chief purpose of such depths is to suppress weed growth. The water around rice plants should never be stagnant, but should flow gently through the field. Rice in fields submerged in still water for three weeks or more is benefited by draining or by fresh water supplies [118]. Most of the fields in the southern United States are submerged from 4–8 inches from the time the seedlings are about 6–10 inches high until the crop is ready to drain for harvest about two weeks prior to full maturity, a period of 3–5 months. Some of the rice is sown in flooded fields. In California, nearly all of the rice is sown in 4–6 inches of water, and the water level is maintained at a depth of 6–8 inches during the latter part of the season until the rice is nearly ripe.

Deep water generally increases plant height but reduces tillering. The number of tillers, total leaf area, total dry matter, and grain yield might be greatest where the water barely covers the soil surface, but such a depth cannot be maintained in the field, and weed growth would be so excessive that yields would be low [36].

Quantity of Water

From 3 to 5 acre-feet of water usually is needed to produce a crop of rice on suitable land. Since light porous soils may require 12–15 acre-feet of water per season, such soils are uneconomical for rice production in the United States. In Arkansas, an average of 32.9 acre-inches of water was applied to rice fields. This seasonal total consisted of 10.9 inches supplied by rainfall and 22 inches by pump irrigation. In Louisiana and Texas, the total requirement may be 4–5 acre-feet of water. The usual seasonal irrigation in these three states is 1.5–3 acre-feet. In California, where little rain falls in summer, the amount necessary may be 3–8 feet, usually 5–6 acre-feet. The total water applied has been reduced to some extent by growing earlier varieties. In Japan, the seasonal water requirement ranges from 2.3–4.3 acre-feet [83, 6].

The water required is increased by permeability of the soil, seasonal evaporation, transpiration, and by a long growing season. Transpiration of water by the plant is relatively constant regardless of the degree of soil saturation so long as available moisture is present. Transpiration may be increased by phosphate applications, or decreased by barnyard manure applications [38]. About 450 gallons per minute (one second-foot) of water will maintain about 50 acres of rice during the growing season in California.

Quality of Water

Water that contains more than 35 grains of salt per gallon (600 parts per million) should not be used to irrigate rice when the soil is dry or when the water is to remain on the field. Rice irrigated continuously with water that contained 35 and 75 grains of salt per gallon (600 and 1300 parts per million) was reduced in yield about 25 and 70 per cent, respectively. The rice also was of lower quality than when water containing 25 grains per gallon was used. Older plants can tolerate higher concentrations of salt than can seedlings, although very high concentrations may kill the plants or make them sterile. Salinity at the tillering stage inhibited the growth of the Caloro variety twice as much as during heading [111]. The Blue Rose variety is more tolerant to salt than are some other varieties. It has made satisfactory yields when the water contained salt concentrations of 75, 150, 200, and 250 grains per gallon in the tillering, jointing, booting, and heading stages, respectively. Some of the newer varieties probably would be damaged seriously by comparable amounts of salt [6].

When a field has been watered with fresh water and the supply is then replenished with salt water, the damage will be less than when the salt water is put on dry soil. In the latter case, the salt is more concentrated in the dry soil and more of it moves into the root zone, whence it is taken up by the plants. Rice grown on clay soils may not be injured by salt water to the same extent as on lighter soils, because less water is used and less is lost by seepage [6].

About three tons per acre of salt are added when water that contains 50 grains of salt per gallon is used for the whole growing season. The accumulations of salt over the years may deflocculate the soil, so that stickiness, compactness, and impermeability increase. The deflocculated soil is hard to cultivate and produces low yields [6].

When the rainfall is below normal in the gulf coast of Louisiana and Texas, the water level in the streams that supply irrigation water in these areas often is so low that brackish water seeps in from the Gulf. The concentration of chloride salts may become so high that the yield and quality of the rice are reduced or the crop ruined [6].

Well water, used to irrigate a large part of the rice acreage in Arkansas, usually is low in chlorides. However, in the lower basin of the Vermillion River in Louisiana, salt encroaches on the Chicot Reservoir when the river is intruded by salty water [6].

Water from shallow wells in Arkansas that contains 75 parts per million of calcium and 22 parts per million of magnesium was applied to rice fields for many years. The soil increased in pH from about 5 up to as high as 8. That change from a highly acid to a highly alkaline reaction is due to the annual addition of about 1500 pounds per acre of limestone equivalent. The increase in available calcium and magnesium lowered the availability of phosphorus in the soil [6].

Rice has been grown in order to reclaim saline or alkali lands in California. It is successful when the water is appreciably lower in dissolved minerals than is the soil, the soil is relatively permeable, and drainage is adequate. Crops that are not salt-tolerant can be grown on the alkali soils after two or three years of rice [6].

Effect of Temperature

The temperature may be too low early in the season, or too high late in the season, for maximum emergence of rice sown in the water. Germination is retarded when the temperature of the water is below 70°F. Roots often develop poorly when the temperature is above 85°F, perhaps because warm water has a low oxygen content. The temperature of the water from shallow wells in Arkansas and from streams in California is usually 65°F or lower. When such cool water goes directly into the field, the rice growing near the water inlet usually is retarded. Such "cold water" rice may ripen 7–10 days later than that in the rest of the field. Cold water can be held in shallow basins until it is warm enough to turn into the rice field [6].

In tropical regions, the temperature of irrigation water may be raised as high as 104°F without injury to rice. The optimum temperature for grain yield in southern Japan is about 90°F. Adverse effects, such as lowered spikelet fertility, occur below 77°F. The critical temperature of irrigation water in northern Japan is about 70°F. The adverse effects of low water temperatures can be offset to some extent in the cooler areas by an increase in water depth to about four inches [103].

Source of Water

The water for rice fields may be diverted or pumped from streams, reservoirs, or lakes; pumped from wells; or impounded in the field by building levees or dikes. In India, many rice growers use water that has been impounded during the rainy season in earthen reservoirs called "tanks." Such a water supply often is inadequate. The famous terraced rice fields on Luzon Island in the Philippines receive water in the upper terraces from small mountain streams, and the water passes successively to the terraces below.

Pumping from bayous supplies most of the surface water in Louisiana and Texas. Diversion from large streams is the main source of water in California. The main surface water supply in Arkansas is from reservoirs that range in size from 20 acres to more than 4000 acres and are filled during periods of high runoff.

More than 40 per cent of the 1953 rice acreage in the United States was irrigated from wells. About 90 per cent of the 485 thousand rice acres in Arkansas, 40 per cent of the 604 thousand acres in Louisiana, 20 per cent of the 573 thousand acres in Texas, 10 per cent of the 394 thousand acres in California, and most of the 75 thousand acres in Mississippi were irrigated from wells.

In the rice areas of the southern United States, large pumping plants— powered by steam, diesel, gas, or electric motors—lift the water from bayous or large reservoirs into canals. The water flows from the canals into laterals and ditches to reach the upper borders of many rice fields. Well pump motors are powered by electricity, diesel oil, natural gas, or other fuels. Modern pump bowls with an efficiency of 83 per cent are more economical of power than were the bowls used about 1915 that had efficiencies of 20–40 per cent. Each acre of rice in the United States requires a continuous flow of water of from 5–16 gallons per minute during the entire growing season. Less would be required in regions of higher seasonal rainfall.

On many small farms of Asia, where electric power is unavailable, water often is lifted several feet to the rice fields from ditches or streams using primitive water wheels operated by water power, animal power, or human foot power. Some water also is lifted in bags or buckets hoisted by animal or man power.

CULTURAL PRACTICES IN THE UNITED STATES

All the commercial rice (almost entirely lowland rice) grown in the

United States is produced by machine methods. Many of the operations are completely mechanized.

Crop Rotations

Single cropping to rice is the rule in California, but rotation with other crops is advantageous where other crops make suitable returns.

In Louisiana and Texas, the most common practice is to grow 1–3 rice crops, pasture the land with or without seeding legumes and grasses for 1–3 years, and then use the field for rice again. The pasture land is not flooded, which helps to eliminate aquatic weeds from the rice land. Also the soil is improved in physical condition by the root and top residues from the grasses. The rotation of rice with improved pastures that contain clovers, grasses, and lespedeza enhances the productivity of the soil, increases rice yields, and provides much better grazing for beef cattle than do unimproved pastures [133]. However, much of the rice land is pastured without seeding, because the natural vegetation provides considerable growth.

In rotation experiments in Louisiana, the highest average yields of rice were obtained when rice followed pastured stubble or improved pastures. The yields of rice were higher after Italian rye grass or clovers on stubble pasture than after corn or soybeans.

Rice may be grown in rotation with soybeans or green manure crops [61, 65]. Cotton is an unsatisfactory crop to grow in rotations with rice where the cotton has been dusted for many years with calcium arsenate to control the boll weevil, for calcium arsenate materially reduces subsequent rice yields [45].

Approximately one-half the land on rice farms in Arkansas in 1947 was sown to rice, a fourth was idle or pastured, and the remainder was cropped to oats, soybeans, lespedeza, corn, or cotton [65]. About 70 per cent of the rice farmers surveyed grew one or more of these crops in rotation with rice. The most prevalent cropping systems on farms of less than 360 acres of crop land were: rice–idle, rice–oats–lespedeza, and rice–soybeans. The rotations generally were 4–6 years in length, with rice grown on the land for two or three consecutive years [99]. Much less land has been left idle in recent years.

In California, the heavy soils on which rice is grown are poorly adapted to the production of other crops. Most of the fields are cropped to rice for one, two or three years and then fallowed or left idle for a year. The idle land often is pastured. The fallowed land sometimes is sown to wheat or barley in the fall, and rice grown again the following year. One rice crop in three years is grown on such land [64]. A rotation often followed is rice, beans, wheat, beans, and again to rice [28]. Sometimes Ladino clover, strawberry clover, or black medic is grown for a winter cover crop or for pasture between rice crops. Grain sorghum or safflower may be grown on the medium-textured soils.

Fertilizer Applications

Commercial fertilizers are widely used for rice production in the United States, but only since about 1940. Nitrogen fertilizers give the best response. Ammonium sulfate has been the standard fertilizer, but some growers use cynamide, ammonium phosphate, and anhydrous ammonia [65]. Complete fertilizers also are used on some soils.

Prairie soils cropped to rice for many years usually respond to applications of nitrogen and additions of organic matter. Nitrogen and phosphorus, applied to rice land singly or in combination, usually give increased yields, but potash increases yields only occasionally [65]. Nitrogen fertilizers alone usually increase yields in Arkansas [67, 68, 69]. Ammonium forms of nitrogen are applied almost universally because the nitrate form is unavailable to rice on submerged soils [9]. Nitrates are soon reduced to unavailable nitrites after the soil is submerged. The soils are low in all forms of nitrogen at the end of the rice season [114].

In Arkansas, yields on old rice lands have been increased by the application, 6–8 weeks after seeding, of a complete 4-8-4 fertilizer at the rate of 500 pounds per acre [65]. Increased yields have been obtained with 40–100 pounds of nitrogen per acre when applied on fields of medium to low fertility as a topdressing on drained land before the second flooding. Nitrogen fertilization usually hastens the maturity of rice, but single applications of 135 pounds per acre or more may delay maturity. Yield responses to phosphate and potash, with or without irrigation, vary considerably from farm to farm in Texas [15].

In Louisiana, complete fertilizers drilled about 2.5 inches below the seed when sowing have given marked increases in rice yields. On the lighter-colored fine sandy loam and silt loam soils, rice yields have been increased by the application, at seeding time, of an 8-8-8 grade at the rate of 300 pounds or more per acre. On the darker-colored silty clay loam and clay loam soils, the application of 4-12-8 or 5-10-5 grades at the rate of 200–300 pounds per acre have given marked increases in yield. Nitrogen topdressed on drained land at the rate of 20–30 pounds per acre, before the rice plants reach the boot stage, has materially increased yields when 200 pounds per acre of 4-12-8 or 5-10-5 grades had been applied at seeding time [65]. On the root-rot infested areas of southwestern Louisiana, 40-pound per acre applications of nitrogen and phosphorus fertilizer were of little benefit unless the root-rot areas were drained before the fertilizers were applied [21].

In Texas, nitrogen applied to heavy clay soils at the rate of 80 pounds per acre at seeding, or topdressed 30–70 days after seeding, has materially increased the yields of rice. On clay loam or loam soils, an additional 40 pounds of P_2O_5 has been recommended [65].

The Stockton clay-adobe soil, as well as other California rice soils, usually shows a response to applications of nitrogen when cropped to rice, but nonnitrogenous fertilizers have failed to increase rice yields materially [64]. Fertilization of rice with ammonium forms of nitrogen is a common practice in California except on the most fertile soils, new lands, or where rice follows a heavy legume cover crop such as vetch, peas, burclover, or ladino clover. Surface application of ammonium sulfate at the rate of 150–200 pounds per acre is widely practiced. Topdressings applied by airplane when the rice is in the tillering stage, or up to 65 days after seeding, are almost as effective [64]. Ammonium nitrogen drilled at 2–4 inches in the soil produces better yields of rice than similar applications on the soil surface [86]. The application of anhydrous ammonia in irrigation water is rather impractical because of the uneven distribution of nitrogen [28].

Seedbed Preparation

In the southern United States, the land is plowed 4–6 inches deep in the fall, winter, or spring. In the spring the field is disked, harrowed, and floated. Heavy soils usually require more subsequent tillage to obtain a good seedbed when spring-plowed than when plowed during the winter. Early fall or winter plowing of rice land is common in Louisiana and Texas, but most of the land is spring-plowed in Arkansas. In a good seedbed, the surface soil is in a mellow but firm condition with moisture near the surface. In such soils, germination usually occurs promptly [61, 65].

The heavy adobe rice soils in California usually are spring-plowed to a depth of 4–6 inches as early as possible after the winter rains. Moldboard plows generally are used, but disc plows may be feasible where rice follows row crops or cultivated fallow. The plowed land is worked down into a seedbed after it has dried for 7–10 days. The roots of some dangerous weeds are killed more readily in dry soils than in moist soils. The land may be disked, harrowed, or dragged with a heavy float or landplane (Fig. 20-8) for final seedbed preparation. A slightly rough seedbed with clods 0.5–4 inches in diameter is preferred to one that is finely pulverized.

In the southern United States, the contour levees that divide the fields into subfields are spaced according to a difference in elevation of about 0.2 foot or less. The levees usually are built with gentle slopes, but high enough to hold an average depth of 4–6 inches of water on the subfields without overflow (Fig. 20-9). Gently sloping levee banks permit the field to be

FIGURE 20-8. **Land plane leveling the field between levees in preparation for sowing rice.**
(*Courtesy US Department of Agriculture*)

FIGURE 20-9. **Building a rice levee in California.**
(*Courtesy US Department of Agriculture*)

worked as a unit. Farm machinery can pass readily over such levees without damage to them or to the machinery (Fig. 20-10) [61, 65].

Field levees in California usually are constructed by large dikers drawn by one or two heavy tractors. The levees are built on a 0.2–0.3 foot contour [28], and often are too high for the machinery to pass over them.

Seeding Practices

Seed treatment, with Arasan at the rate of one ounce, or Ceresan M at the rate of 0.25–0.50 ounce per bushel, usually improves stands of rice, especially when sowing in cold soil. In California, soaking seed in a sodium hypochlorite solution (5.25 per cent by weight) at the rate of one gallon per 100 gallons of water is recommended as a seed protectant, but also for deactivating germination inhibitors (organic acids and aldehydes) that diffuse from the hulls into the embryo.

All rice in the United States is sown directly in the field, either before or after the land is flooded.

In the southern United States, rice usually is sown with a grain drill, which is favorable to uniform germination. Airplanes have replaced endgate seeders for sowing in the water. Airplane seeding is on the increase, particularly when soil or weather conditions make it difficult to prepare a seedbed suitable for the use of a drill, or where grass infestation is a problem [65]. The rice usually is sown between April 1 and May 30, although some may be seeded in early March or late in June. Rice germinates more rapidly when sown in warm soil. Because lower temperatures retard germination, early-sown rice is more subject to seedling blight. There usually is sufficient moisture in rice soils of the United States to germinate the drilled seed as well as to maintain the plants until they are flooded [72, 65]. Flooding to bring up the rice is necessary only when the soil is dry.

FIGURE 20-10. **This self-propelled combine is harvesting rice on the side of a levee.**
(*Courtesy J. I. Case Company*)

Although higher rates often are used, a rate of 90–100 pounds of recleaned viable seed sown with a grain drill, or 110–140 pounds sown broadcast, is sufficient for satisfactory stands in the Southern states. Experiments with drilled rice indicate that 80 pounds of seed per acre usually is sufficient for good stands under very favorable conditions. The rate of seeding should be sufficient to produce stands that are thick enough to check weed growth as well as to prevent late tillering. Less seed is required when rice is sown late than when it is sown early in the spring [61, 65]. The average rate of seeding is about 120 pounds per acre, but it ranges from 101 pounds in Texas to 150 pounds in Missouri.

Rice is drilled 1–2 inches deep. There is less danger from rots from shallow than from deep seeding, especially when it is necessary to irrigate the land after seeding to induce germination.

Most of the rice in California is sown broadcast on the water by airplanes as a means of controlling water grass and other weeds (Fig. 20-11). Some fields are sown with broadcast seeders and then submerged [64]. Seed broadcast in water from airplanes usually is presoaked to eliminate floating and drifting and thus assure a more uniform stand. The seed is generally soaked in burlap bags for 18–24 hours, and drained for 24–48 hours. Seeding is done immediately after the field is flooded. Rice occasionally is drilled early on new (nonweedy) light-textured soil that is moist enough to obtain stands without irrigation. Such direct drilling provides better root anchorage with less subsequent lodging [28]. Rice may be sown in California between April 15 and May 30, but the optimum period is between April 15 and May 10. Seeding later than May 30 is hazardous because of the danger of crop

FIGURE 20-11. **Soaked rice seed, broadcast from the airplane, is falling into the water that floods the field.**

(*Courtesy US Department of Agriculture*)

losses from fall rains. The average rate of seeding in California is 140 pounds per acre.

No rice is transplanted in the United States. Experiments showed no advantage for transplanting over direct field sowing when the weeds were controlled in the plots planted by both methods [4].

Irrigation Practices

In the Southern states, rice land is submerged for 60–90 days or longer during the growing season. Normally, the field is flooded to a depth of about four inches when the rice plants reach a height of 4–6 inches. The field may be irrigated after seeding in occasional years when the soil is too dry to germinate the rice seed promptly. Where water grass (Barnyard grass, *Echinochloa crusgalli*) is a problem, growers usually flood the field to a depth of four inches or more as soon as the rice plants emerge. This practice controls water grass fairly well. An average depth of about 4–5 inches is maintained on the field throughout the rest of the growing season. Water is supplied from time to time to replace that lost by evaporation, transpiration, and seepage. Sometimes the field is drained for disease or insect control or to topdress the field with fertilizers, and is again submerged after a short period. About 10–14 days before harvest, or when the heads turn down, the water is drained from the land to allow the field to dry for harvest [65, 132]. In experiments, the highest average yields of rice have been obtained on land submerged 20 days after the seedlings emerged. Early continuous submergence of the land, beginning 10 days after seedling emergence, gave higher yields in Louisiana than did intermittent drainage of the land followed by continuous submergence [45].

In California, the rice field is submerged continuously to a depth of 4–8 inches until the crop is ready to drain shortly before harvest. Submergence at seeding time to a depth of 4–8 inches controls most types of water grass [53, 56]. The highest average grain yields have been obtained from rice grown in soil submerged four inches, but higher straw yields were obtained from a six-inch depth [58]. The rice field is drained 10–18 days before harvest to permit the ground to become firm enough to support heavy harvesting machinery. The rice usually is ready for the field to be drained, with the least loss in yield and quality, when the panicles are well turned down or when the lower grains on the panicles are in the soft-dough stage. At this stage, the upper two-thirds of the grains on the panicles have started to turn yellowish [64].

Weed Control

Aquatic or semiaquatic plants must be controlled in order to produce high yields of rice. They are least troublesome when the seedbed is well prepared and the rice stands are good. The growth of grasses and spike rush (*Eleocharia* spp.) is checked on land submerged 10–20 days after seeding emergence. Barnyard grass (*Echinochloa,* spp.) is one of the most dangerous grass weeds [45]. It can be controlled with 4–8 pounds per acre of 3, 4-dichloroproprionanalide (DPA) applied when the rice is four weeks old.

It is now a common practice to spray rice fields to control broadleaved weeds through use of 0.25–1.25 pounds of 2,4-D (acid equivalent) of sodium or amine salts per acre [65]. Germinating rice seeds are very sensitive to 2,4-D injury, as also are plants in the boot and flowering stages. It is considered relatively safe to spray 0.25–0.75 pound (acid equivalent) of 2,4-D per acre when the rice seedlings are 3–4 weeks old. When using field sprayers, the herbicide must be applied before the field is submerged or after the land is drained. The field should be flooded from 3–6 days after treatment [117]. Sometimes 2,4-D is applied two or three weeks after fields are submerged when the plants are 6–8 weeks old in order to control Mexican weed (*Caperonia palustris*), curly indigo (*Aeschynomene virginica*), and tall indigo or coffee weed (*Sesbania exaltata*). Under such conditions, 0.50–1.0 pound of 2,4-D usually kills the weeds with little injury to the rice. Older rice plants will tolerate as much as 1.0–1.25 pounds of 2,4-D [65].

Among other rice weeds are red rice, mudplantain (*Heteranthera* spp.), arrowhead (*Sagittaria* spp.), gooseweed (*Sphenoclea zeylanica*), redstem (*Ammannia coccinia*), bulrush (*Scirpus* spp.), and umbrella sedge (*Cyperus* spp.)

Scum on the water in rice fields is due mostly to the growth of blue-green algae, which are capable of fixing atmospheric nitrogen. The algae are present on the soil surface of rice fields during the winter. A heavy, top-dried scum floating on the surface will prevent rice seedlings from emerging above the water. Early sowing of rice enables the plants to emerge before warm weather has stimulated the algal growth. The algae can be largely controlled by applying chemicals such as 8–9 pounds per acre of Delrad 50 (50 per cent dehydroabietylamine) in the irrigation water. However, this dosage is somewhat toxic to fish [107].

Harvest

Most early, medium, and late varieties of rice ripen in 110–180 days after seeding. Rice is ready to harvest when the kernels in the lower part of the heads are in the hard-dough stage, when the kernels in the upper parts of the heads are fully ripe and free from chalky opaque areas [65].

Nearly all of the rice in the United States is harvested with self-propelled or tractor-drawn combines which range in width of cut from 6–21 feet [85, 65]. The rice is harvested when the moisture content of the grain is from

18–25 per cent, and then dried gradually down to 12 or 13 per cent moisture in artificial driers. Drying must start within 24 hours after combining to avoid spontaneous heating of the grain. Heated air at 100–130°F is passed through the grain, often two, three, or more times at intervals, in order to dry it to a safe moisture level without damage to the milling quality [39]. Between runs through the drier, which take 12–36 hours, the partly dried grain is stored in a bin where the moisture content is equalized throughout the grain to avoid checking. Any checks (fine cracks) in the grain cause it to break during milling.

Some rice formerly was cut with swathers, dried in the windrow for 3–6 days, and threshed with combines equipped with pickup attachments. While artificial drying is unnecessary by this method, the rice is often of poorer milling quality than that combined direct and artificially dried. Rice is exposed to weather while drying in the windrow.

The binder, formerly used to harvest rice, has been replaced by the combine.

CULTURAL PRACTICES IN OTHER COUNTRIES

Rice is grown on small, medium, and large farms in most or all countries that produce the crop. Small farms prevail in the heavily populated rural areas of the world, such as in southeast Asia. Thus, the rice-growing practices within many countries range from primitive hand culture in small plots, through the use of animal power and simple implements, to completely mechanized operations. Different regional patterns of rice culture are based on topographical features of the land, availability of water for irrigation, availability of labor, and local customs. The two general types of rice culture are direct seeding and transplanting [103].

Cropping Practices

Single cropping (one crop of rice in one year) is the common practice in northern Japan and other cool temperate regions. Double or even triple cropping to rice often prevails in the warmer climates when ample water is available. Some rotations with other crops also are followed [44, 84].

Much of the lowland rice in the warmer parts of southeast Asia is grown continuously—often two or three crops a year on the same land. Upland rice usually is grown in rotation with other crops because soil fertility is more critical and weed control more of a problem. In Japan, both upland and lowland rice is rotated with barley, wheat, sweet potatoes, soybeans, or millet in three-year or four-year rotations. In Indonesia, rice may be grown in two-year rotations with maize, cassava, peanuts, pulses, or vegetables. In the Po valley of Italy, rice may be rotated with legumes, maize, wheat, or other crops, but sometimes two or three crops of rice may be grown before shifting to the other crops [116].

Sometimes rice culture alternates with fish culture in the submerged field. This procedure conserves, and presumably increases, the productivity of the soil. A practice in many countries is the growing of fish along with the rice. This requires supplemental ponds, tanks, or streams into which the fish can be moved when the rice field is drained. Carp, suckers, goldfish, and other species are grown in rice fields in many countries of the world, but particularly in Japan and China.

Fertilizers

Most of the tropical rice soils are deficient in nitrogen and organic matter, but some soils (particularly in Thailand and Burma) also are deficient in phosphorus. Rice yields in tropical areas usually are stabilized at a rather low level because of infertile soils. Animal manures, compost, and green manures are used to a considerable extent throughout southeast Asia as well as elsewhere. Commercial fertilizers are not generally applied to much of the rice crop in Asia, except in Japan, Korea, and Taiwan.

Rice fields in Japan are heavily fertilized with organic matter as well as with mineral fertilizers, particularly ammonium sulfate and superphosphates. Manures usually are applied before flooding, but other fertilizers are put on after leveling or puddling. Nitrogenous fertilizers often are applied in split applications—*i.e.,* about half when the paddy field is being prepared and the balance before the rice reaches the jointing stage. Chinese vetch or soybeans, usually grown for green manures, are turned under about three weeks before the rice is transplanted. Other fertilizers include barnyard manure, compost, and "night soil." Rates of application per acre of the three principal fertilizer elements range about as follows: Nitrogen (N), 58–135 pounds; phosphoric acid (P_2O_5), 35–90 pounds; and potash (K_2O), 50–100 pounds [83].

Although commercial fertilizers seldom are used for rice production in India, numerous experiments show that yields are increased by nitrogen fertilizers, particularly ammonium sulfate, in nearly all tests. Organic matter is most effective when applied in conjunction with ammonium sulfate. Phosphorus applications of 30–40 pounds of P_2O_5 per acre have increased rice yields in India by only 8–10 per cent. A much higher average response has been obtained with nitrogen fertilizers [112].

In Java, the application of manures to paddy fields is not customary except on very infertile soils, although experiments show that mineral fertilizers and green manures often produce large increases in rice yields. Phosphatic and nitrogenous fertilizers have given the greatest responses. Nitrogen can be supplied by leguminous green manures, such as *Crotalaria* species [136].

Indica types of rice tend to have tall weak culms that are susceptible to lodging, particularly after heavy applications of nitrogen. In many places, as in the Philippines, heavy nitrogen applications have caused early lodging in rice which often nullifies part or all of the benefits derived from the use of nitrogen fertilizers. Japonica rices have shorter and stronger stalks that tend to resist lodging so that these rices benefit from heavy nitrogen fertilization.

Initial Seedbed Preparation

The initial seedbed preparation for rice is plowing with tractor, or animal power, or hand spading or digging, usually to a depth of 4–6 inches or more. The land is then tilled by discs and harrows, or hand hoes to break up clods. The next operation is the leveling or floating of the land between the levees or terraces wherever necessary. Then follows the building (or repairing) of levees for all lowland rice. The field is then ready for direct sowing by drilling, broadcasting on the soil surface, or dribbling the seed into opened furrows by hand. Otherwise the field is flooded in preparation for sowing in the water, or transplanting from the nursery seedbed.

In Japan and other Asiatic countries, preparation of the paddy field often consists of plowing, irrigation, construction of levees (boundary foot paths or bunds), and leveling. The field is either hand-spaded, or plowed with animal power to a depth of 3.5–4.7 inches. After plowing, the clods are broken down with a hoe. The soil is then stirred, irrigated, and leveled or puddled [83, 84]. In many countries the flooded field is puddled with a rakelike implement pulled by animal or man power (Fig. 20-12). The water buffalo (carabao) is well-suited to this operation.

In the warmer southern portions of southeast Asia, where two or even three crops of rice can be grown in one year, seeding may be done in any month of the year that the monsoon seasons permit. Plowing must be done before heavy rains start, and water from rains or other sources must be available for the growing of rice. Varieties are chosen for sowing on the basis of their fitness for the particular growing season.

Direct Seeding Methods

Direct seeding is the oldest form of culture for both upland and lowland rice. It is practiced where labor is scarce or expensive or where water

FIGURE 20-12. **Puddling rice field previous to planting in Japan.**
(*Courtesy US Department of Agriculture*)

supplies are adequate for the entire season. Often there are no further cultural operations until harvest, except for weeding and the control of pests and diseases. Direct seeding is used entirely under mechanized rice culture.

Upland rice is almost always grown by direct seeding. It is grown on uplands or on rough topography where irrigation water is not available. The cultural methods often are primitive.

Lowland rice is grown by direct seeding in many countries. It is the common practice in rain-fed culture in southeast Asia, particularly where the land is poor or the water supply uncertain. The seed is broadcast before or after the field is flooded. Direct seeding is practiced on nearly 70 per cent of the rice area of India. In Japan, rice often is sown between the rows of fall-sown wheat or barley in May, about 30 days before harvest. After the small grain is removed, the rice is fertilized, intertilled, and flooded [103]. In many countries, rice is seeded with a drill before the field is flooded.

Transplanting Method

The transplanting method, widely practiced in Japan, involves sowing rice in small nursery seedbeds with subsequent transplanting to the regular paddy field.

Rice for transplanting is sown in seedbeds which require only from 3.5 to 10 per cent (usually about 4 per cent) of the area to be transplanted. The seedbed usually is plowed or dug to a depth of 4 or 5 inches and then tilled and flooded. The seedbed is then worked up to a consistency of fine mud. The seeds often are soaked to promote uniform germination. Sometimes the seed is allowed to sprout before sowing. The seed is sown by hand in rows 2–3 inches apart, or is broadcast (Fig. 20–13). Seeding in seedbeds usually is done from 30 to 50 days before transplanting to permit the seedlings to attain a height of 7–12 inches suitable for transplanting. In Hokkaido, the northern-most island of Japan, the seedbeds sometimes are covered with oiled paper to warm the soil and thus promote seedling growth. The seedbed is irrigated with about one or two inches of water after the seedlings emerge. The water level is gradually raised as the seedlings grow. In some areas the seedbeds are kept moist but not flooded. Medium or light soil is preferred for seedbeds because the seedlings can be pulled with less root injury. The seedbeds are much more likely to be fertilized than are the fields. Animal manures, composts, green manures, oil-seed meals, or mineral fertilizers may be applied. The seedbed is weeded by hand.

There are various modifications for nursery seedbeds. Dryland nurseries are sometimes used, but they should be sown about two weeks earlier than irrigated nurseries because of slower plant growth. In Indonesia, seeding often is done with rice panicles instead of threshed seeds. Recently, electrically heated nursery beds have come to be used in the cooler areas of Japan to speed up seedling growth [103].

Most of the paddy rice in southeastern Asia and much of that in Europe and Africa is grown from transplanting (Fig. 20-14). Yields often

FIGURE 20-13. **Sowing rice seedbeds by hand in Japan.**

(Courtesy US Department of Agriculture)

FIGURE 20-14. **Transplanting rice in Japan.**

(Courtesy US Department of Agriculture)

are higher [112], chiefly because of better weed control. The plowed and flooded field is tilled thoroughly with rakelike implements operated by hand or animal power, or with a small rotary hoe. This puddles the soil and smothers the weeds just before the seedlings are transplanted. The seedlings are large enough to compete with weeds that emerge later. Furthermore, the plants are spaced in rows 7–12 inches apart, which permits weed control by pulling, hoeing, or wheel-hoe cultivation. Weeds cannot be controlled by cultivation in a broadcast field. Hand weeding is difficult in a field that is either broadcast or close-drilled. Also, weeds emerge about the same time as the rice seedlings from direct sowing and thus compete with the crop during the entire growing season.

In many experiments conducted to compare transplanting with direct seeding, the field seeding was done at the time of transplanting, which gave the latter plants an advantage of a some six week longer growing period. In other experiments, in which the rice was sown in the field and seedbed at the same time, weed control was found to be more effective under the transplanting method. An advantage of transplanting is that it makes double cropping more feasible because the alternate crop can remain in the field for about a month while the rice seedlings are growing in the seedbed. Also there is a saving in water because the field is not flooded until just before transplanting [83, 84].

The chief disadvantage of transplanting is the four or five days of labor required to pull, trim, transport, and transplant the seedlings for an acre of rice. This limits a family to the production of not more than 5–10 acres of rice in a season unless help is hired. However, this is no handicap to millions of farmers in Asia who are farming a total area of 10 acres or less. The process of transplanting is of no benefit to the rice seedling. In fact, it takes several days for the plants to recover from the injuries from root breaking and top trimming.

The seedlings are transplanted in Japan from 20–50 days (usually 30–45 days) after sowing the seedbeds, when the seedlings are 7–12 inches tall and have six or more leaves. For transplanting, the seedlings are uprooted, tied in small bundles, up to one-third of the top trimmed off, and carried to the paddies. The seedlings are pushed into the mud by hand. They usually are planted in rows 8–12 inches apart, in hills 3–8 inches apart in the row, with 3–6 seedlings per hill. About 55 per cent of the rice fields in Japan are planted in hills or checks, 35 per cent in rows, and the balance is broadcast [83].

Experiments in West Java indicate that the best time for transplanting is when the plant is from 30–40 days old, depending on the variety. A planting distance of 25–30 cm (9–12 inches) gave the best yields for the Tjina and Oentoeng varieties [128]. Some growers plan for the rice plants to occupy the seedbed for about one week for each month of their total growing period. Thus, a variety requiring 140–150 days from seeding to maturity would be transplanted from the seedbed 35 days after seeding. Varieties of medium maturity give the best yields when the seedlings are transplanted at the age of 30–40 days. The older seedlings reach maturity sooner than the younger seedlings transplanted at the same time, but a difference of 10 days in seedling age may make a difference of only five days in the time of maturity.

Broad-leaved weeds also are killed in Japan by use of 2,4-D applied 20 to 30 days after transplanting. It should be applied after the tillering stage but before heading. The sodium or amine salt of 2,4-D is used at the rate of 160–200 grams per acre. The paddy field is first drained, the chemical sprayed on the weeds between the rows, and the land left dry for two or three days after spraying [103].

Harvest

In most of the Asiatic countries, rice is harvested with hand sickles with 1–2 feet of straw usually being cut with the panicles which are tied in bundles (Fig. 20–15). In Indonesia and some other countries of southeast Asia, each panicle is cut separately with a special type of knife, the straw being left on the field to be burned or plowed under [134]. The grain harvested with a sickle may be left on the ground for several days for drying when the weather is dry, but often the bundles are hung on racks to dry for about 20 days (Fig. 20-16). After drying, the bundles are shocked out-of-doors or carried indoors and threshed later [83].

FIGURE 20-15. **Harvesting rice with hand sickles.**
(*Courtesy US Department of Agriculture*)

FIGURE 20-16. **Drying bundles of rice on poles.**
(*Courtesy US Department of Agriculture*)

FIGURE 20-17. **A small motor-power rice thresher in Japan.**
(*Courtesy US Department of Agriculture*)

FIGURE 20-18. **Threshing rice with foot-treadle thresher in Japan.**
(*Courtesy US Department of Agriculture*)

FIGURE 20-18. **Threshing rice with foot-treadle thresher in Japan.**
(*Courtesy US Department of Agriculture*)

FIGURE 20-19. **Drying threshed rice on straw mats.**
(*Courtesy US Department of Agriculture*)

Threshing often is done on threshing floors. In some areas, farm animals or humans tread out the grain. In other areas, the grain is beaten out by flails. The tramped or beaten material is then winnowed—*i.e.,* allowed to fall gently from a height while the wind carries away the chaff, dust, short pieces of straw, and the lighter grains. The crop is marketed as paddy or rough rice, or as stalk paddy in Java. Foot-powered or motor-powered threshers (Figs. 20-17 and 20-18) are in common use in Japan, and are being adopted in other Asiatic countries. The threshed grain often is dried for 3–4 days on straw mats until the moisture in the grain is reduced to 13 or 14 per cent before it is ready for hulling (Fig. 20-19). The grain sometimes is hulled on the farm and then marketed as brown (husked) rice in rice-straw bags.

The hand methods just described may require up to 160 hours of man labor to harvest and thresh an acre of rice. With large mechanized equipment, an acre of rice can be harvested, threshed, hauled, and dried with three hours of man labor. Mechanized harvesting methods are practiced on some or most of the larger farms in many countries.

The very time-consuming method of harvesting single panicles of rice with special knives ensures that each panicle is ready for harvest when it is cut. A rice plant that bears six or more panicles seldom ripens all of them uniformly. Traditionally, the gods are displeased when the later maturing heads are cut before they are ripe. This necessitates repeated harvests in

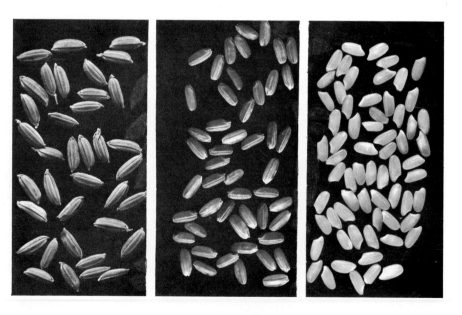

FIGURE 20-20. **Left: paddy or rough rice; center: brown rice; and right: milled rice.**
(Courtesy US Department of Agriculture)

a field but, where this practice prevails, rice harvest is a festivity in which everyone participates. Often the harvester receives a share of the crop as pay for his labor and thus obtains his yearly supply of his favorite food.

COMMERCIAL CLASSES

Standards have been established in the United States for rough rice, brown rice, and milled rice (Fig. 20-20).

Rough Rice

Under United States standards, rough rice consists of 50 per cent or more of kernels of rice from which the hulls have not been removed. Rough rice is divided into classes, based upon varieties, as follows: Rexoro (includes Rexark), Patna, Bluebonnet, Toro, Century Patna, Blue Rose (includes Improved Blue Rose, Greater Blue Rose, Kamrose, Arkrose, and Gulfrose), Magnolia, Zenith, Calrose, Nato, Pearl, and Mixed [127].

Numerical grades for rough rice ranged from No. 1–No. 6 (inclusive), with sample grade added for rice that fails to meet the requirements of the numerical grades. Several factors used for the determination of grades are percentages of heat-damaged kernels, red rice, objectionable seeds, damaged kernels, chalky kernels, and rice of contrasting classes. The grade requirements for all classes of rough rice are shown in Table 20-2.

Special grades have been established for parboiled, damp, and weevily rough rice.

Other Rice Types

Numerical grades are established for brown rice, in which the principal grading factors are objectionable seeds, damaged kernels, red rice, chalky kernels, broken kernels, moisture, rice of contrasting classes, and milled rice. Damaged kernels include heat damage and damage other than heat. Red rice is objectionable because it has an adverse effect on general appearance, while chalky kernels break more readily in milling than do normal kernels,

Milled rice is classified and graded as Head Rice, Second Head, Screenings, and Brewers Milled Rice, listed in order of decreased size of kernel particle.

CHEMICAL COMPOSITION

Rough rice consists of about 20 per cent hulls and 80 per cent grain

TABLE 20-2. **Grades and Grade Requirements for All Classes of Rough Rice.**

Grade[1]	Maximum Limits of					
	Seeds and Heat-Damaged Kernels		Red Rice and Damaged Kernels (Singly or Combined)	Chalky Kernels[2]	Rice of Contrasting Classes[3]	Rice of Non-contrasting Classes[3]
	Total (Singly or Combined)	Heat-Damaged Kernels and Objectionable Seeds (Singly or Combined)				
	(Number in 500 grams)	(Number in 500 grams)	(Per cent)	(Per cent)	(Per cent)	(Per cent)
U.S. No. 1	2	1	0.5	1.0	1.0	5.0
U.S. No. 2	4	2	1.5	2.0	2.0	5.0
U.S. No. 3	7	5	2.0	4.0	3.0	5.0
U.S. No. 4	15	10	3.0	6.0	5.0	5.0
U.S. No. 5	30	30	6.0	10.0	10.0	10.0
U.S. No. 6	75	75	15.0[4]	15.0	10.0	10.0

U.S. Sample Grade: U.S. Sample Grade shall be rough rice which does not meet the requirements for any of the grades from U.S. No. 1 to U.S. No. 6, inclusive; or which contains more than 18.0 per cent of moisture; or which is musty, or sour, or heating; or which has any commercially objectionable foreign odor; or which is otherwise of distinctly low quality.

[1] Color requirements: U.S. No. 1 shall be white or creamy. U.S. No. 2 may be slightly gray. U.S. No. 3 may be light gray. U.S. No. 4 may be gray or slightly rosy. U.S. No. 5 and U.S. No. 6 may be dark gray or rosy.

[2] The rice in grade U.S. No. 1 of the class Pearl Rough Rice may contain not more than 2.0 per cent, grade U.S. No. 2 not more than 4.0 per cent, grade U.S. No. 3 not more than 6.0 per cent, and in grade U.S. No. 4 not more than 8.0 per cent of chalky kernels.

[3] These limits do not apply to the class Mixed Rough Rice.

[4] The rice in grade U.S. No. 6 may contain not more than 6.0 per cent of damaged kernels.

(hulled or brown rice). About 10 per cent of the weight of brown rice is removed in milling off the bran, germ, and some of the endosperm with modern equipment. The proximate chemical composition of brown and milled rice is as follows [77].

Component	Brown	Milled	Losses on Milling
	(Per cent)	(Per cent)	(Per cent)
Fat	2.20	0.34	84.6
Crude fiber	1.10	0.23	79.1
Ash (minerals)	2.09	0.45	78.5
Protein	9.78	8.64	11.4
Carbohydrates	84.83	90.33	6.5

The conversion of brown rice to polished rice thus removed approximately 10 per cent of the protein, 85 per cent of the fat, 70 per cent of the minerals, and 30 per cent of the pentosans.

Proteins in Rice

Most of the protein in rice consists of glutelins. In Louisiana, fertilizer treatments—especially with nitrogen and phosphorus—increased the rice yields but did not increase the protein content significantly. The protein content was increased by treatments that limited yield, such as late seeding, or excessive nitrogen-phosphorus fertilizer ratios. The yields and protein contents from none of the treatments were correlated. The protein content of brown rice of different varieties ranged between 6.4 and 9.4 per cent. Differences in protein content were greater among different varieties than among different soil conditions or fertilizer treatments [121].

Vitamins in Rice

The important B vitamins in rice are thiamine, riboflavin, and niacin. Modern milling removes most of these vitamins, as indicated below [74], because these vitamins are found largely in the bran and germ.

Type of Rice	Thiamine	Riboflavin	Niacin
	(Micrograms per gram)		
White, milled	0.60	0.25	18.1
Brown	3.69	0.50	53.8
Parboiled, milled	2.57	0.36	39.8

The vitamin content in micrograms per gram of 17 varieties of rice grown in Arkansas was as follows: Thiamine, 2.98; niacin, 51.22; biotin,

0.81; and pantothenic acid, 10.62. Milling removed 72.25 per cent of the niacin, 86.27 per cent of the biotin, and 50.96 per cent of the pantothenic acid. The vitamin losses from milling parboiled rice were only 27.55, 48.60, and 24.55 per cent, respectively [76].

Approximately 50–70 per cent of the B vitamins are removed in the first milling operation—*i.e.*, from brown rice to first break rice—whereas the other three operations removed only an additional 10 per cent [135]. The low thiamine content of milled rice is particularly serious in Asiatic countries in which rice is the chief food. Insufficient thiamine causes a deficiency disease known as beriberi. Therefore, undermilling, or parboiling prior to milling, are helpful in the retention of more of the thiamine. The artificial enrichment of white rice with minerals and synthetic vitamins is a common practice. The consumption of enriched rice has reduced the incidence of beriberi in some areas. The consumption of large quantities of brown rice induces digestive disturbances, a fact well known to the people of Asia for centuries but still unknown to numerous advocates of roughage diets.

MILLING PROCESS

In Asia, much of the rice for home or local consumption is milled by hand with a wooden pounder and hollow block (Fig. 20-21). With such equipment, parts of the bran layer and germ are left on the milled rice, which means that much of the rice consumed in Asia is undermilled. Rice is machine-milled in the United States, in most other Occidental countries, and—to a considerable extent—in Asia, too.

FIGURE 20-21. **A primitive rice mill, with pounder or pestle.**
(*Courtesy US Department of Agriculture*)

Modern Machine-milling Process

The milling of rice removes the hulls, bran, germ, and some of the endosperm. An efficient mill cleans, scours, and polishes the grains with a minimum of breakage [23]. The first operation is the removal of any chaff, weed seeds, mud lumps, or other foreign material from the threshed grain as it is marketed. The hulls are then separated from the kernels in a sheller by paired rubber rolls that revolve at different speeds, or by hulling stones, only one of which revolves (Fig. 20-22). These stones are placed horizon-

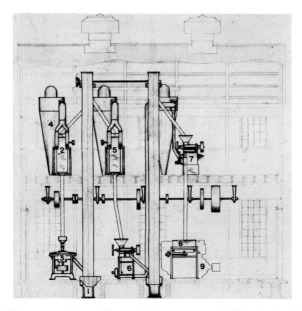

FIGURE 20-22. **Diagram of rice mill operated by power unit (9): elevator boot (1), carries rice to cleaner (2), the cleaned rice passes down to sheller (3), then up again to dust collector (4). The rice then passes to separator (5), to huller (6), to polisher (7), and to grader (8).**
(Courtesy US Department of Agriculture)

tally one above the other. They are adjusted far enough apart so that the longest grains of rice are not broken as they pass between the stones. The rice is fed onto the stones from the center. As the grains pass between the stones, the motion of the revolving stone whips the grains on end so that the tips of the hulls are cracked and removed without kernel breakage. The material then passes through a fanning machine which removes the hulls from the rice.

The brown rice, together with some unhulled grains, next passes to a paddy machine which removes the rough rice and returns it to stones set closer together for removal of the hulls.

The next machine in the milling process is the "huller," a misnomer because it removes the bran layers rather than the hulls. It is a modification of the machine used to hull coffee (hence the name). The brown bran coat is rubbed or milled off of the kernel, and the material then passes to an aspirator and bran duster for removal of the bran from the rice.

Pearling may be the next process, but it is now rarely followed in the United States. The pearling machine consists of a cone covered with a composition stone. This is surrounded by a sieve composed of close-meshed heavy iron wire which passes much of the material that is removed from the kernel. The rice fed into this machine is thoroughly rubbed or scoured before it goes out at the bottom. The milled rice is again sent through the bran duster.

The last scouring of rice in the milling process is done by a machine commonly called "the brush." It consists of a vertical cylinder covered with over-lapping pieces of pigskin or cowhide which revolves at high speed, thus giving the rice a highly polished surface.

From the brush, the milled rice is passed to the brewers' reel to be graded and sized. Some millers coat the milled rice with glucose and talc to give it an even higher polish.

The milling of rough rice yields about 64 per cent of whole and broken kernels, 13 per cent bran, 3–4 per cent polish, and 20 per cent hulls. Adapted varieties give similar total yields of whole and broken rice, but the yields of unbroken (head) rice may be very different [119]. Rice that consists mostly of half and three-quarter kernels is called "second head." That mostly of half and third kernels is called "screenings." Finely broken grains are called "brewers rice," and fine powdery fragments are "rice flour." Long-grained rough rice yields about 50 per cent of head and second-head kernels, but medium-grain and short-grain varieties may yield up to 60 per cent. The slender grain types are broken most easily. Parboiling increases the head rice yields by at least 5 per cent.

Parboiling and Related Treatments

Premilling treatments of rough rice to improve its milling, nutritional, and keeping qualities have been used for generations in India, Burma, Ceylon, Malaya, and British Guinea. These treatments, known as "parboiling," are essentially soaking, steaming, and drying the grain to cause the water-soluble minerals and vitamins in the bran to soak into the endosperm of the kernel. The siddha, sela, and josh treatments used in India are similar to parboiling except that the soaked rice is steamed, but not under pressure. The parboiled rice is dried and then milled in the usual manner. Fermented rice, known locally as "Sierra Rice," is used in the Andes highlands of South

America. The result is comparable to parboiling. Rice is allowed to ferment for several days after which it is dried in the open. Fermentation also softens the rice which reduces the time required for cooking at high altitudes [42].

"Converted" rice is the trade name for a parboiled rice produced by a process used in the United States since 1942. The soaking period is shortened by exhausting the air from rough rice in a vacuum chamber, then soaking under pressure, and finally steaming under pressure. "Malekized" rice is another trade name for a processed rice that has been parboiled.

Parboiling toughens the endosperm of rice so that the mill yield of head rice (unbroken kernels) is increased some 25 per cent. Highly milled samples of parboiled rice have been found to retain 4.5 times as much thiamine as the untreated lots. Processed rice also has a higher content of niacin, calcium, phosphorus, and iron. Parboiling improves the cooking quality so that the grains remain whole even after severe boiling [63]. Parboiling also reduces insect infestation. During storage for 16 weeks, processed rice lost 17 per cent of its vitamin content; brown rice, 33 per cent; white rice, 34 per cent [131].

UTILIZATION OF RICE AND ITS BY-PRODUCTS

Milled rice is consumed largely in the boiled state. In the United States, some rice is sold in a precooked or partly precooked condition. It also is used in the manufacture of breakfast foods such as puffed rice, flaked rice, and rice krispies. Broken rice is used as human food as well as for the making of alcoholic beverages. The flour is a common ingredient in griddle-cake mixtures. In Japan, rice also is used in cakes (mochi), salted bean paste (miso), soysauce (Shoyu), and for making rice wine (sake). Rice cakes made from glutinous rice are a delicacy. Brown rice is seldom consumed as human food, except for adding variety to diets and food recipes, or by some food fanaticists.

Because of its high thiamine content, recipes have been prepared for the use of rice polish in biscuits, corn bread, griddle cakes, muffins, and many other products [43], but it is seldom so used.

Rice starch, generally made from broken rice, is used in face powders. Rice bran and polish are used largely as feed for livestock. Polish also is used to make buttons, while the germ fraction of the bran may eventually provide rice oil, and ultimately soap.

Rice hulls are used for fuel, for insulation material, and for making furfural, cardboard, rayon, and linoleum. They are sometimes used for polishing metal castings or as packing material, soil mulches, and in the manufacture of certain gases.

Rice straw is widely used for thatching roofs of buildings in China,

Japan, and other Asiatic countries. It also is used to make paper, hats, baskets, brooms, and other products. Other uses include mulches, fertilizer, fuel, and livestock feed [83].

DISEASES

The most serious diseases of rice in the United States are seedling blight, brown leaf spot, narrow brown leaf spot, blast, stem rot, root rot, and straighthead. These diseases as well as others occur in many countries where rice is grown [110, 38, 10].

Seedling Blights and Root Rots

Seedling blights attack rice in the southern United States and many other countries. Seedling blight is caused by several fungi which include *Sclerotium rolfsii, Helminthosporium oryzae, Rhizoctonia solani, Pythium* species, *Fusarium* species, *Curvularia lunata,* and *Trichoconis candata.* Seedlings attacked by these fungi often fail to emerge in cold wet soil and thus reduce stands. Diseased seedlings are discolored. The fungus, *Sclerotium rolfsii,* attacks apparently healthy seedlings at the ground line and produces an abundant growth of white mycelium over the soil surface as well as on the lower portion of the plant. This disease is common during moist warm weather after the rice seedlings have emerged but before flooding. Affected seedlings are slightly discolored. Later, small, round, light-brown fungus bodies are found on the lower portions of the seedlings. Severely affected seedlings are killed, which results in reduced stands. Immediate submergence of the land checks the disease, but seed treatment is ineffective [10].

Some of the seedling blights can be largely controlled by seed treatment with fungicides, such as Arasan SFX, Ceresan M, Spergon XL, Agrox, Ceresan 100 and 120, M2X, MEMA, Panogen 15, and Yellow Cuprocide. Increased stands often result, particularly of early-sown seed. These fungicides are used in slurry or liquid form. Shallow seeding is helpful when sowing early in cold wet soil [10].

Root rots are caused by several fungi which include those causing seedling blight. They are reduced by good cultural practices and fertilizer treatments that favor vigorous growth and by seed treatment.

Brown Leaf Spot

Brown leaf spot, Helminthosporium blight, or sesame spot, is one of the most serious diseases of rice in the southern United States. It is particularly serious in the Orient, but it also is widespread in many other countries where rice is grown. It is caused by the fungus, *Cochliobolus* (*Ophiobolus*) *miyabeanus,* whose conidial stage is *Helminthosporium oryzae* [30]. In Japan it is most prevalent on infertile, shallow, or sandy soils.

Brown leaf spot attacks the seedlings, leaves, peduncles, hulls, and kernels. It may cause seedling blight until the plants attain a height of about four inches. Brownish discolorations first appear on the sheaths between the germinated seed and the soil surface, or on the roots. Badly affected seedlings die.

Circular to elongate sesamelike spots appear on the sheaths, stems, and panicles. The small spots are dark reddish brown, while the larger ones have dark reddish-brown margins with grayish centers. The leaves dry up on severely infected plants before the crop is fully mature. This fungus also causes a condition known as "rotten neck"—that is, the branches of the head may break over as with the blast disease. It also causes spots on the hulls and kernels [125, 10].

The seedling blight phase of the brown leaf spot is partly controlled by treating seeds with mercurial disinfectants. However, the fungus also is carried in the soil on plant refuse [81, 83]. The growing of resistant varieties is the most satisfactory means of control, but all varieties grown in the United States in 1958 were at least moderately susceptible [10]. In Japan, infected straw is removed from the fields and the land is fertilized for partial control.

Narrow Brown Leaf Spot

The narrow brown leaf spot caused by the fungus, *Cercospora oryzae,* is perhaps the most widespread leaf spot disease on rice in the southern United States. Ordinarily, the disease does not reduce yields but it may contribute to lodging. It also occurs in Japan, China, and in many other countries where rice is grown.

This disease may be found on the leaves, sheaths, peduncles, and floral bracts of the rice plant. The symptoms appear as narrow reddish-brown linear spots. The disease usually is apparent in late August or in September. Early varieties escape much of the damage when sown early. Injury to affected plants is confined mainly to the reduction of leaf area. The disease may be reduced by growing partly resistant varieties, such as Century Patna 231, and Nato [3, 10].

Blast

Blast, rotten neck, or brusone, caused by the fungus, *Piricularia oryzae,* occasionally causes serious losses of rice in the United States. It is the most serious disease of rice in Japan, and it occurs in nearly all countries where rice is grown.

There are several manifestations of the blast disease on the leaf, nodes, peduncles, and panicles of the rice plant. The leaf spots tend to be long and narrow on young leaves, but more or less circular in outline on old leaves. The spots become brown with age, but finally the leaf dies. Infected areas on the peduncle, nodes, or panicle branches are dark brown. The panicle may fall over when the peduncle (neck) is decayed.

Long-continued cloudy humid weather, excessive nitrogen fertilization, thick stands, late planting, and cold irrigation water may favor the blast disease [81]. In the United States, blast usually occurs on new land or on land that has not been cropped to rice for several years. Such soils tend to be high in nitrogen.

Blast injury on seedlings may be reduced by submerging the field when the disease becomes evident. Excessive quantities of nitrogen fertilizers should be avoided on infected land or on new land. Zenith, Arkansas Fortuna, Bluebonnet, and Nira are resistant to some races of the blast organism [126]. In Japan, organic mercury compounds are recommended for seed treatment as well as for dusting or spraying of rice fields. These compounds are not used in the United States because of the residue of mercury on the grain.

Stem Rot

Stem rot is caused by the fungus, *Sclerotium oryzae,* called also *Leptosphaeria salvinii, Helminthosporium sigmoideum,* and *H. sigmoideum irregulare.* It is widespread in the United States as well as in other countries where rice is grown.

Symptoms of stem rot usually appear in late July or early August as small black discolored areas on the leaf sheaths at or above the water line. The disease attacks the culms as they approach maturity. As the spots enlarge, the inner sheaths are discolored. Dark masses of fungus threads soon develop on the stems, followed by the development of brown to black streaks in the stems. A white mass of mycelium soon appears within the stems from which sclerotia arise. Plant damage occurs through lodging, but lightweight panicles are produced when infection occurs early [126].

The fungus bodies live over in the stubble and in the soil where they remain alive for as long as six years. In Japan, stem rot is observed where excessive amounts of nitrogenous fertilizers have been applied or where the plants have been attacked by stem borers [83].

Control measures for stem rot include drainage of the infected fields before infections reach the rice stem. Water is added from time to time to keep the soil saturated but not submerged [10]. In Japan, recommended controls are removal of affected plant material from the field, limiting nitrogen fertilization, Bordeaux mixture sprays, drying the fields late in the maturing stage, extermination of leafhoppers and stem borers, and cutting the plants near the ground line at harvest time [81, 83]. Application of organic mercury dusts at the base of rice hills also is effective.

Gibberella Blight or "Bakanae Disease"

Gibberella blight or "Bakanae disease" is caused by the fungus, *Gibberella fujikuroi* (*Fusarium moniliforme*). The disease is well known in Japan, but it occurs in other humid rice regions of Asia as well as in the southern United States. Damage to rice is in the form of reduced germination, seedling blight, and kernel blight. In the humid rice areas of the United States, *Fusarium* has been isolated from discolored and chalky rice kernels.

Plants affected by Gibberella blight are characterized by yellow-green foliage color, fewer tillers, and taller stems as compared with normal plants.

Control measures include seed treatment with mercurial dusts and the elimination of infected seedlings at the time of transplanting.

Cultures of the causal fungus, *Gibberella fujikuroi,* produce gibberellins, which are marketed as plant growth regulators.

Straighthead

Straighthead is an important physiological disease caused by abnormal soil conditions. It is found in the United States, Japan, and other rice-growing countries. Affected plants are vigorous and green, but fail to set seed except in some flowers. As a result, the heads remain erect instead of bending over as they do when filled with grain [10] (Fig. 20-23). The hulls may be distorted into a crescent shape, or some hulls and other floral parts may be missing. Some of the panicles may be very small or may fail to emerge.

Straighthead is most prevalent on new land, or land uncropped to rice for several years on which heavy growths of grass, legumes, or weeds have been plowed under. Affected areas produce little or no grain, but the injury often occurs only in spots in a field. Land on which the disease is likely to occur should be drained at least once and allowed to dry before the rice plants reach the boot stage. It is important that the soil become thoroughly dry on the surface for the treatment to be effective. Texas Patna is resistant to straighthead, while Bluebonnet 50, Lacrosse, and Fortuna are moderately resistant. Caloro, Cody and Nato are moderately susceptible, while Zenith and Century Patna 231 are susceptible.

FIGURE 20-23. **Panicles of rice: Normal (left), and affected by straighthead (right).**
(Courtesy US Department of Agriculture)

White Tip

White tip of rice is caused by a small nematode (eelworm), *Aphelchoides besseyi* or *A. oryzae*. The nematodes live over winter under the hulls of the rice seed. They become active and invade the rice seedling when infested seed is sown. They reproduce and infest the young leaves near the growing point of the culm. The nematodes spread to the panicles in the boot and after panicle emergence. The tips, and sometimes other parts, of the infested leaves turn white and later become frayed and dark colored. The flag leaf shows the most conspicuous symptoms just before heading. Severely attacked plants may fail to head or produce only a few grains. The nematodes invade the flower during the heading stage and remain inside the hulls of the developing grain. They are spread in infested seed. Some are carried to other fields by water that drains from an infested area to adjacent fields. The nematodes do not overwinter in the soil.

White tip is controlled by sowing nematode-free seed, or by seeding in water and keeping the field flooded. Seed treatment with hot water or chemicals such as N-244 (3-p-chlorophenyl-5-methyl rhodadine) will kill most of the nematodes with little seed injury, but are recommended only for small special experimental seed lots that become infested. N-244 is not in commercial use. The Bluebonnet, Fortuna, Rexoro, Sunbonnet, Texas Patna, and other varieties are resistant [10].

Other Diseases

Leaf smut of rice caused by the fungus, *Entyloma oryzae,* occurs in the southern United States and in other countries, but it is not very destructive. This smut is evident as small black spots on the leaves, leaf-sheaths, and upper stems. Control measures are not warranted [10].

Brown-bordered leaf spot, caused by the fungus *Phyllostica glumarum,* is found in the southern United States, Japan, and the Philippine Republic. The spots at first are light brown but their centers become lighter as the spots enlarge. The disease causes very little damage. Most commercial varieties of rice are rather resistant to the disease [126].

Bordered sheathspot, caused by the fungus *Rhizoctonia oryzae,* is a minor rice disease in the United States, because only occasional plants in a field are affected. Various diseases caused by the same genus have been reported in Asia. The disease appears mainly on the leaf sheaths above the water line. The spots are irregular in shape, cream-colored in the centers, and reddish-brown on the borders. Control measures are not warranted [10].

Black sheath rot, caused by the fungus *Ophiobolus oryzinus,* is a minor disease on rice in the southern United States. It is more active on certain sandy soils than on heavy soils. In the early stages, the leaf sheaths are blackened but the affected tissues soon begin to rot. In severe cases, the leaf sheaths are rotted away. The fungus overwinters on rice stubble [126].

Kernel smut, caused by the fungus *Neovossia horrida,* sometimes occurs in southern United States, and has been reported in many other countries. It reduces grain yields, and may reduce quality by blackening the milled rice. All or part of the endosperm of diseased kernels consists of a mass of black spores, but the embryo is not destroyed. Usually only 2–8 kernels per panicle become smutted. Early-sown rice seldom is affected.

Sheath blight (*Corticium sasakii*) is a serious disease in Japan. The symptoms are spots on the leaf sheaths which later may spread to the leaves. At first, the spots are greenish-gray but they gradually enlarge and become grayish-white with brownish-black margins. Affected leaves die. Control measures include avoiding excess nitrogen fertilization, allowing full fermentation of affected straw in compost, and spraying plants with Bordeaux mixture or dusting with copper compounds two or three times.

Of several kernel spots, Black kernel smut caused by the fungus *Curvularia lunata* either blackens the entire kernel or causes only surface discoloration. Two other fungi, *Trichoconis caudata* and *Monascus purpureus,* produce pink or red color in the rice grain. Many of the diseased kernels are chalky in texture, and thus readily broken when milled [126].

The hoja blanca ("white leaf") disease, first reported in Panama in 1952, has caused serious losses of rice in Cuba, Venezuela, Costa Rica, and Columbia, and has been reported also in most countries in Central America as well as in the United States. The first symptoms are white stripes or mottled patterns on the leaf, or whitening of entire leaves. The diseased plants are stunted, while the panicles are small, often poorly emerged, and are nearly sterile and thus upright. The plants do not die but continue to develop tillers, some of which are not diseased. The symptoms are very similar to those of the stripe disease in Japan, mentioned below. The disease is caused by a virus which is transmitted by a plant hopper, *Sogata orisicola.* The disease may be largely controlled by growing resistant varieties. Lacrosse, Colusa, Asahi, Missouri R-500, and many Japanese varieties are resistant [7, 10].

Four virus diseases affect the rice plant in Japan: dwarf, yellow dwarf, stripe, and black streak diseases. They are transmitted by leafhoppers. Control measures consist of destroying leafhoppers, avoiding very early or late seeding, and roguing diseased plants.

An important rice disease in Java is the so-called "Mentek" disease, described as nonparasitic in nature. The symptoms are arrested plant growth accompanied by the spread of a rusty color over the leaves, particularly the older ones. The disease occurs most frequently on marl or old volcanic soils. These are heavy soils on which rice plants are unable to develop an adequate root system. Such soils generally are low in phosphates, especially in relation to nitrogen. The "akiochi" disease in Japan is due to iron and manganese deficiencies in the soil.

INSECT AND OTHER PESTS

Rice Stinkbug

The rice stinkbug (*Solubea pugnax*) does considerable damage in the southern United States each year. It is a straw-colored, shield-shaped insect which sucks the contents of the rice kernel in the milk stage to cause a total loss. When kernels are attacked in the soft dough stage, only portions of the kernels are consumed, but this results in a spotted or distorted grain known as "pecky rice." Affected kernels often break when milled. Since the adult stinkbug hibernates over winter in heavy grasses, the numbers are decreased when these grasses are burned or plowed under in the fall or winter. Winter mortality also keeps down the number of bugs. Parasites are effective against the fall generation in Louisiana [31]. This insect also attacks sorghum.

Similar insects, called shield bugs, are found in Asia. *Scotinophara lurida* occurs in China where it is controlled by flooding the field for one day to a depth of five inches every fourth day. *S. coarctata,* prevalent in Malaya, has been controlled by applications of DDT or BHC dusts, or by spraying with kerosene emulsion [38].

Rice Bugs

The rice bug (*Leptocorisa acuta*) is widely distributed in many countries. It is one of the most serious pests in the Philippines, particularly on early varieties of rice. The insect sucks the juices of the grains in the milk stage. Control measures include light traps, collection of insects in nets, derris-soap spray, and DDT-oil emulsion spray [109].

Four rice bugs are serious pests in Japan: black rice bug (*Scotinophora lurida*), rice stinkbug (*Lagynotomus assimulans*), rice bug (*Leptocorisa varicornis*), and slender rice bug (*Cletus trigonus*). The bugs hibernate in the adult stage. They migrate to paddy fields in June or July. The bugs suck the juices from the rice plants, particularly from the immature seeds. Among effective controls are BHC dust with 3 per cent gamma isomer, and parathion dust (1.5 per cent). Tobacco dust is effective for the control of the black rice bug, while late varieties escape attack by the rice stinkbugs [73].

Stalk or Stem Borers

Stem borers are moth larvae. Several different borers attack rice. The two most important species in the United States are the rice stalk borer (*Chilo plajadellus*) and the sugarcane borer (*Diatrae saccharalis*), both of which feed within the rice stem. Losses result from the destruction of the rice panicle before it matures, a decrease in growth of affected plants, breaking off of injured panicles, and the lodging of injured stems. Losses in Louisiana are estimated as 7 per cent of the crop. The adult moths deposit eggs on the leaves of the rice plant, from which the larvae hatch. The larvae soon bore into the stem. Both stalk borers hibernate in rice stubble as well as in other grasses. There is a heavy mortality of these borers during cold weather. The number of borers that overwinter is decreased when rice stubble fields are pastured, plowed, or burned during the winter months. A 100 per cent mortality of borers has resulted when stubble fields were dragged and then submerged [31].

The rice stem borer (*Chilo simplex*) is a serious pest in northern rice areas, particularly in China, Japan, and Korea. There are usually two generations a year in Japan. The first brood moths emerge in June, while the second brood moths appear in late August. The larvae usually overwinter in the straw or stubble. First-generation moths may be controlled in Japan by spray or dust applications of parathion two weeks after the rice is transplanted, or of benzene hexachloride (BHC) just after transplanting. Insecticides should be applied at the peak of moth emergence for control of the second-generation borers [73]. Other control methods include destroying egg clusters, setting light traps to collect the moths, destroying volunteer rice plants, submerging the plants for 24 hours, and burning rice stubble.

The yellow stem borer or paddy borer (*Schoenobius incertellus*) is widespread in Asia, where it causes heavy losses. Three generations per year occur in Japan. The larvae bore into the stems which die or fail to produce grain. The larvae overwinter in rice stubble. An effective control for this pest is to plow under the stubble as soon as the rice crop is harvested, followed by submergence for as long as three months [38]. Insecticides such as DDT, BHC, and parathion have been effective as controls in Japan. Where the pest is serious, seeding in nursery beds is delayed in order to escape early infestation [73].

Other rice stem borers fround in Asia are the white rice moth borer (*Scirophaga innotata*) and the noctuid borer (*Sesamia inferens*).

Sugarcane Beetle

The sugarcane beetle (*Eutheola rugiceps*) is sometimes a serious pest on rice in the United States. The adult beetle gnaws and thus kills young rice plants prior to flooding in the spring. Newly emerged adults attack the nearly mature stalks when the fields are drained prior to harvest, and the affected plants often fall over so that harvesting machinery misses them. Many species of birds, frogs, toads, and armadillos feed on the beetles. Seed treatment with kerosene or commercial coal tar has been effective against spring injury under controlled conditions. Application of irrigation water drives the beetles from the field. Prior to harvest, delayed drainage or immediate reflooding after the appearance of the beetles has reduced losses. Plowing of sodland breeding areas also is helpful [31].

Leafhoppers and Related Insects

Leafhoppers (*Nephotettix* spp.) are widespread pests on rice in Asia. The green rice leafhopper (*N. apicalis cincticeps*) is the vector for the dwarf and yellow dwarf diseases of rice in Japan. This species also is a serious pest in the Philippines. The zigzag-striped leafhopper (*Inazyma dorsalis*) is another pest of rice in Japan [73].

The white-backed plant hopper (*Sogata furcifera*) is a pest of rice in Japan, Taiwan, and Malaya. Plant hoppers suck the juices from the stems, after which the plant often dies. *Sogata* species are vectors of the hoja blanca virus disease in Cuba, Central America, Columbia, and Venezuela. The smaller brown plant hopper (*Delphacodes striatella*) is the vector for the stripe virus disease of rice in Japan. It also is found in the Philippines. Another related species found in both countries is the brown planthopper (*Nilaparvata lugens*) [109, 73].

Control measures for leafhoppers or related insects consist of light traps; application of kerosene to the rice paddies so that a thin film covers the water surface; clean culture to destroy wild grasses near rice paddies; and spraying with a soap solution of 150 to 300 grams of yellow laundry soap per gallon of water, to which nicotine sulfate, derris, or pyrethrum may be added. DDT-oil emulsion also may be used [109]. Planthoppers are controlled in Japan by 0.5 to 1.0 per cent BHC, or 2.5 per cent DDT dust. Since the green rice leafhopper is resistant to BHC, either DDT or phosphorus compounds are recommended for this insect [73].

Leaf Beetles

The rice leaf beetle (*Lema oryzae*) is a serious pest in northern Japan. The adults overwinter in grasses near paddy fields. In the spring, the adults attack the leaves of rice plants in nursery beds. The beetles lay eggs from which larvae soon emerge. The young larvae also feed on the leaves of the rice plant. Injured leaves split, after which they turn a whitish-yellow color. This insect may be controlled by two or three applications of calcium arsenate dust or spray at 10-day intervals in the larval or adult stages. Other effective insecticides are BHC and DDT applied in a similar manner [73].

Another leaf beetle (*Hippa armigera*) is common in India, Taiwan, and southeast Asia. It causes severe injury by mining the leaves. The beetles may be netted, or sprayed with insecticides [38].

Stored Grain Insects

Several insect pests attack stored rice grain. Those most destructive in rough rice in the United States are the Angoumois grain moth (*Sitotroga cerealella*), the lesser grain borer (*Rhizopertha dominica*), and the rice weevil (*Sitophilus oryzae*). These insects bore into the kernels. Several other species feed on the surface of the kernels, on broken grains, and on grains damaged by boring insects. The most common of these species are the cadelle (*Tenebroides mauritanicus*), the flat grain beetle (*Laemophloeus surinamensis*), almond moth (*Ephestia cautella*), and the rice moth (*Corcyra cephalonica*) [11].

Insects that attack brown or milled rice include the saw-toothed grain beetle, the flour beetles (*Tribolium castaneum* and *T. confusum*), the cadelle, the almond moth, the rice moth, the corn sap beetle (*Carpophilus dimidiatus*), the lesser grain borer, and the rice weevil [11].

Rough rice in bins may be fumigated with crude granular calcium cyanide. A dosage of eight pounds of the chemical to 360 bushels of rice, or 16 pounds per 1000 cubic feet of space will kill the insects in covered wooden cribbed bins. Methyl bromide, liquid hydrocyanic acid, and chloropicrin may be used for warehouse fumigation or for atmospheric-vault fumigation of milled rice. Vacuum fumigation of rice may be accomplished with the same chemicals, or with ethylene oxide [11].

Other Pests

In the United States, the rice water weevil (*Lissorhoptrus simplex*) causes slight damage to rice. Sometimes rice plants are damaged by the fall armyworm (*Laphygna frujiperda*), southern corn rootworm (*Diabrotica duodecipunctata*), and the chinch bug (*Blissus leucopterus*). These insects are destroyed when the field is flooded. Recently, root parasitic nematodes have been found in rice in Texas and Louisiana, particularly *Radopholus oryzae.*

Rice armyworms (*Spodoptera mauritia* and *Prodenia litura*) and rice case worms (*Nymphula depunctalis*) are harmful rice pests in the Philippines. The rice grasshopper (*Hieroglyphus banian*) and the eelworm (*Tylenchus angustatus*) are troublesome pests in India. Two leaf miners attack rice in Japan; *i.e.,* the rice leaf miner (*Agromyza oryzae*), and the smaller rice leaf miner (*Hydrellia griseola*).

The rice crop suffers considerable damage each year in all countries from birds, rodents, moles, and crabs. In the United States, rice is attractive to blackbirds, cowbirds, grackles, and wild ducks [106, 64]. Blackbirds feed on the germinating seed as well as on the ripening grain. In California, the tadpole shrimp (*Apus oryzphagus* and *A. biggai*), a Crustacean, has been a pest of rice since 1946. It pulls up or devours rice seedlings before they emerge through the water, and muddies and litters the water so that other seedlings are retarded. The tadpole shrimp eggs overwinter in the soil and hatch in from 5–7 days after the field is submerged. The shrimp are controlled by applying 10 pounds of granular copper sulfate per acre, with an airplane, about two weeks after the field is submerged.

CYTOGENETICS

The haploid chromosome number of cultivated rice (*Oryza sativa*) and many wild species is 12, but *O. latifolia, O. minuta, O. corarctati, O. eichingeri,* and other species have 24 chromosomes. Some cytologists have suggested that *O. sativa* is a balanced allotetraploid which originated through hybridization between two different five-paired species in which two chromosomes are duplicated [112], but this theory has not been fully accepted.

Intersubspecies Crosses

The two so-called subspecies or botanical varieties of *Oryza sativa,*

Indica and *Japonica,* have been grown under different environmental conditions so long that they may have accumulated gene changes or rearrangements which make them largely incompatible when intercrossed [47]. The mean fertility of the F_1 plants of crosses between *Indica* and *Japonica* types was 9.34 per cent, while crosses with these types had a fertility of 77.4 per cent [80].

A third type includes certain Indian varieties which give high fertility in some crosses with the the other two types, but high sterility in other crosses [124]. Some Javanese varieties behave similarly, which has led to the suggestion that the third type be considered a new botanical variety named *Javanica* [98]. Despite low fertility in many intergroup crosses, the occurrence of a few fertile segregates has resulted in the development of numerous improved varieties in Japan, Taiwan, and the United States.

Interspecies Hybrids

The F_1 plants of crosses between cultivated and wild species of rice usually are highly sterile and produce no seed. Irregularities in chromosome behavior are common in the F_1 hybrids of such crosses. Some cultivated rice varieties cross more readily with wild species than do others. Among the 12-chromosome species of *Oryza,* crosses of *O. sativa* with *O. glaberrima* were usually sterile, but those with *O. longistaminata* were fertile or partly fertile. The F_1 hybrids of crosses of *O. sativa* with *O. officinalis* and *O. cubensis* were sterile [112].

Although cultivated rices (*O. sativa*) also have been crossed with the wild tetraploid species, *O. latifolia* and *O. minuta,* the hybrids are sterile. The suggested genome constitutions of the three species are: *O. sativa,* AA; *O. minuta,* BBCC; and *O. latifolia,* CCDD [95, 96, 97].

Haploids, Polyploids, and Aneuploids

Haploid plants, that arise naturally, are characterized by slow growth and small culms, leaves, and florets. Such plants are sterile [47].

Tetraploid rice plants ($4n = 48$) have been found as natural mutants, some of which are partly fertile [62]. Triploid plants ($3n = 36$) also occur in rice fields, some of which may arise from crosses between tetraploid and diploid plants. The triploid plants are at least as large as normal diploid plants, while the florets are larger with a tendency to have an awn or to have it more pronounced. Triploids are highly self-sterile, but probably give rise to aneuploids by natural pollination with diploid plants [46].

Colchicine-induced autotetraploids produced in Texas were distinctly coarser in all plant parts, and less vigorous and productive than comparable diploid plants [12]. Induced-autotetraploid plants in Japan had larger spike-lets, longer awns, and larger pollen grains than their diploid counterparts. Although the grains of tetraploids are larger, their number per panicle is less and the plants yield less than diploids. Long ligules of the flag leaf readily distinguished tetraploids from diploids. The fertility of four tetra-ploid varieties ranged from 10–50 per cent, and the number of tetravalents in the pollen mother cells at meiosis ranged from 3–12. Autotetraploids have no practical value because of the reduced number of spikelets, fewer tillers, and partial sterility [26].

Intersubspecies tetraploids have been produced between *Japonica* and *Indica* types. Some of the F_2 tetraploid progeny showed more than 90 per cent fertility. Some of these tetraploids may offer possibilities as cultivated varieties [27].

Aneuploid rice plants with from 1–6 extra chromosomes, in addition to the normal diploid number of 24, produce only an occasional seed [62].

GENETICS

Several summaries of rice genetics have been published [59, 104, 112, 47]. A later summary is "Rice gene symbolization and linkage groups, USDA, ARS 34–28. 1963".

Color Inheritance

Color inheritance probably has been studied more than all other phases of rice genetics. Anthocyanin pigmentation, particularly purple and red, is found in the stems, leaves, and floral bracts. The apiculus is the tip of the lemma and palea.

Apiculus color genes are basic for anthocyanin formation because color fails to develop in most other organs unless the apiculus is colored. The chromogen Gene C and a reducer Gene A are necessary for pigment forma-tion, giving a red color. In the absence of C, there is no color other than green [55]. Ratios of 3:1 and 9:7 for red and green are common in the F_2 generation, but ratios of 9 purple:3 red:4 green apiculus color were obtained in crosses between Japanese varieties in California. Thus, a third gene is necessary to produce color when C and A are present. Shades of color in rice hulls result from a series of multiple alleles for Gene C [104]. Other work indicates duplicate genes for apiculus color [122]. Three com-plementary genes give 9:7 or 27:37 ratios in the presence of Gene C [19].

Purple vs. nonpurple color has segregated into 3:1, 9:7, and 27:37 ratios in the internodes, leaf sheaths, and leaf blades. A 15:1 ratio for duplicate genes also has been reported for color in the leaf sheath.

Single and duplicate gene segregations for red vs. white pericarp have been reported, but two complementary genes are necessary for the production of red color [19]. One of these genes gives a speckled brown coloration. While the other gene alone has no expression, it acts in the presence of the first gene to produce a uniform bright red. Thus, a cross of red × white would be expected to segregate 9 red:3 speckled:4 white.

Inflorescence, Flower, and Kernel Characters

Panicles with long exsertion, as well as entire plants, often break over in high winds. Varieties with panicles that remain enclosed in the leaf-sheath are uncommon, and may be partly sterile. In some cases, enclosed panicles are more subject to leaf-spot diseases. Panicle exsertion vs. nonexsertion has been reported as being controlled by three gene pairs with exsertion dominant, or possibly by one major gene and two modifiers [112].

Dense rice panicles appear to be controlled by a simple recessive gene in Burma rices. In a cross between lax-panicled wild rice and a cultivated variety with a dense panicle, complementary gene action is indicated by an F_2 ratio of 9:7 for lax vs. dense [112].

In many crosses, earliness *v.* lateness of flowering behaves as a single-gene difference, with earliness dominant in some crosses and recessive in others. More frequently, multiple and modifying genes appear to be involved in other crosses.

Flower fragrance in rice appears to be inherited as a single dominant gene.

Normal vs. long outer glumes usually have segregated in a 3:1 ratio in F_2, but a 15:1 ratio with duplicate factors also has been reported.

Inheritance of awned vs. awnless lemmas has been reported as controlled by one, two, or three gene pairs with the awned character dominant. Some F_2 ratios recorded are 3:1, 15:1, 9:6:1, 12:3:1, and 63:1 [112]. A ratio of 13 awnless to 3 with some degree of awnedness indicates that an inhibitor may be involved in some cases [47].

Glabrous or smooth hull is due to a single gene recessive to pubescent hull.

Ratios of 3:1, 1:3, or 13:3 have been obtained in crosses between non-shattering and shattering rices. Shattering is dominant in some crosses.

Grain length usually appears to be governed by multiple genes, with short grain usually dominant over long grain. However, in some crosses a 3:1 ratio of short grain to long grain occurs, with the short grain of a characteristic round shape [112].

The glutinous (waxy) character of the rice kernel is due to a single recessive gene. Xenia occurs in glutinous × nonglutinous crosses. The starchy condition, which is dominant over glutinous, appears immediately in the endosperm.

Chalky vs. normal endosperm segregates in F_2 in a 9:7 ratio, which indicates the operation of two complementary factors.

Vegetative Characters

Albino, yellow, and striped chlorophyll deficiencies have been reported as being controlled by single, complementary, or duplicate genes.

Morphological characters include many types of dwarfs which usually are single-gene recessives. In crosses between tall and dwarf varieties, plant height often has segregated in a 3:1 ratio for tall to short, but a 1:3 ratio also has been reported. In some crosses, plant height has been explained by the presence of three gene pairs.

Floating growth habit of deep-water rice is reported to be dependent on duplicate recessive genes. Segregation ratios of 15:1 for normal to floating have been obtained in F_2 [112].

In crosses between rice varieties with hairy and nonhairy leaves, the segregation often is a 3:1 ratio, but a 15:1 ratio also has been reported.

Absence of the ligule, auricle, and collar is inherited as a unit. A 3:1 ratio has been reported for normal plants and those that lack these characters. Four duplicate genes have been reported in India in a liguleless mutation.

Tillering of rice plants is influenced particularly by environmental conditions. When low and high tillering strains are crossed, the behavior in F_2 indicates that three, four, or more genes may be involved [112].

Nonlodging habit has been reported as controlled by a single recessive gene, but environmental conditions usually determine the amount of lodging.

Disease Resistance

Inheritance of resistance to the Cercospora leaf spot (*Cercospora oryzae*) disease is controlled by single or duplicate genes for resistance to various physiologic races [47].

Inheritance studies of blast (*Piricularia oryzae*) indicate that resistance may be due to a single recessive gene in some crosses, but to complementary genes with a 9:7 ratio for resistance to susceptibility in others [112].

Resistance to Helminthosporium blight (*Helminthosporium oryzae*) has been reported to segregate as a 3:1 ratio for resistance to susceptibility. Other reports suggest that reaction to the disease is controlled by several factors with resistance recessive [3].

Susceptibility to stem rot (*Sclerotium oryzae*) is dominant to resistance, with reaction to the disease controlled by a single gene pair.

Linkage Relations[1]

Linkage studies, based primarily on Japanese varieties, have been reported by Nagao and Takahashi [105]. They postulate 12 linkage groups that correspond to the haploid chromosome number. Their groups, together with pertinent results by other workers, are as follows:

1. *Waxy (Glutinous) Group:* Dwarf 4, waxy, chromogen, and purple-leaf inhibitor [105]. Other factors that probably belong to this group are virescent, cluster, colored hull furrows, and late flowering.
2. *Purple-Leaf Group:* Dwarf 2, dwarf 3, purple leaf, liguleless, phenol staining, and purple hull [105]. Other factors in this group are white hull and purple-colored apiculus, and possibly purple-leaf margin, purple axis, and gold hull.
3. *Activator Group:* Activator, red bran, and purple node [105]. Purple internode also belongs to this group.
4. *Long Glume Group:* Dwarf 6, long glume, brown bran, and also Dwarf 7 [105]. Some other data indicate the possible linkage of brown (?) bran with purple internode, internode lines, and late flowering.
5. *Brown Furrow Inhibitor Group:* Inhibitor and purple stigma [105]. Other data indicate that purple sheath also is linked with purple stigma in this group.
6. *Dwarf 1 Group:* Variegated, dwarf 1, gold hull, awn, and dwarf 8 [105]. Other data indicate that purple hull and apiculus may belong to this group. (See Group 2).
7. *Fine Stripe Group:* Undulate rachis, fine stripe, and dense panicle [105].
8. *Lazy Group:* Lazy and recessive shattering [105].
9. *Neck Leaf Group:* Neck leaf and whorled rachis [105].
10. *Black Leaf Group:* Black leaf and dwarf 5 [105].
11. *Brittle Culm Group:* So far, brittle culm has not been found to be linked with any character included in crosses studied by Nagao and Takahashi [105].
12. *Glabrous Plant Group:* Possibly glabrous and awn, but none located in this group by Nagao and Takahashi [105].

BREEDING

Yield has been the primary consideration in rice breeding in the Orient, whereas in the United States additional demands have included stiff straw, smooth hull, semishattering for combine harvest, disease resistance, high milling quality, attractive bright clear grain, and cooking quality characterized by grains that remain separate. The consistency of varieties grown in the United States ranges from slightly sticky ("moist cooking") in most of the

[1] Taken largely from "Report by FAO Rice Breeders Working Party Committee on Symbolism and Linkage." 1959.

short- and medium-grain varieties to nonadhering flaky ("dry cooking") in the long-grain varieties.

Introductions

Many thousands of rice varieties have been introduced from one country to another, but only a few are found suitable to the new environment. Practically all of the rice now grown in the United States consists of varieties that were selected or bred from introduced varieties, although introduced varieties were grown exclusively before about 1912. At least three American varieties, Caloro, Fortuna, and Bluebonnet 50, have been grown successfully in other countries. The Joya variety, introduced from India during the last century, has yielded well in Trinidad [101].

Some rice varieties of Chinese origin have been successfully introduced into India where they have yielded well in the Kashmir Valley [112].

Selection

In the United States, panicle or plant selections often are made from commercial varieties or introductions. Selections now grown as varieties in this country include Zenith, Bluebonnet 50, Sunbonnet, Rexoro, Caloro, and Colusa.

Pure-line selection in Japan began in 1910. Ruku-u No. 20, selected from the Aikoku variety, is resistant to cool temperatures but it also matures early [84]. Many varieties were developed through pure-line selection.

Isolation from naturally variable populations, together with multiplication of pure strains, has been the principal mode of rice improvement in India. Among 284 improved high-yielding varieties, 255 were evolved by selection. Improved varieties have increased average yields 12–20 per cent [113]. Reports indicate that 127 new varieties have been developed by selection in China, of which 38 now are being grown by farmers in the different provinces. It has been estimated that yields of rough rice in China have been increased from 2.81–23.52 per cent by means of pure-line selections [79].

Hybridization

The desirable qualities of two or more varieties were combined in varieties selected from crosses in the United States to produce Texas Patna, T. P. 49, Bluebonnet, Prelude, Arkrose, Lacrosse, Calrose, Magnolia, Nato, Gulfrose, Belle Patna, and Northrose. The bulk method can be used to advantage in breeding for disease resistance, because the large populations that can be grown increase the possibility of obtaining the desired recombination of disease resistance with other desired characters [5].

Hybridization has been widely used in Japan for the development of new varieties since 1904. Crosses are made at the national agricultural experiment stations where they are grown in the F_1 and F_2 generations. Selection is practiced in F_2 for major desirable characters, such as maturity season, length of culm, and disease resistance. The F_3 seeds of selected lines are sent to various local stations where pedigree selection is continued until pure strains that are adapted to local conditions are obtained. Lines that show promise are included in yield tests. Superior adapted lines with high yields are released as new varieties with "Norin" numbers [84]. Another feature of the Japanese rice hybridization program is that new selections are tested for yield on heavily fertilized soils. Blast-resistant varieties, such as Sinzyu and Hutaba, have been developed from crosses between Japanese varieties with those from tropical countries.

Hybridization is widely used in India for rice improvement by the pedigree method. The backcross method also is used to some extent, particularly in breeding for disease resistance. Two new varieties, Co. 42 and Co. 26, are resistant to blast.

In Indonesia, all crosses are made at the Central selection station at Bogor, and the progenies usually are grown in bulk with little or no selection until the F_6 or F_7 generation. At that stage, many of the plants selected are homozygous for most observable characters. The bulk population is grown at the central station for the first three or four years and then at local substations for two or three years before selections are made. By this procedure, natural selection eliminates the weaker less adaptable types under local conditions. A total of 30 new varieties have been developed for Indonesia by this method [129].

A new hybrid rice variety, Yatsen No. 1, has been reported for China that is characterized by cold resistance, tolerance to high acidity, and with an increased yield of 12.6 per cent. Another hybrid, K-110, is resistant to blast [79].

WILD RICE

The wild rice of North America (*Zizania aquatica*) is not a true rice, and it even belongs to a different grass tribe than do the Asiatic wild rices of the genus *Oryza*. Nearly all of the wild rice is gathered from natural stands, but it frequently is sown in wild fowl preserves and occasionally on Indian reservations. An average of more than one million pounds of the processed grain was harvested in Minnesota and Wisconsin in the United States and Manitoba and Ontario in Canada from 1940–48 [120]. The parched grain is a staple food of certain Indian tribes, and is a luxury delicacy for serving with wild game or other meats. It is an important food for wild birds, especially for migrating wild ducks.

Wild rice is found in shallow lakes from Manitoba, the Dakotas, and Nebraska, eastward to New Brunswick and Maine, and southward in sluggish backwaters along the Atlantic Coast to central Florida, and along the Gulf Coast as far west as Louisiana. It often is called "water oats" or "Indian rice." It is harvested only in the northern Great Lakes region. It grows in tidal waters that fluctuate over a three-foot depth, but will not survive under prolonged absence of flooding or under long flooding with three feet of water over the tops of the plants. It does not thrive in stagnant water, or in water that tastes salty, or contains as much as 0.2 per cent salt.

Wild rice [17, 18] is an annual monecious plant 1–11 feet in height that grows in water, usually 0.5–3 feet deep. The spikelike top of the long panicle bears the pistillate florets, while the long nodding branches in the lower half of the panicle bear the staminate florets. Thus, it is ideally constructed for cross pollination. The pistillate florets are enclosed in a palea and a thin papery awned lemma, but the glumes are vestigal. The cylindrical caryopsis, with a groove on one side, is about 1.5–2 cm long and 1.5 mm thick. The seeds shatter and fall in the water as soon as they are fully ripe. They then lie in the muddy bottom until the next spring when they germinate and produce seedlings that grow up through the water. Some seeds may not germinate until a year later. The seeds lose their viability when dry for more than a few days. Seed for planting is stored in water immediately after it is gathered and is kept wet until sown in the water. Freezing does not injure the wet seed. Wild rice is a short-day plant, but different ecological strains permit the seed to ripen at different latitudes from 30–50°. The plants of Canadian strains are much smaller and earlier than those found in Florida.

Wild rice must be gathered just before it is ripe in order to save it before it drops into the water. Most of it is collected by hand in canoes or boats that are poled through the water. A stick held in one hand is used to bend the stalks over the boat, while another stick is used to beat the stalks so that the seed drops into the boat. Since the grain does not ripen uniformly, two or more harvests may be necessary. Usually one half or more of the seed falls into the water before or after harvesting, or during the harvest operation. Most of the wild rice is gathered by Indians who keep perhaps one-fourth of the crop for food, and sell the remainder. A few harvesting machines with a reel-type beater mounted on the front end of a flat boat are used for gathering wild rice in Canada.

The damp harvested grain must be parched, or dried or partly dried, immediately to prevent spoilage. It is parched in a heated rotating drum, or in a drum or kettle placed over a fire with constant stirring to prevent excessive charring or burning. Parching loosens the hulls, sterilizes the grain, and imparts a roasted flavor. The hulls are separated from the grain by tramping or pounding in a pit or other container, or with small mechanical hullers. The hulls and grain are then separated by winnowing in the wind or in a fanning mill. A 100-pound canoe load of damp wild rice yields about 40 pounds of dry, hulled, parched grain. Most of the black pericarp or bran remains on the grain after hulling.

The composition of the dry matter in the hulled grain of wild rice is as follows:

Item	Per cent	Item	Per cent	Item	Mg./ Lb.
Protein	15.1	Calcium	0.02	Manganese	1.8
Fat	0.7	Phosphorus	0.35	Copper	1.8
Fiber	1.0	Potassium	0.35	Thiamine	2.4
Ash	1.5	Magnesium	0.12	Riboflavin	3.2
N-free extract	81.7	Sodium	0.05	Panothenic acid	5.1
Sulfur	0.16	Chlorine	0.04	Niacin	30.9

Thus, wild rice is perhaps the highest in protein content and the lowest in fat of any of the cereals.

REFERENCES

1. Adair, C. R., "Studies in blooming rice." *J. Am. Soc. Agron.*, **26**: 965–973. 1934.
2. ———, "Effect of time of seeding upon yield, milling quality, and other characters of rice." *J. Am. Soc. Agron.*, **32**: 697–706. 1940.
3. ———, "Inheritance in rice of reaction to *Helminthosporium oryzae* and *Cercospora oryzae*." USDA *Tech. Bul. 772*. 1941.
4. ———, *et al.*, "Comparative yields of transplanted and direct sown rice." *J. Am. Soc. Agron.*, **34**(2): 129–137. 1942.
5. ———, and J. W. Jones, "Effect of environment on the characteristics of plants surviving in bulk hybrid populations of rice." *J. Am. Soc. Agron.*, **38**: 708–716. 1946.
6. ———, and K. Engler, "The irrigation and culture of rice," in *Water*. USDA Yrbk. of Ag., 1955. pp 389–394. 1955.
7. ———, J. U. McGuire, Jr., and J. G. Atkins, "Summary of research on hoja blanca." *Rice J.*, **61**(8). 1958.
8. "Agricultural statistics, 1959." USDA. pp 1–632. 1960.
9. Anderson, M. S., J. W. Jones, and W. H. Armiger, "Relative efficiencies of various nitrogenous fertilizers for production of rice." *J. Am. Soc. Agron.*, **38**: 743–753. 1946.
10. Atkins, J. G., "Rice diseases." USDA *Farmers Bul. 2120*. pp 1–14. 1958.

11. Balzar, A. I., and R. T. Cotton, "Insect pests of stored rice and their control." USDA *Farmers Bul. 1906.* 1947.

12. Beachell, H. M., "Effect of photoperiod on rice varieties grown in the field." *J. Ag. Res.*, **66**: 325–340. 1943.

13. ———, *et al.*, "Extent of natural crossing in rice." *J. Am. Soc. Agron.*, **30**: 743–753. 1938.

14. ———, and J. W. Jones, "Tetraploids induced in rice by temperature and colchicine treatments." *J. Am. Soc. Agron.*, **37**: 165–175. 1945.

15. Beacher, R. L., "Rice fertilization: results of tests from 1946 through 1951." Ark. Ag. Exp. Sta. *Bul. 522.* 1952.

16. Best, R., "Photoperiodism in rice." Commonwealth Bu. Past. and Fld. Crops *Fld. Crop Abs.* **12**(2). pp 85–93. 1959.

17. Chambliss, C. E., "Wild rice." USDA *Cir. 229.* pp 1–16. 1922.

18. ———, "The botany and history of wild rice." *J. Wash. Acad. Sci.*, **30**(5). 1940.

19. Chao, L. F., "Linkage studies in rice." *Genetics*, **13**: 133–169. 1928.

20. Chatterjee, D., "Note on the origin and distribution of wild and cultivated rices." *Ind. J. Gen. and Pl. Breed.*, **11**: 18–22. 1951.

21. Chilton, S. J. P., W. A. Douglas, and T. C. Ryker, "Rice yields in root rot areas improved by application of fertilizer." La. Ag. Exp. Sta. *Bul. 379.* 1944.

22. Clark, F., D. C. Nearpass, and A. W. Specht, "Influence of organic additions and flooding on iron and manganese uptake by rice." *Agron. J.*, **49**: 586–589. 1957.

23. Collier, G. A., "Rice production and marketing in the United States." USDA *Misc. Publ. 615.* 1947.

24. Copeland, E. B., *Rice.* London: Macmillan. pp 1–352. 1924.

25. Crist, R. E., "Rice culture in Spain." *Sci. Mon.*, **84**: 66–74. 1957.

26. Cua, L. D., "Artificial polyploidy in the *Oryzae.* I: Cytogenetical studies on colchicine-induced autotetraploid rice, *Oryza sativa*, L." Kihara Inst. Biol. Res. (Seiken Ziho), *Rpt. No. 4.* pp 43–53. 1950.

27. ———, "Fertile tetraploids of Japonica × Indica in rice." Jap. Acad. *Proc.*, **27**(1): 43–48. 1951.

28. Davis, L. L., "California rice production." Cal. Ag. Ext. *Cir. 163.* 1950.

29. De, P. K., and M. Sulaiman, "Influence of algal growth in the rice fields on the yield of crop." *Ind. J. Ag. Sci.*, **20**: 327–342. 1950.

30. Dickson, J. G., *Diseases of Field Crops*, 2d. ed. New York: McGraw-Hill. pp 1–517. 1956.

31. Douglas, W. A., and J. W. Ingram, "Rice-field insects." USDA *Cir. 632.* 1942.

32. Efferson, J. N., "The market outlook and prospective competition for United States rice in Asia, the Near East, and Europe." USDA FAS *Rpt. No. 35.* pp 1–79. 1949.

33. ———, "The market outlook and prospective competition for United States rice in the Western Hemisphere." USDA FAS *Rpt. No. 43.* pp 1–93. 1949.

34. ———, "The production and marketing of rice." *Rice J.*, New Orleans, La. pp 1–534. 1952.

35. Elst, Van der P., "The 'Mentek' disease of rice." 4th Pac. Sci. Cong. *Proc.*, Vol. 4, Ag. Pprs. pp 329–331. 1929.

36. Ghosh, B. N., "Studies on the physiology of rice. VII: Effect of varying water levels on growth of rice in relation to nitrogen absorption." Natl. Inst. Sci. India *Proc.*, **20**: 371–387. 1954.

37. Green, V. E., Jr., "The culture of rice in organic soils—a world survey." *Agron. J.*, **49**: 468–472. 1957.

38. Grist, D. H., *Rice*. London: Longmans. pp 1–331. 1953.
39. Hall, O. J., "The operation of rice driers in Arkansas, 1946." Ark. Ag. Exp. Sta. *Bul. 474.* 1948.
40. Hector, C. P., "Notes on pollination and cross-fertilization in the common rice plant, *Oryza sativa* L." Dep. Ag. India, *Mem., Bot. Ser.*, **6**: 1–10. 1913.
41. Hector, J. M., *Introduction to the Botany of Field Crops*, Vol. I, *Cereals.* Johannesburg, S. Af.: Central News Agency. pp 1–478. 1936.
42. Herzfeld, H. C., "Rice fermentation in Ecuador." *Econ. Bot.*, **611**: 267–270. 1957.
43. Hollinger, M. E., "The use of rice polishing in cooking." La. Ag. Exp. Sta. *Bul. 355.* 1942.
44. Iso, E., "Rice and crops in its rotation in subtropical zones." Jap. FAO Assn. pp 1–611. 1954.
45. Jenkins, J. M., and J. W. Jones, "Results of experiments with rice in Louisiana." La. Ag. Exp. Sta. *Bul. 384.* 1944.
46. Jodon, N. E., "Sunbonnet and Toro: Two new midseason long-grained rice varieties." La. Ag. Exp. Sta. *Bul. 499.* 1955.
47. ———, "Present status of rice genetics." *J. Ag. Assn. China*, New Ser. No. 10. 1955.
48. ———, "Occurrence and importance of natural crossing in rice." *Rice J.* July, 1959.
49. ———, and D. A. de la Houssaye, "Rice varieties for Louisiana." La. Ag. Exp. Sta. *Bul. 436.* 1949.
50. Johnston, T. H., and E. M. Cralley, "Rice varieties and their yields in Arkansas, 1948–1954." Ark. Ag. Exp. Sta. *Rpt. Ser. 49.* 1955.
51. Jones, J. W., "Observations on the time of blooming of rice flowers." *J. Am. Soc. Agron.*, **16**: 665–670. 1924.
52. ———, "Germination of rice seed as affected by temperatures, fungicides, and age." *J. Am. Soc. Agron.*, **18**: 576–592. 1926.
53. ———, "Experiments in rice culture at the Biggs Rice Field Station in California." USDA *Bul. 1387.* 1926.
54. ———, "Sterility in rice hybrids." *J. Am. Soc. Agron.*, **22**: 861–867. 1930.
55. ———, "Inheritance of anthocyanin pigment in rice." *J. Ag. Res.*, **40**: 1105–1128. 1930.
56. ———, "How to grow rice in the Sacramento Valley." USDA *Farmers Bul. 1240.* 1931.
57. ———, "Effect of depth of submergence on control of barnyard grass and yield of rice grown in pots." *J. Am. Soc. Agron.*, **25**: 278–283. 1933.
58. ———, "Effect of reduced oxygen pressure on rice germination." *J. Am. Soc. Agron.*, **25**: 69–81. 1933.
59. ———, "Improvement of rice," in USDA Yrbk. of Ag. pp 415–441. 1936.
60. ———, "New rices: new practices," in *Science in Farming, 1943–1947.* USDA Yrbk. of Ag. pp 373–378. 1947.
61. ———, *et al.*, "Rice culture in the southern states." USDA *Farmers Bul. 1808.* 1938.
62. ———, and A. E. Longley, "Sterility and aberrant chromosome numbers in Caloro and other varieties of rice." *J. Ag. Res.*, **62**: 381–399. 1941.
63. ———, L. Zeleny, and J. W. Taylor, "Effect of parboiling and related treatments on the milling, nutritional, and cooking quality of rice." USDA *Cir. 752.* 1946.
64. ———, L. L. Davis, and A. H. Williams, "Rice culture in California." USDA *Farmers Bul. 2022.* 1950.

65. ———, et al., "Rice production in the Southern States." USDA *Farmers Bul. 2043*. 1952.
66. ———, et al., "Rice varieties and their yields in the United States, 1939–49." USDA *Cir. 915*. 1953.
67. Kapp, L. C., "Study of rice fertilization." Ark. Ag. Exp. Sta. *Bul. 291*. 1933.
68. ———, "Laboratory and greenhouse studies of rice nutrition." Ark. Ag. Exp. Sta. *Bul. 302*. 1934.
69. ———, "Study of relation of growth to nutrition of the rice plant." Ark. Ag. Exp. Sta. *Bul. 335*. 1936.
70. ———, "A study of factors concerned with rice growth." Ark. Ag. Exp. Sta. *Bul. 349*. 1937.
71. ———, "The effect of common salt on rice production." Ark. Ag. Exp. Sta. *Bul. 465*. 1947.
72. ———, and R. F. Bartholomew, "The effect of controlling weeds by irrigation and seeding practices on rice fields." Ark. Ag. Exp. Sta. *Bul. 467*. 1947.
73. Kawada, A., et al., "Insects and diseases of rice plants in Japan." Natl. Inst. Ag. Sci., Tokyo, pp 1–33. 1954.
74. Kester, E. B., and J. W. Jones, "News of rice, an ancient staple," in *Crops in Peace and War*. USDA Yrbk. of Ag. pp 362–366. 1950–51.
75. Kihara, H., "Considerations on the origin of cultivated rice." Seiken Ziho, **10:** 68–83. 1959.
76. Kik, M. C., "Nutritive studies of rice." Ark. Ag. Exp. Sta. *Bul. 508*. 1951.
77. ———, and R. R. Williams, "The nutritional improvement of rice." Natl. Res. Council *Bul. 112*. 1945.
78. Koch, L., "Past, present, and future in the obtaining and spreading of superior rice varieties in the Dutch East Indies." 4th Pac. Sci. Cong. *Proc.*, Vol. 4, Agricultural Pprs. Batavia-Bondoeng, Java. pp 9–14. 1929.
79. Kuang, H. H., "Studies on rice cytology and genetics as well as breeding work in China." *Agron. J.*, **43**(8): 387–397. 1951.
80. ———, and D. S. Tu, "Studies on the fertile percentage in varietal crosses of rice hybrids." *Agron. J.*, **41**(5): 195–199. 1949.
81. Kuwana, S. L., "Important diseases of the rice crop in Japan." 4th Pac. Sci. Cong. *Proc.*, Vol. 4, Agricultural Prps. pp 203–207. 1929.
82. Laude, H. H., and R. H. Stansel, "Time and rate of blooming in rice." *J. Am. Soc. Agron.*, **19**: 781–787. 1927.
83. Leonard, W. H., "Rice as a crop in Japan." *J. Am. Soc. Agron.*, **40**(7): 579–602. 1948.
84. Matsuo, T., "Rice culture in Japan." Min. Ag. and For., Japanese Government, Tokyo. pp 1–119. 1954.
85. McNeal, X., "When to harvest rice for best milling quality and germination." Ark. Ag. Exp. Sta. *Bul. 504*. 1950.
86. Mikkelsen, D. S., and D. C. Finfrock, "Availability of ammoniacal nitrogen to lowland rice as influenced by fertilizer placement." *Agron. J.*, **49**: 296–300. 1957.
87. Misra, G., "Photoperiodic behavior of medium early varieties of rice." *Sci.*, **118**(3071). 1953.
88. ———, "Photoperiodism in rice. VII: Photoperiodic response of two early varieties of rice." *Agron. J.*, **47**: 393–395. 1955.
89. ———, "Photoperiodism in rice. IV: Effects of short day length on three medium-early varieties of rice of Uttar Pradesh." Natl. Inst. Sci. India *Proc.*, **212**: 1–9. 1955.

90. ———, "Photoperiodism in rice. VI: Effect of long day length on three medium-early varieties of rice of Uttar Pradesh." *J. Ind. Bot. Soc.*, **34**: 67–71. 1955.

91. ———, "Photoperiodism in rice. IX: Response of an early variety of rice to long photoperiod." Ind. Acad. Sci. *Proc.*, **448**: 108–113. 1956.

92. ———, "Effects of long photoperiod on four varieties of late-winter rice." *Sci. and Cult.*, **21**: 383–384. 1956.

93. ———, and B. Samantarai, "Effects of various levels of nitrogen on the vegetative growth and ear emergence of rice plants." *J. Ind. Bot. Soc.*, **34**: 451–454. 1955.

94. ———, and B. Samantarai, "Effects of short photoperiods on a variety of early rice." *Curr. Sci.* (India), **24**: 242–243. 1955.

95. Morinaga, T., "Cytogenetical studies on *Oryza sativa* L. IV: The cytogenetics of F$_1$ hybrid of *O. sativa* L. and *O. minuta* Presl." *Jap. J. Bot.* (Tokyo), **11**: 1–16. 1940.

96. ———, "Cytogenetical studies on *Oryza sativa* L. V: The cytogenetics of F$_1$ hybrid of *O. sativa* L. and *O. latifolia.*" *Jap. J. Bot.* (Tokyo), **11**: 461–478. 1941.

97. ———, "Cytogenetical studies on *Oryza sativa* L. VI: The cytogenetics of F$_1$ hybrid of *O. minuta* and *O. latifolia.*" *Jap. J. Bot.* (Tokyo), **12**: 347–357. 1943.

98. ———, "Classification of rice varieties on the basis of affinity." *Rpts.* for 5th meeting of the Working Party on Rice Breeding. Min. Ag. and For., Jap. Govt. (Tokyo). pp 1–14. 1954.

99. Mullins, T., and M. W. Slusher, "Comparison of farming systems for small rice farms in Arkansas." Ark. Ag. Exp. Sta. *Bul. 498*. 1950.

100. Murneck, A. E., and R. O. Whyte, "Vernalization and photoperiodism." *Chron. Bot.* pp 1–196. 1948.

101. Murray, D. B., "Photoperiodism in rice in Trinidad with reference to a second crop." *Emp. J. Exp. Ag.*, **18**(72): 271–275. 1950.

102. Nagamutsu, T., "Studies on the geographical differentiation of characters in cultivated rice. I: Studies on the behavior of germination." *Jap. J. Gen.*, **19**: 47–56 (Eng. resume). 1943.

103. Nagai, I., *Japonica Rice, Its Breeding and Culture.* Tokyo: Yokondo, Ltd. pp 843. 1959.

104. Nagao, S., "Genic analysis and linkage relationship of characters in rice," in *Advances in Genetics*, Vol. 4. New York: Academic Press. pp 181–212. 1951.

105. ———, and M. Takahashi, "Linkage groups in rice." Rpt. of Pl. Breed. Inst., Hokkaido University. 1959.

106. Neff, J. A., and B. Meanley, "Blackbirds and the Arkansas rice crop." Ark. Ag. Exp. Sta. *Bul. 584*. 1957.

107. Olsen, K. L., "Scum in rice fields and irrigation canals." Ark. Ag. Exp. Sta. *Rpt. Series* **69**: 1–20. 1957.

108. ———, "Mineral deficiency symptoms in rice." Ark. Ag. Exp. Sta. *Bul. 605*. 1958.

109. Otanes, F. O., and P. Sison, "Pests of rice." Philippine Dept. Ag. and Nat. Res. *Popular Bul. 42*. 1952.

110. Padwick, G. W., *Manual of Rice Diseases.* Commonwealth Mycol. Inst. pp 1–198. 1950.

111. Pearson, G. A., and L. Bernstein, "Salinity effects at several growth stages in rice." *Agron. J.*, **51**: 654–657. 1959.

112. Ramiah, K., "Rice breeding and genetics." Ind. Cncl. Ag. Res. Sci. *Monograph No. 19*. pp 1–360. 1953.

113. ———, R. L. M. Chose, and M. V. Vachhani, "Improvement of rice in India." *Emp. J. Exp. Ag.*, **20**: 161–174. 1952.

114. Reed, J. F., and M. B. Sturgis, "A study of the fertilization of rice." La. Ag. Exp. Sta. *Bul. 292.* 1937.

115. ———, and M. B. Sturgis, "Chemical characteristics of the soils of the rice area of Louisiana." La. Ag. Exp. Sta. *Bul. 307.* 1939.

116. "Rice growing in Europe," in *World Crops*, **4**(4): 132–134. 1952.

117. Ryker, T. O., "Weed control in rice with 2,4-D." La. Ag. Exp. Sta. *Bul. 427.* 1948.

118. Sen, P. K., "Studies in the water relations of rice. I: Effect of watering on the rate of growth and yield of four varieties of rice." *Ind. J. Ag. Sci.*, **7**: 89–117. 1937.

119. Slusher, M. W., and T. Mullins, "Rice mill yield and grade in relation to variety and method of harvest." Ark. Ag. Exp. Sta. *Bul. 526.* 1952.

120. Steeves, T. A., "Wild rice—Indian food and modern delicacy." *Econ. Bot.* **6**(9): 107–143. 1952.

121. Sturgis, F. E., R. J. Miears, and R. K. Walker, "Protein in rice as influenced by variety and fertilizer levels." La. Ag. Exp. Sta. *Tech. Bul. 466.* 1952.

122. Takahashi, M., "Analysis on apiculus color genes essential to anthocyanin coloration in rice." *J. Fac. Agr. Hokkaido U.*, **50**: 266–362. 1957.

123. Terao, H., "On the improvement of the techniques of rice cultivation in Japan." 4th Pac. Sci. Cong. *Proc.*, Vol. 4, Agricultural Papers. pp 253–256. 1929.

124. ———, and G. Midusima, "Some considerations on the classification of *Oryza sativa* L. into two subspecies, so-called 'Japonica' and 'Indica.' " *Jap. J. Bot.* (Tokyo), **10**(3): 213–258. 1939.

125. Tullis, E. C., "Fungi isolated from discolored rice kernels." USDA *Tech. Bul. 540.* 1936.

126. ———, "Diseases of rice." USDA *Farmers Bul. 1854.* 1940. Rev. 1951.

127. "United States standards for rough rice, brown rice, and milled rice." Ag. Mktg. Ser., USDA. pp 1–14. 1961.

128. Van der Giessen, I. C., "Culturmethod—Onderzoek bij sawahrijst," Buitenzorg, Java: Mededeelingen van het Algemeen Proefstation vor den Landbouw No. 55. pp 1–66. (Eng. summary.) 1942.

129. Van der Muelen, J. G. J., "Rice improvement by hybridization and results obtained." Contr. Gen. Ag. Res. Sta., Borgor, Indonesia, No. 116. pp 1–38. 1950.

130. Vavilov, N. I., "The origin, variation, immunity, and breeding of cultivated plants." *Chron. Bot.*, **13**(1–6), pp 1–364. 1949–50.

131. Vinacke, W. R., E. Hartzler, and Y. Tanada, "Processed rice in Hawaii." Ha. Ag. Exp. Sta. *Tech. Bul. 10.* 1950.

132. Walker, R. K., *Rice*, 15th ed. La. St. Dept. Ag. and Imm. 1952.

133. ———, and M. B. Sturgis, "A twelve-month grazing program for the rice areas of Louisiana." La. Ag. Exp. Sta. *Bul. 407.* 1946.

134. Wickizer, V. D., and M. K. Bennett, *The Rice Economy of Monsoon Asia.* Stanford U. Food Res. Inst. pp 1–358. 1941.

135. Williams, V. R., and E. A. Fieger, "Rice and the vitamin B complex." La. Ag. Exp. Sta. *Bul. 381.* 1944.

136. Wulff, I. A., "Increasing the yield of rice in Java by means of manuring." 4th Pac. Sci. Cong. *Proc.*, Vol. 4, Agricultural Papers. pp 385–389. 1929.

137. Yeh, B., and M. T. Henderson, "Cytogenetic relationship between cultivated rice, *Oryza sativa* L., and five wild diploid forms of Oryza." *Crop Sci.*, **1**(6): 445–450. 1961.

21. GRAIN SORGHUM

ECONOMIC IMPORTANCE

Grain sorghum (*Sorghum vulgare*, Pers.) is cultivated throughout Africa and extensively in India, China, Manchuria, and the United States. Sorghum also is grown in Asia Minor, Iran, Turkestan, Pakistan, Korea, Japan, Australia, southern Europe, Central America, South America, and some islands of both the East and West Indies. The crop is generally distributed from the tropics to latitudes as high as 45 degrees [55]. The cultivated sorghums include grain sorghum, sorgo (sweet sorghum), broomcorn, and grass sorghum. Grass sorghums include Sudangrass, Johnson grass, and their hybrid progenies, such as sorgrass.

Statistics on world production of sorghums are meager, but the total area devoted to grain production is believed to exceed 120 million acres from 1959–61. The estimated world production of sorghum grain for the period 1934–38 averaged 24,172,105 tons. Of this the United States produced 1,227,783 tons; about 90 per cent of the total world crop was grown in China, India, Manchuria, and French West Africa. Approximately 18,069,-400 tons—75 per cent of the total—was used as human food, and 3,865,-953 tons—16 per cent—as livestock feed [1]. Considerable quantities are also used for making native beer.

Grain sorghum is an important crop in the United States (Table 21-1), particularly in the Southwest, where the climate is too hot and dry for corn [71]. In Kansas, the zone of transition between the predominate acreages of corn and sorghum formerly lay near the 25-inch annual precipitation line, a semiarid zone, but sorghum has now spread into the more humid areas where the annual precipitation exceeds 30 inches. The advent of hybrid sorghum, and the resistance of sorghum to corn borers, enable sorghum to outyield corn in such areas.

The acre yield of grain sorghums increased from 21 bushels in 1940–41 to 41.8 bushels in 1960–61. More than 600 million bushels were produced

TABLE 21-1.   **Average Acreage and Production of Sorghum in the United States, 1952-61 (Grass Sorghums Omitted).**

Sorghum Crop	Acreage Harvested	Unit	Yield per Acre	Total Production
	(1000 A)			(1000)
Grain	12,388	Bushels	28.30	374,685
Forage	4,039	Tons	1.41	5,054
Silage	1,343	Tons	7.38	9,986
Broomcorn	224	Tons	0.14	30.6
Syrup	36	Gallons	75	2,700
Total	18,030	——	——	——

in 1958 and in 1960. The states leading grain production were Texas, Kansas, Nebraska, Oklahoma, California, and New Mexico (Fig. 21-1). The acreage of sorghum harvested for grain in the United States has varied considerably through the past 30 years; recently, acreage has been on the increase.

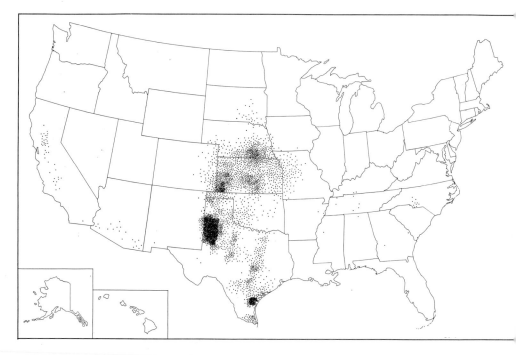

FIGURE 21-1. **Distribution of grain sorghum acreage in the United States in 1959. Each dot represents 5,000 acres. United States total was 14,560,604 acres.**

(*Courtesy US Department of Commerce*)

Developments, mostly since 1940, have made grain sorghum a good supplement to wheat in the southern Great Plains. These improvements include mechanization, development of productive hybrids suitable for combine harvesting, better seedbed preparation, better weed control, and industrial utilization. Sorghum can be planted and harvested with wheat machinery. It is the best single crop to meet the requirements for both roughage and grain for livestock in the southern Great Plains [29]. The excellent response of sorghum to irrigation and heavy nitrogen applications accounts for much of the recent increase in yields.

HISTORY OF SORGHUM CULTURE

The early history of sorghum culture is unknown, but it probably was one of the earliest plants to be domesticated. It is believed that cultivated sorghum probably originated in east-central Africa. Its culture in Egypt goes back to antiquity, and it was grown in Assyria as early as 700 BC. It was an important crop in the Old World long before the Christian era. Sorghum must have been grown in India in the first century AD, for Pliny wrote that sorghum was brought to Rome from India. It is unlikely that sorghum originated in India because the forms grown there show only limited diversity. Apparently, sorghum did not reach China until the thirteenth century AD [134, 1].

Nearly all grain sorghum now grown in the United States is of African origin or derivation. The first grain sorghum, called "guinea corn," reached the West Indies in slave ships from Africa. It later entered the United States long before the introduction of the first sorgo (sweet sorghum) variety, Chinese Amber in 1853. Other grain sorghums came to this country during the colonial period but failed to become permanently established. White durra and brown durra were introduced from Egypt to California in 1874. White and red kafirs were brought to this country in 1876. Milo appears to have been introduced into the United States, probably about 1885, from an area of northeastern Africa within 10 degrees of the Equator. A tall late variety, Yellow milo or Giant milo, it was displaced about 1904 by Standard Yellow milo, a mutation to earlier maturity. Other important introductions included shallu from India about 1890, feterita from Africa in 1906, and hegari from Africa in 1908 [73, 54].

ADAPTATION

Sorghum is grown largely in regions of Africa, Asia, North America, and Australia that are too dry or too hot for successful corn production. In areas of the United States where the yield of corn is as little as two-thirds what grain sorghum could yield farmers have often perferred corn because of the greater certainty of obtaining a stand in poor soil, less risk of damage in storage, higher feeding and market value, ability of the stalks to stand longer after maturity, and better adaptability for feeding to certain classes of livestock without threshing or grinding.

Climatic Factors

Although originally native to the tropics, many present-day sorghum varieties are well adapted to temperate regions. All require warm summer weather for successful growth.

Grain sorghum cultivation in the United States has been extended to the drier, shorter-season areas of the country as a result of the development of new early-maturing varieties [74]. The limits of production have now reached sections where the average annual precipitation is 15–17 inches, the average frost-free season 130-140 days, and the mean July temperature 70°F. Sorgo for forage is grown farther north than grain sorghum because it can be harvested before the seed is mature. Although well adapted to survive drought, sorghum usually fails to produce profitable yields in dry-land regions without summer rainfall; hence it is seldom grown in the far western United States, except under irrigation.

Sorghum can produce a bigger crop than corn under dry hot condi-tions, because it remains dormant during drought but resumes growth when favorable conditions reappear. It has high resistance to desiccation, a low transpiration ratio, a large number of fibrous roots, and the ability to pro-duce a crop from the tillers and branches that develop after rains occur. The relatively impervious corky epidermis of sorghums has a waxy bloom that retards desiccation of stalks and leaves [74].

The minimum temperature for the germination of sorghum seeds is 45–50°F [89], but the minimum for subsequent plant growth is about 60°F. Well-advanced sorghum plants are killed by temperatures slightly below freezing, but newly emerged seedlings have survived temperatures as low as 19°F. Sorghums usually are planted in warm soils after the danger of frost is over.

In the United States, the principal sorghum varieties require 100–120 days to mature, although some very early ones may be ripe 80 days after planting. The grain types generally are unsuccessful as crops where the frost-free season is less than about 160 days for most varieties, or 130 days for the earliest ones. The period from planting to pollination is about twice as long at an average temperature of 68°F as it is at 86°F. A deviation of one hour from an average day length of 12–15 hours will alter the growing period by about 10–14 days with a corresponding difference in plant size.

The optimum temperature for the growth of sorghums has not been established, but the best yields are secured where the mean July temperature is 80–85°F. High yields are seldom obtained where the mean July summer temperature is less than 75°F. Sorghum plants have survived repeated exposures to air temperatures of 120–140°F in the greenhouse in the summer, but observations indicate that maximum temperatures much above 100°F are detrimental, especially as the plants approach the heading stage [74].

Sorghums are short-day plants; *i.e.,* floral initiation is hastened by short days, delayed by long days. When grown in the United States, most varieties from the tropics fail to head under conditions of 14 hours or more of daylight in June. Nearly all sorghum varieties are sensitive to photoperiod (day length), although they differ in degree of sensitivity.

Yields of sorghum fluctuate greatly from year to year, chiefly because of differences in rainfall. In the southern Great Plains, very low yields or even failure of grain sorghum may be expected when the crop-year precipitation is less than 11–12 inches on sandy soils, or less than 13–14 inches on the heavier loam soils [74]. Frequency of failure to produce grain is reduced by thin planting, wide spacing of rows, or by planting drought resistant varieties. Within certain limits, each inch of rainfall above the minimum may result in an average additional production of 2–2.5 bushels of grain per acre under good cultural conditions. Sorghum responds well to supplementary irrigation.

Soil Conditions

Sorghum is grown successfully on nearly all types of soil that range 5.5–8.5 pH. In moist seasons, highest yields are obtained on heavy soils; in dry seasons, the crop does best on sandy soils. Sorghum will tolerate considerable salinity and alkalinity fairly well.

GENUS SORGHUM

Sorghum belongs to the genus *Sorghum,* Tribe Andropogeneae, of the grass family [134]. The genus is characterized by spikelets borne in pairs, one sessile and fertile, the other pedicellate and usually sterile or staminate. The terminal sessile spikelet is accompanied by two pedicellate spikelets. The plant is a robust grass with flat leaf blades and terminal panicles.

Sorghum vulgare (cultivated sorghum) plants are annuals with 10 pairs of chromosomes. *S. halepense* or Johnson grass plants are perennial with creeping rhizomes and 20 pairs of chromosomes. The wild grass sorghum species of Africa, except Johnson grass, have 5–10 pairs [35].

FIGURE 21-2. **A field of Plainsman grain sorghum with plants about three feet tall.**
(Courtesy US Department of Agriculture)

The sorghums often are classified broadly into four agronomic groups: grain sorghums, sorgos, broomcorn, and grass sorghums. Grain sorghum is grown primarily as a cereal, sorgos for forage or syrup, broomcorn for its brush for use in brooms, and grass sorghums for hay or pasture. Cross pollinations readily occur between the groups of cultivated annual sorghums.

BOTANICAL DESCRIPTION OF THE SORGHUM PLANT

Vegetative Characters

A detailed literature review on the botany of sorghums has been published [42]. The sorghum plant is a coarse annual with culms or stems 2–15 feet, sometimes more, in height [134] (Fig. 21-2). The culms are made up of 7–18 or more nodes and internodes. Basal diameters vary from a fraction of an inch to two inches. The stem may be juicy or pithy, sweet or nonsweet. A leaf is borne at each node; nodes are alternate and on opposite sides of the culm. The surface of the culms, sheaths, and leaves is glaucous. Some sorghum varieties tiller profusely under favorable environmental conditions, others do not. The various sorghum groups have been ranked by number of tillers from greatest to least as follows: hegari, feterita, sorgo, milo, kaoliang, kafir, and durra [106]. Recurved or "gooseneck" heads are the result of thick heads forced out of the side of a too-narrow sheath while the peduncle is still flexible and unlignified [72]. Sometimes the peduncles of varieties having thick panicles are not recurved but kinked near the base because of resistance to the pressure of head emergence from the sheath. Recurved heads are undesirable because they are difficult to harvest with machinery, but recurved heads suffer less damage from quelea birds in Africa.

The number of leaves at maturity is highly correlated with length of vegetative period. Each additional leaf adds 3–4 days to the length of the growing period. The number of leaves arising above the soil level ranges from 7–18 or more. The leaf sheaths are long and overlap in dwarf varieties. The margins of the leaves bear sharp, curved teeth. Numerous motor cells are located near the midrib on the upper side of the leaf, which facilitate rapid folding of the blade during periods of drought.

The root system is fibrous, composed of many slender roots of about equal diameter. Lateral roots arise throughout the length of the single seminal root that grows vertically downward. Coronal roots develop in succession from the basal node upward, and aerial roots may arise at nodes above the ground level. Roots usually attain a working depth of 3–4 feet, but may reach a depth of 6 feet [2] and occasionally 9 feet.

The roots of sorghums generally are finer, more fibrous than those of corn. The coronal roots per unit length of seminal root are twice as frequent in sorghum as in corn. Absorption by the root system of a sorghum plant is twice as efficient as that of corn although the sorghum plant has a leaf area only half that of corn [138].

Inflorescence

The inflorescence or "head" of sorghum is a panicle usually ranging from 3–20 inches in length and 1.5–8 inches in width [108], with few-to-many long or short primary branches borne on a hairy axis (Fig. 21-3). The seed branches are borne in more or less definite whorls. The fertile sessile spikelet consists of a short floral axis on which parts occur as follows: first glume, second glume, sterile floret, fertile floret. The glumes are somewhat indurate, about equal length, and more or less thickened (Fig. 21-4). They are usually black, red, brown, or straw-colored. The glumes enclose 2 florets, of which the lower is nearly always sterile, the upper perfect. The sterile floret consists of the lemma only. The fertile floret consists normally of the lemma and palea, 2 lodicules, 3 stamens, and a one-celled ovary with a bifurcated plumose stigma. Both lemma and palea are hyaline and delicate. The 2 lodicules lie adjacent to the fertile lemma in the base of the spikelet. When present, the awn is attached to the lemma of the fertile floret. The sterile pedicellate spikelet is more elongate than the fertile sessile one. It commonly consists of 2 glumes only, but may have anthers or other parts [134]; occasionally it produces a seed. Many of the sterile pedicellate spikelets fall off soon after the fertile spikelets mature.

FIGURE 21-3. **A half-panicle of kafir grain sorghum, showing seed branches borne in about 11 whorls.**

(*Courtesy US Department of Agriculture*)

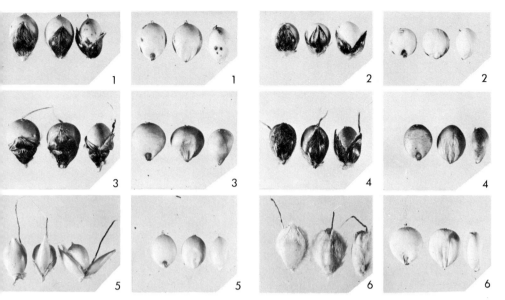

FIGURE 21-4. **Spikelets (left) and kernels (right) of six grain sorghum groups. 1, kafir; 2, hegari; 3, milo; 4, darso; 5, shallu; 6, durra.**

(*Courtesy US Department of Agriculture*)

Multiple-seeded spikelets occur rarely, except in antherless derivatives. In one case in Texas, the spikelets on tillers and side branches of Standard Yellow Milo had 5.8 per cent of twin seeds, 0.27 per cent connate seeds, and 0.23 per cent triple seeds [49].

Caryopsis or Grain

The caryopsis, commonly called the grain or "seed," is the part of commercial importance in grain sorghum. It usually threshes free of the floral bracts. In broomcorn, grass sorghums, and many sorgos the caryopsis usually remains enclosed in the hulls.

The sorghum grain ranges in size from 8–35 mm. There are 12–30 thousand seeds in a pound in most varieties. The true milos as a group have large seeds, the feteritas have very large seeds. The kernel shape is usually obovoid, although some are more or less ovoid or ellipsoid (Fig. 21-4). The seeds of durra are particularly flat, while those of feterita and milo are some-what flat.

The color of sorghum seeds may be white, chalky white, pink, yellow, red, buff or brownish yellow, brown, or reddish brown. Some white-seeded varieties also have red, purple, or brown spots that consist of water soluble pigment washed from the glumes. The pigment of sorghum kernels is formed in the pericarp, testa, and endosperm. The testa or subcoat, sometimes erroneously called the nucellar layer, is absent in many varieties, but is always colored brown when present at maturity. Brown seeds usually contain considerable amount of tannin and related compounds. Yellow and red seeds have color in the pericarp (epicarp). Varieties with a yellow endosperm have been known only since 1951. In the buff or light-brown varieties, the testa is present along with a genetic spreader factor that causes the testa pigment to diffuse out to the pericarp. In dark brown or reddish-brown varieties, the testa is present with the spreader factor and a colored epicarp. Chalky white varieties have the brown testa, without the spreader factor, and thus no color in the epicarp [134]. Yellow and red feterita have a colored pericarp and testa, without the spreader factor.

The caryopsis consists of about 84 per cent endosperm, 10 per cent germ, and 6 per cent pericarp [9]. The endosperm starch usually is composed of 22–24 per cent amylose, a straight-chain starch; the remainder is amylopectin, a branch-chain starch component. The starch of waxy (or glutinous) varieties consists wholly of amylopectin. Sorghums with sugary endosperms also have been reported. Yellow-endosperm varieties that contain carotene and xanthophyll are being bred from crosses with the Short Kaura variety introduced from Nigeria in 1951.

POLLINATION

Sorghum flowers begin to open 2 days or less after the inflorescence or head is entirely out of the sheath, sometimes before it is fully emerged. The first flowers to open are those at or near the apex of the panicle, followed by a downward progression to the base at a rate of 2–5 cm per day [76]. The anthers usually become pendant and dehisce when the glumes are spread or soon thereafter (Fig. 21-5). The entire process of blooming of a single spikelet may be completed in as little as 20–30 minutes, but flowers frequently remain open for 2–3 hours [113, 99]. When not fertilized, the flowers remain open for several days.

In Texas, the stimulus that causes anthesis appeared as early as midnight in some varieties, but as late as 4–5 AM in others. Blooming is delayed by cool temperatures, i.e., it may take place as late as midmorning in cool weather. The blooming of a single panicle normally is completed in 4–7 days [113, 99], but often it requires even 15 days, under cool conditions.

There are approximately 5000 pollen grains per anther in Spur feterita, an estimated 24 million pollen grains per panicle. Pollen deteriorates rapidly. Texas studies indicate that seed failed to set when pollen was used five hours or more after it was collected from dehiscing anthers. Stigmas were re-

FIGURE 21-5. **Sorghum florets in bloom.**
(*Courtesy US Department of Agriculture*)

ceptive 8–16 days after the flowers bloomed. Fertilization was found to take place within 6–12 hours after pollination [113]. After fertilization, the zygote rests for about four hours. Organ differentiation in the embryo begins on the seventh day and is completed on the twelfth day. The embryo continues to grow until the seed is mature [3].

Sorghums are normally self-fertilized, with no known barrier to cross-fertilization. When sorghum varieties are grown in adjacent rows, the amount of cross-pollination has been reported to average 6 per cent [99]. There may be considerable variation in the amount of natural crossing in different varieties or under different climatic conditions. Wind is the chief agency in natural crossing. One report on milo indicates a range of from less than 2 per cent to 35 per cent with an average of 6.18 per cent under conditions favorable for cross-pollination [50]. Another study indicates that 5.38 per cent of cross-pollination occurred between yellow and white milo varieties grown in adjacent rows [105]. Natural cross-pollination is considerably higher in Sudan grass [36], and in certain grain sorghums with large open florets such as Dwarf Freed. Sudan grass pollen also is widely disseminated by wind, and is responsible for considerable contamination in commercial hybrid sorghum seed fields.

SORGHUM TYPES

An agronomic classification of sorghums is now the only practical one because of widespread hybridization between groups. Based on crop utilization, the agronomic groups are the grain sorghums, sorgos, grass sorghums, and broomcorn.

Grain sorghums are characterized by stalks that vary from dwarf to tall in different varieties. About 98 per cent of the grain sorghums now grown in the United States are dwarf types suitable for combine harvest with stalks usually less than 56 inches tall. Varieties grown in many other countries often are 8 or more feet in height. Grain sorghums generally have comparatively dry stalks at maturity, but they may vary from juicy to dry and from slightly sweet to nonsweet in different varieties. Although grown for grain, varieties with juicy stalks have high forage value when grain production is limited. Grain sorghums generally have larger seeds and produce more seed in proportion to total crop than do the sorgos [73]. The seeds, which are palatable, may be white, yellow, or red in color. Some varieties show splashes of red or purple on the outer coat.

Sorgo plants generally have tall, juicy, sweet stalks. The seeds range in color from mahogany red to light brown to white. They may be bitter. Sorgo is valued primarily for forage, silage, or sirup.

Grass sorghums may be either annuals or perennials. Sudan grass is an annual with slender stems 4–6 feet high with many tillers, numerous rather soft leaves, and open panicles. Johnson grass is a perennial with similar plant characteristics. Grass sorghums are grown for hay or pasturage.

Broomcorn plants have woody stalks, dry pith, and scant foilage. They are characterized by a very short rachis (main axis) with extremely long panicle branches. Broomcorn is grown for its brush.

GRAIN SORGHUM GROUPS

Grain sorghums introduced into the United States from different areas of Africa and Asia have been classed into groups called kafir, milo, feterita, durra, shallu, kaoliang, and hegari (Fig. 21-6).

The *kafir*s generally have thick juicy stalks, relatively large leaves, and beardless cylindrical heads. The seeds are white, pink, or red, and of medium size. The chaff is either black or straw-colored. South Africa is their main habitat.

The *milos* from east-central Africa have wavy leaf blades with a yellow midrib and the stalks are less juicy than those of kafir. The heads of the true milos are bearded, compact, and rather oval, with dark brown glumes having a transverse wrinkle. The seeds are large and salmon color or creamy white. The plants tiller considerably. In general, the milos are more tolerant to heat and drought than the kafirs.

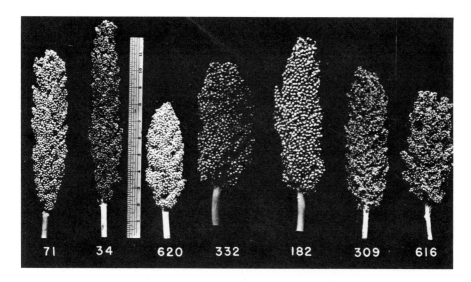

FIGURE 21-6. **Heads of several groups of grain sorghum. Left to right: Blackhull kafir, Red kafir, Legari, milo, feterita, Darso, Schrock.**

(*Courtesy US Department of Agriculture*)

The *feteritas,* from Sudan, have few leaves and relatively slender dry stalks that are slightly sweet, but also somewhat bitter. The heads are rather oval, compact, and contain very large chalky-white seeds.

The *durras* have bearded, fuzzy heads, large flat seeds, and dry stalks. Most of the varieties have compact heads but some have open heads with long branches. These are the characteristic sorghums in North Africa, Southern Europe, The Near East, and Middle East.

Shallu, from India, has tall, slender, dry stalks, loose heads, and pearly white seeds, and usually is relatively late in maturity.

Most of the *kaoliangs* are tall with dry, woody, slender, and sparsely-leaved stalks and wiry semicompact heads, and bitter brown seeds. These are the typical sorghums in China, Manchuria, Korea, and Japan.

Hegari, from Sudan, differs from kafir in having more nearly oval heads, chalky white seeds, and plants that tiller abundantly.

Most of the grain sorghum hybrids and varieties grown in the United States were derived from crosses that involved milo and kafir and occasionally other groups, and are not fully typical of any of the above groups.

VARIETIES

More than 50 varieties of grain sorghum have been grown in the United States in certain years. There was a drastic change in grain sorghum varieties after 1940 when combine types became popular. The sorghum hybrids introduced since 1956 have replaced most other varieties.

The grain sorghum varieties most widely grown in the United States from 1947–57 included Martin, Midland, Westland, Plainsman, Caprock, Early Hegari, Bonita, Combine Kafir-60, Redbine-60, Redbine-66, Redlan, and Reliance. These are all combine types that vary in height from 24–50 inches [140].

Medium-height (4–6 feet) grain sorghum varieties that previously were popular include Dwarf hegari, Blackhull kafir, Texas Blackhull kafir, Hydro kafir, Pink kafir, Red kafir, Texas milo, darso, Sagrain, Early Kalo, Ajax, and shallu.

Combine-type grain sorghum hybrids have been widely grown since 1956. These hybrids are all single crosses. Characteristics of several grain sorghum hybrids are given in Table 21-2 [18, 99].

TABLE 21-2. **Characteristics of the Leading Open-Pedigree Grain Sorghum Hybrids Released in 1957 or 1958.**

Hybrid[1]	Pedigree	Seed Color	Maturity
RS 501	ms Combine Kafir-60 × Norghum	Yellow	Same as Reliance
RS 608	ms Martin × Combine 7078	Brownish yellow	Three days earlier than Martin
RS 610	ms Combine Kafir-60 × Combine 7078	Light red	Heads about 3 days earlier than Martin
Texas 620	ms Combine Kafir-60 × Texas 07	Red	About same as Martin
RS 630	ms Combine Kafir-60 × White Feterita	White	"
RS 650	ms Combine Kafir-60 × Plainsman	Light red	"
Texas 660	ms Combine Kafir-60 × Caprock	"	Late

[1] RS designates "Regional Sorghum."

Commercial closed-pedigree hybrids comprised a substantial portion of the grain sorghum acreage in the United States by 1960.

Most combine grain sorghum hybrids and varieties are adapted to conditions in several states. The early-maturing hybrids are best suited to regions with a short growing season, and to seasons with insufficient moisture.

GROWTH OF THE SORGHUM PLANT

Normal development of the sorghum plant is similar to that of other cereals except for a few characteristic reactions.

Sorghum seedlings are smaller in proportion to the ultimate plant size than are those of corn and the common small grains. This results from the small seed size as compared with the size of the mature plant. The sorghum plant also has the ability to produce branches from buds that develop at each node on the culm. These branches start to elongate shortly before the seed on the panicle of the main stalk is fully mature. The branches usually produce panicles that often form ripe grain before the plant is harvested. Under extremely humid conditions, branches may develop aerial roots. As a result, it is possible to propagate sorghum plants vegetatively. The first branch to develop arises from the bud at the next node below the one that bears the peduncle. Branching then proceeds downward on the stalk. In contrast, tillers develop first from the lowest bud in the crown after which tillering proceeds upward.

Compared with corn, the leaves of sorghum have smaller stomata and the number of stomata per unit area is 50 per cent greater [71]. The epidermis is coated with a heavy bloom of white wax which, together with the more complete cutinization, limits evaporation so that the leaves wilt more slowly than do those of corn. The root system of sorghum is profusely branched and rebranched, which enables the plant to exhaust the moisture from the soil.

A curvilinear relationship exists between grain yield and leaf area in sorghum. A greater yield reduction results from removal of leaf area from the upper than from the lower portions of the plant. Removal of alternate leaves is more deleterious than removal of half of each leaf. Mean yield decreases of 23, 35, 43, and 95 per cent, respectively, were obtained in Kansas in 1959 from removal of approximately 33, 50, 67, and 100 per cent of the leaf area at the late boot or anthesis stages [122]. The accumulation of dry matter, total sugars, acid hydrolyzable carbohydrates, and nitrogen were reduced in plants as well as in the grain of Plainsman grain sorghum where the plants had been defoliated at the boot or anthesis stage [87]. In Kansas studies, grain yields of main culms of three grain sorghum varieties were not significantly influenced by defoliation of the tillers, and vice versa. Yield compensation for loss of leaf blade area was restricted to the defoliated culms [88].

Compared to corn, sorghum has a lower osmotic concentration of the leaf juices, but the stalk, crown, and root juices are higher in sorghum. Sorghum stalks have a lower moisture content. Sorghum has a lower transpiration ratio which, together with the slower drying rate, permits sorghum plants to withstand drought longer than corn. Sorghum plants suffering from drought usually recover and resume growth when moisture again becomes available. Early grain sorghum varieties may partly escape drought to produce some grain before the soil moisture is exhausted [71].

Sorghum grain with 10–20 per cent moisture was not reduced in viability by freezing temperatures of 14, 20, and 26°F maintained for 4–72 hours in Iowa studies. Grain with 30–45 per cent moisture content was reduced markedly in germinability under these conditions. Seedling vigor was not reduced appreciably by the freezing treatments [15].

Seed of Standard Blackhull kafir stored in envelopes in western Texas, where the humidity and rainfall are low, germinated 88 per cent after 7 years, and 65 per cent after 10 years [48], but only one seed in 200 germinated after 19 years of storage [52].

CROP ROTATIONS

Sorghum readily follows other crops in rotations, but often has a depressive effect on a subsequent crop seeded too soon after the sorghum is harvested.

Cropping Systems

In northeastern New Mexico [14], and other dryland sections of the Great Plains, fields have been cropped to sorghum for 20–30 years without a decline in yield. On the eastern Colorado drylands, sorghum yields more grain when planted after sorghum than after a small-grain crop [10]. Sometimes grain sorghum is alternated with sorgo, Sudan grass, broomcorn, or corn. In Oklahoma, grain sorghum usually produces more after small grains, corn, cowpeas, or cotton than in continuous culture. The reduction in yield of winter wheat sown soon after sorghum harvest was especially severe [69].

Sorghums respond very well to fallow, but fallowed land usually is sown to wheat. A three-year rotation of sorghum-fallow-wheat is a popular rotation where fallow is a desirable preparation for winter wheat. In dryland rotation studies in the Texas Panhandle, the total pounds of grain produced per acre in the two crop years of the same three-year rotation approximately equalled the total pounds of grain in three years of continuous cropping [99]. On sandy soil in western Oklahoma, the yield of sorghum after wheat was higher than after row crops, and nearly equal to the yield on fallowed land [69]. However, under those conditions the fallowed land contained little more moisture than did the cropped land at planting time.

Effects of Sorghums on Subsequent Crops

Sorghum is reputed to be hard on the land, the effect being particularly noticeable when fall grains are sown immediately after sorghum harvest.

Some of the injurious aftereffects of sorghum can be explained by the persistent growth of the sorghum plant, killed only by frost. Thus, sorghum depletes soil moisture to a greater extent than do other crops.

Sorghum injury to subsequent crops under irrigation, where soil moisture is ample, has been attributed to the depletion of available nitrates in the soil as a result of the high sugar content of sorghum residues left on the land [22]. The sugars in the roots of sorghum at maturity ranged from 15 to over 55 per cent on a dry-matter basis, whereas corn roots ranged from less than 10 to about 4.5 per cent [24]. These sugars furnish the energy for the multiplication of soil microorganisms which compete with crop plants for the available soil nitrogen. The result is retarded crop growth. This condition lasts for only a few months, or until the sorghum residues have decayed. Ground-up sorghum roots added to the soil depress nitrate accumulation but increase bacterial development more than corn roots [141].

The injurious aftereffects of sorghum on irrigated land may be overcome by planting an inoculated legume after sorghum, or by the application of nitrogen fertilizers for the next corp. Both alfalfa and fenugreek have made practically normal growth after sorghums in California [23]. The detrimental effect of sorghum on drylands may be avoided by fallowing the next season, or by planting a late spring crop such as sorghum or corn. By the next May after sorghum harvest available nitrates will have accumulated, while much of the soil-moisture deficiency caused by the sorghums will have been replenished by normal precipitation.

FERTILIZERS

In the Great Plains, where most of the sorghum is grown, fertilizer was seldom used on the crop until after 1945. The limiting factor for yields in this region is moisture rather than soil fertility. Consequently, fertilizers often are uneconomical. Barnyard manure also has been of little benefit on most soils of the Great Plains. However, when ample soil moisture is present, sorghum responds to applications of 25–50 pounds of nitrogen per acre.

Grain sorghum grown under irrigation in the western states generally responds to fertilizers, particularly to nitrogen. In eastern Washington, applications of 80 and 160 pounds of nitrogen (N) per acre increased the sorghum grain yields by 31.4 and 40.7 bushels, respectively, over the yields of untreated plots [83]. Yields of grain sorghums often decline after 3–5 years of production under irrigation in southwestern Kansas unless nitrogen fertilizers are used. High grain yields generally were obtained in tests with 80–90 pounds of nitrogen per acre, but there was little response to phosphorus [44]. In northeastern New Mexico, the highest yield was obtained from a combination of 240 pounds of nitrogen and 80 pounds of phosphorus

(P_2O_5), plants spaced 4 inches apart in 36-inch rows, and 8 irrigations. Closer spacing of plants favored larger yield responses at the higher nitrogen rates [86].

In humid regions, sorghum generally responds to fertilizers beneficial to corn under local conditions. Growers may apply 300–500 pounds per acre of a 4-8-4 or a 5-10-5 mixed fertilizer before planting, and later 20–30 pounds of nitrogen as a side dressing before the plants reach a height of 30 inches. This represents a total annual fertilizer application of 30–40 pounds of nitrogen, 30–40 pounds of phosphorus, and 20 pounds of potash [124]. High nitrogen content of the fertilizer is desirable where forage is grown.

On the alluvial soils of the Yazoo-Mississippi Delta in Mississippi, Sa-grain sorghum responded to an application of 150 pounds of ammonium sulfate per acre when the plants were approximately 12 inches tall [80].

SEEDBED PREPARATION

Sorghums for grain should be planted in a well prepared seedbed free from weed growth. A warm, mellow seedbed is essential for good seed germination. A weed-free seedbed is important because the seedlings are small for several weeks after emergence. Weeds are difficult to eliminate by cultivation when they grow concurrently with sorghum seedlings [10].

FIGURE 21-7. **A 5-bottom lister stirring sorghum stubble land in the spring.**
(Courtesy US Department of Agriculture)

Experiments indicate that in general higher yields are obtained from fall or winter seedbed preparation. The land may be disked, plowed, one-wayed, subsurface tilled, or blank listed in preparation for sorghum with very little difference in sorghum yields, where a suitable seedbed is prepared just before planting time. Subsurface tillage is sometimes used on cropped land, especially after wheat. Plowing is the common method of seedbed preparation in the eastern portion of the grain sorghum region, but the other implements are used in the important semiarid grain sorghum area.

In central and western Kansas, the highest sorghum grain yields are obtained from listing in late fall or early spring and the ridges leveled as soon as the weeds start growth in the spring (Fig. 21-7). The seed is planted with a lister or furrow-opener planter in the filled original furrows. The average yields of kafir at the Hays Branch Station (1924–31) by this method were 36.5 bushels per acre when listed in the fall, and 35.6 bushels for early spring listing. The yield was only 21.9 bushels when the land was listed and planted in one operation without previous tillage [60]. Similar results were obtained at the Nebraska Station [25]. In the Texas Panhandle, land preparation is delayed until early spring [99]. In northeastern New Mexico, spring listing in March or early April is advocated, the ridges being leveled in May [14].

In eastern Kansas, where the rainfall averages 30–32 inches, the seedbed for sorghums ordinarily is prepared by plowing the land in the fall, disking once or twice in the spring, and harrowing just before the seed is planted [60]. This method is satisfactory in eastern Nebraska also.

Seeding Practices

Sorghums usually are planted after the soil becomes warm, generally 10–20 days after corn-planting time in a particular locality. Planting may be done on the Gulf Coast as early as February 15, but it usually is delayed until March or April. The crop can be planted in the southern part of the grain sorghum region as late as September 1 with a good chance to mature [55, 99]. In north-central Texas, the soil does not become warm until after April 15, and in northern Kansas and southern Nebraska after May 15. In general, sorghums are planted between May 15 and July 1 [77]. In the Texas Panhandle much of the grain sorghum is planted from June 10–25, while in Kansas the date varies from May 25 to June 20 [103]. In most parts of Nebraska, the crop should be planted in late May or early June [25]. In eastern Colorado, the critical date ranges from May 20 to June 8 [10]. In the southern parts of Arizona and California the best yields are obtained from July plantings.

Sorghum for grain usually is planted in cultivated rows, 36 to 44 inches

FIGURE 21-8. **A 6-row lister planter.**
(*Courtesy J. I. Case Company*)

FIGURE 21-9. **Furrow-opener discs attached to a shoe-type planter.**
(*Courtesy US Department of Agriculture*)

apart. They may be surface planted or seeded in lister rows [Fig. 21-8]. A corn planter equipped with furrow openers combines the advantages of planting in warm soil with the better weed control that results from planting in a furrow (Fig. 21-9). In western Kansas and Oklahoma, the Texas Panhandle, and eastern New Mexico, some of the combine types are frequently planted with furrow drills in rows 14–21 inches apart without subsequent cultivation, or with one or two harrowings or a chemical spray to control early weeds. The planted seed is generally covered with 1–2 inches of soil. Grain sorghum yielded favorably in 20-inch rows in eastern Kansas with populations of 78,000 plants per acre [90], the average yield advantage of 20-inch rows over 40-inch rows being 6 per cent [121]. Higher yields were obtained with wide row spacings (40 inches) than with 10- or 20-inch rows in central Kansas in years of extreme drought [12]. (Fig. 21-10). Irrigated grain sorghum on the High Plains of Texas grown in 12- or 20-inch rows produced significantly higher grain yields than that planted in 30- or 40-inch rows [90]. Where wind erosion is a problem, sorghum rows should be planted at right angles to the direction of the prevailing winds as a protective measure [142].

Proper spacing of grain sorghum in the row depends upon the soil moisture supply and the tillering habits of the variety. In Texas, milo yielded 21 per cent more grain per acre when the seeds were planted 18–36 inches apart than when planted 3–9 inches apart; kafir yielded 13 per cent more grain planted 3–8 inches apart than when spaced more than 18 inches apart. The difference in response to spacing was attributed to the fact that milo tillers profusely while kafir tillers sparsely. Spacings between plants for the sorghum groups were advocated as follows: milo, 12–24 inches; hegari and feterita, 6–12 inches; kafir, about 6 inches. In general, the grain sorghum hybrids now grown produce the highest yields when plants are spaced 6–8 inches in rows 40–44 inches apart on semiarid nonirrigated land [57], or 19–26 thousand plants per acre. For irrigated or humid conditions this

FIGURE 21-10. **First cultivation of grain sorghum planted in lister furrows. The discs are set to throw the soil away from the plants up on the ridges. The discs will be reversed to level off the ridges and fill the furrows for the next cultivation when the plants are taller.**
(*Courtesy US Department of Agriculture*)

FIGURE 21-11. **Combining a field of grain sorghum in which most of the leaves are dead and dried.**

(Courtesy J. I. Case Company)

plant population should be doubled or trebled by thicker planting in narrower rows.

The pounds of seed per acre required for an adequate stand is one of the most uncertain features in sorghum production, because of the variable conditions of seedbed, seed viability, seed size, and weather at planting time. The seeding rate for grain sorghum varies from 2–10 pounds per acre. For average dryland conditions, 2–4 pounds of seed are sufficient to assure a stand. The dwarf combine hybrids require 3–4 pounds of seed per acre under usual conditions. From 8–15 pounds of seed per acre generally are planted on fertile irrigated land [103], and in the humid areas.

Harvesting

Most of the grain sorghum used for grain in the United States is now harvested by combine. This was made possible by the breeding of dwarf or double-dwarf varieties, followed by hybrids suitable for combine harvest with wheat machinery. Grain sorghum is mature when the seeds are fully colored, at which time they have begun to harden. At this stage the grain may contain as much as 18–20 per cent moisture. When combined, the crop should be allowed to dry until the grain contains 13 per cent or less of moisture, unless provision is made for drying the grain. The stalks often remain green with a high moisture content until killed by drought or frost. In the northern Great Plains, most grain sorghum is harvested after frost. Grain combined after a few days of dry weather following a severe freeze will usually have a moisture content low enough for safe storage (Fig. 21-11). Some varieties have a tendency to lodge soon after the stalk has been killed, which may result in heavy grain losses when harvested with a combine. In order to reduce the amount of cracked grain, it is usually advisable to reduce the cylinder speed of the thresher. Cracked grain is likely to go out of condition in storage.

Tall grain types may be cut with a row binder and the cured bundles threshed with a combine or grain separator. Grain bundles are topped with a special vertical-blade sickle attached to a combine that is pulled up to each shock at threshing time. Much of the grain sorghum grown in Asia and Africa is cut with a hand sickle or knife. The dried heads are later cut from the stalk and threshed with a flail, or by treading with animals, or with simple threshing devices.

Many elevator operators in the grain sorghum region have installed drying equipment to reduce the moisture content to 13 per cent or less. It has been found practical to take grain up to 18 per cent moisture and put it in storable condition by running it through a heater-drier [29]. Other methods of drying sorghum grain are to mix it with dry oats where later separation of the two grains is unnecessary, bin drying in thin layers, sun drying, and drying of small amounts in grain sacks [28].

SORGHUM PRODUCTION IN OTHER COUNTRIES

Sorghum (Jowar, Juar, or Cholam) is one of the most important cereals in India. It is the food crop of the common people; the stalks are fed to cattle. Sorghum is grown in most parts of India, but chiefly on the Deccan Plateau and in central India, because it resists drought well. A large sorghum area in Pakistan on the lower banks of the Indus river is irrigated, but in most regions of India the crop is grown without irrigation [1].

Sorghum (kaoliang) is a staple food in China where the crop is grown extensively. Kaoliang is grown over most of central, west, and north China, and in Manchuria. The chief production provinces are Shantung, Honan, and Hopei, where 60 per cent of the crop is produced [1]. It is widely grown where the rainfall is too low for rice. About 29 per cent of the total grain production of kaoliang is used for human food, 20 per cent for livestock feed, 7 per cent for seed, and 24 per cent for kaoling wine and its byproducts. Farmers usually sell their wheat and keep kaoliang for their own daily consumption. The crop is usually planted in the latter part of April. Kaoliang heads and blooms in July. When the average July temperature is below 24°C (75.2°F), the yield is usually low. Scanty summer rainfall also affects the crop adversely. Early fall frost is another limiting factor in the growth of this crop, which makes it necessary to grow varieties that mature early. Kaoliang is harvested in September in the northern area of production [104].

Sorghum is an important crop in most of Africa. In South Africa, the excellent health of the Bantu children often is ascribed to the kafir mush that they eat. Grain sorghum, locally called dura, is the staple food crop of the Sudan. Feterita is the best-adapted type because of its early or medium maturity, fine stems, and profuse tillering. Small areas of other grain sorghums are grown, particularly a dwarf white milo. The crop is grown extensively under rain-fed conditions, on flood lands, and under irrigation. It is generally planted in June or July. Grain sorghums are planted by hand with a pointed sowing stick in hills at rates that vary from about 4–10 pounds per acre. The plants are thinned later to 3–4 per hill. In the Gezira region, grain sorghum is grown on old cotton ridges with about 30 inches between rows and about 18 inches between hills in the row. In the Tokar and Gash deltas, the spacing is about 36 by 36 inches between hills. The crop is usually harvested in November or later. The heads are cut, piled, and later the grain is flailed out [128].

Sorghum is grown primarily for grain in Japan, but the acreage is small, *i.e.,* about 7500 acres. The crop was probably introduced into Japan from China in the Tenshō Period (1573–92). The waxy type has been cultivated in preference to the nonwaxy type. Kaoliang is seeded in rows from about May 1–15. The grain is harvested from September 15 to October 15, the heads being cut with a hand sickle. The heads are tied together in groups of 5 or 6 and sun-dried for several days.

PRUSSIC ACID POISON[1]

The young plants, particularly the leaves, of sorghums contain a glucosside called dhurrin which, when it breaks down, releases a poisonous substance known as prussic acid or hydrocyanic acid (HCN). Some losses of cattle, sheep, and goats occur each year from sorghum poisoning when they graze upon the green plants. Silage and well-cured fodder and hay usually may be fed with safety [131]. Silage may contain toxic quantities of prussic acid, but it escapes in gaseous form while the silage is being moved and fed. The prussic acid content of sorghum hay and fodder decreases during curing so that it is dangerous only occasionally.

[1] Based on Martin, J. H., and W. H. Leonard, *Principles of Field Crop Production.* (New York: Macmillan, 1949), pp. 404–405.

The prussic acid content decreases as the plant approaches maturity [78]. Small plants, young branches, and tillers are high in prussic acid. The prussic acid content of the leaves is 3–25 times greater than that of the corresponding portions of stalks of plants in the boot stage. Heads and sheaths are low in prussic acid. The upper leaves contain more prussic acid than the lower leaves. The amount of prussic acid varies in different sorghums. Sudan grass contains about 40 per cent as much as many sorghums grown under the same conditions. Sudan grass rarely kills animals unless contaminated with sorghums or sorghum-Sudan grass hybrids, except occasionally in the northern states. Even there it usually is safe after the plants are 18 inches high. Freezing does not increase the prussic acid content of sorghum. It does cause the prussic acid to be released more quickly from the glucoside form, thus making frosted sorghum very dangerous until it begins to dry out. An abundance of soil nitrates causes sorghum to be high in prussic acid. Drought-stricken and second-growth plants are dangerous because they consist largely of leaves, which are high in prussic acid.

Since a mere half-gram of prussic acid can kill a cow, 7.6 pounds of sorghum containing 0.0164 per cent HCN can be fatal. Sheep seem to be slightly less susceptible than are cattle, while horses and hogs apparently are not injured. Individual animals differ in their susceptibility to sorghum poisoning. Sorghum is unsafe as pasturage except after the plants are mature

FIGURE 21-12. **Longitudinal section of a sorghum grain.**

(*Courtesy Corn Products Company*)

and no new growth is present. Poisoning is less likely to occur when the animals eat some ground grain before they are turned into the pasture.

The antidote for cyanide poisoning is intravenous injection of a combination of sodium nitrite and sodium thiosulfate: for cattle, 2–3 grams of sodium nitrite in water, followed by 4–6 grams of sodium thiosulfate in water; for sheep, up to 1 gram of sodium nitrite and 2–3 grams of sodium thiosulfate are recommended.

CHEMICAL COMPOSITION

Composition of the Kernel

Basically, the sorghum kernel resembles other cereal grains in composition. The pericarp of a typical grain variety constitutes about 6 per cent by weight of the average kernel, the endosperm about 84 per cent, and the germ about 10 per cent [30] (Fig. 21-12). Since the endosperm comprises the bulk of the kernel, its properties in large measure determine the utility of the kernel. It consists mainly of starch which may be sugary, waxy, or nonwaxy (common) in character. The germ of a typical grain sorghum kernel contains approximately 70 per cent of the fat and 13 per cent of the protein present in the entire kernel.

Average chemical compositions, weights per 1000 kernels, and weights per bushel of 3 types of grain sorghums, as compared with maize and wheat, are given in Table 21-3 [63].

TABLE 21-3. **Percentage Composition of Various Grain Sorghums Grown in Texas.**

Crop	Water	Ash	Protein	Fat	Fiber	Carbo-hydrates	Weight per 1000 Kernels, gm
Durra	9.50	1.73	13.63	3.47	1.49	70.30	28.2
Kafir	9.70	1.76	13.13	3.30	1.54	70.30	20.7
Milo	9.39	1.64	12.50	3.18	1.52	71.88	23.9
Maize	10.04	1.55	10.39	5.20	2.09	70.69	267.4
Wheat	10.62	1.82	12.23	1.77	2.36	71.18	38.6

These analyses indicate that sorghum grain has a composition similar to that of hard wheat. Sorghums have less fiber but more fat than wheat, while the ash content is about the same. The protein in grain sorghums contains no gluten. It is possible to produce good bread from a mixture of 25 per cent milo, kafir, and other grain sorghum meal, and 75 per cent wheat flour. The crumb color is similar to that of wheat-rye bread.

Several studies have been conducted on the vitamin content of sorghum grain. In Oklahoma, 29 varieties of sorghum were analyzed for riboflavin, niacin, and pantothenic acid contents. The variation in riboflavin and pantothenic acid was small within groups. The niacin content of the brown-coated varieties was much higher than that of the other varieties [59, 43]. Another series of analyses for B-complex vitamins indicated that sorghum grain contained approximately the same quantities of riboflavin and pyridoxine as corn, but more of pantothenic acid, nicotinic acid, and biotin [127].

The composition of the component parts of the sorghum kernel is of importance to industries that utilize the crop, because it determines the value of the derivatives as well as of the by-products for food or food uses. Component analyses for the average of five varieties are given in Table 21-4 [45].

TABLE 21-4. **Percentage of Various Constituents in the Sorghum Grain as Average of Five Varieties.**

Fraction	Ash	Pro-tein	Oil	Starch	Niacin	Panto-thenic Acid	Ribo-flavin	Biotin	Pyri-doxine
Endo-sperm	20.6	80.9	13.2	94.4	75.6	64.8	50.5	52.7	75.8
Germ	68.6	14.9	76.2	1.8	17.1	28.1	27.7	31.6	16.3
Bran	10.8	4.0	10.6	3.8	7.3	7.1	21.8	15.7	8.0

The proportion of endosperm in the sorghum varieties separated ranged 80.0–84.6 per cent; germ, 7.8–12.1 per cent; and bran, 7.3–9.3 per cent. In general, sorghum grain and its fractions were found to resemble corn in the proportions of starch, protein, oil, and ash. Vitamin content varied much more among varieties than did the proportion of major constituents. The germ, which is richest of the fractions in vitamin content, contained a general concentration from 2 to 5 times as high as that of the endosperm or bran. Riboflavin in the bran was exceptionally high, being equal to that in the germ. Niacin, pantothenic acid, and pyridoxine occurred in the bran as well as in the endosperm in essentially the same concentration.

Composition of Dried Forage

The composition of the dried forage of various sorghums is compared to that of corn in Table 21-5 [31].

TABLE 21-5. **Percentage Composition of Dried Forage of Various Sorghums in Comparison with Corn.**

Foodstuff	Mois-ture	Ash	Crude Protein	Ether Extract	Crude Fiber	N-Free Extract	Cal-cium	Phos-phorus
Hegari								
fodder	13.5	8.2	6.2	1.7	16.7	53.7	0.17	0.18
stover	15.1	9.7	4.5	1.9	26.6	42.2	0.38	0.09
Kafir								
fodder	9.1	7.8	6.6	2.1	28.4	46.0	0.31	0.05
stover	12.6	9.0	5.8	1.7	27.5	43.4	—	—
Sorgo								
fodder	11.6	6.0	5.3	2.4	26.0	48.7	0.27	0.15
hay	5.8	9.5	9.5	1.9	26.8	46.5	0.31	0.09
Corn								
fodder	11.8	5.8	7.4	2.4	23.0	49.6	—	—
stover	10.7	6.1	5.7	1.5	30.3	45.7	—	—

MARKET GRADES

For market purposes, grain sorghums are divided by the Official Grain Standards of the United States into five classes, all of which are based on color. These classes are as follows: Class I, White Grain Sorghums; Class II, Yellow Grain Sorghums; Class III, Red Grain Sorghums; Class IV, Brown Grain Sorghums; and Class V, Mixed Grain Sorghums [40].

Subclasses are provided for some of these classes as follows: Class I—White Kafir, White Durra, and White Grain Sorghums; Class II—Yellow Milo, and Yellow Grain Sorghums; Class III—Red Kafir, and Red Grain Sorghums.

Under each class or subclass, there are 4 numerical grades and Sample grade. The grade requirements for grain sorghums are given in Table 21-6.

In addition, special grade designations are applied for certain conditions as follows: Bright, Discolored, Weevily, and Smutty.

TABLE 21-6. **Market Grades of Grain Sorghums.**

Grade No.	Minimum Test Weight per Bushel, Lb	Mois- ture	Maximum Limits of Damaged Kernels (Grain Sorghums, Nongrain Sorghums, and Other Grains), %		Nongrain Sorghums	Total Cracked Kernels, Foreign Material and Other Grains, %
			Total	Heat- Damaged		
1.	55	14	2	0.2	1	4
2.	53	15	5	0.5	3	8
3.	51	16	10	1.0	5	12
4.	49	18	15	3.0	10	15

Sample Grade: Sample grade shall include grain sorghums of any class or subclass which do not come within the requirements of any of the grades from No. 1 to No. 4, inclusive; or which contain inseparable stones and/or cinders; or which are musty, or sour, or heating, or hot; or which are badly weathered; or which have any commercially objectionable foreign odor except of smut; or which are otherwise of distinctly low quality.

UTILIZATION

Most sorghum grain produced in the United States is used for livestock feed, except for about 9 million bushels annually that are used in industries. It is an important human food in many countries of the Eastern Hemisphere.

Livestock Feed

Sorghums are utilized by livestock as grain, fodder, silage, hay, and pasture.

Sorghum grain is similar to corn in feeding value, but it contains slightly more protein and slightly less fat. Unlike yellow corn, most sorghum grain contains very little vitamin A. However, sorghum grain with a yellow endosperm, unknown until 1951, contains fair amounts of vitamin A precursor. Sorghum grain can be substituted for corn in almost all places where corn is used as a livestock feed. The grain is used on farms as feed for all types of livestock. Before World War II, about 20 per cent of the grain sorghum that reached terminal markets was used in poultry feeds [126].

Sorghum forage or fodder is fed to all classes of livestock. Sorgo forage usually contains less than 20 per cent of the grain by weight, whereas grain sorghum forage is usually about one-third grain. Sorghum forage contains slightly less digestible nutrients than does corn fodder but is more palatable [55].

Sorghum silage is considered to be nearly equal to corn silage in feeding value. Much of the silage produced is fed to dairy cattle.

Human Food

Sorghum grain is the most important food in parts of China, India, and Africa. The grain is consumed in the form of bread, porridge, confectionaries, and as an alcoholic drink similar to beer.

In Bombay Province in India, sorghum grain in some form is eaten at each meal. The grain is ground each day in the home; otherwise the flour would become rancid because of the presence of the embryo. The flour is made into flat thin cakes. Kafir mush is eaten in South Africa by Bantu children [55]. African natives prefer palatable white and yellow varieties for food [79]. Kaoliang ground into flour or groats for consumption as bread or porridge is an important food in north China. Sometimes kaoliang is mixed with wheat flour to make bread [1]. Since 1945, American-grown grain sorghum has found wide use as food for people in war-stricken as well as in underdeveloped countries. In many cases, 1 part of sorghum flour is blended with 4 parts of wheat flour [79].

The use of sorghum grain for human food has never been widespread in the United States. In the pioneer days of the American West, grain sorghum used as bread or porridge frequently allowed a family to remain on the land after drought or other calamity had destroyed the wheat or corn crops. Recipes for the use of sorghum grain as food were published by several states and by the Federal government at the time of World War I, but it was found that Americans preferred other cereals [56].

Waxy sorghum varieties have been used as special food delicacies in China for several centuries. The release in Kansas in 1944 of the Cody sorghum variety, which has a waxy endosperm, first stimulated interest in the conversion of the crop into a special starch as a substitute for the cassava starch obtained from the Dutch East Indies before World War II. The product was used in the manufacture of "minute dessert" which is similar in quality to tapioca. Production of waxy sorghum for this purpose was largely discontinued in 1947 as cassava was imported from Brazil.

The natives of Africa have made beer from sorghum grain since prehistoric times. Varieties with brown or red seedcoats or subcoats were used for making native beers because the tanninlike substance in the colored

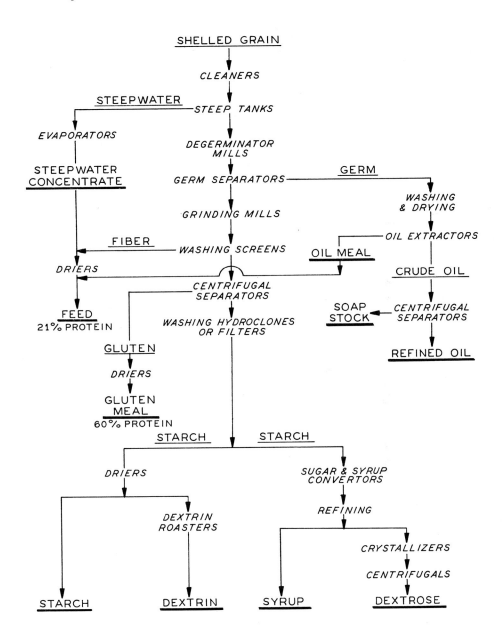

SHELLED GRAIN

CLEANERS

STEEPWATER

EVAPORATORS

STEEP TANKS

STEEPWATER
CONCENTRATE

DEGERMINATOR
MILLS

GERM SEPARATORS

GERM

GRINDING MILLS

WASHING
& DRYING

FIBER

WASHING SCREENS

OIL EXTRACTORS

DRIERS

OIL MEAL

CRUDE OIL

CENTRIFUGAL
SEPARATORS

FEED
21% PROTEIN

WASHING HYDROCLONES
OR FILTERS

SOAP
STOCK

CENTRIFUGAL
SEPARATORS

GLUTEN

REFINED OIL

DRIERS

GLUTEN
MEAL
60% PROTEIN

STARCH

STARCH

DRIERS

SUGAR & SYRUP
CONVERTORS

DEXTRIN
ROASTERS

REFINING

CRYSTALLIZERS

CENTRIFUGALS

STARCH

DEXTRIN

SYRUP

DEXTROSE

FIGURE 21-13. **Flow sheet for generalized wet milling operation for grain sorghum,
which also applies to corn.**

(Courtesy Corn Products Company)

grains supplies the bitterness that in American and European beers is derived from hops.

Industrial Products

Grain sorghum long has been a potential source of industrial raw material. It contains 11.5–16.5 per cent protein, and the starch content is 63 to 73 per cent [79]. Sorghum grain in the United States is processed into starch, paste flour, dextrose, dextrose syrup, alcohol, edible oils, gluten meal, and gluten feed.

Sorghum grain can be made readily into starch by a wet-milling process similar to that used for corn (Fig. 21-13). A factory in Texas uses some 6 million bushels of grain sorghum annually. The starch from sorghum can then be converted into dextrose for use in food products.

Waxy starch is used as a postage stamp adhesive, and for sizing for paper or fabrics. Another use of waxy starch is in drilling muds. The drilling mud mixture is circulated through the bit during the drilling of oil wells. The muds remove the cuttings rapidly from the well, lubricate and cool the drill, and seal the walls so as to retard the entrance of water. A ton or more of starch is used in each new oil well [79].

Dry milling plants in Kansas and Texas manufacture flour and livestock feed from the crop. Flour from sorghum grain is used to make gypsum lath or wall board. Grits obtained from the endosperm by dry milling can be used in brewing, just as corn grits and broken rice are now used.

Considerable grain sorghum was used as a source of grain alcohol during World War II [56]. Alcohol is produced from sorghum grain in quantities quite comparable to that obtained from wheat or corn. The manufacture of butyl alcohol from sorghum grain was begun in 1944. Butyl alcohol, when combined with certain organic acids, forms butyl esters used as lacquer solvents and in the manufacture of 2,4-D weed killer [59].

The seedcoat of grain sorghum contains a wax similar to carnauba wax extracted from the carnauba palm of the tropics. It is used to make polishes for furniture and shoes, carbon paper, sealing wax, and other products [59].

DISEASES

Head or Panicle Diseases

The three sorghum smuts found in the United States are covered kernel smut, loose kernel smut, and head smut. Johnson grass smut occasionally attacks second-growth sorghum (Fig. 21-14). In India, long smut (*Toly-*

FIGURE 21-14. **Sorghum smuts. Left to right: sound head, covered kernel smut, loose kernel smut, head smut.**

(Courtesy US Department of Agriculture)

sporium chronbergii), which is transmitted by floral infection, also attacks sorghum.

Covered kernel smut caused by the fungus, *Spaceletheca sorghi,* is probably the most destructive sorghum disease in the United States. Usually all of the kernels on a smutted plant are destroyed. Large cylindrical or cone-shaped smut galls are formed instead of the kernels. These are covered with a light-gray or brown membrane which later breaks to release the dark brown spores. Some of the spores are scattered in the field to nearby healthy heads, but most of them remain in the galls until the crop is threshed when the spores are spread to sorghum seed [67].

When smut-contaminated seed is planted, the spores germinate at the same time as does the seed. The heaviest infection often occurs when the seed germinates at a low soil temperature (50–70°F) [130]. The fungus invades the seedling, grows within the plant undetected, and becomes apparent when the heads appear [67].

The five known strains or races of covered smut attack different sorghum varieties. Most of the sorghums are susceptible to all five races. Hegari and the true milos are attacked by Race II and certain feteritas and their derivatives are attacked by Race III. A few varieties are attacked by Races IV and V, but these varieties differ in their susceptibility to the other races. Spur feterita and some of its derivatives are highly resistant to or immune from all races of covered kernel smut [67].

Covered kernel smut can be controlled by seed treatment, use of smut-free seed, or planting resistant varieties. Several dust, slurry, and liquid treatments are effective. Copper carbonate or basic copper sulfate dusts, applied at the rate of 2–3 ounces per bushel of seed, will generally control the disease. Ceresan M is effective when applied at the rate of one-half ounce per bushel in a slurry [13, 67].

Loose kernel smut caused by the fungus *Sphacelotheca cruenta,* is much less common than covered kernel smut. It occurs occasionally, particularly in the southern Great Plains.

Long pointed galls are formed in the spikelets. The thin membrane that covers the galls usually breaks soon after they reach full size. Most of the dark-brown spores are soon blown away, leaving a long, dark, pointed, curved central structure called a columella.

Spores of loose kernel smut on the sorghum seed germinate soon after the seed is planted, and the fungus grows within the sorghum plant where it becomes apparent after heading. Unlike covered kernel smut, this disease stunts infected plants and frequently induces the development of abundant side branches. It may also cause secondary infection; that is, spores from a smutted head may cause the smut development in late heads on otherwise healthy plants [67].

There are at least two races of loose kernel smut which differ in their ability to attack different groups of sorghum. Certain varieties of feterita and milo are resistant to both races, while other varieties are susceptible to one race but resistant to the other [67].

Control measures for loose kernel smut are the same as those for covered kernel smut. The varieties which are resistant to the five races of covered kernel smut usually are resistant also to the races of loose kernel smut.

Head smut, caused by the fungus *Sphacelotheca reiliana,* damages certain sorghum varieties and has been particularly destructive since 1952. Some of the best sorghum hybrids, such as RS 610, are susceptible to head smut.

This smut destroys the entire head, transforming it into a large mass of dark brown powder spores. The smut first becomes evident when the sorghum heads emerge. The large gall bulges out of the boot. At first the gall is covered with a whitish membrane, but it soon breaks and allows the spores to be scattered. The fungus carries over in the soil for several years and may infect a plant in the seedling or later stages [67].

The growing of resistant hybrids or varieties offers the only control of head smut, but the treatment of seed from infected fields prevents the spread of the smut to uninfected areas. Smutted plants or heads should be cut and burned before the spores are disseminated. Head smut attacks the durras, kafirs, and some hybrids that involve these varieties [100, 67].

Root Diseases

Periconia root rot or milo disease is caused by the fungus *Periconia circinata.* The disease was formerly attributed to *Pythium arrhenomanes,* or to other organisms. It was discovered in the United States in 1925 and caused heavy damage in the 1930's, especially in Texas, Kansas, New Mexico, and California. It is the most serious disease known on milo, darso, and certain of their derivatives [67].

In heavily infested soil, Periconia root rot may kill sorghum seedlings but usually the damage appears later. The first indications of the disease are stunted plants, slight rolling of the leaves, and a light yellow color at the tips and margins of the older leaves. However, the roots and crowns are badly damaged by that time. The disease progresses until all leaves are discolored or dead. The diseased plants usually die before heading, but the affected plants may form small, poorly filled heads [67].

The outer part of the roots of affected plants reveals a water-soaked brown or reddish discoloration, but later most or all of the finer roots as well as the outer part of the large roots are rotted. The central part of the large roots, crown, and lower stalk turn dark red [67].

Soil becomes heavily infested with Periconia root rot only when susceptible varieties are grown, but it may build up very rapidly. Losses in yield of 50–60 per cent can be expected whenever a susceptible variety is grown on an infested soil, but under irrigation losses up to 100 per cent are the usual occurrence. The organism may remain in the soil for 7 years or longer [96]. The disease is spread by soil or carried in runoff or irrigation water. It is also spread by farm implements, windblown soils, or any agency that transports soil from infested fields. [67].

Losses from Periconia root rot are avoided when resistant varieties are grown (Fig. 21-15). All of the susceptible varieties have been replaced with resistant varieties or hybrids that were selected or bred for resistance [82, 67].

FIGURE 21-15. **Double Dwarf milo: Selected strain resistant to Periconia root and stalk rot (above); unselected variety destroyed by the disease (below).**

(*Courtesy US Department of Agriculture*)

Stalk Diseases

Charcoal rot, caused by *Macrophomina phaseoli,* has resulted in serious losses to sorghum fields in the semiarid regions, but it also occurs in many other areas. The disease is more destructive when extreme heat or drought occurs [67]. The fungus causes a seedling blight as well as a stalk rot.

The most conspicuous symptom of charcoal rot is the disintegration of the pith and numerous small black sclerotia on the loosely attached fibers which remain in the otherwise hollow stem, as the crop approaches maturity. Severely damaged plants lodge badly, particularly in areas of moderate winds. Pith in badly lodged stalks is disintegrated. The rot may extend for some distance up the stalk as well as down into the roots. Heads of diseased plants fail to develop normally, which results in a poor yield of shrunken grain [135].

A soil temperature of 107.6°F is most favorable for the seedling blight, whereas a soil temperature of 100.4°F was most favorable for the development of stalk rot of mature plants [68].

The milos and quick-maturing and dry-stalked varieties suffer the greatest damage. Most varieties of kafir and sorgo are rather resistant [67]. Damage is limited where the soil is well supplied with moisture [135]. Charcoal rot attacks corn, sweet potatoes, cowpeas, field beans, sunflowers, alfalfa, and other crops so that crop rotation is of little benefit.

Colletotrichum stalk rot is caused by the fungus, *Colletotrichum graminicolum*. The same fungus also causes leaf anthracnose. The disease has been more destructive to broomcorn and sorgos than to grain sorghum, but the milos are susceptible.

Colletotrichum stalk rot follows evidence of leaf anthracnose and usually appears first in the lower part of the stalk, but it may spread upward as the plant approaches maturity. Diseased stalks frequently break over at or near the base. The lesions formed on the outside of diseased stalks usually have reddish to purplish margins and white centers. The pith of infected stalks is red or purplish red in most sorghum varieites [67].

The fungus lives over on field residues of susceptible crops and weeds and on seeds. It enters the stalks directly through the rind and spreads in the interior of the stalks, especially in the conducting tissues.

Control measures for Colletotrichum stalk rot are based on clean culture, crop rotation, and the use of resistant varieties [62]. Hegari, Western Blackhull kafir, Club kafir, and Early Kalo were resistant to the disease [67].

Weak neck causes stalk breaking of dry-stalked varieties in the central and southern Great Plains.

Weak neck is the result of the drying and subsequent overdecay of the peduncle of certain dwarf varieties of sorghum after maturity. Affected tissues become so weakened that the heads break over, usually at the base of the peduncle. Sometimes the panicles are lying on the ground where they cannot be harvested satisfactorily with a combine. Poorly developed heads with lightweight lusterless seeds sometimes are associated with the disease [125, 66, 41, 67].

Weak neck was induced in Colby milo by subjecting the plants to drought stress periods, by artificial defoliation, or by partial shading of the leaves during the growing season. Resistant varieties maintained a higher concentration of carbohydrates in the peduncles throughout the growing season than did susceptible varieties [41].

The use of resistant varieties is the most practical control measure. The peduncles of resistant varieties remain green and solid after the seeds are ripe and dry. Midland and most of the kafirs have this characteristic.

Other stalk diseases. Fusarium stalk rot, caused by the fungus *Gibberella fujikuroi,* produces symptoms similar to those of charcoal rot [129]. Rhizoctonia stalk rot, caused by *Rhizoctonia solani,* is a soil-borne fungus. This disease differs from charcoal rot in that it first attacks the pith where it produces a reddish discoloration. The fibers remain as light streaks in the discolored pith. The sclerotia are on the outside of the stalk instead of the inside as occurs in charcoal rot. Both diseases have been reported in northern Texas [67].

Leaf Diseases

Bacterial leaf diseases are likely to be found wherever sorghum is grown. Organisms that cause these diseases are believed to be carried over from season to season on the seed, on infected plant material in or on the soil, and occasionally on plants that overwinter. They may be spread from one plant to another by wind, splashed rain, or insects. Infection occurs through the stomata of the leaves. Bacterial diseases seldom cause serious losses, but they may destroy one-half to two-thirds of the leaf surface during warm moist seasons. Three bacterial diseases of sorghum are known in the United States: bacterial stripe, bacterial streak, and bacterial spot [67].

Bacterial stripe, caused by *Pseudomonas andropogoni,* is the most widespread of the three bacterial diseases. It attacks all sorghum groups. The disease is characterized by long, rather narrow, somewhat irregular stripes, which usually are red and first apparent on the lower leaves. The stripes, 0.25–9 inches or more in length, are confined between the leaf veins. Bacterial exudate occurs on the stripes which often dries to form red crusts or thin scales. The color of the stripes varies somewhat in different varieties of sorghum [67].

Bacterial streak is caused by *Xanthomonas holcicola.* This disease occurs on sorghum plants from the seedling stage to near maturity as narrow water-soaked translucent streaks about 0.125 inch wide and 1–6 inches long. At first the streaks are colorless, except for the light yellow beadlike drops of exudate on the young streaks. Later, narrow red-brown margins or blotches of color appear in the streaks; after a few days the streaks are red throughout. When numerous, the streaks may join to form long, irregular areas that cover a considerable part of the leaf blade. In the advanced stage, the bacterial exudate dries to thin white or cream colored scales [67].

Bacterial spot, caused by *Pseudomonas syringae,* attacks the leaves of all sorghums. Spots appear first on the lower leaves, but infection gradually spreads to the upper leaves as the plants approach maturity. The spots are circular to irregularly elliptical and from 0.04 to 0.33 inch in diameter. They first appear as dark green water-soaked areas which soon turn to red. Later, the spots become dry and light-colored in the center, each usually surrounded by a red border. The smaller lesions are often red throughout. When numerous, the spots may coalesce into large diseased areas which may kill the entire leaf [67].

Recommended control measures for the three bacterial leaf diseases are sanitation, seed treatment, and the use of resistant varieties. Disposal of old infected plant litter, destruction of infected plants that overwinter, and crop rotation will reduce the quantity of inoculum present in sorghum fields the next season. Seed treatment will prevent the disease from being carried over on the seed. Varieties somewhat resistant to all three of these bacterial diseases are: Shallu, Cody, and other varieties and hybrids that carry a tan plant pigment. Kafirs are relatively resistant to bacterial streak.

Fungus leaf diseases. Fungus leaf spots usually are more or less roughened due to the presence of fungal fruiting bodies. Eight distinct leaf diseases are commonly found on sorghum in the United States: rough spot, anthracnose, leaf blight, zonate leaf spot, gray leaf spot, target spot, sooty stripe, and rust.

The rough spot disease, caused by *Ascochyta sorghina,* is rather widespread in the southeastern states where it was first reported in 1937. It is first observed as circular or oblong light-colored spots, which later turn red or tan. As the spots enlarge, they grow together so that the size of diseased areas is extremely variable. The disease is particularly characterized by the abundant development of pycnidia, usually on the surface of the diseased discolored area. Severely diseased leaves die. Control measures include crop rotation, use of resistant varieties, and seed treatment. Sorghum after sorghum should be avoided on land where the disease has occurred. The Schrock variety is relatively resistant to the disease [67].

Anthracnose, *Colletotrichum graminicolum,* occurs on the leaves of sorghum in the humid areas of the South. This fungus also causes a stalk rot. The fungus is carried on the seed as well as on plant refuse on or in the soil. The leaves seldom are affected severely until about the middle of the growing season when the plants have reached the jointing stage. Infection appears on the leaves as small, circular to elliptical, tan to reddish-purple spots. Later these spots enlarge and may unite to involve large leaf areas. The leaf midrib is often strikingly discolored. Centers of the leaf spots finally fade to a grayish-tan color. Spores are spread from these spots by wind or rain to other leaves. Control measures include crop rotation to avoid sorghum after sorghum, clean culture to destroy infected plant material, and the use of resistant varieties. Resistant grain sorghums include hegari, Western Blackhull kafir, and Martin [67].

Other sorghum fungus leaf diseases, together with the causal fungus, are: Leaf blight, *Helminthosporium turcicum*; zonate leaf spot, *Gleocorcospora sorghi*; gray leaf spot, *Cercospora sorghi*; target spot, *H. sorghicola*; sooty stripe, *Ramulispora sorghi;* and rust, *Puccinia purpurea.* These diseases usually occur in humid areas such as eastern United States and the tropical zone of Africa.

Seed Rot or Seedling Blights

Seed rot is most severe when sorghum is planted in cold wet soil. Some fungi that invade the endosperm are species of *Fusarium, Aspergillus, Rhizopus, Rhizoctonia, Penicillium,* and *Helminthosporium.* Most of these thrive at temperatures below 70°F [65]. Some fungi, especially species of *Pythium,* attack the young sprout before it emerges. Fungi that also attack seedlings include species of *Fusarium, Penicillium, Pythium,* and *Helminthosporium.*

Controls include the use of sound, well-matured seed, seed treatment, and proper cultural practices. Seed with the seedcoats cracked or otherwise damaged in threshing is readily invaded by seed rotting fungi. To insure good stands, seed should not be planted until the soil is warm enough for prompt germination. Planting in cold soil at the bottom of freshly opened lister furrows often results in excessive seed rotting. These rots are most common in feterita, hegari, Club, Wonder, and similar soft-seeded types [67]. Dust fungicides, especially copper carbonate, applied at the rate of two ounces per bushel resulted in increased seedling emergence [66].

INSECT PESTS

Chinch Bug

The chinch bug, *Blissus leucopterus,* is widely distributed in the northern Mississippi valley as well as the adjacent areas in North America [85]. In outbreak stages, it is one of the most destructive insects to sorghum in the United States [136]. Outbreaks usually occur at intervals of 5–10 years, and usually coincide with times of drought [85]. This insect is also destructive on small grains, corn, and some other grasses.

Chinch bugs are small black sucking insects about 0.125 inch long when full grown. The adults have white wings folded on their backs to form a sort of X [84]. They winter over on bunch grasses or other plant debris. In the spring the adults fly to small-grain fields in the cooler areas, or directly to sorghum or corn in the warmer areas such as Texas or southern Oklahoma. They mate, laying eggs on the leaves of the plants or on the soil adjacent. The hatched bugs feed on the plants. In grain fields, most of the bugs crawl to sorghum (or corn) when the small grains begin to ripen. A second generation is usually produced, and it continues to feed on the sorghum plant. A third generation develops in the South in the fall. The adults from the last generation overwinter [136].

Chinch bugs suck the juices of sorghum plants. Injury to sorghum results from a combination of one or more of at least four factors as follows:

> (1) The direct withdrawal of plant fluids from cells and especially from the xylem and phloem tubes; (2) the exudation of plant fluids from punctures left open after the feeding of the insects, with attendant possible interference with root pressure and translocation; (3) a clogging of the plant conductive tissue with stylet sheath material deposited by the bugs; and (4) openings in the plant tissue are provided through which fungi and bacteria can enter [107].

Differences in composition doubtless account for the preferences that chinch bugs show for certain varieties and for their ability to thrive on and destroy susceptible varieties. However, research workers have been unable to identify the chemical compounds that are responsible [139]. Old plants are more difficult to kill than younger ones [107].

Chemical or mechanical barriers prevent the migration of chinch bu⁓ The best barriers into or across sorghum fields are a narrow band of a repellant or insecticide on the soil surface or on a stiff paper fence about 2 inches high. Coal-tar creosote repellants have been replaced by insecticidal dusts, especially those which contain 4 per cent of dinitro-o-cresol, 10 per cent of DDT, or 1 per cent of benzene hexachloride. They may be applied in a narrow band on smooth hard-packed soil at the rate of 1–2 pounds per rod. The dust line should be patrolled daily to remove debris that may have blown onto it, or to repair breaks caused by wind, water, or soil cracks [84].

They are rather expensive, but several new insecticides used as dusts or sprays have given effective control when the insecticide hits the chinch bug. Control of adults has been obtained with toxaphene applied as a spray or dust at the rate of 1.5 pounds per acre. One of the most effective dusts

FIGURE 21-16. **Chinch bugs destroyed the susceptible varieties in the 2 rows where the stakes are standing, but did little damage to the 3 resistant strains.**

(Courtesy US Department of Agriculture)

consists of 4 per cent by weight of sabadilla powder in pyrophyllite applied at the rate of 50 pounds per acre [84].

Some sorghum varieties are more resistant to chinch bug injury than others. In general, the milos are very susceptible and feteritas susceptible. The Redlan variety, and the kafirs are resistant to injury [107] (Fig. 21-16).

Sorghum Midge

The sorghum midge (*Centarinia sorghicola*) is abundant in the southern states. It is also recorded from Mexico, South America, Dutch Antilles, Italy, and Anglo-Egyptian Sudan. It may be identical with *C. caudata* from southern Asia. The midge attacks all sorghums. It made grain sorghum production unprofitable in the southern states until nearly 1940 when a larger acreage and the presence of parasites reduced the severity of the damage.

The sorghum midge is a small, orange colored fly which deposits its eggs in the spikelets of sorghum or Johnson grass at flowering time. The small white larvae, which hatch a few days later, feed on the young seed. They pupate after 9–11 days. The adult midge emerges to start a new generation every 14–20 days under favorable conditions. The midge overwinters in the larval stage in a cocoon. The species is probably disseminated in seed or hay in the form of dormant cocoon larvae. The adult emerges in time to lay eggs on blooming sorghum heads [137].

The only control measures are early planting and a large acreage of sorghum. Varietal resistance has not been definitely established.

Corn-Leaf Aphid

The corn-leaf aphid (*Aphis maidis*) is a pest in North and South America, Japan, South Africa, and Hawaii [85]. In some seasons, this aphid causes serious damage to sorghum in the United States, particularly when large numbers occur in the leaf curl. This hinders the exsertion of the head from the boot. Badly infested heads usually produce a small amount of low vitality seed. The secretion of honey dew by the aphid forms a sticky mass about the heads which encourages mold growth, which in turn prevents the production of high quality seed. Aphids apparently overwinter in the southern states, migrating north in the spring [60]. Resistant varieties offer promise as a control measure. The Norghum variety shows considerable resistance [85].

Sorghum Webworm

Severe damage to grain sorghum crops is frequently caused by the sorghum webworm (*Celama sorghiella*). It has been reported from most of the southeastern states, but it is known to range northward to Missouri, Illinois, Nebraska, and Maryland.

Sorghum webworm injury is caused by the larvae which destroy the seed. In Texas, the insect has proved most troublesome in regions where the annual rainfall averages 30 inches or more, but outbreaks are periodic. They are most likely to occur in seasons characterized by prolonged spells of rainy weather [101].

This insect overwinters in the larval stage on sorghum plants. Pupation occurs the next spring, while the adults begin to emerge about April 1 in Texas. Shortly afterwards, the moths start to lay eggs, but multiplication proceeds slowly until about the middle of the growing season. The insect increases rapidly after that time. Consequently, sorghums planted late are injured more severely than those planted early. Records indicate that six generations or broods may be produced during a season [101].

Control of the sorghum webworm by the use of insecticides may be impractical. Helpful cultural measures include a thorough cleanup of crop residues to destroy the worms that overwinter, and planting early to mature the crop before injurious infestations occur. Dry weather accompanied by high temperatures is the most effective factor in natural control [101].

Other Insect Pests

Some other insects that injure sorghums are the rice stinkbug (*Solubea pugnax*) and the corn earworm (*Heliothis armigera*). The corn earworm is an important pest, especially in varieties with a compact head. Occasionally farmers spray or dust with insecticides to save the crop.

Stem borers (*Chilo* species) have attacked sorghum in California and are very destructive in India and North Africa. A few varieties are resistant to this insect.

Grasshoppers cause little injury to sorghum even where nearby cornfields are wholly destroyed. Grasshoppers seem to prefer the leaves of milo or hegari to those of most other sorghums. They will eat the sorghum grain as it develops, but they may be controlled with chlordane or toxaphene sprays.

Other stem borers (*Sesamia* species) are destructive in India and Africa. The sorghum maggot (*Atherigonia indica*) feeds heavily on young sorghum plants in India. Ants, beetles, and other insects that eat sprouting sorghum seeds in the soil, can be controlled by treating the seed with insecticides such as benzene hexachloride.

Other Pests

Birds devour large quantities of grain sorghum, and are particularly destructive when they invade fields of grain in the milk stage. The chief bird pests are sparrows in the United States and queleas in Africa. Attempts to control the birds by trapping, shooting, poisoning, electrocution or frightening are only partly effective. Numerous large fields of grain sorghum in a locality limit the bird losses on individual farms.

Witchweed (*Striga lutea* or *S. asiatica*) is a flowering (phanerogamous) plant parasite of sorghum, corn, and some other grass species. It is prevalent over Africa and India and has invaded North and South Carolina in the United States. Haustoria from germinating witchweed seedlings enter the sorghum roots and sap the growth of the plants before the witchweed stems emerge above the soil surface. Herbicidal control of the witchweed after emergence in helpful but cannot prevent considerable crop loss. The planting of trap crops such as cowpeas, which stimulate the germination of witchweed seeds but are not parasitized, is helpful where the practice is feasible.

CYTOLOGY — CYTOGENETICS

The genus *Sorghum* is comprised of three groups: one, with a somatic chromosome number of 10 (2*n*), includes *S. versicolor;* another, with a somatic number of 20, is represented by *S. vulgare;* the third, a group of 40, is represented by *S. halepense* [70, 51, 34]. These groups might be considered as the diploid, tetraploid, and octoploid forms of the genus, since quadrivalents have been found among the meiotic chromosomes of *S. vulgare,* while chromosomes higher numbers than quadrivalents have been reported in *S. halepense* [46, 47]. However, all chromosomes of *S. vulgare* usually associate as bivalents, and most of the chromosomes of *S. halepense* associate as bivalents with a few quadrivalents [70, 47, 34]. Consequently, *S. vulgare* is commonly referred to as the diploid form, and *S. halepense* as the tetraploid form.

Occasional haploid plants with only 10 chromosomes are found in sorghum fields. These haploids are short and weak with small plant parts, and are nearly sterile since they bear only an occasional seed [11].

Tetraploid and octoploid plants of *S. vulgare* have been produced by colchicine treatment, and they are stouter and shorter than the diploids. The tetraploid plants flower about 20 days later, while the octoploids flower more than 30 days later than do the diploids. The relative sterility of polyploid sorghum makes them of doubtful economic value [17].

Varieties of *S. vulgare* with 20 somatic chromosomes cross freely with one another, but attempts to cross the 10-chromosome *S. versicolor* with the two higher chromosome groups have been unsuccessful [51, 34]. *S. vulgare* and *S. halepense* can be crossed, and they hybridize occasionally under natural conditions. Johnson grass, which has 40 somatic chromosomes, evidently has chromosomes or segments of chromosomes that are homologous with 20-chromosome sorghums [98].

The meiotic behavior of crosses that involve Sudan grass and Johnson grass indicates *S. halepense* probably is an autotetraploid of some variety of *S. vulgare* [16], or is a segmental allopolyploid that arose from 2 species closely related cytologically [38].

A cross between Texas Blackhull kafir (*S. vulgare*) and Johnson grass (*S. halepense*), produced some 30-chromosome (triploid) hybrids that were sterile, but one hybrid produced a few seeds when pollinated with *S. vulgare* [38]. Most of the backcross progeny had only 20 somatic chromosomes, but some of these showed various Johnson grass characteristics except rhizome formation [39].

GENETICS

Most of the research on the genetics of sorghum has been done in India and the United States [73, 4, 98, 76].

Seed or Plant Colors

Pigments in sorghum grain may occur in the epicarp and testa. At least nine genes are involved in seed color. Two gene pairs were reported in India to account for red, yellow, and white seed colors. The genotypes of the three colors are RRYY, red; rrYY, yellow; and RRyy and rryy, white [37]. A third gene pair (I, i) was added later which, in the dominant condition, intesifies color and differentiates between red and pink when both R and Y are present [7]. Two additional genes in the dominant condition, BW_1 and BW_2, cause a brown tinge in the pericarp in some Indian varieties. The gene M that causes an intensification of color independent of the three major factors (RYI) also was reported in India. Two gene pairs, B_1b_1 and B_2b_2, are known to control presence or absence of the testa. In the presence of the brown testa, the epicarp is brown when a dominant gene S (spreader) is present along with dominant B_1 and B_2. Recessive S prevents brown in the epicarp in the presence of B_1 and B_2 [98, 76].

Glume color is green until the plant approaches maturity, when different colors may appear such as straw, red, black, sienna, or mahogany. Red and black glume colors have been explained as an allelic series, Q, q, and q^r. Red is dominant to black in some varieties, but red is recessive in others. The genotypes of this series would be as follows: Q, red; q^r, red; and q, black [110].

There are purple and brown plant colors, to which the factor pair Pp has been assigned. Plants with dominant P are reddish purple in the presence of dominant Q, or blackish purple in the presence of recessive q. Plants with recessive p are brown or tan. The brown plant color modifies the red and black colors caused by the Qq factor pair. Modified black plants have mahogany colored glumes. Some sorghum varieties have straw-colored glumes, a character that appears to be controlled by two or three genes [98].

Vegetative Characters

Sorghum varieties range in height 2–15 feet or more. Tall varieties are preferred for forage because of greater fodder yields, but dwarf varieties are preferred for grain in the United States, Australia, and Argentina. Numerous dwarf types have been developed from mutations or hybrid segregations. Four independently inherited genes and a modifying complex have been found to influence elongation of the internodes. The shortening of the internodes is the only visible effect of these recessive genes, and the number and size of leaves are unaffected. Combine varieties now grown are recessive for either two or three genes for dwarfness, while some of the tall forage sorghums are recessive for only one gene [97]. There are sixteen possible genotypes from the independent assortment of four gene pairs, and at least ten of these genotypes have been recognized among common varieties. Under dryland conditions in Texas, plants recessive for four genes usually are 40 cm in height from the ground to the upper leaf; those with three recessive genes about 50 cm tall; those with two recessive genes, 100 cm tall; and those recessive for one gene, 150–200 cm tall [97]. Late varieties are taller than early varieties that carry the same genes for internode length because late varieties have more nodes and internodes. So-called Four Dwarf or Quadruple Dwarf hybrids are now in production.

Crosses between the erect variety Sart and the weak-stalk variety Iceberg indicate that a single factor pair (E, e) is involved, with erect stalk dominant [20].

Sorghum stem pith is dry or juicy, and sweet or nonsweet. Dry pith is controlled by a single factor pair (D, d). Dry stalks have white leaf midribs, whereas the water in juicy pith causes the midribs to appear gray. A juicy stalk may contain 70 to 80 per cent moisture, while a similar plant with dry pith contains 65 to 70 per cent moisture. The characters sweet and nonsweet juice are controlled by a single factor pair (X, x) with nonsweet dominant [4]. However, additional genes control the degree of sweetness or sugar content.

Duration of Growth

Three genes, ma, ma_2, and ma_3, were found to influence duration of growth in milo. Lateness is dominant to earliness, except that recessive ma is epistatic to dominant Ma_2 and Ma_3, and Ma_2 is epistatic to Ma_3. This results in 8 homozygous genotypes, but only 4 phenotypes for maturity as indicated in Table 21-7.

TABLE 21-7. **Phenotypes and Genotypes of Milo in Relation to Time of Blooming.**

Phenotypes	Homozygous Genotypes	Days to Anthesis
Early	ma ma Ma_2 Ma_2 Ma_3 Ma_3	50
	ma ma ma_2 ma_2 Ma_3 Ma_3	50
	ma ma Ma_2 Ma_2 ma_3 ma_3	50
	ma ma ma_2 ma_2 ma_3 ma_3	50
Intermediate	Ma Ma ma_2 ma_2 ma_3 ma_3	70
Late	Ma Ma ma_2 ma_2 Ma_3 Ma_3	82
Ultra Late	Ma Ma Ma_2 Ma_2 ma_3 ma_3	98
	Ma Ma Ma_2 Ma_2 Ma_3 Ma_3	98

These phenotypes bloom at approximately 50, 70, 82, and 98 days when planted in June in Texas when the days are longer than 14 hours. All four phenotypes for maturity are identical for both size and duration of growth when grown under 10-hour photoperiods. Thus, these genes govern the response of milo to photoperiod [92].

Another gene, ma_4 from Kalo, has been reported in this maturity series. Early Kalo has the dominant allele, Ma_4 [95]. The very early Ryer Milo is recessive for the fourth maturity gene.

The maturity of the plant is directly associated with the number of nodes and leaves on the stalk. Each additional leaf formed delays the time of flowering about 3–4 days. Also each additional internode adds several inches to the plant height.

Sorghum varieties differ in their sensitivity to photoperiod although all are short-day plants. In crosses of sorghums that exhibited differences in sensitivity to photoperiod, it has been observed that all F_1 hybrids were hastened in maturity when subjected to 10-hour photoperiods where one parent was sensitive. Thus, sensitivity to short photoperiod is a dominant characteristic. Hybrids that were relatively insensitive to short photoperiods always had two relatively nonsensitive parents [94].

Inflorescence, Flower, and Seed Characters

The character for loose or compact panicle has been reported as being controlled by a single-factor pair.

Cytoplasmic male sterility in grain sorghum appears to be controlled by a single recessive nuclear gene (ms_c) that interacts with sterile cytoplasm. The pollen grains in male-sterile plants tend to shrivel after being partially formed. The anthers are reduced in size and lack viable pollen prior to dehiscence [81].

Seed shedding due to callus formation has been studied in hybrids between Tunis grass, Sudan grass, and several sorghum varieties. Seed shedding was found to be dominant to nonshedding. One or two gene pairs appear to be involved in different crosses [55, 56].

Waxy endosperm is a simple recessive to starchy. Sugary endosperm in sorghum is similar to that in maize. The sugary gene has been reported as a simple recessive.

Disease Resistance

Susceptibility to milo disease (*Periconia circinata*) has been found to be partially dominant to resistance. It is controlled by a single gene pair [82].

Reaction to leaf anthracnose (*Colletotrichum graminicolum*) is controlled by a single factor pair (L, l) with resistance dominant to susceptibility [61].

In a cross between two sorgo varieties, disease reaction to stalk red rot (*Colletotrichum graminicolum*) has been found to be controlled by a single factor pair (Ls, ls) in which resistance was dominant. This factor pair is closely linked with leaf anthracnose reaction (L, l) with a crossover value of 9.57 per cent [19].

Resistance to Insect Pests

There are marked differences in reaction of sorghums to chinch bugs (*Blissus leucopterus*). Sometimes resistance indicates simple dominance, but in other crosses transgressive segregation for resistance suggests that complementary genes are involved. There is ample evidence that chinch-bug resistance is heritable [107, 26].

Hybrid Vigor or Heterosis

First generation (F_1) sorghum hybrids generally are vigorous, and many of them are late in maturity and tall. Lateness, due to complementary gene action, affects time of floral initiation, and a similar genetic explanation applies to tallness. This complementary gene action is often confused with heterosis that causes more vigorous growth and increased head size and consequent grain yield. Such plants are somewhat larger, tiller more, and produce more grain or forage than do pure varieties of comparable growth duration [98]. Hybrid vigor is particularly marked in crosses between widely different groups or varieties of grain sorghums [21]. Increases in plant size as great as 300–400 per cent have been reported as a result of complementary action of height and maturity genes and growth vigor (Fig. 21-17).

Milo-hegari hybrids invariably have expressed extreme vigor, especially in increased vegetative growth as well as in extreme lateness of maturity. Hybrids between certain other types failed to show extremes of height or lateness, but manifested their vigor mainly in grain production. From these observations it follows that the different degrees of heterosis represent differences in the number of dominant genes favorable to growth [53].

In sorghum involving the factor pair, Ma ma, which controls plant response to photoperiod and influences the time of floral initiation, the heterozygous condition, Ma ma, produces plants that are later and larger than the homozygous genotypes. They also tiller more. Heterosis that did not involve later maturity was concluded to be a stimulation of tillering and of more rapid cell division [93]. In most hybrids in which later maturity is not involved, hybrid vigor is expressed chiefly in larger heads that contain more grains, with some increased tillering, and a slight increase in grain size.

Tests in Arizona of 19 first-generation sorghum hybrids showed that the Double Dwarf milo 38 × Ajax hybrid yielded 54 per cent more than the average of the two parents. The increases in plant height over the means of the parents ranged 6.2–113.8 per cent in the hybrids. The hybrids that ranked highest in vigor as expressed by grain yield, stover yield, plant height, number of leaves, maturity, and other characters, had either hegari or Double Dwarf milo 38 in their parentage [8].

An F_1 sorghum hybrid, Texas Blackhull kafir × Day Selection, characterized by vigor without lateness of maturity or tall height, was tested for grain yield in Texas for 8 years. The hybrid was produced by hand pollination of male sterile Blackhull kafir carrying the gene ms_1 [108]. The hybrid was grown at the Chillicothe Station for 6 years in an April 15 planting, and for 8 years in a June 15 planting. The hybrid yielded 27 per cent above the average of all varieties in the April planting, and 44 per cent above the variety average in the June planting. These data provided a measure of heterosis to be expected in sorghum hybrids grown for grain [117].

Induced Mutations

New variants induced by colchicine treatment of the seedlings without

FIGURE 21-17 **Extreme example of hybrid vigor in sorghum (center) in a cross between kafir (left) and hegari (right). Complementary genes for late maturity (and resultant plant size), as well as for heterosis (expressed chiefly in increased kernel number) produced this large panicle.**

(Courtesy US Department of Agriculture)

a change of chromosome number, have been reported. In general, the variant characters bred true. It was proposed that somatic reduction of the chromosome number took place with a concurrent chromosome rearrangement and a subsequent restoration of the diploid number [102].

Numerous mutants of mature plant characters have been induced by irradiation [91]. Studies on the effects of thermal neutron irradiation on dormant sorghum seed indicated that the frequency of seedling mutations ranged from 2.7–7.3 per cent after treatment with different radiation dosages. Albino was the most common mutation [58].

Linkage Groups

Seven of the ten possible linkage groups in sorghums have been reported. Four of these groups have three or more known genes, whereas the other three groups are now represented by only two.

The *Q-B-Gs Group* was reported by Stephens and Quinby [114]. Factor pairs located in this group include reddish or blackish plant color that is conspicuous in the glumes (Q, q), presence or absence of a brown testa (B, b), and normal green or green-striped plants (Gs, gs). The order of genes with crossover percentages was as follows: Q (13.2) B (11.3) Gs. At least one of the gene pairs, Bw_1 bw_1 and Bw_2 bw_2, also appears to be located in this group very close to the Q locus. In the dominant condition, these genes cause brown color in the epicarp and dry anthers, even in the absence of a testa that develops when B_1 and B_2 are present in the dominant condition [98].

The *D-Rs-P Group* was reported by Stephens and Quinby [116]. Factor pairs found in this group are dry or juicy stalks (D, d), red or green seedling stem color (Rs, rs), and purple or brown stem color (P, p). The indicated order of genes, together with crossover percentages, is D (10.9) Rs (16.4) P. The crossover percentage between D and P was 27.3, which agrees well with the 30 per cent reported by Ayyangar [6].

The *Ms_2-A-V_{10} Group* was reported by Stephens and Quinby [117]. Green Striped-2 was added to the group by Stephens [109]. Factor pairs located in this group are as follows: normal or male-sterile flowers (Ms_2, ms_2), awnless or awned lemmas (A, a), green or virescent-yellow plants (V_{10}, v_{10}), and normal or green-striped plants (Gs_2, gs_2). The order of genes with crossover percentage is Gs_2 (11.0) Ms_2 (10.9) A (9.1) V_{10}.

The *$Y-V_{11}-G_2$ Group* was described in sorghum by Stephens [111]. The factor pairs found in this group are red or white seed color (Y, y), green or virescent-yellow plant color (V_{11}, v_{11}), and green or golden plant color (G_2, g_2). The order of genes, together with cross-over percentages, is Y (6.0) V_{11} (3.0) G_2. A linkage has also been reported between the gene that controls white or red seed color in milo (Y, y) and the maturity gene, Ma_3. Because the population observed was small an accurate estimate of the crossover value was impossible, but Ma_3 appears to be closely linked with Y [92].

A genetic linkage also has been reported between the maturity gene Ma_1 and a gene Dw_2 that influences length of internode [92].

A linkage has been reported between green or yellow seedling (Y_2, y_2) and starchy or waxy endosperm (Wx, wx). The crossover percentage between wx and y_2 was estimated as 26.5 [98].

A linkage has been reported between the factor pair for loose or compact head shape (Pa_1 pa_1) and one that controls thickness of the mesocarp (Z, z). The crossover percentage between these genes was estimated as 1.07 [5].

SORGHUM IMPROVEMENT

Most of the sorghum improvement work now being done is based on a knowledge of the inheritance of specific genes for desired characters in productive sorghum varieties. As a result, it is possible to choose parents with reasonable assurance that a desirable strain will emerge from the cross as the result of recombination of the desired genes [55].

Objectives of Sorghum Improvement

Some of the objectives of sorghum improvement are: earlier maturity, more palatable seed, dwarf types for easy machine harvest, improved forage quality, seed that will stand exposure with the least damage, insect resistance, disease resistance, resistance to lodging, resistance to drought, lower prussic acid content, better syrup production, resistance to cool temperatures, and endosperms with waxy type of starch [73, 55].

Seeds of all brown-seeded sorghums contain a bitter substance that makes them less palatable than white-, yellow-, or red-seeded varieties. Consequently, much effort has been devoted to breeding strains that lack this bitter taste. For combine harvest, the most valuable grain sorghum varieties are characterized by dwarf plants less than 4 feet tall, lodging resistance, and erect heads. Much effort has been expended to obtain combine varieties with good head exsertion and quick-drying rachis or secondary seed branches as in Martin. These are important characteristics south of the region where sorghums are combined after frost.

Standard Breeding Methods

Since sorghum was introduced into the United States from Africa, selection was widely practiced in order to obtain improved strains. The frequency of natural cross-pollination necessitated the selection of seed heads in order to keep the varieties reasonably uniform. A crop from bulk seed nearly always contains some off-types or outcrosses that must be eliminated by selection. Consequently, nearly every sorghum variety released by an experiment station has undergone some selection before it was distributed. Among the varieties produced by selection were Dwarf Yellow milo, Double Dwarf milo, Dawn kafir, Sunrise kafir, Spur feterita, and Dwarf feterita [73]. The Martin variety which is resistant to Periconia root rot, was selected from a field of the susceptible Wheatland milo [75]. Other resistant selections include Texas milo, Double Dwarf 38, and Westland.

Artificial hybridization of sorghum varieties, started in 1914, resulted in Chiltex and Premo which were released to growers in 1923. They were selections from a feterita-kafir cross [98]. Several varieties, which included Wheatland, Kalo, Plainsman, and Caprock, were selected from milo-kafir crosses. Norghum is an early grain sorghum developed from a Dwarf ferterita-Dwarf Freed × Yellow kafir cross [33]. Rancher is a low-prussic-acid sorgo developed from a cross of high and low acid strains of Black Amber sorgo [32]. Dwarf kafir 44-14, selected from a Sharon kafir × Early feterita cross, is suitable for combine harvest as well as being chinch bug resistant [27].

A method of progeny row selection, described in 1921, has been widely used in the development of several sorghum varieties distributed since that time [133].

Controlled Pollination Techniques

Controlled self-pollination to avoid contamination by foreign pollen is readily accomplished with paper bags placed over the heads before blooming begins. Special bags are made of heavy Kraft paper glued with waterproof adhesive. Insects frequently eat much of the grain on bagged heads. They may be controlled by spraying the bags with insecticides such as aldrin, dieldrin, or malathion.

Most crosses for sorghum improvement are made by hand emasculation and pollination because the breeder usually desires only a few F_1 plants. In crossing, the immature spikelets and the pedicellate spikelets that contain anthers are trimmed from a branch of the head with dissecting scissors before the flowers bloom. The anthers are then extracted with tweezers or a blunt awl. The emasculated spikelets are covered by a small glassine bag (Fig. 21-18), and are ready for pollination about two days later. Viable pollen collected from the male parent is dusted on the exposed stigmas, and the branch is again bagged [132].

Pollen is collected in a paper bag placed over a head that is in bloom. The bag is shaken to free pollen from the anthers and the bag is carried to the plant to be pollinated. The pollen is dusted on the receptive head, preferably on 2–3 successive days. The bag is then placed over the entire pollinated head if it is a male-sterile head [98].

Sorghum flowers can be emasculated by immersing the panicle, just prior to the first blooming, in water at a temperature of 48°C (118.4°F) for 10 minutes which kills the pollen. The water temperature may drop as low as 42–44°C (107.6–111.2°F) by the end of the 10-minute period [112]. The emasculated head is then bagged to prevent undesirable pollination. The method is suitable for mass pollination of crosses in which any self-pollinated plants, which occasionally occur, may be detected.

Hybrid Sorghum Seed Production

Research on methods for the production of hybrid seed in quantity has been underway in Texas since the early 1930's. A genetic male-sterile character, discovered in Texas Blackhull kafir in 1935, offered promise for the production of hybrid seed [108], but a better genetic male-sterile was found in Day milo in 1943. It produced sterile F_1 plants when crossed with some varieties, but gave fertile F_1 plants when pollinated with others. This provided a procedure for the production of hybrid sorghum seed by a three-way cross [118].

FIGURE 21-18. **Placing a bag over the emasculated florets at the top of a sorghum panicle. The lower unemasculated spikelets have been removed.** (*Courtesy US Department of Agriculture*)

Then a cytoplasmic male-sterile was isolated from crosses between milo and kafir, in which milo was the female parent. The cytoplasmic male-sterility resulted from the interaction between milo cytoplasm and kafir nuclear factors. The results indicate that the degree of sterility is increased as the proportion of kafir chromosomes in milo cytoplasm is increased [119]. Cytoplasmic male-sterility lines now used for hybrid seed production are nearly completely sterile. Many varieties or selections may serve as pollen-restorer strains in making hybrids [98].

The method now generally followed for the production of hybrid sorghum seed on a field scale was outlined in 1954 [119]. With minor modifications, it is as follows:

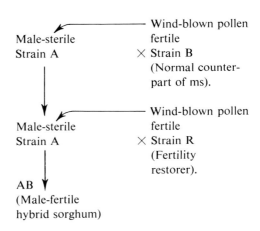

I. Maintenance or increase of cytoplasmic male-sterile strain (ms) in a crossing block.

Male-sterile Strain A
— Wind-blown pollen fertile
× Strain B (Normal counterpart of ms).

II. Crossing block for production of single-cross seed.

Male-sterile Strain A
— Wind-blown pollen fertile
× Strain R (Fertility restorer).

III. Single-cross hybrid seed planted by farmers for grain or forage production.

AB (Male-fertile hybrid sorghum)

Male-sterile Strain A is produced in an isolated crossing block in which normal Strain B is the pollen parent. Hybrid sorghum is produced in a second crossing block with male-sterile Strain A and a fertility restorer Strain R. The seed from the second block is planted by growers for commercial hybrid sorghum production. Cross-pollination in sorghum is effective over at least twelve 40-inch rows. At present, the most common ratio of seed to pollen rows is 3:1 with either 6:2 or 12:4 modifications based on whether 2-row or 4-row harvesting equipment is available for harvesting the rows of the pollen parent [99].

REFERENCES

1. Anderson, E., and J. H. Martin, "World production and consumption of millet and sorghum." *Econ. Bot.*, **3**(3): 265–288. 1949.
2. Artschwager, E., "Anatomy and morphology of the vegetative organ of *Sorghum vulgare*." USDA *Tech. Bul. 957.* 1948.

3. ———, and R. C. McGuire, "Cytology of reproduction in *Sorghum vulgare*." *J. Ag. Res.*, **78**(12): 659–673. 1949.

4. Ayyangar, G. N. R., "The description of crop plant characters and their ranges of variation. IV: Variability of Indian sorghum (Jowar)." *Ind. J. Ag. Sci.*, Vol. XII, Part IV, pp 527–563. 1942.

5. ———, and M. A. S. Ayyar, "Linkage between a panicle factor and the pearly-chalky mesocarp factor (Zz) in sorghum." Ind. Acad. Sci. *Proc.*, **8**: 100–107. 1938.

6. ———, M. A. S. Ayyar, and V. P. Rao, "Linkage between purple leaf-sheath colour and juiciness of stalk in sorghum." Ind. Acad. Sci. *Proc.*, **5**(B): 1–3. 1937.

7. ———, *et al.*, "Inheritance of characters in sorghum—the great millet. III: Grain colors: red, yellow, and white." *Ind. J. Ag. Sci.*, **3**: 594–604. 1933.

8. Bartel, A. T., "Hybrid vigor in sorghum." *Agron. J.*, **41**(4): 147–152. 1949.

9. Bidwell, G. L., E. E. Bopst, and J. D. Bowling, "A physical and chemical study of milo and feterita kernels." USDA *Bul. 1129*. 1922.

10. Brandon, J. F., J. J. Curtis, and D. W. Robertson, "Sorghums in Colorado." Colo. Ag. Exp. Sta. *Bul. 449*. 1938.

11. Brown, M. S., "Haploid plants in sorghum." *J. Hered.*, **34**(6): 163–166. 1943.

12. Brown, P. L., and W. D. Shrader, "Grain yields, evapotranspiration, and water use efficiency of grain sorghum under different cultural practices." *Agron. J.*, **51**: 339–343. 1959.

13. Buchholtz, W. F., "Sorghum seed treatment." S. Dak. Ag. Exp. Sta. *Cir. 51*. 1944.

14. Burnham, D. R., and R. W. Leamer, "Dryland tests with sorghums at Tucumcari, New Mexico." N. Mex. Ag. Exp. Sta. *Bul. 393*. 1954.

15. Carlson, G. E., and W. H. Atkins, "Effect of freezing temperatures on seed viability and seedling vigor of grain sorghums." *Agron. J.*, **52**: 329–333. 1960.

16. Casady, A. J., and K. L. Andersen, "Hybridization, cytological, and inheritance studies of a sorghum cross-autotetraploid Sudan grass × (Johnson grass × 4n Sudan grass)." *Agron. J.*, **44**(4): 189–194. 1952.

17. Chin, T. C., "The cytology of polyploid sorghum." *Am. J. Bot.*, **33**: 611–614. 1946.

18. Clegg, M. D., O. J. Webster, and P. H. Grabouski, "Performance of grain sorghum hybrids and varieties in Nebraska, 1957." Nebr. Ag. Exp. Sta. *Outstate Test Cir. 67*. 1958.

19. Coleman, O. H., and I. E. Stokes, "The inheritance of resistance to stalk rot in sorghum." *Agron. J.*, **46**: 61–63. 1954.

20. ———, and I. E. Stokes, "The inheritance of weak stalk in sorgo." *Agron. J.*, **50**: 119–120. 1958.

21. Connor, A. B., and R. E. Karper, "Hybrid vigor in sorghum." Tex. Ag. Exp. Sta. *Bul. No. 359*. 1927.

22. Conrad, J. P., "Some causes of the injurious after-effects of sorghums and suggested remedies." *J. Ag. Res.*, **19**: 1091–1111. 1927.

23. ———, "Fertilizer and legume experiments following sorghums." *J. Am. Soc. Agron.*, **20**: 1211–1234. 1928.

24. ———, "The carbohydrate composition of corn and sorghum roots." *J. Am. Soc. Agron.*, **29**: 1014–1021. 1937.

25. Cushing, R. L., T. A. Kiesselbach, and O. J. Webster, "Sorghum production in Nebraska." Nebr. Ag. Exp. Sta. *Bul. 329*. 1940.

26. Dahms, R. G., and J. H. Martin, "Resistance of F_1 sorghum hybrids to the chinch bug." *J. Am. Soc. Agron.*, **32**: 171–174. 1940.
27. Davies, F. F., and J. B. Sieglinger, "Dwarf Kafir 44-14 and Redlan." Okla. Ag. Exp. Sta. *Bul. B-384.* 1952.
28. DeLong, H. H., and E. I. Whitehead, "Storing grain sorghum." S. Dak. Ag. Exp. Sta. *Bul. 396.* 1949.
29. Doll, R. J., "Grain sorghum in the Great Plains economy." Fed. Res. Bnk. of Kansas City. pp 1–51. 1952.
30. Edwards, W. M., and J. J. Curtis, "Grain sorghums, their products and uses." USDA Bur. Ag. and Ind. Chem. *Cir. ACE-193.* March 1943.
31. Ellis, N. R., W. R. Kauffman, and C. O. Miller, "Composition of the principal feedstuffs used for livestock," in *Food and Life.* USDA Yrbk. of Ag. pp 1065–1074. 1939.
32. Franzke, C. J., "Rancher sorghum." S. Dak. Ag. Exp. Sta. *Cir. 57.* 1945.
33. ———, "Norghum sorghum." S. Dak. Ag. Exp. Sta. *Bul. 397.* 1949.
34. Garber, E. D., "A cytological study of the genus *Sorghum:* Subsections Para-sorghum and Eu-sorghum." *Am. Nat.*, **78**: 89–94. 1944.
35. ———, "Cytotaxonomic studies in the genus *Sorghum.*" U. Calif. Pub. Bet., **23**: 283–362. 1950.
36. Garber, R. J., and S. S. Atwood, "Natural crossing in Sudan grass." *J. Am. Soc. Agron.*, **37**: 365–369. 1945.
37. Graham, R., "Pollination and cross-fertilization in the juar plant (*Andropogon sorghum,* Bret.)." Dept. Ag. India, Bot. ser. *Mem.*, **8**: 201–216. 1916.
38. Hadley, H. H., "Cytological relationships between *Sorghum vulgare* and *S. halepense.*" *Agron. J.*, **45**: 139–143. 1953.
39. ———, and J. L. Mahan, "The cytogenetic behavior of the progeny from a back-cross, (*Sorghum vulgare* × *S. halepense* × *S. vulgare*)." *Agron. J.*, **48**: 102–106. 1956.
40. "Handbook of official grain standards of the United States." USDA SRA-AMS-177. 1960.
41. Hansing, E. D., L. E. Melchers, and J. C. Bates, "Weak neck of sorghum." *Agron. J.*, **42**(9): 437–441. 1950.
42. Hector, J. M., *Introduction to the Botany of Field Crops*, Vol. I. *Cereals*, Johannes-burg, South Africa: Central News Agency, Ltd. pp 360–391. 1936.
43. Heller, V. G., and J. B. Sieglinger, "Chemical composition of Oklahoma grain sorghums." Okla. Ag. Exp. Sta. *Bul. 274.* 1944.
44. Herron, G. M., and A. B. Erhart, "Effects of nitrogen and phosphorus fertilizers on the yield of irrigated grain sorghum in southwestern Kansas." *Agron. J.*, **52**: 499–501. 1960.
45. Hubbard, J. E., H. H. Hall, and F. R. Earle, "Composition of the component parts of the sorghum kernel." *Cer. Chem.*, **27**(5): 415–420. 1950.
46. Huskins, C. L., and S. G. Smith, "A cytological study of the genus *Sorghum* Pers. I: Somatic chromosomes." *J. Gen.*, **25**: 241–249. 1932.
47. ———, and S. G. Smith, "A cytological study of the genus *Sorghum* Pers. II: The meiotic chromosomes." *J. Gen.*, **28**: 387–395. 1934.
48. Karper, R. E., "Longevity and viability of kafir seed." *J. Am. Soc. Agron.*, **20**: 527 (note). 1928.
49. ———, "Multiple-seeded spikelets in sorghum." *Am. J. Bot.*, **18**: 189–195. 1931.

50. ———, and A. B. Conner, "Natural cross pollination in milo." *J. Am. Soc. Agron.*, **11**: 257–259. 1919.

57. ———, *et al.*, "Grain sorghum date of planting and spacing experiments." Tex. Ag. Exp. Sta. *Bul. 424.* 1931.

51. ———, and A. T. Chisholm, "Chromosome number in sorghum." *Am. J. Bot.*, **23**: 369–374. 1936.

52. ———, and D. L. Jones, "Longevity and viability of sorghum seed." *J. Am. Soc. Agron.*, **28**: 330–331. 1936.

53. ———, and J. R. Quinby, "Hybrid vigor in sorghum." *J. Hered.*, **28**: 83–91. 1937.

54. ———, and J. R. Quinby, "The history and evolution of milo in the United States." *J. Am. Soc. Agron.*, **38**: 441–453. 1946.

55. ———, and J. R. Quinby, "The inheritance of callus formation and seed shedding in sorghum." *J. Hered.*, **38**:(7): 211–214. 1947.

56. ———, and J. R. Quinby, "Sorghum—its production, utilization, and breeding." *Econ. Bot.*, **1**(4): 355–371. 1947.

58. Kaukis, K., and O. J. Webster, "Effects of thermal neutrons on dormant seeds of *Sorghum vulgare* Per." *Agron. J.*, **48**: 401–406. 1956.

59. Knox, G., V. G. Heller, and J. B. Sieglinger, "Riboflavin, niacin, and pantothenic acid contents of grain sorghums." Stanford U. Food Res. Inst., **9**(2): 89–91. 1944.

60. Laude, H. H., and A. F. Swanson, "Sorghum production in Kansas." Kans. Ag. Exp. Sta. *Bul. 265.* 1933.

61. LeBeau, F. J., and O. H. Coleman, "The inheritance of resistance in sorghum to leaf anthracnose." *Agron. J.*, **42**(1): 33–34. 1950.

62. ———, I. E. Stokes, and O. H. Coleman, "Anthracnose and red rot of sorghum." USDA *Tech. Bul. 1035.* 1951.

63. LeClerc, J. A., and L. H. Bailey, "The composition of grain sorghum kernels." *J. Am. Soc. Agron.*, **9**: 1–16. 1917.

64. Leukel, R. W., "Chemical seed treatments for the control of certain diseases of sorghum." USDA *Tech. Bul. 849.* 1943.

65. ———, and J. H. Martin, "Seed rot and seedling blight of sorghum." USDA *Tech. Bul. 839.* 1943.

66. ———, L. E. Melchers, and A. F. Swanson, "Weak neck in sorghum." *J. Am. Soc. Agron.*, **35**: 163–165. 1943.

67. ———, J. H. Martin, and C. L. Lefebvre, "Sorghum diseases and their control." USDA *Farmers Bul. 1959.* 1944 (rev. 1951).

68. Livingston, J. E., "Charcoal rot of corn and sorghum." Nebr. Ag. Exp. Sta. *Res. Bul. 136.* 1945.

69. Locke, L. F., and O. R. Mathews, "Cultural practices for sorghums and miscellaneous field crops." USDA *Cir. 959.* 1955.

70. Longley, A. R., "Chromosomes in grass sorghums." *J. Ag. Res.*, **44**: 317–321. 1932.

71. Martin, J. H., "The comparative drought resistance of sorghums and corn." *J. Am. Soc. Agron.*, **22**: 993–1003. 1930.

72. ———, "Recurving in sorghums." *J. Am. Soc. Agron.*, **24**: 501–503. 1932.

73. ———, "Sorghum improvement," in USDA Yrbk. of Ag. pp 523–560. 1936.

74. ———, "Climate and sorghum," in *Climate and Man.* USDA Yrbk. of Ag. pp 343–347. 1941.

75. ——, "Tailor-made sorghums," in *Science in Farming*, USDA Yrbk. of Ag., 1943–1947. pp 413–416. 1947.
76. ——, "Sorghum and Pearl millet," in *Handbuch der Pflanzenzuchtung*, Berlin, Germany: Verlag Paul Parey, II. Bd., 2 Aufl. pp 565–587. 1959.
77. ——, J. S. Cole, and A. T. Semple, "Growing and feeding grain sorghums." USDA *Farmers Bul. 1764*. 1936.
78. ——, J. F. Couch, and R. R. Briese, "Hydrocyanic acid content of different parts of the sorghum plant." *J. Am. Soc. Agron.*, **30**: 725–734. 1938.
79. ——, and M. M. MacMasters, "Industrial uses of grain sorghum," in *Crops in Peace and War*. USDA Yrbk. of Ag. pp 349–352. 1950–1951.
80. ——, and J. C. Stephens, "The culture and use of sorghums for forage." USDA *Farmers Bul. 1844* (rev.). 1955.
81. Maunder, A. B., and R. C. Pickett, "The genetic inheritance of cytoplasmic—genetic male sterility in grain sorghum." *Agron. J.*, **51**: 47–49. 1959.
82. Melchers, L. E., and A. E. Lowe, "The development of sorghums resistant to milo disease." Kans. Ag. Exp. Sta. *Tech. Bul. 55*. 1943.
83. Nelson, C. E., "Effects of spacing and nitrogen applications on yield of grain sorghums under irrigation." *Agron. J.*, **44**(6): 303–305. 1951.
84. Packard, C. M., "Cereal and forage insects," in *Insects*. USDA Yrbk. of Ag. pp 581–595. 1952.
85. Painter, R. H., *Insect Resistance in Crop Plants*. New York: Macmillan. pp 326–356. 1951.
86. Painter, C. G., and R. W. Leamer, "The effects of moisture, spacing, fertility, and their interrelationships on grain sorghum production." *Agron. J.*, **45**: 261–264. 1953.
87. Pauli, A. W., and F. C. Stickler, "Leaf removal in grain sorghum. II: Trends in dry matter, carbohydrates, and nitrogen following defoliation." *Agron. J.*, **53**(2): 102–105. 1961.
88. ——, and F. C. Stickler, "Leaf removal in grain sorghum. III: Main culm-tiller relationships." *Agron. J.*, **53**(5): 319–321. 1961.
89. Pinthus, M. J., and J. Rosenblum, "Germination and seedling emergence of sorghum at low temperatures." *Crop Sci.*, **1**(4): 293–296. 1961.
90. Proter, K. B., M. E. Jensen, and W. H. Sletten, "The effect of row spacing, fertilizer, and planting rate on the yield and water use of irrigated grain sorghum." *Agron. J.*, **52**: 431–434. 1960.
91. Quinby, J. R., and R. E. Karper, "Inheritance of mature plant characters in sorghum." *J. Hered.*, **33**(9): 323–327. 1942.
92. ——, and R. E. Karper, "The inheritance of three genes that influence time of floral initiation and maturity date in milo." *J. Am. Soc. Agron.*, **37**(11): 916–936. 1945.
93. ——, and R. E. Karper, "Heterosis in sorghum resulting from the heretozygous condition of a single gene that affects duration of growth." *Am. J. Bot.*, **33**(9): 716–721. 1946.
94. ——, and R. E. Karper, "The effect of short photoperiod on sorghum varieties and first generation hybrids." *J. Ag. Res.*, **75**: 295–300. 1947.
95. ——, and R. E. Karper, "The effect of different alleles on the growth of sorghum hybrids." *J. Am. Soc. Agron.*, **40**(3): 255–259. 1948.
96. ——, and R. E. Karper, "The effect of milo disease on grain and forage yields of sorghum." *Agron. J.*, **41**(3): 118–122. 1949.

97. ——, and R. E. Karper, "Inheritance of height in sorghum." *Agron. J.*, **46:** 211–216. 1954.

98. ——, and J. H. Martin, "Sorghum improvement," in *Advances in Agronomy*, Vol. 6. New York: Academic Press. pp 305–359. 1954.

99. ——, *et al.*, "Grain sorghum production in Texas." Tex. Ag. Exp. Sta. *Bul. 912.* 1958.

100. Reed, G. M., and L. E. Melchers, "Sorghum smuts and varietal resistance in sorghum." USDA *Bul. 1284.* 1925.

101. Reinhard, H. J., "The sorghum webworm (*Celama sorghiella*, Riley)." Tex. Ag. Exp. Sta. *Bul. 559.* 1938.

102. Ross, J. G., C. J. Franzke, and L. A. Schuh, "Studies on colchicine-induced variants in sorghum." *Agron. J.*, **46:** 10–15. 1954.

103. Ross, W. M., and H. H. Laude, "Growing sorghums in Kansas." Kans. Ag. Exp. Sta. *Cir. 319.* 1955.

104. Shen, T. H., *Agricultural Resources of China.* Cornell U. Press. pp 206–207. 1951.

105. Sieglinger, J. B., "Cross pollination of milo in adjoining rows." *J. Am. Soc. Agron.*, **13:** 280–282. 1921.

106. ——, and J. H. Martin, "Tillering ability of sorghum varieties." *J. Am. Soc. Agron.*, **31:** 475–488. 1939.

107. Snelling, R. O., *et al.*, "Resistance of sorghums to the chinch bug." USDA *Tech. Bul. 585.* 1937.

108. Snowden, J. D., *The Cultivated Races of Sorghum.* London: Adlard & Son, Ltd. pp 1–274. 1936.

109. Stephens, J. C., "Male sterility in sorghums: its possible utilization in production of hybrid seed." *J. Am. Soc. Agron.*, **29:** 690–696. 1937.

110. ——, "Linkage of green-striped 2 in sorghum." *J. Am. Soc. Agron.*, **36**(5): 469–470. 1944.

111. ——, "An allele for recessive red glume color in sorghum." *J. Am. Soc. Agron.*, **39:** 784–790. 1947.

112. ——, "The $YV_{11}G_2$ linkage group in sorghum." *Agron. J.*, **43:** 382–386. 1951.

113. ——, and J. R. Quinby, "Bulk emasculation of sorghum flowers." *J. Am. Soc. Agron.*, **25:** 233–234. 1933.

114. ——, and J. R. Quinby, "Anthesis, pollination, and fertilization in sorghum." *J. Ag. Res.*, **49**(2): 123–136. 1934.

115. ——, and J. R. Quinby, "Linkage of the Q-B-Gs group in sorghum." *J. Ag. Res.*, **57**(10): 747–757. 1938.

116. ——, and J. R. Quinby, "The D-Rs-P linkage group in sorghum." *J. Ag. Res.*, **59**(10): 725–730. 1939.

117. ——, and J. R. Quinby, "The Ms_2-A-V_{10} linkage group in sorghum." *J. Ag. Res.*, **70:** 209–218. 1945.

118. ——, and J. R. Quinby, "Yield of a hand-produced hybrid sorghum." *Agron. J.*, **44**(5): 231–233. 1952.

119. ——, G. H. Kuykendall, and D. W. George, "Experimental production of hybrid sorghum seed with a three-way cross." *Agron. J.*, **44**(7): 369–373. 1952.

120. ——, and R. F. Holland, "Cytoplasmic male-sterility for hybrid sorghum seed production." *Agron. J.*, **46:** 20–23. 1954.

121. Stickler, F. C., and H. H. Laude, "Effect of row spacing and plant population of corn, grain sorghum, and forage sorghum." *Agron. J.*, **52:** 275–277. 1960.

122. ——, and A. W. Pauli, "Leaf removal in grain sorghum. I: Effects of certain defoliation treatments on yield and components of yield." *Agron. J.*, **53**(2): 99–102. 1961.

123. ——, *et al.*, "Row width and plant population studies with grain sorghum at Manhattan, Kansas." *Crop Sci.*, **1**(4): 297–300. 1961.

124. Stokes, I. E., O. H. Coleman, and J. S. Dean, "Culture of sorgo for sirup production." USDA *Farmers Bul. 2100*. 1957.

125. Swanson, A. F., "Weak neck in sorghums." *J. Am. Soc. Agron.*, **30**: 720–724. 1938.

126. ——, "Recent developments in grain sorghum production by plant breeding methods." *Agron. J.*, **41**(5): 179–181. 1949.

127. Tanner, F. W., S. E. Pfeiffer, and J. J. Curtis, "B-complex vitamins in grain sorghums." *Cer. Chem.*, **24**(4): 268–274. 1947.

128. Tothill, J. D., Ed., *Agriculture in the Sudan*. Oxford, England: Oxford U. Press. pp 1–974. 1948.

129. Tullis, E. C., "*Fusarium moniliforme*, the cause of a stalk rot of sorghum in Texas." *Phytopath.*, **41**: 529–535. 1951.

130. Vaheeduddin, S., "The pathenogenicity and genetics of some sorghum smuts." Minn. Ag. Exp. Sta. *Tech. Bul. 154*. 1942.

131. Vinall, H. N., "A study of the literature concerning poisoning of cattle by the prussic acid in sorghum, Sudan grass, and Johnson grass." *J. Am. Soc. Agron.*, **13**: 267–280. 1921.

132. ——, "A method of crossing sorghums." *J. Hered.*, **17**: 297–299. 1926.

133. ——, and A. B. Cron, "Improvement of sorghums by hybridization." *J. Hered.*, **12**: 435–443. 1921.

134. ——, J. C. Stephens, and J. H. Martin, "Identification, history, and distribution of common sorghum varieties." USDA *Tech. Bul. 506*. 1936.

135. Wadsworth, D. F., and J. B. Sieglinger, "Charcoal rot of sorghum." Okla. Ag. Exp. Sta. *Bul. 355*. 1950.

136. Wakeland, C., "The chinch bug," in *Insects*. USDA Yrbk. of Ag. pp 611–614. 1952.

137. Walter, E. V., "The biology and control of the sorghum midge." USDA *Tech. Bul. 778*. 1941.

138. Weaver, J. E., *Root Development of Field Crops*. New York: McGraw-Hill. pp 192–197. 1926.

139. Webster, J. E., J. B. Sieglinger, and F. Davies, "Chemical composition of sorghum plants at various stages of growth and relation of composition to chinch bug injury." Okla. Ag. Exp. Sta. *Tech. Bul. 30*. 1948.

140. Wheeler, W. A., and D. D. Hill, *Grassland Seeds*. New York: Van Nostrand. pp 605–628. 1957.

141. Wilson, B. D., and J. K. Wilson, "Relation of sorghum roots to certain biological processes." *J. Am. Soc. Agron.*, **20**: 747–754. 1928.

142. Zingg, A. W., N. P. Woodruff, and C. L. Englehorn, "Effect of wind-row orientation on erodibility of land in sorghum stubble." *Agron. J.*, **44**(5): 227–230. 1952.

22. MILLETS

ECONOMIC IMPORTANCE

Millets are small-grained cereals, consumed as food by millions of people in the world. They are sometimes referred to as a "poor man's cereal" because people with a choice prefer other cereals such as wheat or rice. Most of the millet of the world is grown in Asia, Africa, and the U.S.S.R., where it is consumed largely as food [1].

While millets have greatly lost in importance over the last 1000 years, they probably will retain their position as a food grain in some countries for a long time. In southeastern Russia, millets are grown where it would be almost impossible to grow any other cereal crop profitably [36]. Millets now have a minor role as crops in the Near East, although parts of this region, now looked upon as useless for peasant agriculture, might possibly be suitable for growing millets on an extensive scale [42]. There is a trend to substitute corn for millets in some areas, particularly in the Orient and in central and southern Africa.

Reliable world statistics on millets are impossible to obtain but probably 25 million tons were produced annually on nearly 120 million acres from 1959–61. The average annual world production from 1934 to 1938 was estimated as 26,164,759 short tons. This production was utilized as follows: seed and waste, 2,276,410 tons; feed, 1,543,430 tons; and human food, 22,299,645 tons, or 85 per cent of the crop. About 88 per cent of the world millet crop was grown in China, India, Manchuria, French West Africa, and the Soviet Union. China and India together produced about 56 per cent of the total production [1].

Millet is a minor crop in the United States. Roughly, about 15 thousand tons of seed, mostly proso, are produced primarily for livestock feed. In general, other cereals in the United States yield more grain than does proso. Foxtail millet, Japanese barnyard millet, and pearl millet are used primarily as forage crops (Fig. 22-1).

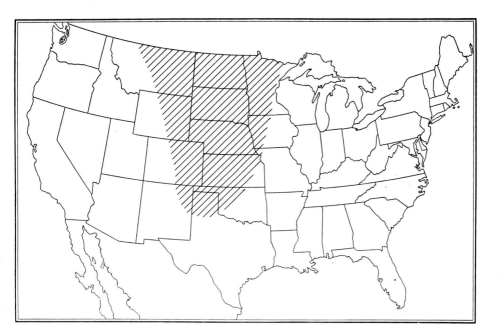

FIGURE 22-1. **Most of the proso and foxtail millet in the United States has been grown in the shaded area.**

(*Courtesy US Department of Agriculture*)

GENERAL ENVIRONMENTAL REQUIREMENTS

Millets often produce a greater quantity of grain than do other cereals under conditions of infertile soil, intense heat, and scanty rainfall. Most millets have an additional advantage: they require only a short growing season. Millet is a very valuable crop in India where much depends on when the monsoon arrives. When the monsoon comes too late for other spring grains, millet may be sown with the assurance that it will produce some kind of crop. It also is valuable as a second or catch crop [1].

Another advantage of the millets is that the seed requirements are low, since the seeds are relatively small. This is important in countries such as India and China where the ratio of people to land is high. Such people often find it difficult to save sufficient seed for the next crop. In Japan, millets are grown in the mountainous areas where the season is too short, cool, and dry for rice production.

HISTORY OF MILLET CULTURE

Millets were consumed in India, China, Egypt, and other countries in prehistoric times, but little is known of their origin. They probably were developed in eastern or central Asia. Some students believe that millet was the first cultivated crop because it was grown in the so-called Hoe Age which preceded the Plow Age.

In ancient and medieval times millet was grown in most of the known world. During the Middle Ages it was one of the principal foods of the poor people of Europe. During the nineteenth century, millet was gradually superseded in western Europe by wheat, rye, rice, maize, and potatoes, which usually produce higher yields. Development of yeast-raised bread contributed to this loss in popularity because millet is not satisfactory for making a good raised bread.

KINDS OF MILLET

Millets are warm-weather annual grasses which, except for pearl millet, range from 1–4 feet in height. They have much smaller seeds in proportion to the size of the mature plant than do small grains or maize. Some millets produce only a single seminal root instead of three or more as in corn and small grains. They are all short-day plants.

The millets include five genera, *Panicum, Setaria, Echinochloa, Pennisetum,* and *Paspalum,* in the tribe Paniceae, and one genus (*Eleusine*) in the tribe Chlorideae. The most important cultivated millet species are proso (*Panicum miliaceum*), foxtail millet (*Setaria italica*), Japanese barnyard millet (*Echinochloa crusgalli* var. *frumentacea*), pearl or cattail millet (*Pennisetum glaucum*), finger millet (*Eleusine coracana*), and koda millet of India or ditch millet of New Zealand (*Paspalum scrobiculatum*). The principal species of cultivated millets grown in the United States are readily separated with the aid of a key (see Chap. 2).

USES OF MILLET

Millet is used as a meal, for making bread and cakes, or as paste from pounded soaked seed, or as boiled gruel. In Asia, glutinous types of proso or foxtail millets are used in cakes, puddings, or other holiday delicacies. In the U.S.S.R., proso millet is eaten mostly in the form of a thick porridge called *kasha* or in flat bread. Millets sometimes are used in making alcoholic drinks. In the United States, proso is grown for feed grain and the other millets are used for forage.

The chemical composition of the grain of three millets, as compared with wheat is as follows:

	Average Composition, Per Cent				
Commodity	Protein	Fat	Fiber	N-Free Extract	Mineral Matter
Foxtail millet	12.1	4.1	8.6	60.7	3.6
Proso	11.9	3.4	8.1	63.7	3.3
Japanese millet	10.6	4.9	14.6	54.7	5.0
Wheat (all types)	13.2	1.9	2.6	69.9	1.9

The mineral content of most millets is higher than that of sorghum, wheat, rice, or rye, but less than that of soybeans. Millets, except pearl millet, are enclosed in the hulls and thus contain considerable fiber before they are processed for food. Millet is used as a whole-grain cereal and thus furnishes more thiamine than does milled rice [1]. In northern China, millet often is mixed with other cereals or legumes. A recommended mixture is maize, millet or other cereals, or soybeans. Sprouted millet supplies part of the Chinese diet.

Proso grown in the United States is used mostly as poultry feeds or birdseed mixtures, or as livestock feed. It is readily eaten by all types of livestock, but it should be ground before it is fed.

PROSO MILLET

Proso (*Panicum miliaceum*) is sometimes called broomcorn millet, hog millet, or Hershey millet. It is the "common" millet of Europe. It is grown in the United States on not more than 150 thousand acres annually, mostly as a late-sown catch crop for grain production.

Adaptation

Proso grows farther north than does any other millet. It is especially suited to a dry climate such as that of central Asia. It thrives in southern and central Russia, the Middle East, northern India, and in Manchuria. Proso is adapted to the cooler portion of the Great Plains of the United States, and is grown chiefly in North Dakota, South Dakota, and Colorado.

Proso makes a rapid growth under warm weather conditions. It is sensitive to frost. The crop requires relatively little water, but demands a better soil than does either pearl millet or finger millet.

Proso grows well on almost any kind of soil except coarse sands. In Michigan, it is adapted to light sandy soils where a June-planted crop is needed, but wheat or barley outyield proso on suitable soils [47].

FIGURE 22-2. **A proso plant.**
(*Courtesy US Department of Agriculture*)

Botanical Description

Proso grows to a height of 1–4 feet. The culms or stems are stout, erect, or decumbent at the base. They also are round or flattened, and generally about one-fourth inch thick (Fig. 22-2). The stems and leaves are covered with hairs. The stems and outer chaff are green or sometimes yellowish or reddish green when the seed is ripe. The leaf sheaths are open and covered with very small protuberances (papillae) from each of which arises a stiff hair. The ligule is short and thick, but auricles are lacking [43].

The proso inflorescence is a rather open panicle similar to that of oats. The panicles are more or less included in the sheath at the base, 10–30 cm long, usually nodding, or nearly erect, and rather compact. The numerous branches are ascending, very scabrous, and bear spikelets near the tips. A single spikelet consists of two unequal glumes, a sterile lemma, and a fertile floret. The fertile floret consists of a lemma, palea, and caryopsis. The seeds thresh out enclosed in smooth shiny hulls (lemmas and paleas) [43].

Proso seeds are 2.25–2.5 mm in length and about 2 mm in width. In outline, the seeds are ovate and rounded on the dorsal side. The hulls of different varieties may be white, cream, yellow, red, green, brown, or nearly black. The caryopsis is a cream color. Certain varieties have glutinous seeds [59].

The seeds of proso are larger, more rounded, and not flattened on the dorsal side as are those of foxtail millets. The caryopsis of proso also is larger and rounder.

The proso flower is normally self-fertilized, although cross-fertilization frequently occurs.

Other millets in the genus *Panicum* include little millet (*P. miliare*) grown in India, and browntop millet (*P. ramosum*) which is sown for feeding game birds in the southeastern United States. Little millet often is confused with proso. It is grown in the south of India on poor, otherwise worthless lands. It can withstand both drought and water-logging. It grows in India up to 7000-feet elevation. The seeds of several other *Panicum* species are gathered for food in India.

Varieties

The three botanical varieties of proso are *P. miliaceum effusum,* with broad panicles having branches spreading to all sides (Fig. 22-3); *P. miliaceum contractum,* with panicles less spreading than effusum, and onesided; and *P. miliaceum compactum,* with panicles compact, thick, and erect (Fig. 22-4).

The principal varieties of proso grown in the United States are Yellow

Manitoba, Turghai, and Early Fortune. Other varieties grown only occasionally are White Siberian, Crown, Black Voronezh, White French, and Red Russian [1]. Hundreds of varieties are grown in other parts of the world. The best types of proso for the Middle East are probably those from southeastern Russia [42].

Characteristics of several important proso varieties are shown below.

Varieties	Character of Panicle	Color of Outer Chaff	Color of Seed Hull	Season of Maturity	Plant Heights
White Siberian	Spreading	Yellowish-green	Lemon Yellow	Early to midseason	Short to midtall
Red Russian (Tambov)	"	Reddish-green	Reddish-brown	"	"
Turghai	"	"	Yellowish-brown	"	Midtall to tall
White French	Loose, one-sided	Yellowish-green	Creamy-white	Midseason to late	"
Yellow Manitoba	"	"	Brownish-yellow	"	"
Black Voronezh	"	"	Brownish-black	"	"
Crown	——	——	Gray	——	——
Early Fortune (Red Lump)	Compact, erect	"	Reddish-brown	Early to midseason	Short to midtall

Cultural Practices

Since proso plants are readily killed by spring frosts, seeding is delayed until all danger of frost is past. In the United States it is sown with a grain drill in late May, in June, or in early July at the rate of 20–40 pounds per acre. Generally the crop is seeded from 2–4 weeks after corn is planted in the locality. Date of seeding tests conducted in Colorado indicate that proso can be seeded in eastern Colorado between June 15–July 1. The crop is almost always planted in close drills. About 35 pounds of seed per acre give satisfactory yields [28]. Proso should be sown in Michigan between June 1–20, or sufficiently early so that the seed will be well matured before cool weather. Satisfactory yields have been obtained with light seedings of 10–15 pounds per acre in drill rows 14 inches apart [47].

Proso is ready for harvest about 60–75 days after seeding, but ripening is not uniform. The seeds in the tips of the earlier heads often are dead ripe and have shattered before the lower seeds and later panicles are mature. The stems and panicle branches are still green when the seeds ripen. Gen-

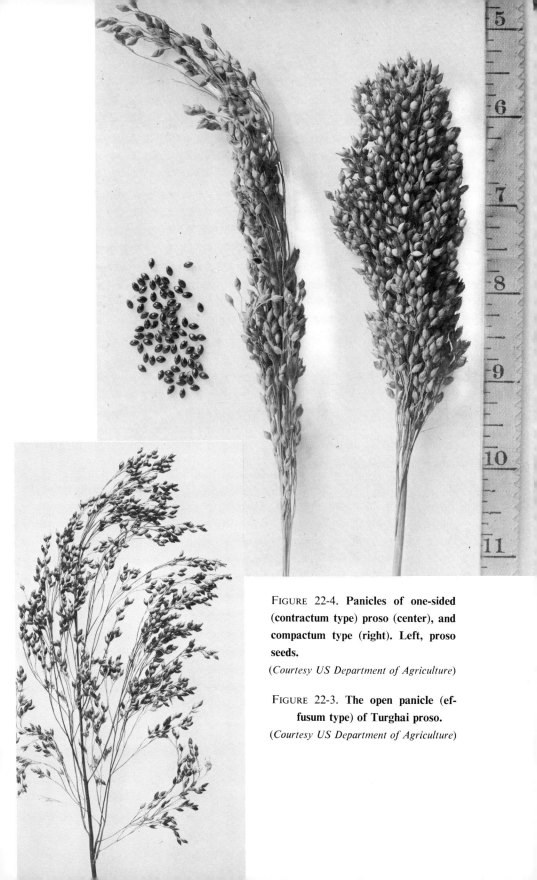

FIGURE 22-4. Panicles of one-sided (contractum type) proso (center), and compactum type (right). Left, proso seeds.

(*Courtesy US Department of Agriculture*)

FIGURE 22-3. The open panicle (effusum type) of Turghai proso.

(*Courtesy US Department of Agriculture*)

erally proso is harvested when the seeds in the upper half of the panicles are ripe. Most of the crop is cut by a swather which permits the crop to cure in the windrows on the cut stubble. The crop is then gathered and threshed by a combine with a pickup attachment. Sometimes it is cut with a binder, cured in long slender shocks, and then threshed. Irregular ripening usually precludes direct harvest by the combine.

Utilization

The feeding value of proso has been reported to be slightly higher than that of oats, but less than that of corn [47], but in feeding tests in Colorado it was equal to shelled corn when used with protein supplements [20]. In human digestion experiments with bread made from proso in the United States, the carbohydrates were as well utilized as in other cereals, but less than one half of the proteins were digested. The seed has an agreeable taste with a slight nutty flavor, different from other cereals, and is well liked by some people [38].

Diseases

Head smut (*Sphacelotheca destruens*) is a widespread disease of proso. It is first evident when the panicles emerge. Affected panicles are noticeably shortened, frequently being exposed only slightly beyond the leaf sheath. The smutted ovaries of the grain are massed together and enclosed by a whitish membrane. The affected panicle resembles a thickened elongated boil. The smut masses generally are ruptured or broken before harvest time [55]. The disease can be controlled by seed treatment with organic mercury dusts.

A bacterial stripe disease (*Phytomonas panici*) has been described on the Early Fortune variety in Wisconsin and South Dakota. Affected plants have water-soaked lesions to brown stripes on the leaves, sheaths, and culms.

FIGURE 22-5. **Seed of 3 millets: (a) proso, (b) foxtail millet, and (c) Japanese millet, compared with (d) barnyard grass.**

(*Courtesy US Department of Agriculture*)

These streaks become shiny. Interiors of stems show an abundance of gummy exudate. The main culms are killed on some plants, while on others only the upper portion and head are killed. The disease, found to develop only on proso, is probably seed-borne. No control measures have been reported [31].

FOXTAIL MILLET

Foxtail millet (*Setaria italica*), sometimes called Italian millet, has been widely grown but is now less important than formerly, except in India, China, Manchuria, and a few other countries. It is the most important millet in Japan, although the acreage is small. It is by far the most widely grown millet in China where it thrives in many regions in which other cereals do not. Foxtail millet is found in the mountainous sections as well as on the plains of many parts of China. Next to rice and wheat in importance, it provides approximately 17 per cent of the total food consumed in China [33]. Foxtail millet is grown in the Middle East on almost as large a scale as proso, either as a crop or as an admixture. In the high altitudes of Armenia, it often supplants proso in dry years and in exhausted soils. Foxtail millet is often mixed with proso in other parts of Turkey [42]. The chief advantage of foxtail over proso millet in these countries is that it produces good yields of grain as well as excellent forage. However, its grain is less satisfactory than that of proso for any form of bread. In the United States, large unthreshed heads, usually of the German variety, are sold in supermarkets and pet food stores for feeding to cage birds.

Adaptation

Foxtail millet is grown in temperate climates of the world. It requires moderate temperatures, but it is somewhat less exacting than proso. It matures quickly when grown in the hot summer months of the northernmost states in the United States. Foxtail millet usually ripens in from 70–90 days after seeding and thus is somewhat later than proso.

Foxtail millet requires a fairly fertile soil for good crops, although it will grow in poor land. It will not stand water-logging or extreme drought.

Botanical Description

Foxtail millet is an annual grass with slender, erect, and leafy stems. The plant may vary in height from 1–6 feet. Under semiarid conditions in

Colorado, foxtail millet was found to vary in height from one to slightly over three feet. Height depended upon variety and season [29].

The inflorescence of foxtail millet is a dense, cylindrical, and bristly panicle from 2–12 inches long. The spikelet consists of a thin papery much-reduced first glume, a longer second glume, a sterile lemma of like texture, and a fertile floret with hardened lemma and palea. The spikelet is sub-tended by an involucre of from one to several bristles. The spikelet falls free from the bristles so that these seldom appear in the harvested seed [50].

The hull color of seeds may be creamy white, pale yellow, orange, reddish-orange, green, dark purple, or mixtures of various colors. The seeds vary from 2–3 mm in length and from 1–2 mm in width, and are ovate in outline. Free caryopses are evident when threshing is severe. The cultivated millets are distinguished from the common wild species of *Setaria, S. viridis* (green foxtail), *S. lutescens* (yellow foxtail), *S. faberi* (giant foxtail), and others by their large seeds or by the minutely tuberculate or finely undulate surface of the lemma [59].

Pollination

The first flowers of foxtail millet may open when three-fourths of the panicle emerges from the sheath, or as many as five days after full emergence [10, 33]. Flowering proceeds from the top of the head downwards, and similarly from the tip downwards in each of the panicle branches. A large head may take 8–16 days to complete flowering. A peak in flowering occurs on the fourth day after flowering begins. A single floret may remain open about 30 minutes. About 80 minutes are required for the complete blooming process. Flowering is hastened by high temperatures and low humidity [33].

Most of the flowers open from 8:00 PM to 10:00 AM, although a few may open throughout the day. Daily blooming is checked as the temperature rises and the humidity drops [10, 33].

The floral arrangement in foxtail millet favors self-pollination, but some crossing occurs. In Canada, an average of 0.69 per cent of natural crossing occurred when two strains were grown in alternate rows, with a range of 0–9.86 per cent [46].

Varieties

Numerous varieties are grown in Asia and Europe. The varieties of foxtail millet grown in the United States include German, Common, Hungarian, Goldmine, White Wonder, Siberian, and Kursk (Fig. 22-6). German

FIGURE 22-6. **Heads of foxtail millet varieties. Left to right: Kursk, Hungarian, Common, Siberian, Turkestan, and Golden Wonder.**

(*Courtesy US Department of Agriculture*)

is the most widely grown variety. The so-called Golden variety is either German, Common, or a mixture of the two, and much of the German millet grown is mixed with Common. German millet that has been grown in the Northern states for several years usually is earlier than that grown in the South as a result of natural selection under different photoperiods. Plant characters of American varieties of foxtail millet are shown in Table 22-1.

Cultural Practices

Foxtail millet often is sown late as an emergency feed crop in the United States [54], frequently on land where other small grain crops have failed. The field should be free from weeds at seeding time [29]. A firm seedbed is necessary because of the small size of the seeds. It should be

TABLE 22-1. **Plant Characters of American Varieties of Foxtail Millet**

Variety	Growth Period (Days)	Size of Stem	Size of Head	Character of Head	Length of Bristles	Color of Bristles	Outline of Seeds	Color of Seeds
Common	60	Slender	Medium	Not lobed	Long	Pale yellow	Narrowly to broadly elliptical	Pale golden yellow
German	87	Stout	Large	Distinctly lobed	Long	Green to purple	Rounded or broadly elliptical	Pale straw to golden yellow
White Wonder	—	Stout	Large	Distinctly lobed	Short	Green to purple	"	Grayish white or yellowish
Goldmine	69	Medium	Medium	Not lobed	Long	Pale yellow	Narrowly to broadly elliptical	Golden yellow
Hungarian	69	Slender	Small	Not lobed	Long	Purple	"	—[1]
Siberian	72	Medium	Medium	Not lobed	—	Purple	"	Orange to golden yellow
Kursk	64	Slender	Small	Not lobed	Long	Purple	"	Orange

[1] Mixed yellowish straw, light brown mottled with dark brown, dark brown and purple.

sown in warm soil, some two or three weeks after corn planting time. In the United States, the crop usually is sown between May 15–June 15, but may be seeded as late as August 1 where 60–70 or more days remain before an expected frost [56]. Where the growing season is short, foxtail millet should be sown as soon as possible after May 15, and before July 1, whenever there is sufficient moisture in the surface soil to germinate the seed. In semi-arid regions, conditions usually are favorable after a rain of 0.75 inch or more. Ten-year average yields of foxtail millet sown on corn-stubble land on six dates at Akron, Colorado, are as follows [29]:

	Average Acre Yields	
Seeding Date	*Hay Yields, Lb*	*Seed Yields, Bu*
May 15	2352	7.0
June 1	2126	6.7
June 15	1985	5.1
July 1	1464	5.7
July 15	895	4.9
August 1	217	1.0

Foxtail millet for hay production is nearly always sown with a grain drill at a depth of one inch or less, with the seed placed in moist soil. Drills spaced 6–8 inches apart are preferable to wider drills because close spacing helps the crop to compete with weeds. The usual seeding rate is 25–30 pounds per acre in humid areas, and 15–20 pounds per acre in semi-arid regions on weed-free soil [56]. In western Texas and eastern New Mexico, foxtail millet usually is drilled at a rate of about four pounds per acre in cultivated rows three feet or more apart for seed production [1]. A similar spacing is desirable for producing large unthreshed heads for the cage bird feed market.

When harvested for seed, foxtail millet usually is cut with a binder or windrower. Binder-harvested foxtail millet may be threshed with a small combine that is pulled from shock to shock. When the crop is windrowed, a combine with pickup attachment is used [29].

In southern Manchuria, millet is planted in May. A furrow is made in each middle between rows of the previous year. A man following a plow drops seed from a gourd-kaoliang stalk planter. Soil is kicked into the furrow to cover the seed. It is then compacted with an oval stone roller drawn by a donkey or other draft animal. The millet is harvested and then placed on the threshing floor or ground with the heads toward the center and threshed with stone rollers [1]. In China, foxtail millet sown in 12-inch rows produced the highest yields when the plants were spaced not more than two inches apart in the row [39].

Diseases

The important diseases on foxtail millet are smut and downy mildew.

Kernel smut (*Ustilago crameri*) is commonly found on foxtail millets in the United States as well as in Asia and Africa. It is severe in Asiatic countries, especially where the spores overwinter in the soil. Affected plants usually are stunted, while the heads frequently are abnormal in shape. Smutted plants have yellowish heads early in the season which become somewhat darkened in the fall. The disease is evident in the heads even before they emerge from the sheath. The bracts that enclose the spore masses appear whitish and translucent. The caryopsis is replaced by the dark spore mass. In most cases, every grain of the head is destroyed [55]. The floral bracts often break to release the spores as the plant approaches maturity, but in some cases the spore masses persist in the threshed grain. Crop rotation is a recommended control measure, especially in dry areas where the spores persist in the soil. Seed treatment with volatile organic mercury compounds generally will control the disease.

Downy mildew (*Sclerospora graminicola*) is destructive on foxtail millet, especially in some of the Asiatic countries. It has been reported on this millet in India, China, Manchuria, Japan, and Korea. Losses of as much as 50 per cent of the crop occur in serious cases [35]. The disease was abundant on foxtail millet in Minnesota in 1935 [57]. Diseased plants are dwarfed with excessive development of tillers. Malformations of the floral bracts and failure of kernel development are other symptoms. Yellow-green streaks may run the entire length of the leaf on diseased plants. Secondary infection consists of chlorotic local lesions. Probably the most effective control is seed treatment with organic mercury compounds [57, 30].

Bacterial spot (*Pseudomonas alboprecipitans*) has been reported on foxtail millet. The common symptoms are small grayish-green spots with brown pigmentation. The disease is of little importance in the United States.

Genetics

Foxtail millet plants may be either green or tinged with purple. The dominant purple character occurs in the presence of a basic factor, P. Different patterns of purpling are determined by 6 factors, P_1 to P_6. The P_1 plants are purple throughout, while the P_6 plants have green seedlings and show only occasional light purple on the leaf blades of mature plants. A factor I causes intense color. Two other factors, V and H, determine the alacrity with which P is manifested in the vegetative parts or in the inflorescence. Interactions of P, I, V, and H factors produce the diversity of forms that characterize the varieties of foxtail millet [18]. In Canada, the inheritance of purple and green plant colors has been explained on a monogenic basis, with purple (P) dominant over green (p) [46].

The genotypes for six seedcoat (lemma and palea) colors are as follows: Black, BBIIKK; sepia, BBIIkk; tawny buff, bbIIKK; Korra buff, BBiiKK and bbiiKK; red, bbIIkk; and tawny red, BBiikk and bbiikk [2].

Endosperm characters, nonwaxy vs. waxy (Wx, wx) and white vs. yellow (W, w), showed simple Mendelian inheritance [40].

A palmatic type of head, in which the branches on the main axis of the inflorescence gradually lengthen from the tip of the axis downward, is inherited on the basis of the complementary action of two factor pairs, P_1p_1 and P_2p_2. The F_2 segregation was 9 palmatic to 7 normal heads [40].

The primitive type of lax head, characterized by fewer spikelets and chronic sterility, is recessive to the economic dense type. The Aa factor pair is responsible for normal and lax heads [12].

The bristles on the spike may range in length from about 2.2–14 mm in different strains. The dwarf 2.2–4.5 mm bristle factor X is present in all *Setaria species*. Three other factors, E, L_1, and L_2 act on X to form three longer classes of bristle length. Factor E expression occurs only in the presence of factor L_2. The factor X alone or with E produces a dwarf bristle. The factors L_1 or L_2 produce a short bristle, but together produce a medium bristle. The E factor produces a short bristle with L_1, a medium bristle with L_2, and a long bristle with L_1 and L_2 together [11].

Interspecific crosses between *S. italica* and *S. viridis,* both of which have 9 pairs of chromosomes, appear to pair normally in the F_1 generation, but may have about 70 per cent of pollen sterility. *S. viridis* was suggested as the probable progenitor of cultivated foxtail millet [41]. Three linkage groups were postulated on the basis of factor pairs determined in this interspecific cross as follows:

1. In (9.11) Pr_1 (20.93) Pr_2. In this group, *In* is an intensifier for P, while Pr_1 and Pr_2 are factors for purple bristles.
2. S (19.37) P (27.09) Pr_3. In this group, P is purple plant color, while Pr_3 is a factor for purple bristles. The factor X may be B, Vi, or R which are involved in seedcoat color.
3. G^a (36.80), W (12.32) *br*. In this linkage group, G^a is a gametophyte factor for differential pollen tube growth; W is a factor for white pericarp; and Br is a gene for brown, another color.

PEARL MILLET

Pearl millet (*Pennisetum glaucum* or *P. typhoideum*), is also known as cattail millet, pencillaria, or Mands Forage Plant, in the United States; bulrush millet or Dukhn in Africa; bajra, cumbo, or sajja in India; and candle millet or dark millet in Europe [44].

Economic Importance

Pearl millet has been cultivated in Asia and Africa since prehistoric times and probably originated in tropical Africa. It is widely grown in Africa where it replaces sorghum as the principal cereal crop on sandy soils and in the drier areas. In the Sudan, pearl millet ranks second to sorghum as a cereal crop for human food. It is grown on about 27 million acres in India. The crop is seldom grown in the Middle East, although at one time it seems to have been produced extensively in Mesopotamia [42]. A small acreage is grown for forage on the coastal plain in the southeastern United States where it appears to be the best summer temporary grazing crop [25].

Adaptation

Pearl millet is an annual warm weather grass that is resistant to drought. It grows in some regions with less than 15 inches of annual rainfall. Pearl millet grows in areas that have extended dry periods, such as western Ghats and the plains of Rajputana in India and in the Sudan near the Sahara desert in Africa [42]. It is reported to be grown occasionally in desert sections of western India where the average annual rainfall is only 5–7 inches. In the United States, the crop is confined largely to the humid areas of the Southeastern states, but some is grown in semiarid and irrigated areas of the Southwest.

Pearl millet thrives better than most crops on poor soils. It often replaces sorghum on light sandy soils in the Sudan and other parts of Africa. The crop is unusually well adapted to the sandy soils of the coastal plain in the United States [22].

Botanical Description

The genus *Pennisetum* contains grasses whose spikelets are solitary or in groups of two or three, surrounded by an involucre of bristles that are united at the base and attached to the spikelets. Pearl millet (*P. glaucum*) is an annual with the bristles of the involucre about as long as the spikelets.

Pearl millet usually ranges in height from 5–10 feet or higher. The stems, about an inch in thickness, are densely villous below the panicle. The blades are flat, cordate, and sometimes three feet or more in length and two or three inches wide. The leaf sheaths are open and hairy, while the ligule is short. The leaf margins, like those of sorghum, bear small sawlike teeth.

The stiff cylindric head or spike of pearl millet usually is from 8–18 inches long and about one inch thick (Fig. 22-7). The heads are similar in size and shape to those of the common cattail that grows in shallow waters. However, pearl millet heads have a beaded appearance that results from the exposed white seeds. The fasicles are peduncled. The spikelets are short-pedicelled, with two in a facicle. There is one fertile floret per spikelet.

The spikelets consist of a short lower glume which is broader than it is long. The inner glume is longer, about half the length of the spikelet, oval, and 3–4-nerved. Each spikelet has two flowers, the lower one being imperfect, staminate, sometimes without stamens, or wanting. The lemma of the fertile flower is oval, pointed, 5–6-nerved, and hairy on the margins. The palea is rounded above, thin, and membranous. Unlike other millets, the lemma and palea of the perfect flower of pearl millet do not clasp the caryopsis, which threshes free [59].

The seeds or caryopses of pearl millet are much larger than the hulled seeds of other millets. Typical seeds are obovoid, 3–4 mm long and 2.25 mm wide. Many seeds are nearly as broad as long. They are yellowish-gray in color, while the embryo has a reddish tinge [59].

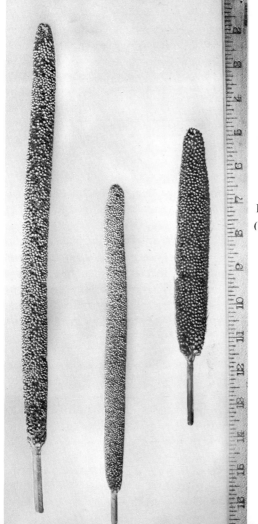

FIGURE 22-7. **Panicles of pearl millet.**
(Courtesy US Department of Agriculture)

Pearl millet is related to the perennial Napier grass (*P. purpureum*), introduced into the southeastern United States in 1913. Hybrids have been made between pearl millet with 14 somatic chromosomes and Napier grass with 28 somatic chromosomes, but all hybrids were highly sterile [22].

Pollination

Pearl millet is highly cross-pollinated. In blooming, the stigmas come out several days before the anthers appear, which facilitates crosspollination.

Anthesis occurs throughout the day and night, with maximum blooming between 10:00 PM and midnight, and a second slight rise prior to 10:00 AM in India. High humidity and falling temperature stimulate anthesis [13]. In Georgia, blooming is most abundant over a two-hour period about sunrise [58].

Varieties

Common pearl millet was grown in the United States before the Starr variety, which soon became the most widely grown variety in the Southern states, was distributed in 1950. Starr is a synthetic variety developed in Georgia. An extremely leafy selection with short internodes was crossed with broad-leafed common pearl millet. Mass selection of the hybrid progeny resulted in strains which were combined in the Starr variety. This variety is shorter but more leafy than common pearl millet. Since it matures 4–6 weeks later, Starr outyields the common type in clipped herbage. It is about six feet tall when mature [34].

Gahi 1 (Georgia Hybrid No. 1), which consists of about 65 per cent hybrid seed, yields about 50 per cent more forage than the commercial check when planted at a rate of 10 pounds of seed per acre in 30–36-inch rows so as to crowd out the less vigorous inbreds [26].

In other countries numerous local varieties differ chiefly in height and in maturity. There are two general types in the Sudan: (a) relatively short plants with slender stems and numerous lateral heads, grown on Riverain soils in the Northern Province; and (b) relatively tall plants with large stems and few laterals which are grown under rainfed conditions. Heads of the first type ripen over a period of several weeks, whereas those of the second type ripen together [53].

Cultural Practices

Pearl millet often responds to fertilizer applications of nitrogen, phosphorus, and potash on soils of low fertility, but is less responsive to fertilizers than is corn or sorghum. The crop is planted in the United States after all danger of frost is past, or usually in April in the Gulf States [19]. Pearl millet may be sown in close drills for hay or pasture, but it also may be planted in cultivated rows for seed, pasture, or silage. For seed production, the crop usually is planted in rows from 20–42 inches apart at a rate of 5–6 pounds per acre. As much as 10 pounds may be planted in rows for pasture or soiling [58]. In Georgia, pearl millet often is planted at rates of 10–20 pounds of seed per acre in rows 30–36 inches apart. A rate of 10 pounds in 30-inch rows places approximately four seeds per inch of row [23]. The seed crop generally is cut with a corn binder, cured in shocks, and threshed with a small combine with a bundle-topping attachment [58].

In the Sudan, the crop is planted by hand in June or July after the first good rains, in hills spaced 18 × 18 to 36 × 36 inches apart. About four seeds are dropped per hill with a pointed sowing stick. In India the seed usually is dropped by hand in furrows opened with a wooden plow. In both Sudan and India the crop is harvested by hand in October or November. The heads are cut by hand and the grain flailed out on a threshing floor.

Utilization

Pearl millet is ground into meal, cooked as a gruel or porridge, and eaten with a sauce or stew [53], or is baked into bread. In the Sudan, balls of pearl millet cake are used in the diet.

Pearl millet is widely used as a temporary pasture plant in the southeastern United States, and in Georgia it produces more beef per acre than other annual crops generally grazed there [22]. It is used only occasionally for hay, silage, or soiling. The coarse stalks cure very slowly when cut for hay in humid areas. The dry stover or straw has a low feeding value.

Inheritance

Single-factor differences have been reported for purple seedlings (dominant) vs. green seedlings [52]; pale green (dominant) vs. albino seedlings [15]; bristled spike (dominant) vs. basal branching spike [18]; fertile anthers (dominant) vs. sterile anther; and normal spike (dominant) vs. partly-flowered spike [37]. In some crosses, seedlings have segregated into a dihybrid ratio of 9 green: 3 pale green: 4 albino [15, 16]. Also some induced albino and yellow seedlings segregate in dihybrid ratios [37].

In F_1 crosses in Georgia, heterosis was manifested for plant yield, stem diameter, head length, plant height, and internode length. Few stems per plant was dominant over many stems, early maturity over late maturity, and wide leaves slightly dominant over narrow leaves. A minimum of one gene was estimated as responsible for head length and leaf width, while 2–8 genes appeared to control most other characters [24].

Breeding

Increased yields of pearl millet are obtained from hybrids between suitable lines. Seed mixtures containing 50–90 per cent of hybrid seed yield about as much forage as does pure hybrid seed [23]. Gahi 1 (Georgia No. 1) pearl millet is produced by planting an equal seed mixture of four inbred lines, 13, 18, 23, and 26 [26]. Large-scale production of hybrid pearl millet seed likewise has been accomplished in India. In Madras and Bombay provinces, hybrid pearl millet has yielded 25–40 per cent more grain than the crop as commonly grown [51].

A cytoplasmic male-sterile pearl millet has been reported in Georgia. This line might be crossed either with a sterility maintainer strain, or with a fertility restorer to produce a complete F_1 hybrid single cross. A sterile hybrid might tend to remain in a vegetative condition. Possibilities of such hybrids are still under study [26].

JAPANESE MILLET

Japanese millet (*Echinochloa crusgalli* var. *frumentacea*) also has been called Japanese barnyard millet and Billion Dollar Grass in the United States. It is known as Sawan millet in India. It is grown to some extent in Japan and in other Asiatic countries, and occasionally in Australia and the United States. It is a minor cereal crop in several parts of India [49]. In Egypt, Japanese millet is grown occasionally, usually on lands that are too salty for rice or other grains, chiefly in Behera and Fayum. It occurs almost everywhere that other millets are found, often as a weed [42].

In Australia, Japanese millet is the most widely grown millet in New South Wales where it is used primarily as a catch crop [32], and is grown widely both in southern Victoria and the northern irrigated areas [45].

In the United States, Japanese millet is grown sparingly in Pennsylvania and New York, and occasionally elsewhere, and has been reported as the best late-season green feed for most of the North Pacific Slope [21].

Adaptation

Japanese millet is best adapted to temperate climates with humid or subhumid conditions. It makes the most rapid growth of all millets under favorable weather conditions, occasionally producing ripe grain in 45 days after seeding. In the Pacific Northwest in the United States, the crop has never been known to lodge, in spite of heavy rains and winds that occur there in September [21].

Japanese millet is adapted to a wide variety of soils, but makes its

FIGURE 22-8. **Plant and detached raceme of Japanese millet.**

(*Courtesy US Department of Agriculture*)

best growth on mellow soils high in organic matter. In Japan, awnless varieties are grown on upland soils, while awned types are grown in water-filled paddy fields.

Botanical Description

Japanese millet (*Echinochloa crusgalli* var. *frumentacea*) is sometimes difficult to distinguish from the weed, barnyard grass, or water grass (*E. crusgalli*).

The spikelets are borne on one side of each branch of rather compact racemes (Fig. 22-8). The spikelets are two-flowered, and consist of a short, sharp, pointed, mucronate lower glume, a wider upper glume as long as or longer than the "seed," a lower floret which is staminate or sterile, and a perfect floret. The lemma of the lower floret is thick, while the palea is thin and not easily seen. The veins of both the upper glume and lemma of the first floret are armed with long stiff bristles, smaller bristles being scattered between the veins [59].

The lemma and palea of the upper floret are hard and parchment-like, quite shiny, and yellowish-straw color, or sometimes greenish-gray. The lower glume of the sterile floret often remains attached to the "seed." Japanese millet is awnless, but is difficult to distinguish from the long-awned barnyard grass whose awns usually are broken off [59].

The seeds of Japanese millet are 2.75–3 mm long and 2 to 2.25 mm wide and are larger and more plump than those of barnyard grass. The caryopses of Japanese millet are larger and somewhat lighter in color than those of barnyard grass, but the 2 species are almost impossible to separate.

A related cultivated species is the Shama millet or "jungle rice" (*E. colonum*) of India.

Cultural Practices

In the United States, Japanese millet usually is drilled in the late spring at the rate of 20–25 pounds of seed per acre. When harvested for seed, the crop generally is cut with a binder or windrower to be threshed with a pickup combine.

In the Middle East, Japanese millet is sown about June 15 when the soil is moist. Rain is needed until about August 15 when the crop is cut. This presupposes a monsoon climate with rain in the summer [42]. In Victoria, Australia, Japanese millet is sown shallow with a grain drill at the rate of 12–15 pounds per acre on a carefully prepared warm moist seedbed. An application of 60–100 pounds of superphosphate per acre is sometimes made.

Utilization

In India, the grain of Japanese millet usually is eaten by the poorer classes of people, either parched or boiled in milk with sugar. In eastern India, it is mixed with rice in the manufacture of rice beer. The crop is also a valuable forage [49]. The crop is used in similar ways in Japan.

Japanese millet is grown almost entirely as a hay crop in the United States. The crop is used for hay, green fodder, or pasture in Australia. It is particularly popular there as an early grazing plant. It is often grazed in 6–8 weeks after planting, or when the plants are 6–12 inches tall, because the nutritive value for grazing decreases at later stages. Japanese millet is cut at the blossoming stage for the best quality of hay [45]. Its thick stems cure slowly in humid regions.

Diseases

Japanese millet is free from fungus diseases of major importance. Three smuts may cause damage in India: *Ustilago panici-frumentacei, U. paradoxa,* and *U. crusgalli* [49].

FINGER MILLET

Finger millet (*Eleusine coracana*) also is known as ragi, nagli, birdsfoot millet, coracana millet, and African millet. It is cultivated for human food in Africa and in southern Asia. Finger millet ranks second in importance among the millets in India. It is grown in the southern part of the country, more than half of it in Madras and nearby states, and much of the remainder in Mysore state. Finger millet also is grown in many parts of Africa, particularly in Ethiopia, Somaliland, and the Sudan.

Adaptation

Finger millet usually is found in India wherever rice grows. It is a hardy plant that grows in almost any soil. In contrast with other millets, it thrives in a moist climate but not where there are very heavy rains. It grows at altitudes of 6000–7000 feet on rocky soil in the rainy foothills of the Himalayas. Damp mountain slopes seem to be especially favorable [1].

Botanical Description

Finger millet (*Eleusine coracana*) is an annual that grows to a height of 3–4 feet with a capacity to tiller and branch freely. The stems are some-

what compressed, elliptic, tough, and smooth. The stems are much en-
sheathed with very little exposure of the internodes. The base of the leaf
sheath develops a ring of swollen tissue referred to as the nodal band. The
sheath and blade join together to form a light-colored triangular tissue known
as the junction. The leaf blade has a prominant midrib, in spite of which
many well-grown leaves have a tendency to break and hang down. These
bent or broken leaves gradually cease to function and dry up.

The inflorescence of finger millet is borne on a long peduncle from
which 4–6 spikes radiate in a raceme or whorl. The base of the peduncle
from which these radiate is referred to as the basal ring, because of the
presence of an irregular ring of slightly swollen tissue. The spikes are called
"fingers," while the odd one often found attached to one edge of the flattened
peduncle a little lower than the basal ring is called the "thumb." The spikes
are either straight or curved inward. In each finger there are 60–80 spikelets
in two rows, alternately attached to one side of the flattened rachis [7].

The spikelets of finger millet are sessile, generally with 4–5 florets,
and subtended by two glumes. Each floret consists of a lemma, palea, ovary
with two feathery stigmas, and three stamens. During dehiscence, the anther
sacs split longitudinally. The ovule develops into a globular seed enclosed
in a membranous pericarp [7].

Finger millet flowers open from 1:00 to 4:00 PM. An inflorescence usually completes its flowering in 7–8 days. Self-pollination is the rule, but
occasional crosspollination occurs in nature [14].

Cultural Practices

Finger millet in India is sometimes sown between the rows of maize
which often fails to produce a crop. Sometimes it is grown under irrigation.
It is seeded after the rainy season, or the seed is sown in May in irrigated
beds. The young plants are then transplanted at the beginning of the rainy
season.

In Sudan, finger millet is grown on thin or wet soils. It is planted in
pure stands or is mixed with grain sorghum, maize, or sesame. The crop is
sown broadcast and covered with a hoe. It is sown either in April or in
September, usually at the rate of 8–10 pounds of seed per acre. It matures
in 3–4 months and is harvested in July or in December when it attains
a height of about 40 inches. The heads generally are cut with a small knife,
dried, and the seed flailed out [53].

Utilization

Finger millet is commonly used as a food grain. In India it is used in
bread as well as for making cakes and puddings. In Gujarat, the unripe

ears are eaten as a vegetable. In Ethiopia, only the white-seeded kind is used for human food. Finger millet is sometimes used for making beer, for which it is well suited.

Diseases

A helminthosporium disease (*Helminthosporium nodulosum*) has been reported on finger millet. It is a serious and widely distributed disease in India. *H. leucostylum* was also found to attack the crop, but causes much less damage than *H. nodulosum*. Both fungi cause leaf spots, seedling blight, and head blight. *H. nodulosum* also causes foot rot, seed blight, and root rot. All parts of the finger millet plant are susceptible to attack by both species. The optimum temperature for the infection of the aerial parts by *H. nodulosum* was found to be 30–32°C (86–89.6°F), with a range of 10–37°C (50–98.6°F) [48].

A grain smut (*Melanopsichum eleusinis*) is also reported to attack finger millet.

Genetics

Purple pigmentation, mostly in the earhead, which gives certain varieties a characteristic violet color when in full bloom, is dominant to the unpigmented (green) condition [7]. Localized purple and green are differentiated by a single factor pair, Pp. One intensifier factor, I_1, acts with PP basic purple to form dilute purple. Another intensifier factor, I_2, acts only in the presence of I_1 to produce full purple in the floral bracts and nodal bands.

Purple Groups		*Green Groups*	
$PPi_1i_1i_2i_2$	local purple	$ppI_1I_1I_2I_2$	Green
$PPi_1i_1I_2I_2$	local purple	$ppi_1i_1I_2I_2$	Green
$PPI_1I_1i_2i_2$	dilute purple	$ppI_1I_1i_2i_2$	Green
$PPI_1I_1I_2I_2$	full purple	$ppi_1i_1i_2i_2$	Green

Brown is the predominant grain color in finger millet, although some varieties have white grain. The brown pigment is confined to the testa or outer layer of the seedcoat. In a cross between white-grained green plants and brown-grained purple plants, duplicate factors, B_1 and B_2, either alone or together, produced brown grain. A third factor, S, in association with either B_1 or B_2, or both, produced purple plant pigmentation. A fourth factor, D, deepens the brown color and behaves as a simple dominant and is independent of the purple pigmentation factors [7].

Green pericarp is determined by a single factor, Cx. The recessive factor cx produces a light-green pericarp color [5].

Chronic partial sterility, occasionally found in finger millet, results in very poor seed set. Such plants grow profusely, flower late, and have a low bushy appearance. The sterility results from nondehiscence of the anthers or agglutination of pollen grains. The absence of a dominant factor X causes nondehiscence, while the absence of the dominant factor Y causes pollen agglutination [4].

Albinism occurs in the absence of either C_1 or C_2 or both dominant independent factors for green plant color. These factors segregate in a dihybrid 15:1 ratio [6].

Incurving and crowding of the digitate spikes of some forms of finger millet are conditioned by the dominant factor Q_1. An independent factor E causes elongation of the rachis to produce top curving in the presence of factor q_1. The Q and E factors are independent of the factors for purple pigmentation [8].

Two dominant complementary factors, E_1 and E_2, determine whether the spikes are long, short, or very short length [11, 13].

KODA OR DITCH MILLET

The koda millet of India, or ditch millet of New Zealand (*Paspalum scrobiculatum*) resembles certain forage grasses of the genus *Paspalum* grown in the southeastern United States. These closely related grasses include Dallis grass, Vasey grass, and Bahia grass. The seeds of koda millet are borne in two rows on one side of the rachis of spikelike racemes [1].

BROWNTOP MILLET

Browntop millet (*Panicum ramosum*) is grown in the United States on some 100 thousand acres annually, chiefly in Georgia, Florida, and Alabama [27]. It is used for hay and pasture, while the seed provides feed for quail, doves, and other game birds. This crop, a native of India, was brought to the United States about 1915, being first grown under the name "German hay grass." Later it was identified, incorrectly, as *Panicum fasiculatum,* then called "browntop millet." The latter species, a grass native to Central and South America, is now called "browntop panicum."

The browntop millet plant is a quick-growing annual 2–4 feet tall, with a yellow to bronze-brown open panicle 2–6 inches long. It yields much less forage than does pearl millet, but it has a shorter growing season, with finer stems that permit easier curing for hay. Seed yields up to 1500 pounds per acre or more have been obtained.

Browntop millet is sown from May to July. It can be sown in disced crimson clover sod after the latter crop matures, and thereafter both crops may be self-seeding. Its reseeding habit may make browntop millet a pest when grown in rotation with cultivated crops. Natural reseeding often maintains its stands on game preserves and conservation areas.

For seed production, this millet may be sown in cultivated rows two feet apart at a rate of 4–10 pounds per acre. When forage is desired, it should be sown in drills at the rate of 10–20 pounds per acre. The seed crop is harvested with a combine after some shattering has occurred. Even then some of the seeds are not fully mature and must be dried after threshing.

REFERENCES

1. Anderson, E., and J. H. Martin, "World production and consumption of millet and sorghum." *Econ. Bot.*, **3**: 265–288. 1949.
2. Ayyangar, G. N. R., and T. R. Narayanan, "Inheritance of characters in *Setaria italica* (Beauv.), the Italian millet. I: Grain color." *Ind. J. Ag. Sci.*, **1**: 586–608. 1931.
3. ———, P. Krishna, and U. A. Wariar, "Inheritance of characters in ragi, *Eleusine coracana* (Gaertn.). II: Grain color factors and their relation to plant purple pigmentation." *Ind. J. Ag. Sci.*, **1**: 538–553. 1931.
4. ———, and N. Krishnaswami, "Inheritance of characters in ragi, *Eleusine coracana* (Gaertn.). III: Sterility." *Ind. J. Ag. Sci.*, **1**: 554–562. 1931.
5. ———, P. K. Rao, and N. Krishnaswami, "Inheritance of characters in ragi, *Eleusine coracana* (Gaertn.). IV: Depth of green in pericarp." *Ind. J. Ag. Sci.*, **1**: 563–568. 1931.
6. ———, and P. K. Rao, "Inheritance of characters in ragi, *Eleusine coracana* (Gaertn.). V: Albinism." *Ind. J. Ag. Sci.*, **1**: 569–576. 1931.
7. ———, and P. Krishna, "Inheritance of characters in ragi, *Eleusine coracana* (Gaertn.). I: Purple pigmentation." *Ind. J. Ag. Sci.*, **1**: 434–444. 1931.
8. ———, and U. A. Rao, "Inheritance of characters in ragi, *Eleusine coracana* (Gaertn.). VI: Earhead shapes." *Ind. J. Ag. Sci.*, **2**: 254–265. 1932.
9. ———, P. K. Rao, and U. A. Wariar, "Inheritance of characters in ragi, *Eleusine coracana* (Gaertn.). VII: Fist-like earheads." *Ind. J. Ag. Sci.*, **3**: 1072–1079. 1933.
10. ———, T. R. Narayanan, and P. S. Sarma, "Studies in *Setaria italica* (Beauv.), the Italian millet. I: Anthesis and pollination." *Ind. J. Ag. Sci.*, **3**: 561–571. 1933.
11. ———, T. R. Narayanan, and T. N. Rao, "Inheritance of characters in *Setaria italica* (Beauv.) the Italian millet. III: Bristles." *Ind. J. Ag. Sci.*, **3**: 207–218. 1933.
12. ———, and P. S. Sarma, "Inheritance of characters in *Setaria italica* (Beauv.), the Italian millet. V: A type of lax earhead." *Ind. J. Ag. Sci.*, **3**: 557–558. 1933.
13. ———, C. Vijiaraghavan, and V. G. Pillai, "Studies on *Pennisetum typhoideum* (Rich.), the pearl millet. I: Anthesis." *Ind. J. Ag. Sci.*, **3**: 688–694. 1933.

14. ———, and U. A. Wariar, "Anthesis and pollination in ragi, *Eleusine coracana* (Gaertn.), the finger millet." *Ind. J. Ag. Sci.*, **4**: 386–393. 1934.

15. ———, and P. V. Hariharan, "Chlorophyll deficiencies in *Pennisetum typhoides* (Stapf and Hubbard) the pearl millet." *Madras Ag. J.*, **23**: 394–397. 1935.

16. ———, P. V. Hariharan, and S. R. Pamakrishnan, "Basal branching in the ear-heads of the pearl millet, *Pennisetum typhoides*, Stapf and Hubbard." *Curr. Sci.*, Palghat, India, **4**: 237–238. 1935.

17. ———, and P. V. Hariharan, "Bristled cumbri (Pearl millet)." *Madras Ag. J.*, Palghat, India, **24**: 235–237. 1936.

18. ———, *et al.*, "Inheritance of characters in *Setaria italica* (Beauv.), the Italian millet. VII: Plant purple pigmentation." *Ind. J. Ag. Sci.*, **5**: 176–194. 1935.

19. Ball, C. R., "Pearl millet." USDA *Farmers Bul. 168*. 1903.

20. Brandon, J. F., *et al.*, "Proso or hog millet in Colorado." Colo. Ag. Exp. Sta. *Bul. 383*. 1932.

21. Bressman, E. N., and E. S. Fry, "Differences between barnyard grasses and Japanese millet." *J. Am. Soc. Agron.*, **24**: 123–128. 1932.

22. Burton, G. W., "Hybrids between Napier grass and cattail millet." *J. Hered.*, **35**: 227–232. 1944.

23. ———, "Performance of various mixtures of hybrid and inbred pearl millet, *Pennisetum glaucum*." *J. Am. Soc. Agron.*, **40**: 908–915. 1948.

24. ———, "Quantitative inheritance in pearl millet (*Pennisetum glaucum*)." *Agron. J.*, **43**: 409–417. 1951.

25. ———, "Immediate effect of gametic relationship upon seed production in pearl millet, *Pennisetum glaucum*." *Agron. J.*, **44**: 424–27. 1952.

26. ———, "Cytoplasmic male-sterility in pearl millet (*Pennisetum glaucum*) (L.) R. Br." *Agron. J.*, **50**: 230. 1958.

27. Craigmiles, J. P., and J. M. Elrod, "Browntop millet in Georgia." Ga. Ag. Exp. Sta. *Leaflet 14*. 1957.

28. Curtis, J. J., J. F. Brandon, and D. W. Robertson, "Proso or hog millet." Colo. Ag. Exp. Sta. *Bul. 438*. 1937.

29. ———, J. F. Brandon, and R. M. Weihing, "Foxtail millet in Colorado." Colo. Ag. Exp. Sta. *Bul. 461*. 1940.

30. Dickson, J. G., *Diseases of Field Crops*. 2d ed. New York: McGraw-Hill. pp 1–517. 1956.

31. Elliott, C., "A bacterial stripe disease of proso millet." *J. Ag. Res.*, **26**: 151–160. 1923.

32. Harrison, L. S., "Millet, a useful catch crop." N. S. Wales *Ag. Gaz.* **43**: 887–889. 1932.

33. Heh, C. M., T. F. Mei, and S. S. Yang, "Anthesis of millet, *Setaria italica* (L.) Beauv." *J. Am. Soc. Agron.*, **29**: 845–853. 1937.

34. Hein, M. A., "Registration of varieties and strains of pearl millet (*Pennisetum glaucum*) (L.) R. Br." *Agron. J.*, **45**: 573–574. 1953.

35. Hiura, M., "Mycological and pathological studies on the downy mildew of Italian millet." Hokkaido Imp. U. *J. Fac. Ag.*, **36**: 121–283. 1935.

36. Jasny, N., *Competition Among Grains*. Stanford U. Food Res. Inst. pp 1–358. 1940.

37. Krishnaswami, N., and G. N. R. Ayyangar, "Certain abnormalities in millets induced by X-rays." Ind. Acad. Sci. *Proc.*, **14**, Section B, pp 1–9. 1942.

38. Langworthy, C. F., and A. D. Holmes, "Experiments in the determination of the digestibility of millets." USDA *Bul. 525.* 1917.
39. Li, H. W., and C. J. Meng, "Experiments on the planting distance in varietal trials with millet, *Setaria italica* (L.) Beauv." *J. Am. Soc. Agron.*, **29**: 577–583. 1937.
40. ———, J. C. Meng, and C. H. Li, "Genetic studies with foxtail millet, *Setaria italica* (L.) Beauv." *J. Am. Soc. Agron.*, **32**: 426–438. 1940.
41. ———, C. N. Li, and W. K. Pao, "Cytological and genetical studies of the interspecific cross of the cultivated foxtail millet, *Setaria italica* (L.) Beauv., and the green foxtail millet, *S. viridis* L." *J. Am. Soc. Agron.*, **37**: 32–54. 1945.
42. Mann, H. B., "Millets in the Middle East." *Emp. J. Exp. Ag.*, **14**: 208–216. 1946.
43. Martin, J. H., "Proso or hog millet." USDA *Farmers Bul. 1162.* 1920, 1929, 1937.
44. ———, "Sorghum and pearl millet," in *Handbuch der Pflanzenzuchtung*, II Bd., 2 Aufl., pp 565–589. 1959.
45. McDonald, W. J. B., "Summer fodder crops: Maize, millet, and sorghum." *Victoria Dep. Ag. J.*, **45**: 449–454. 1947.
46. McVicar, R. M., and H. R. Parnell, "Inheritance of plant color and the extent of natural crossing in foxtail millet." *Sci. Ag.*, **22**: 80–84. 1941.
47. McGee, C. R., "Proso—a grain millet." Mich. Ag. Exten. *Bul. 231.* 1941.
48. Mitra, M., and P. R. Mehta, "Diseases of *Eleusine coracana* (Gaertn.) and *E. aegyptiaca* (Def.) caused by species of *Helminthosporium*." *Ind. J. Ag. Sci.*, **4**: 943–975. 1934.
49. Mundkar, B. B., "Studies in India cereal smuts. VI: The smuts on Sawan (*Echinochloa frumentacea*)." *Ind. J. Ag. Sci.*, **13**: 631–633. 1933.
50. Musil, A. F., "Seeds of grasses cultivated for forage or occurring incidentally with crop seeds: The genus *Setaria*." USDA Leaflet (mimeo), pp 1–4. 1944.
51. Pal, B. P., "Advances in plant breeding and genetics in relation to crop improvement in India in the last twenty-five years." *Emp. J. Exp. Ag.*, **26**: 123–135. 1958.
52. Rao, P. K., A. Kunhikoran, and I. V. G. Krishnamurthy, "Natural crossing in cumbri, *Pennisetum typhoides* Stapf and Hub." *Madras Ag. J.*, Palghat, India, **36**: 526–592. 1949.
53. Tothill, J. D., *Agriculture in the Sudan*. Oxford, England: Oxford U. Press. pp 1–971. 1948.
54. Trotter, I. P., "Millet for forage and grain." Mo. Ag. Exten. Serv. *Leaflet 41.* 1937.
55. Vasey, H. E., "Millet smuts and their control." Colo. Ag. Exp. Sta. *Bul. 242.* 1918.
56. Vinall, H. N., "Foxtail millet: Its culture and utilization in the United States." USDA *Farmers Bul. 793.* 1917 (rev. 1924).
57. Wang, C. S., "*Sclerospora graminicola* on millet in Minnesota." *Phytopath.*, **26**: 462–464. 1936.
58. Wheeler, W. A., and D. D. Hill, *Grassland Seeds*. New York: Van Nostrand. pp 1–734. 1957.
59. Wright, W. H., "Millets (*Panicum, Setaria*, and *Pennisetum*)," in *Handbook on Seed Testing*, Assoc. Off. Seed Analysts. pp 1–4. 1941.

Appendix

TABLE A-1. **Corn: Average Acreage, Yield, and Production in Specified Countries, with World Total, 1955–59.**

Country	Thousands of Acres	Yield per Acre	Production
		(Bushels)	(1000 Bushels)
Canada	516	59.7	30,780
El Salvador	431	14.5	6,240
Guatemala	1,549	11.3	17,500
Honduras	822	11.7	9,634
Mexico	14,292	13.3	190,630
Nicaragua	369	12.5	4,620
United States	66,409	48.7	3,234,891
Cuba	432	15.7	6,800
Austria	125	47.0	5,874
France	1,455	41.8	60,766
Greece	537	19.1	10,274
Italy	3,272	42.6	139,282
Portugal	1,187	15.0	17,772
Spain	934	34.5	32,179
Albania	357	19.0	6,780
Bulgaria	1,787	22.6	40,340
Czechoslovakia	434	40.7	17,670
Hungary	3,194	36.2	115,600
Rumania	8,764	20.7	180,000
Yugoslavia	6,627	29.8	185,502
U.S.S.R.	11,925	26.8	320,000
Turkey	1,737	17.7	30,690
China	—	—	435,000
India	9,881	13.0	128,100
Pakistan	1,097	16.4	18,020
Indonesia	5,611	14.8	82,850
Japan	121	32.2	3,900
Philippines	3,889	9.8	38,190
Thailand	275	21.7	5,960
Congo	1,182	16.7	19,686
Kenya	500	26.2	13,110
Egypt	1,921	33.3	63,916
Morocco	1,147	10.1	11,622
Former French West Africa	1,705	9.6	16,316
Malagasy	204	13.0	2,643
Angola	1,453	8.4	12,220
Rhodesia and Nyasaland	2,960	17.6	52,000
South Africa	9,540	14.9	141,946
Argentina	5,855	29.7	173,710
Brazil	15,152	19.7	299,000
Chile	169	28.2	4,762
Columbia	1,585	19.0	30,170

TABLE A-1. **Corn: Average Acreage, Yield, and Production in
Specified Countries, with World Total, 1955–59. (Cont.)**

Ecuador	481	12.3	5,900
Peru	605	19.1	11,530
Uruguay	777	8.9	6,920
Venezuela	702	19.1	13,380
Australia	180	31.7	5,700
New Zealand	6	55.2	332
World Total	227,720	32.1	6,465,000

TABLE A-2. **Wheat: Average Acreage, Yield, and Production in Specified Countries, with World Total, 1955–59.**

Country	Thousands of Acres	Yield per Acre	Production
		(Bushels)	(1000 Bushels)
Canada	22,704	20.5	465,437
Mexico	2,214	20.6	44,615
United States	49,128	22.3	1,095,357
Austria	634	32.8	20,802
Belgium	496	53.6	26,672
Denmark	179	58.8	10,521
Finland	314	23.9	7,514
France	10,432	34.3	358,210
Germany, West	3,045	45.5	138,676
Greece	2,704	21.4	57,762
Ireland	361	42.3	15,279
Italy	12,145	27.2	329,880
Netherlands	250	57.8	14,446
Norway	35	32.4	1,134
Portugal	2,009	12.1	24,286
Spain	10,728	15.4	165,400
Sweden	831	33.7	28,030
Switzerland	243	44.7	10,860
United Kingdom	2,098	48.5	101,720
Bulgaria	3,466	19.6	68,100
Czechoslovakia	1,818	30.0	54,500
Germany, East	1,026	41.1	42,160
Hungary	3,112	22.0	68,500
Poland	3,581	23.4	83,900
Rumania	7,302	16.2	118,600
Yugoslavia	4,750	21.5	102,000
U.S.S.R.	159,000	12.0	1,910,000
Iran	—	—	95,950
Iraq	2,540	10.7	27,118
Israel	137	17.6	2,418
Jordan	638	8.6	5,458
Lebanon	162	10.4	1,682
Syria	2,540	10.0	25,392
Turkey	16,990	13.7	232,000
China	—	—	900,000
India	30,448	10.9	330,926
Pakistan	11,496	11.6	133,192
Japan	1,551	32.5	50,482
Korea, South	317	14.1	4,469
Algeria	4,658	10.0	46,364
Egypt	1,561	34.4	53,778
Morocco	3,888	9.2	35,723

TABLE A-2. **Wheat: Average Acreage, Yield, and Production in Specified Countries, with World Total, 1955–59. (Cont.)**

Tunisia	2,908	6.1	17,798
South Africa	2,906	9.5	27,554
Argentina	11,598	19.5	225,676
Brazil	2,386	10.3	24,460
Chile	2,030	20.0	40,597
Columbia	412	12.8	5,288
Peru	365	14.2	5,166
Uruguay	1,604	11.8	18,950
Australia	9,629	17.5	168,320
New Zealand	103	46.7	4,814
World Total	493,020	16.1	7,955,000

TABLE A-3. **Rye: Average Acreage, Yield, and Production in Specified Countries, with World Total, 1955–59.**

Country	Thousands of Acres	Yield per Acre	Production
		(Bushels)	(1000 Bushels)
Canada	576	16.3	9,393
United States	1,729	15.6	27,030
Austria	525	31.0	16,254
Belgium	170	45.5	7,732
Denmark	270	40.5	10,946
Finland	217	22.9	4,969
France	888	20.3	18,055
Germany, West	3,634	40.5	147,130
Greece	115	14.9	1,719
Italy	178	23.5	4,190
Netherlands	380	46.2	17,540
Norway	2	33.0	66
Portugal	636	11.3	7,185
Spain	1,425	14.0	20,110
Sweden	258	32.2	8,320
Switzerland	31	44.6	1,362
United Kingdom	22	37.1	816
Bulgaria	320	13.9	4,440
Czechoslovakia	1,278	29.8	38,140
Germany, East	2,672	30.4	81,152
Hungary	1,019	18.1	18,410
Poland	12,668	22.5	285,280
Rumania	395	15.1	5,960
Yugoslavia	626	15.7	9,864
U.S.S.R.	44,735	14.2	635,000
Turkey	1,611	15.0	24,086
Argentina	2,660	12.0	31,816
World Total	79,480	18.1	1,440,000

TABLE A-4. **Barley: Average Acreage, Yield, and Production in Specified Countries, with World Total, 1955–59.**

Country	Thousands of Acres	Yield per Acre	Production
		(Bushels)	(1000 Bushels)
Canada	8,956	26.6	238,000
Mexico	602	14.1	8,500
United States	14,391	29.5	424,448
Austria	419	40.8	17,110
Belgium	229	63.4	14,520
Denmark	1,692	65.1	110,090
Finland	518	29.0	15,010
France	4,452	44.4	197,890
Germany, West	2,142	52.1	111,700
Greece	491	22.3	10,950
Ireland	279	57.7	16,110
Italy	571	23.2	13,240
Netherlands	183	70.9	12,970
Norway	312	43.2	13,480
Portugal	370	10.4	3,850
Spain	3,785	21.8	82,470
Sweden	655	40.9	26,760
Switzerland	63	54.4	3,430
United Kingdom	2,611	56.8	148,200
Bulgaria	656	28.6	18,770
Czechoslovakia	1,639	37.6	61,700
Germany, East	825	45.8	37,760
Hungary	1,172	31.8	37,280
Poland	1,857	28.9	53,630
Rumania	781	21.7	16,940
Yugoslavia	923	23.7	21,890
U.S.S.R.	25,000	39.4	440,000
Cyprus	142	21.5	3,046
Iran	2,015	21.1	42,530
Iraq	2,821	15.9	44,992
Israel	134	22.0	2,949
Syria	1,213	13.2	16,064
Turkey	6,295	22.1	139,000
China	—	—	311,000
India	8,274	15.2	125,356
Pakistan	561	11.8	6,620
Japan	2,356	40.0	93,528
Korea, Republic of	1,933	18.8	36,260
Algeria	3,111	10.9	34,000
Egypt	141	43.2	6,090
Morocco	4,438	12.4	55,250
Tunisia	1,550	5.4	8,440

TABLE A-4. **Barley: Average Acreage, Yield, and Production in Specified Countries, with World Total, 1955–59. (Cont.)**

South Africa	68	16.9	1,150
Argentina	2,213	22.8	50,510
Chile	157	31.4	4,932
Colombia	120	27.4	3,293
Ecuador	295	13.3	3,928
Peru	439	19.5	8,551
Uruguay	116	12.3	1,457
Australia	2,183	20.8	45,400
New Zealand	58	51.2	2,972
World Total	136,510	23.8	3,255,000

TABLE A-5. **Oats: Average Acreage, Yield, and Production in Specified Countries, with World Total, 1955-59.**

Country	*Thousands of Acres*	*Yield per Acre*	*Production*
		(Bushels)	(1000 Bushels)
Canada	9,735	38.5	375,000
Mexico	231	23.0	5,308
United States	33,093	38.6	1,278,145
Austria	447	53.1	23,740
Belgium	365	86.2	31,470
Denmark	575	89.1	51,210
Finland	1,111	43.3	48,160
France	4,424	50.7	224,270
Germany, West	2,211	70.8	156,630
Greece	355	31.0	11,000
Ireland	490	70.2	34,380
Italy	1,039	36.1	37,490
Luxembourg	49	59.0	2,890
Netherlands	368	87.3	32,140
Norway	157	59.4	9,320
Portugal	756	9.9	7,450
Spain	1,408	26.3	37,000
Sweden	1,299	45.2	58,750
Switzerland	48	80.2	3,850
United Kingdom	2,348	69.6	163,310
Bulgaria	394	28.8	11,340
Czechoslovakia	1,290	50.2	64,800
Germany	1,152	57.9	66,740
Hungary	374	37.6	14,080
Poland	4,139	40.7	168,640
Rumania	833	27.6	22,960
Yugoslavia	880	27.4	24,090
U.S.S.R.	36,080	23.5	845,000
Syria	19	24.0	456
Turkey	866	29.3	25,406
China	—	—	65,000
Japan	216	56.4	12,188
Algeria	257	18.8	4,840
Morocco	69	22.8	1,570
Tunisia	55	12.0	660
South Africa	400	15.1	6,040
Argentina	2,016	32.1	64,620
Chile	259	30.8	7,970
Uruguay	189	14.8	2,798
Australia	3,183	20.0	63,630
New Zealand	39	62.3	2,430
World Total	116,910	34.9	4,060,000

TABLE A-6. **Rice: Average Acreage, Yield, and Production of Rough Rice in Specified Countries, with World Total, 1955-59.**

Country	Acreage	Yield per Acre	Production
	(1,000 Acres)	(Pounds)	(1,000 Short Tons)
Mexico	285	1,854	264.2
United States	1,547	3,189	2,467.0
Costa Rica	112	835	46.8
Nicaragua	55	1,175	32.3
Panama	224	1,018	114.0
Cuba	314	1,720	270.0
Dominican Republic	125	1,940	122.4
Argentina	138	2,956	204.0
Bolivia	54	1,330	35.9
Brazil	6,527	1,370	4,472.4
British Guiana	166	1,912	158.7
Chile	84	2,130	89.4
Colombia	485	1,653	400.8
Ecuador	268	1,226	164.3
Peru	167	3,575	298.5
Surinam	67	2,334	78.2
Uruguay	43	2,884	62.0
Venezuela	78	1,096	42.8
France	66	3,782	124.8
Greece	39	3,359	65.5
Italy	347	4,666	809.6
Portugal	91	3,960	180.2
Spain	164	5,167	423.8
Congo	383	959	183.6
Guinea	960	677	325.0
Ivory Coast	478	581	138.8
Malagasy Republic	2,031	1,210	1,228.8
Egypt	679	3,734	1,267.6
Iran	800	1,750	700.0
Iraq	475	1,099	261.0
Turkey	121	2,474	149.7
Burma	11,100	1,387	7,700.0
Cambodia	3,080	1,002	1,542.4
Ceylon	1,018	1,542	785.0

TABLE A-6. **Rice: Average Acreage, Yield, and Production of Rough Rice in Specified Countries, with World Total, 1955-59 (Cont.)**

Country	Acreage	Yield per Acre	Production
	(1,000 Acres)	(Pounds)	(1,000 Short Tons)
China (Taiwan)	1,926	2,765	2,676.1
India	80,273	1,189	47,722.0
Indonesia	17,263	1,535	13,248.6
Japan	8,081	4,040	16,325.6
Korea (South)	2,725	2,450	3,338.5
Laos	1,663	724	602.2
Malaya	893	1,916	855.6
Pakistan	22,767	1,242	13,140.0
Philippines	7,158	1,062	3,799.8
Thailand	12,778	1,209	7,721.2
Vietnam (South)	—	—	—
Australia	50	4,762	119.0
World Total[1]	201,881	1,431	144,475.0

[1]Excluding Communist China, North Korea, North Vietnam, and U.S.S.R. which together produced fully 75,000 tons.

TABLE A-7. **Some Foreign Names for the Cereals.** (Additional names are used in some of these languages).

Language	Barley	Corn (maize)	Oats	Rice	Rye	Wheat
				Cereal		
English	Barley	Corn (maize)	Oats	Rice	Rye	Wheat
Latin	*Hordeum*	*Zea*	*Avena*	*Oryza*	*Secale*	*Triticum*
Arabic	Sha'ir	Dhurah shamyah	Hartaman	Ruz	Ales	Quamhh
Danish	Bug	Korn	Havre	Ris	Rug	Hvede
Dutch	Gerst	Turkische koren	Voy	Ryst	Rogge	Weit
Finnish	Ohra	Maissi	Karra	Riisi	Ruis	Vehna
French	Orge	Blé de Turquie	Avione	Riz	Seigle	Blé: Froment
German	Gerste	Turkische korn	Hafer	Reis	Roggen	Weizen
Italian	Orzo	Gran turko	Vena	Riso	Segale	Frumento
Japanese	Omugi	To-morokoshi	Embaku	Ine	Raimugi	Komugi
Jugoslavian	Yetcham	Kukuruz	Zob	Riza	Raz	Pshenitsa
Norwegian	Bug	Korn	Havre	Ris	Rug	Hvede
Portuguese	Cevada	Maiz	Veia	Arroz	Centeio	Trigo
Russian	Iachman	Kukuruza	Oves	Ris	Rozh	Pshenitsa
Spanish	Cebada	Maiz	Avenas	Arroz	Centano	Trigo
Swedish	Korn	Majs	Havre	Ris	Rag	Hvete
Turkish	Arpa	Misir bugdayi	Yulav	Pirinc	Cavdar	Bugday

TABLE A-7. **Some Foreign Names for Cereals (Cont.)**

Cereal

Language	Sorghum / *Sorghum*	Pearl millet / *Pennisetum*	Proso / *Panicum*	Finger / *Eleusine*	Foxtail / *Setaria*	Barnyard / *Echinochlea*
English	Sorghum	Pearl millet	Proso	Finger	Foxtail	Barnyard
Latin	*Sorghum*	*Pennisetum*	*Panicum*	*Eleusine*	*Setaria*	*Echinochlea*
Arabic	Dhurah nili	Dukhn	Dukhn	Bisnah	Dukhn	Dhunaybah
Dutch	Zorgzaad	Paarl gierst	Gierst	Eleusine gierst	—	—
Finnish	Durra	—	Vilja hirssi	—	—	—
French	Sorgho	Millet à chandelles	Panic millet	Coracan	Panic d'Italio	Panic pied de coq
German	Mohrhirse	Negerhirse	Rispenhirsa	Africanski hirse	Welsche hirse	Huhnerhirse
India (dialects)	Jowar; cholam	Bajra; Cumbo	Chena; Warree	Ragi	Korra; Kangni	Sanwak
Italian	Saggina	Miglio d'Indie	Panico miglio	Eleusina	Panico d'Italia	Panico pie di gallina
Japanese	Morokoshi	—	Kibi	—	Awa	Hie
Jugoslavian	Sirak	—	—	—	—	—
Portuguese	Trigo de guine	—	—	—	—	—
Russian	Sorgo	—	Proso	—	Italianskago proso	—
Spanish	Sorgo	Panizo negro	Mijo comun	—	—	—
Swedish	Durra	—	Akta hirs	—	—	—
Turkish	Dari	Hind darisi	Ak darisi	Ragi darisi	Konak darisi	Pirine otu

TABLE A-8. **Measures in Other Countries Equivalent to Some Measures Used in the United States.**

System of Measurement	One United States Acre	One United States Bushel	One United States Gallon	One United States Pound	One United States Short Ton (2000 Pounds)
	1 United States acre equals	1 United States bushel equals	1 United States gallon equals	1 United States pound equals	1 United States ton (2000 lbs) equals
Metric measures[1]	0.40 hectare	0.35 hectoliter	3.79 liters	0.45 kilogram	0.91 metric ton
United Kingdom measures[2]	0.40 hectare	0.97 imperial bu	0.83 imperial gal.	1.00 pound	0.89 ton (long)
Spanish measures	0.58 manzana	0.63 fanega	0.06 fanega	0.99 libra	0.99 tonelada
Other measures, countries using:					
Afghanistan[2]	—	—	—	0.10 mahn	—
Argentina[2,4]	0.24 cuadra	0.26 fanega	0.05 baril	0.04 arroba	0.91 tonelada
Australia[2,3]	—	—	—	0.01 cental	—
Chile[2,4]	—	0.36 fanega	—	—	—
China	6.07 mow (shih)	—	—	0.91 catty (shih)	—
Colombia[2]	0.63 fanegada	0.09 fanega	—	0.91 libra	—
Costa Rica[2,4]	0.03 caballeria	0.33 fanega	—	0.04 arroba	—
Cuba[2,4]	—	—	—	—	—
Cyprus[3]	3.02 donum	—	0.10 kile	0.36 oke	16.23 cantars
Denmark[2]	0.73 tonde	0.25 tonde	—	0.009 centner	—
Dominican Republic[2]	6.43 tarea	—	—	0.91 libra	—
Egypt and Anglo-Egyptian Sudan[2]	0.96 feddan	0.18 ardeb	0.23 kilah	1.01 cantar	0.96 dariba
Eritrea[2]	—	—	—	16.21 okia	—
Germany[2]	—	—	—	0.91 pfund	9.07 double zentner
Greece[2]	4.05 stremma	0.93 kile	—	1.00 pound	—
Haiti[2]	—	—	—	0.91 libra	1.00 ton
Hong Kong[2,3]	—	—	—	0.75 catty	—
Hungary[2]	0.70 yoke (joch)	—	—	—	—

TABLE A-8. **Measures in Other Countries Equivalent to Some Measures in the United States (Cont.)**

System of Measurement	One United States Acre — 1 United States acre equals	One United States Bushel — 1 United States bushel equals	One United States Gallon — 1 United States gallon equals	One United States Pound — 1 United States pound equals	One United States Short Ton (2000 Pounds) — 1 United States ton (2000 lbs) equals
Indonesia, United States of [2]	0.57 bouw (bahoe)	—	—	—	—
Iran [2]	0.40 jerib	0.54 artaba	0.46 collothun	0.15 batman	305.45 batman
Iraq [2]	1.62 donum	—	—	0.02 man	36.29 man
Japan and Korea [2]	0.41 cho	0.20 koku	0.02 koku	0.76 kin	15.12 picul
Libya [2]	4.40 donum	—	—	0.35 oke	17.69 cantar
Malaya, Federation of [2,3]	—	—	—	0.75 catty	15.00 picul
Manchuria [2]	—	—	2.10 sho	0.75 catty	15.00 picul
Mexico [2,4]	0.11 fanega	0.39 fanega	—	—	—
Paraguay [2,4]	—	0.12 fanega	—	0.04 arroba	61.76 arroba
Portugal [2]	—	2.55 alqueire	0.23 almude	0.99 arratel	15.00 picul
Straits Settlements [2,3]	—	—	—	0.75 catty	15.00 picul
Syria and Lebanon [2]	4.04 donum	—	—	0.35 oke	3.54 cantar
Taiwan (Formosa) [2]	0.42 ko	0.20 koku	0.02 koku	0.76 kin	15.12 picul
Thailand (Siam) [2]	—	—	—	0.75 catty	15.12 picul
Turkey [2]	4.40 donum	0.93 kile	—	0.35 oke	16.07 cantar
Union of South Africa [2,3]	0.47 morgen	0.32 muid	—	—	—
Union of Soviet Socialist Republics [2]	0.37 desiatina	0.17 chetvert	0.30 vedro	0.03 pood	5.54 berkovets
Venezuela [2,1]	0.58 fanegada	0.30 fanega	—	—	—
Yugoslavia [2]	5.78 donum	—	—	0.35 oke	708.74 oke

[1] U.S. foot = 0.30 meter; 1 U.S. mile = 1.61 kilometers.　　　[3] Also uses United Kingdom system.
[2] Also uses metric system.　　　[4] Also uses old Spanish system.

TABLE A-9. **Usual Rates-Per-Acre of Seeding Cereals in the United States.**[1]

State	Corn (Lb)	Winter Wheat (Bu)	Durum Wheat (Bu)	Other Spring Wheat (Bu)	Oats (Bu)	Barley (Bu)	Rye (Bu)	Grain Sorghum (Lbs)	Rice (Lbs)
Maine	15.8	—	—	—	2.9	2.2	—	—	—
New Hampshire	14.6	—	—	—	2.3	—	—	—	—
Vermont	15.4	—	—	—	2.3	—	—	—	—
Massachusetts	15.1	—	—	—	2.2	—	—	—	—
Rhode Island	15.1	—	—	—	—	—	—	—	—
Connecticut	15.6	—	—	—	2.2	—	—	—	—
New York	13.8	2.0	—	—	2.3	2.0	1.9	—	—
New Jersey	10.2	2.0	—	—	2.2	2.0	1.8	—	—
Pennsylvania	9.8	2.0	—	—	2.4	2.1	1.7	—	—
Ohio	8.7	2.0	—	—	2.3	2.0	1.7	—	—
Indiana	8.6	1.7	—	—	2.2	1.7	1.5	10.3	—
Illinois	8.3	1.5	—	—	2.6	1.8	1.5	—	—
Michigan	8.5	1.9	—	—	2.2	1.8	1.5	—	—
Wisconsin	9.9	1.7	—	1.7	2.7	2.0	1.6	—	—
Minnesota	9.0	1.6	1.5	1.4	2.8	1.9	1.6	—	—
Iowa	9.0	1.5	—	1.7	3.0	2.1	1.5	11.5	—
Missouri	7.9	1.4	—	—	2.4	1.9	1.6	12.7	150
North Dakota	8.5	—	1.4	1.2	1.9	1.5	1.2	—	—
South Dakota	7.5	1.1	1.4	1.2	2.4	1.6	1.3	9.0	—
Nebraska	7.2	1.1	—	1.1	2.4	1.5	1.1	7.2	—
Kansas	7.1	0.9	—	—	2.1	1.4	1.1	5.6	—
Delaware	8.5	1.8	—	—	2.3	2.0	1.6	—	—
Maryland	9.1	1.8	—	—	2.3	2.0	1.6	—	—
Virginia	9.4	1.7	—	—	2.2	1.9	1.6	—	—
West Virginia	9.6	1.9	—	—	2.1	2.0	—	—	—

TABLE A-9. **Usual Rates-Per-Acre of Seeding Cereals in the United States (Cont.)**

State	Corn	Winter Wheat	Durum Wheat	Other Spring Wheat	Oats	Barley	Rye	Grain Sorghum	Rice
	(Lb)	(Bu)	(Bu)	(Bu)	(Bu)	(Bu)	(Bu)	(Lb)	(Lb)
North Carolina	8.8	1.7	—	—	2.8	2.1	1.5	9.0	—
South Carolina	7.7	1.6	—	—	2.9	2.2	1.5	11.0	—
Georgia	8.0	1.5	—	—	2.8	1.9	1.5	11.0	—
Florida	7.0	—	—	—	2.3	—	—	—	—
Kentucky	7.7	1.5	—	—	1.9	1.8	1.7	11.3	—
Tennessee	7.7	1.5	—	—	2.4	2.0	1.7	11.3	—
Alabama	10.0	1.6	—	—	2.8	—	—	12.5	—
Mississippi	9.3	1.6	—	—	2.9	2.0	—	12.0	120
Arkansas	8.3	1.6	—	—	3.0	1.9	—	12.0	134
Louisiana	10.3	1.6	—	—	3.0	—	—	10.5	123
Oklahoma	8.3	0.9	—	—	2.1	1.4	1.1	8.6	—
Texas	7.5	0.7	—	—	1.9	1.2	0.9	6.5	101
Montana	8.2	0.9	0.9	0.9	1.7	1.2	0.9	—	—
Idaho	11.7	1.2	—	1.5	2.4	1.6	1.3	—	—
Wyoming	7.6	0.8	—	1.1	2.1	1.6	0.8	—	—
Colorado	8.0	0.6	—	1.1	2.2	1.3	0.7	9.5	—
New Mexico	8.7	0.6	—	1.0	1.9	1.4	1.0	6.7	—
Arizona	10.0	1.2	—	—	2.0	2.1	—	9.0	—
Utah	12.7	1.2	—	1.6	2.5	2.0	0.8	—	—
Nevada	13.5	1.6	—	1.7	2.4	2.0	—	—	—
Washington	11.4	1.1	—	1.2	2.6	1.7	1.0	—	—
Oregon	9.8	1.2	—	1.5	2.7	1.8	1.1	—	—
California	13.0	1.3	—	—	2.6	1.7	1.0	14.0	140
United States	8.6	1.00	1.30	1.17	2.51	1.61	1.36	7.1	123

¹ Average rate per acre for caryopses (without hulls): wheat, 60–78 lbs.; oats 60–72 lbs.; barley, 60–70 lbs.; rye 76 lbs.

TABLE A-10. **Average Composition of the Caryopses of the Cereals.**[1]
(Based on dry weight; figures in italics are for grain that includes hulls.)

Composition	Corn	Wheat	Rice	*Rice*	Rye	Barley	*Barley*	Oats	*Oats*	Sorghum	Pearl Millet	Proso	*Proso*
Protein (%)	10.4	14.3	9.4	*9.0*	13.4	14.5	*13.4*	19.3	*13.3*	12.7	13.4	14.8	*11.6*
Fat (%)	4.5	1.9	1.8	*1.9*	1.8	2.1	*2.1*	7.4	*5.1*	3.3	5.1	3.5	*4.2*
Fiber (%)	2.4	2.9	0.9	*9.7*	2.6	2.1	*6.0*	2.0	*12.0*	2.4	2.5	2.4	*10.2*
Ash (%)	1.5	2.0	1.1	*5.2*	2.1	2.3	*3.1*	2.9	*4.1*	2.0	2.2	2.3	*3.6*
N-free extract (%)	81.2	78.9	86.8	*74.2*	80.1	79.0	*75.7*	68.4	*65.5*	79.6	76.8	77.0	*70.4*
Energy calories/lb	2,059	2,043	1,833	*1,566*	1,767	—	*2,086*	—	*2,138*	2,005	—	—	*1,816*
Total sugars (%)	1.9	3.2	0.6	—	4.5	—	*2.5*	—	*1.6*	1.4	—	—	—
Starch (%)	71.8	63.8	—	—	63.8	62.0	*64.6*	—	*44.7*	70.2	—	—	—
Pentosans (%)	6.2	7.4	2.1	*6.2*	10.6	10.3	*10.3*	—	*7.5*	2.5	—	—	—
Minerals													
Calcium (%)	0.03	0.06	0.05	*0.09*	0.07	0.08	*0.09*	—	*0.11*	0.03	0.06	—	*0.05*
Phosphorus (%)	0.31	0.41	0.29	*0.36*	0.38	0.40	*0.47*	—	*0.39*	0.35	0.43	—	*0.33*
Copper mg/lb	1.1	3.7	2.2	—	4.0	—	*3.9*	—	*3.0*	3.6	—	—	—
Potassium (%)	0.33	0.58	0.23	*0.38*	0.52	0.60	*0.63*	—	*0.42*	0.37	—	—	*0.48*
Magnesium (%)	0.14	0.18	0.10	*0.16*	0.13	0.13	*0.14*	—	*0.19*	0.02	—	—	*0.18*
Iron (%)	0.002	0.006	0.006	—	0.009	—	*0.006*	—	*0.008*	0.005	0.001	—	*0.009*
Manganese mg/lb	2.6	24.9	2.2	—	34.2	—	*8.3*	—	*19.5*	8.5	—	—	*4.5*
Sulfur (%)	0.14	0.19	0.04	—	0.17	—	*0.19*	—	*0.23*	0.18	—	—	—
Sodium (%)	0.01	0.10	0.05	—	0.02	—	*0.02*	—	*0.07*	0.05	—	—	—
Chlorine (%)	0.06	0.08	0.06	*0.10*	0.04	—	*0.13*	—	*0.11*	0.10	—	—	—
Cobalt mg/lb	0.010	0.035	—	—	—	—	*0.053*	—	*0.029*	0.138	—	—	—
Zinc mg/lb	8.9	7.0	—	—	15.6	—	*7.8*	—	—	7.0	—	—	—

TABLE A-10. **Average Composition of the Caryopses of the Cereals (Cont.)**

Composition	Corn	Wheat	Rice	Rye	Barley	Oats	Sorghum	Pearl Millet	Proso
Vitamins									
Thiamine mg/lb	2.1	2.5	1.5	2.0	2.6	3.2	2.1	—	3.6
Riboflavin mg/lb	0.7	0.6	0.4	0.8	1.0	0.8	0.7	—	1.9
Pantothenic acid mg/lb	2.8	6.2	5.5	3.5	3.3	6.6	5.7	—	—
Niacin mg/lb	11.3	28.9	22.4	6.6	29.3	8.1	22.0	—	11.7
Pyridoxine mg/lb	3.8	2.4	3.6	—	1.5	0.6	2.7	—	—
Choline mg/lb	284	424	—	—	526	548	346	—	—
Carotene mg/lb	2.0	0.0	—	0.0	0.2	0.0	0.6	—	—
Folic acid mg/lb	0.11	0.22	0.07	0.33	0.28	0.15	0.11	—	—
Biotin mg/lb	0.03	0.05	0.04	0.03	0.08	0.15	0.13	—	—
Tocopherol mg/lb	—	7.9	5.4	7.9	3.1	3.0	—	—	—
Amino acids									
Arginine (%)	0.4	0.8	0.6	0.6	0.6	0.08	0.4	—	0.4
Histidine (%)	0.2	0.3	0.1	0.3	0.3	0.2	0.3	—	0.2
Isoleucine (%)	0.5	0.6	0.3	0.6	0.6	0.6	0.6	—	0.5
Leucine (%)	1.2	1.0	0.6	0.8	0.9	1.0	1.6	—	1.2
Lycine (%)	0.3	0.5	0.3	0.5	0.6	0.4	0.3	—	0.3
Phenyl alanine (%)	0.5	0.7	0.3	0.7	0.7	0.7	0.5	—	0.6
Threonine (%)	0.3	0.4	0.2	0.4	0.4	0.4	0.3	—	0.4
Tryptophane (%)	0.1	0.2	—	0.1	0.2	0.2	0.1	—	0.2
Valine (%)	0.5	0.6	—	0.7	0.7	0.7	0.6	—	0.6
Methionine (%)	0.2	0.2	—	0.2	0.2	0.2	0.1	—	0.3
Cystine (%)	0.1	0.2	—	0.2	0.2	0.2	0.2	—	—
Glutamic acid (%)	2.7	4.9	—	3.8	3.4	3.0	2.8	—	—

TABLE A-10. **Average Composition of the Caryopses of the Cereals (Cont.)**

Composition	Corn	Wheat	Rice	Rye	Barley	Oats	Sorghum	Pearl Millet	Proso
Serine (%)	0.8	0.4	—	0.7	0.5	0.4	0.6	—	—
Tyrosine (%)	0.5	0.5	—	0.3	0.4	0.6	0.4	—	—
Glycine (%)	0.5	1.0	—	—	—	—	—	—	—
Alenine (%)	—	0.7	—	—	—	—	—	—	—
Aspartic acid (%)	—	0.2	—	—	—	—	—	—	—
Cysteine (%)	—	0.3	—	—	—	—	—	—	—
Proline (%)	—	1.4	—	—	—	—	—	—	—

[1] Adapted from Miller, D. F., *Composition of Cereal Grains and Forages*. Washington, D.C.: Natl. Acad. Sci. — Natl. Res. Council Publ. 585. 1958.

TABLE A-11. **Chemical Composition of Processed Cereal Food Products.**[1]

Cereal food description	Water (%)	Food Energy (Cal[2])	Protein (%)	Fat (%)	Carbohydrate Total (%)	Carbohydrate Fiber (%)	Ash (%)	Calcium (mg[3])	Phosphorus (mg)	Iron (mg)	Vitamin A value (I.U.)	Thiamine (mg)	Riboflavin (mg)	Niacin (mg)
Barley:														
Pearled, light, dry	11.1	349	8.2	1.0	78.8	0.5	0.9	16	189	(2.0)	(0.0)	0.12	0.08	3.1
Corn:														
Meal, yellow or white,														
Whole ground:														
Unbolted	12.0	355	9.2	3.9	73.7	1.6	1.2	10	256	2.4	510	0.38	0.11	2.0
Bolted	12.0	362	9.0	3.4	74.5	1.0	1.1	6	(178)	1.8	440	0.30	0.08	1.9
Degermed:														
Unenriched	12.0	363	7.9	1.2	78.4	0.6	0.5	6	99	1.1	300	0.14	0.05	1.0
Enriched	12.0	363	7.9	1.2	78.4	0.6	0.5	6	99	2.9	300	0.44	0.26	3.5
Oats:														
Oatmeal or rolled oats	8.3	390	14.2	7.4	68.2	1.2	1.9	53	405	4.5	(0.0)	0.60	0.14	1.0
Rye:														
Flour, medium	11.0	326	11.4	1.7	74.8	1.0	1.1	(27)	262	2.6	0.0	0.30	0.12	2.5
Meal or whole grain	11.0	321	12.1	1.7	73.4	2.0	1.8	(38)	376	3.7	0.0	0.43	0.22	1.6

TABLE A-11. **Chemical Composition of Processed Cereal Food Products (Cont.)**

Cereal Food Description	Water (%)	Food Energy (Cal²)	Protein (%)	Fat (%)	Carbohydrate Total (%)	Carbohydrate Fiber (%)	Ash (%)	Calcium (mg³)	Phosphorus (mg)	Iron (mg)	Vitamin A value (I.U.)	Thiamine (mg)	Riboflavin (mg)	Niacin (mg)
Wheat: Flour														
Whole (hard wheats)	12.0	333	13.3	2.0	71.0	2.3	1.7	41	372	3.3	(0.0)	0.55	0.12	4.3
80% extraction	12.0	365	12.0	1.3	74.1	0.5	0.65	24	191	1.3	(0.0)	0.26	0.07	2.0
Straight, hard wheat	12.0	365	11.8	1.2	74.5	0.4	0.46	20	97	1.4	(0.0)	0.12	0.07	1.4
Straight, soft wheat	12.0	364	9.7	1.0	76.9	0.4	0.42	20	97	1.1	(0.0)	0.08	0.05	1.2
Patent bread flour														
Unenriched	12.0	365	11.8	1.1	74.7	0.3	0.44	16	95	0.9	(0.0)	0.08	0.06	1.0
Enriched	12.0	365	11.8	1.1	74.7	0.3	0.44	16	95	2.9	(0.0)	0.44	0.26	3.5
Wheat: Products														
Flakes	3.8	355	10.8	1.6	80.2	1.7	3.6	46	329	3.0	(0.0)	0.08	0.18	4.8
Germ	11.0	361	25.2	10.0	49.5	2.5	4.3	84	1096	8.1	(0.0)	2.05	0.80	4.6
Wild rice	8.5	364	14.1	0.7	75.3	1.0	1.4	19	339	—	(0.0)	0.45	0.63	6.2

¹ Per 100 grams edible portion. Watt, B. K., and A. L. Merrill. *Composition of Foods — Raw, Processed, Prepared.* USDA Agricultural Handbook No. 8, pp 147. 1950.
² Calories per 100 grams.
³ Number per 100 grams.

TABLE A-12. **Performance of Farm Implements for Grain Production**

Implement or Operation	Working Width	Normal Power[1] Required or Used	Acres in 10 hours		Draft in Pounds	
			Average	Range	Normal	Range
Plow, moldboard walking	8 in.	1 horse	1.0	0.8–1.1	240[2]	200–400
" moldboard walking	14 in.	2 horses	1.9	1.5–2.1	420[2]	350–840
" moldboard, 2 bottom	28 in.	5 horses	4.5	4–5	840[2]	700–1680
" moldboard, 2 bottom	28 in.	10 h.p. tractor	8.0	6–10	840[2]	700–1680
" disk, 4 bottom	50 in.	20 h.p. tractor	13.0	10–16	1500[2]	1250–3000
" one-way disk	10 ft.	20 h.p. tractor	28.0	20–40	1800	1500–3500
Lister, 2-row	7 ft.	6 horses	12.0	10–14	1100	800–1500
" 3-row	10.5 ft.	15 h.p. tractor	30.0	25–40	1650	1200–2250
Chisel or Graham-Hoeme plow	10 ft.	20 h.p. tractor	25.0	20–35	1800(?)	—
Subtiller or blade	10 ft.	20 h.p. tractor	25.0	20–35	1800(?)	—
Stalk cutter	3-row	10 h.p. tractor	32.0	30–45	550	390–750
Harrow, disk, single	8 ft.	4 horses	15.0	12–18	560	320–1040
" disk, single	20 ft.	20 h.p. tractor	60.0	40–70	1400	800–2600
" disk, tandem	10 ft.	"	30.0	20–35	1200	800–1600
" disk, tandem, cutaway	10 ft.	"	28.0	20–35	1360	910–1820
" springtooth	10 ft.	4 horses	15.0	12–18	800	350–1500
" spiketooth, 2 sections	10 ft.	2 horses	15.0	14–20	400	300–600
" spiketooth	20 ft.	4 horses	30.0	28–40	800	600–1200
" spiketooth	24 ft.	10 h.p. tractor	70.0	50–90	960	720–1440
" spiketooth	32 ft.	15 h.p. tractor	90.0	60–120	1280	960–1920
Roller or packer	10 ft.	4 horses	20.0	15–25	500	300–600
Field cultivator	10 ft.	10 h.p. tractor	30.0	20–40	1000	900–1600
Rod weeder	24 ft.	20 h.p. tractor	60.0	50–70	2160	1920–2640
Cultivator, walking	½-row	1 horse	3.7	2–10	100	60–150

[1] Tractor power based on drawbar horsepower of modern rubber-tired tractors.
[2] Plow draft based on 5-inch depth of plowing, a popular depth in grain regions.

TABLE A-12. **Performance of Farm Implements for Grain Production (Cont.)**

Implement or Operation	Working Width	Normal Power Required or Used [1]	Acres in 10 hours Average	Acres in 10 hours Range	Draft in Pounds Normal	Draft in Pounds Range
" riding	1-row	2 horses	7.0	4–10	220	130–300
" riding	2-row	3 horses	12.0	10–18	440	260–600
" mounted or drawn	2-row	10 h.p. tractor	20.0	16–30	440	260–600
" mounted or drawn	4-row	15 h.p. tractor	35.0	30–50	880	520–1200
Rotary hoe	14 ft.	15 h.p. tractor	60.0	40–70	—	—
Lister cultivator	6-row	20 h.p. tractor	60.0	50–70	—	—
Field sprayer	30 ft.	15 h.p. tractor	75.0	60–90	—	—
Airplane sprayer, seeder, or spreader	30 ft.	—	700.0	600–900		
Grain drill	7 ft.	3 horses	11.0	9–15	350	210–560
"	10 ft.	6 horses	20.0	16–24	500	300–800
"	10 ft.	10 h.p. tractor	25.0	20–36	500	300–800
"	20 ft.	15 h.p. tractor	50.0	40–60	1000	600–1600
" furrow	20 ft.	20 h.p. tractor	50.0	40–60	1500	900–2400
Corn planter, drilled	1-row	1 horse	5.5	4–8	100	80–120
" checkrow	2-row	2 horses	12.0	8–18	200	160–240
" checkrow	2-row	10 h.p. tractor	17.0	12–22	200	160–240
" checkrow	4-row	10 h.p. tractor	33.0	25–40	400	320–480
" drilled	4-row	10 h.p. tractor	40.0	30–50	360	300–450
Lister, planter	2-row	10 h.p. tractor	20.0	14–25	700	200–1200
"	6-row	25 h.p. tractor	55.0	40–70	2000	600–3600
Grain binder	6 ft.	3 horses	9.0	7–12	600	390–900
"	8 ft.	4 horses	14.0	12–20	800	520–1200
" power takeoff	10 ft.	15 h.p. tractor	25.0	20–30	1000	650–1500
Shocking grain	—	By hand	8.0	5–10	—	—
Combine	40 in.	15 h.p. tractor	7.0	5–10	—	—
" power takeoff	5 ft.	15 h.p. tractor	11.0	9–13	—	—

TABLE A-12. **Performance of Farm Implements for Grain Production (Cont.)**

Implement or Operation	Working Width	Normal Power[1] Required or Used	Acres in 10 hours		Draft in Pounds	
			Average	Range	Normal	Range
Combine power takeoff	10 ft.	20 h.p. tractor	22.0	18–25	—	—
" auxiliary motor	16 ft.	20 h.p. tractor	30.0	25–40	2400	1600–3200
" self-propelled	14 ft.	85 h.p. motor	32.0	25–45	—	—
Corn binder	1-row	3 horses	6.0	4–8	300	250–350
Shocking corn or grain sorghum	—	By hand	4.0	3–6	—	—
Cutting and stacking corn	—	By hand	1.2	0.7–1.4	—	—
Picking corn, mechanical	1-row	15 h.p. tractor (PTO)	7.0	4–10	—	1000–1800
" mechanical	2-row	20 h.p. tractor (PTO)	12.0	8–20	—	2000–3600
" by hand	—	2 horses	1.5	1–2	—	—
Husking corn, from shock	—	—	1.2	0.7–1.5	—	—
Snapping corn, by hand	—	2 horses	2.0	1–3	—	—
Thresher, 16 men	32 in.	7 teams, 2 trucks / 20 h.p. tractor	37.0	30–50	—	—

TABLE A-13. **Recommended Batch Size to Match Different Sizes of Crop Driers; and Estimated Time and Fuel Consumption Required for Drying Ear Corn from the Moisture Content Stated Down to 13 Per Cent.**

Air Temperatures			Initial Moisture Content of Kernels	Size of Fan Motor		Recommended Batch Size²	Estimated Amount of Fuel Oil and Time Required to Dry a Batch to 13-per cent Moisture Content, Using— A Direct-heat Drier			Estimated Amount of Water that Will Be Evaporated per Gallon of Fuel Oil Burned Using— A Direct-heat Drier
Atmosphere¹	Amount of Rise	Drying		Power Rating	Rate of Air Delivery		Fuel Consumption per Hour	Fuel Consumption for 1000 Bushels	Time per 1000 Bushels	
(°F)	(°F)	(°F)	(Pct)	(HP)	(Cfm)	(Bushels)	(Gallons)	(Gallons)	(Hours)	(Lb)
30	40	70	30	3	9,000	1,500– 1,800	3	500	167	43
			25			2,000– 2,600		340	113	
			20			2,400– 4,700		190	63	
60	40	100	30	3	9,000	1,000– 1,500	3	310	103	70
			25			1,200– 2,100		210	70	
			20			1,600– 3,700		120	40	
30	80	110	30	3	9,000	950– 2,400	6	440	73	50
			25			1,200– 3,500		300	50	
			20			1,500– 6,000		160	27	
60	80	140	30	3	9,000	700– 1,800	6	330	55	66
			25			900– 2,600		230	38	
			20			1,200– 4,900		120	20	
30	40	70	30	5	15,000	2,600– 3,000	5	500	100	44
			25			3,300– 4,400		340	68	
			20			4,200– 8,000		190	38	

TABLE A-13. **Recommended Batch Size to Match Different Sizes of Crop Driers; and Estimated Time and Fuel Consumption Required for Drying Ear Corn from the Moisture Content Stated down to 13 Per Cent (Cont.)**

| Air Temperatures | | | Initial Moisture Content of Kernels | Size of Fan Motor | | Recommended Batch Size² | Estimated Amount of Fuel Oil and Time Required to Dry a Batch to 13-per cent Moisture Content, Using— A Direct-heat Drier | | | Estimated Amount of Water that Will be Evaporated per Gallon of Fuel Oil Burned Using— A Direct-heat Drier |
| Atmosphere¹ | Amount of Rise / Drying | | | Power Rating | Rate of Air Delivery | | Fuel Consumption per Hour | Fuel Consumption for 1000 Bushels | Time per 1000 Bushels | |
(°F)	(°F)	(°F)	(Pct)	(HP)	(Cfm)	(Bushels)	(Gallons)	(Gallons)	(Hours)	(Lb)
60	40	100	30	5	15,000	1,600– 2,400	5	310	62	70
			25			2,100– 3,500		210	42	
			20			2,600– 6,000		120	24	
30	80	110	30	5	15,000	1,600– 4,000	10	440	44	50
			25			2,000– 6,000		300	30	
			20			2,400–11,000		160	16	
60	80	140	30	5	15,000	1,200– 3,000	10	330	33	66
			25			1,400– 4,500		230	23	
			20			1,900– 8,000		120	12	

¹ Relative humidity 70 per cent.

² If a larger quantity of ear corn is dried than the maximum recommended for each range, there may be some mold growth in that part of the batch that dries last. If a smaller quantity than recommended is dried, the amount of fuel required per 1000 bushels will be greater than the estimates given in this table.

For a batch half the size of the minimum recommended in each range, the fuel requirement per 1000 bushels will be increased by about half.

³ Total fuel consumption required to dry a batch averages approximately 40 per cent more for an indirect-heat drier than for a direct-heat drier.

TABLE A-14. **Comparison of Cereal Grains**
(a) **Relative Feed Value per cent.**

Grain	Dairy Cows	Fattening Beef Cattle	Fattening Hogs	Fattening Lambs
Corn	100	100	100	100
Wheat	100	105	105	85
Barley	100	88	91	87
Sorghum	100	95	95	100
Oats	95	85	85	90

(b) **Size of Grains.**

	Number Per Gram Average	Number Per Pound Average	Number Per Pound Usual Range
Corn (dent)	3	1,200	900– 1,500
Barley	30	13,000	10,000–15,000
Oats	30	14,000	11,000–17,000
Rice	33	15,000	12,000–18,000
Wheat	35	16,000	8,000–24,000
Rye	40	18,000	10,000–21,000
Sorghum	50	20,000	13,000–24,000

Maximum acre-yield in bushels in any farm field in the United States: corn—304, rice—210, sorghum—204, wheat—155; oats—150; barley—130.

Index

Åberg, E., 485, 493
Abruzzes rye, 457
Abyssinia, wheat origins in, 304
Aceria tulipae, 401, 419
acetone, 214
acreage and production data, 6-12, 733-83
adhesives, corn in, 215; grain sorghum, 710; wheat, 381
adjunomoto, 381
adlay, 147
adobe soils, rice culture in, 631
aeciospores, 230, 386
Aegilops, 304, 471; *A. cylindrica*, 429; *A. speltoides*, 304, 430; *A. squarrosa*, 305, 428, 430
Aeolus mellilus, 238
aeration, corn damage from, 142; in storage, 101-102
Aeschynomene virginica, 636
Africa, corn culture in, 135; barley culture in, 4, 483, 495, 498; grain sorghum, 679, 681, 702; oats, 562; wheat, 4, 389
Agonoderus lecontei, 240
agricultural machinery, *see* machinery
Agriculture Department, U.S., 114, 160, 202, 265, 388
Agriotes mancus, 238
Agromyza oryzae, 664
Agropyron, 428; *A. cristatum*, 430; *A. elongatum*, 430; *A. intermedium*, 430; *A. junceum*, 430; *A. repens*, 430; *A. trichophorum*, 430
Agrotis gladiaria, 238; *A. orthogonia*, 419; *A. ypsilon*, 236
Agrotriticum hybrids, 430
Agrox, 654
air drying, 103-104
airplane, as farm implement, 81, 188
akiochi disease, of rice, 613, 660
Alabama, browntop millet in, 766
albumen, 206, 317, 366, 462
alcohol and alcoholic beverages, from barley, 513; corn, 214; grain sorghum, 710; millet, 742; rice, 653;

rye, 464
aldrin, 235, 238, 248, 416, 419, 731
aleurone layer, corn, 153, 160, 206, 256
alfalfa, 173, 324, 329, 405, 566, 695
algae, in rice culture, 624, 636
alkali soils, 30
allelic factors, corn, 256
almond moth, 663
alpha-amylase, 367, 514
Alternaria, 94, 96
amino acids, 44; in corn, 169, 204, 206, 208; in wheat, 367
Ammannia coccinia, 636
ammonium nitrogen, in rice culture, 631
ammonium sulfate, in sorghum culture, 696
amylopectin, 206, 260
amylose, 259-60
Anabrus simplex, 416
Andes mountains, 9, 140
Angoumois grain moth, 110, 249, 663
Anguina tritici, 420-21
anthocyanin, 489
anthracnose, of oats, 590; rye, 467; sorghum, 717, 726
Anuraphis maidi-radicis, 239
Aphelchoides besseyi, 658
aphids, 527, 589, 720; corn-root, 239-240; grain, 414-15
Aphidus testaceipes, 415
Aphis maidis, 248, 720
apogeotropic stimulus, 33
Appleby twine knotter, 72
Apus oryzphagus, 664
Arasan, 220, 222, 394
Arasan SFX, 654
Argentina, corn production in, 131; oat culture, 547, 561; rye production, 449; wheat culture, 355; wheat varieties in, 307
Arizona, sorghum culture in, 697
Arkansas, oats culture in, 574; rice production, 20, 612, 627, 629-30, 649
armyworm, 237, 247, 418, 664
asbestos, 216